CYTOTOXIC T CELLS

BIOLOGY AND RELEVANCE TO DISEASE

ANNALS OF THE NEW YORK ACADEMY OF SCIENCES
Volume 532

CYTOTOXIC T CELLS

BIOLOGY AND RELEVANCE TO DISEASE

Edited by Jack R. Battisto, Janet Plate, and Gene Shearer

The New York Academy of Sciences
New York, New York
1988

Library of Congress Cataloging-in-Publication Data

Cytotoxic T cells.

(Annals of the New York Academy of Sciences, ISSN 0077-8923 ; v. 532)
Result of a conference held in Bethesda, Md. on May 13-15, 1987, by the New York Academy of Sciences.
Includes bibliographies and index.
1. T cells—Congresses.   2. Cell-mediated cytotoxicity—Congresses.   3. Killer cells—Congresses.
I. Battisto, Jack R. (Jack Richard), 1922-   . II. Plate, Janet.   III. Shearer, Gene M.   IV. New York Academy of Sciences.   V. Series.   [DNLM: 1. Killer Cells, Natural—immunology—congresses.   2. T Lymphocytes, Cytotoxic—immunology—congresses.
W1 AN626YL v.532 / QW 568 C9975 1987]
Q11.N5 vol. 532   [QR185.8.T2]   500 s   88-19487
ISBN 0-89766-460-4   [616.07'9]
ISBN 0-89766-461-2 (pbk.)

BCP/PCP
Printed in the United States of America
ISBN 0-89766-460-4 (cloth)
ISBN 0-89766-461-2 (paper)
ISSN 0077-8923

ANNALS OF THE NEW YORK ACADEMY OF SCIENCES

Volume 532
August 30, 1988

CYTOTOXIC T CELLS
BIOLOGY AND RELEVANCE TO DISEASE[a]

Editors and Conference Organizers

JACK R. BATTISTO, JANET PLATE, and GENE SHEARER

CONTENTS

[a] This volume is the result of a conference entitled Cytotoxic T Cells: Biology and Relevance
to Disease, held in Bethesda, Maryland on May 13-15, 1987, by the New York Academy of
Sciences.

Part III. Requirements for Generation and Down-Regulation of Cytotoxic T Lymphocytes

Part IV. Cytotoxic T Lymphocytes and Immunopathology

Part V. Mechanisms of Killing

**Part VI.   Molecular Aspects of Cytotoxic T Lymphocytes and Effects on
Tumor Growth**

Part VII.   Poster Papers

Induction and Regulation of Cytotoxic Cells

Major funding for this conference was provided by:

- UNITED STATES ARMY MEDICAL RESEARCH AND DEVELOPMENT COMMAND

Financial assistance was received from:

- BOEHRINGER INGELHEIM CORPORATION
- EASTMAN KODAK COMPANY
- HOFFMANN-LA ROCHE INC.
- LILLY RESEARCH LABORATORIES
- MERCK SHARP & DOHME RESEARCH LABORATORIES
- ORTHO PHARMACEUTICAL CORPORATION
- SCHERING CORPORATION
- SQUIBB CORPORATION
- WARNER-LAMBERT COMPANY

Introduction

JACK R. BATTISTO

Cleveland Clinic Foundation
Cleveland, Ohio 44106

Dr. Janet Plate, Dr. Gene Shearer, and I welcome each of you to this conference on cytotoxic T cells. Each of us shares with you a feeling of anticipation concerning what shall be accomplished here.

No single meeting has yet dealt with the complete range of topics that we selected to be covered in this special conference. Instead, there have been sporadic meetings and publications that have addressed single subtopics separately. Furthermore, our knowledge of this effector cell, the discovery of which is now some 27 years old, is maturing rapidly. For these two major reasons, the conveners of this meeting felt that the time was appropriate to bring together the international community of scientists who were currently addressing the questions relative to this killer cell. The timely information presented orally, as well as in printed form in this *Annal*, is important to cancer and transplant-rejection research as well as to the study of virological, parasitological, and autoimmune diseases.

Our conference was in the planning stage for slightly more than one-and-a-half years. During that time, the organizing committee put together a team of speakers and fashioned a poster session that was representative of a wide cross section of thought on the subject of cytotoxic T cells, and their biology and relevance to disease. In the process of constructing the meeting, we had to cope with limitations of program time, distances over which prospective participants had to travel, and availability of funds. These three items severely restricted our capability to have additional investigators on the program. Thus, some individuals who contributed to our concepts and who should have been represented, unfortunately, were not.

Within a relatively short span of time, considerable effort has been expended toward understanding the newest effector cell in our immunological armamentarium. As a consequence, knowledge has been and is being acquired concerning its functioning in protection as well as in general homeostasis of the organism. As is true for T cells in general, considerable importance is attached to ontogeny, receptors, and triggering. Genetic aspects of the killer cell and its involvement in transplantation is a special area of interest, as are the diverse cells and cytokines needed for generation, maintenance, and down-regulation. The mechanism by which this unique cell achieves killing of targets without apparent self-harm is a fascinating topic, as are the clinically relevant situations in which it induces pathology or where it functions beneficially. These, then, are the several topics with which the conference was concerned.

We thank our session chairs who preceded each session with a short introduction and general review of the upcoming topic. In addition, they were responsible for seeing that each of the presentations was properly introduced, timed, and discussed so as to meet our tight schedule. Special thanks go to Dr. Janet Plate for preparing a summary statement delivered on the last day. She highlighted some of the more important and/ or controversial points made in the presentations and discussions and indicated some of the directions that future work may take.

Over and above his many contributions to the success of this meeting, Dr. Gene Shearer must receive credit for having ably selected our meeting site. Furthermore, this conference would not have been possible without the support of the officers of the New York Academy of Sciences: namely, Dr. Fleur Strand, president; Dr. Walter Scott, chairman of the conference committee; and Dr. Heinz Pagels, executive director. Review and approval of the program was done by a subcommittee consisting of Dr. Pat Mongini, Dr. P. Sehgal, and Dr. C. Burrell. Dr. Mongini, in particular, questioned, probed, and prodded the conveners on every aspect of the program. Without doubt, she was a fourth (although unseen) convener of this conference. Another unheralded individual who must receive special tribute is Dr. Subhash Gautam, with whom many conversations relative to this program took place. In addition, highly competent advice came from the Academy's conference director, Ellen Marks, and her staff. One of her staff, Renée Wilkerson, must be singled out for her exceptional talent and service. The help of each of these individuals is gratefully acknowledged. Finally, we must acknowledge the diligent and professional work of the Editorial Department, and in particular Steven Bohall, for their help in seeing this book through the press.

Regulation of Human T-Cell Proliferation and CTL Development by Human Recombinant Interleukin-4

R. BRUCE ACRES, MICHAEL B. WIDMER,[a]

KENNETH H. GRABSTEIN, AND STEVEN GILLIS[b]

Immunex Corporation
51 University Street
Seattle, Washington 98101

INTRODUCTION

Interleukin-4 (IL-4), also known as B-cell stimulatory factor-1 (BSF-1), was originally characterized by its growth stimulatory properties for murine B cells in the presence of membrane receptor cross-linking reagents such as anti-immunoglobulin.[1] Murine IL-4 was also shown to stimulate the proliferation of cell types, not of B-cell lineage, such as T cells and mast cells.[2,3] Murine IL-4 has recently been shown to be a potent helper factor for the generation of murine cytotoxic T lymphocytes (CTL) in mixed leukocyte cultures (MLC).[4]

In this paper we extend our murine studies to a human experimental system. Human peripheral blood T-cell populations and an antigen specific T-cell line proliferated in response to human IL-4. As in the murine system, an initial period of activation was required in order for the cells to proliferate optimally to IL-4. Like IL-2, IL-4 augmented the development of antigen-specific CTL in MLC. In the absence of antigenic stimulus, however, IL-4 failed to induce the generation of lymphokine-activated killer cells (LAK). These results provide evidence for a role of IL-4 in the amplification of the human T-cell response.

EXPERIMENTAL PROCEDURES

Material

Preparation of human, recombinant IL-2 and IL-4 has been described elsewhere.[5,6] Phytohemagglutinin (PHA) was purchased from Grand Island Biologicals Company, Grand Island, NY. The tissue culture medium was RPMI 1640 (Gibco) supplemented with 10% fetal bovine serum (Rehatuin, Armour Pharmaceuticals, Kankakee, IL), 50 U/ml penicillin, 50 μg/ml streptomycin, 2 mM glutamine, and 5×10^{-5} 2-mercaptoethanol. Tissue culture plates were purchased from Costar (Cambridge, MA). Preparation of the monoclonal antibody 2A3, which has specificity for the human IL-2 receptor and blocks the binding of IL-2 to its receptor, has been described elsewhere.[7] Peripheral blood mononuclear cells (PBM) were prepared by centrifugation of freshly drawn human blood over a Hypaque-Ficoll gradient (specific gravity = 1.077) as described elsewhere.[6] The

---

[a] Scholar of the Leukemia Society of America.
[b] To whom correspondence should be addressed.

antigen-specific, cytotoxic T-cell line 24/7, maintained *in vitro* has been described elsewhere.[8] The cell line Daudi was purchased from the American Type Culture Collection and kept in continuous culture. Tritiated thymidine ([^{3}H]TdR) and Na ^{51}CrO$_4$ were purchased from New England Nuclear (Boston, MA).

Methods

Proliferation assays were performed as follows: Human PBM or cells from line 24/7 were distributed in 200 μl volume 96-well, flat-bottom tissue culture plates at 2×10^3 or 2×10^4 cells/well, respectively. Plates were incubated for two (24/7) or three (PBM) days and pulsed with 1 μCi/well [^{3}H]TdR for 8 hours, after which they were harvested onto glass fiber filter strips and [^{3}H]TdR incorporation determined by liquid scintillation counting.

Where indicated, cells were preincubated for seven days in tissue culture medium supplemented with 1% PHA. Generation and assessment of antigen-specific CTL or LAK have been described in detail elsewhere.[6] Briefly, freshly prepared PBM were incubated in 2 ml volumes for 7 days in 24-well tissue culture plates at 10^6 cells/well. Where indicated, irradiated (3000 R) stimulator cells were added at 10^6 per well. Lymphokines were added at the times indicated in a 20 μl volume, to a final concentration of 10 ng/ml, or to the final concentrations indicated.

Cytotoxicity assays have been described elsewhere.[6] Briefly, cells from MLC were titrated into 200 μl volume 96-well V-bottom plates, and 2000 ^{51}Cr-labeled target cells were added to each well. After 4 hours at 37°, plates were centrifuged, and 150 μl was removed from each well and counted using a Gamma 5780 gamma counter (Packard Instruments, Laguna Hills, CA). Target cells for the CTL assays were prepared by stimulating PBM for 2 days at 37°, 10% CO$_2$, in tissue culture medium supplemented with 1% PHA and then washed twice prior to ^{51}Cr labeling. One lytic unit (LU$_{25}$) of cytotoxicity is defined as the fraction of the initial culture required for 25% specific ^{51}Cr release and was determined from the linear region of the dose response curves.

RESULTS

Proliferation of Human PBM in Response to IL-2 and IL-4

Recombinant IL-4 was compared with recombinant IL-2 for its ability to induce proliferation of freshly isolated or PHS-preactivated human PBM. The data shown in FIGURE 1A indicate that both IL-2 and IL-4 are able to induce proliferation of PHA-prestimulated PBM. By contrast, freshly isolated, unstimulated PBM cells were unable to proliferate in response to IL-4, but did respond to IL-2 (FIG. 1B).

Proliferation of Human T Cells in Response to IL-4 Is Independent of IL-2

To determine whether IL-4 causes T-cell proliferation directly or through the production of IL-2, the following experiment was performed. Cells from the human alloantigen-specific, IL-2-dependent T-cell line 24/7[8] were stimulated to proliferate with either IL-2 or IL-4 in the presence or absence of the monoclonal antibody 2A3, which binds with high affinity to the human IL-2 receptor.[7] The IL-

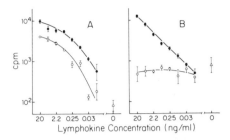

FIGURE 1. A. Proliferation of human PBM in response to IL-2 (●—●) or IL-4 (○—○). Single donor PBM were isolated as described. Cells were incubated for seven days in medium supplemented with 1% PHA, washed extensively, and incubated for a further 3 days in the presence of lymphokine at the concentrations shown. Proliferation was assessed by uptake of [³H]TdR during an 8 hour pulse on the third day of culture. **B.** Freshly isolated, single-donor PBM were cultured as above, but without the 7 days PHA preactivation. △, background proliferation in medium alone; error bars indicate standard deviation.

2-induced proliferation of 24/7 cells was effectively inhibited by 10 μg/ml 2A3 antibody (95% reduction in [³H]TdR incorporation in the linear portion of the IL-2 titration curve) (FIG. 2). IL-4-induced proliferation, however, was virtually unaffected by the same concentration of 2A3 antibody. These data indicate that human T cells that have been activated either by mitogen or antigen (and IL-2) will

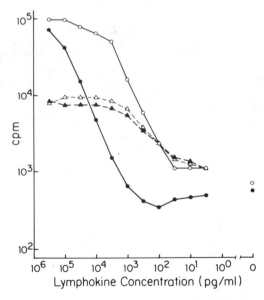

FIGURE 2. Inhibition of IL-2, but not IL-4-driven proliferation, by anti-IL-2 receptor antibody. Cells from the human cytotoxic T-cell line 24/7 were taken from continuous culture 5 days after the last exposure to antigen (allogeneic Epstein-Barr virus (EBV)–transformed B cells) and IL-2. Cells were washed and dispensed in 96-well microtiter plates in 200 μl volumes and incubated for 2 days with lymphokines as shown. Where indicated, 2A3 antibody was at a final concentration of 10 μg/ml. Proliferation was assessed by incorporation of [³H]TdR during 40 to 48 hours of culture. ○, IL-2; ●, IL-2 + 10 μg/ml 2A3; △, IL-4; ▲, IL-4 + 10 μg/ml 2A3.

TABLE 1. Induction of LAK Activity by IL-2 but not IL-4[a]

Lymphokine	Concentration (ng/ml)	LU_{25}/Culture
—	0	~3
IL-2	0.1	~4
IL-2	1.0	80
IL-2	10	286
IL-2	100	714
IL-4	0.1	<1
IL-4	1.0	<1
IL-4	10	<1
IL-4	100	<1

[a] PBM from a single donor were prepared as described and incubated for 7 days at 10^6 cells/2 ml culture with lymphokine concentrations as shown. LAK activity was assessed by cytotoxic activity against ^{51}Cr-labeled cells from the LAK-sensitive target cell line, Daudi.

proliferate in response to recombinant, human IL-4. Moreover, T-cell proliferation in response to IL-4 does not appear to depend upon the production of, and subsequent proliferation in response to, IL-2.

Inability of IL-4 to Generate LAK Activity

In the absence of an overt antigenic stimulus, IL-2 will activate a population of cytotoxic cells from human peripheral blood.[9] These LAK lyse a variety of tumor target cells and show poorly defined antigenic specificity. LAK have been the subject of intense investigation in recent years because cell populations enriched for LAK appear to be effective in the treatment of some forms of cancer.[10] It was of interest to compare the effects of IL-2 and IL-4 on the generation of LAK activity. The data in TABLE 1 confirm that IL-2 is very effective at inducing LAK activity (as defined operationally by the ability to lyse Daudi cells), with significant activity occurring in cultures supplemented with 1 ng/ml or more IL-2. IL-4, on the other hand, was unable to induce measurable LAK activity in PBM isolated from healthy donors at any dose tested.

To determine whether the apparent absence of LAK in IL-4-supplemented cultures was due to a shift in the kinetics of the response to an earlier peak, we assessed LAK activity at three time points after initiation of cultures of fresh

TABLE 2. Kinetics of LAK Cell Development[a]

Lymphokines	Day of Culture	LU_{25}/Culture
0	3	<1
0	5	<1
0	7	<1
IL-2	3	22
IL-2	5	172
IL-2	7	263
IL-4	3	<1
IL-4	5	~2
IL-4	7	<1

[a] Cells were prepared and cultured as for TABLE 1. Lymphokines were at a final concentration of 10 ng/ml. LAK activity was assessed by lysis of Daudi cells.

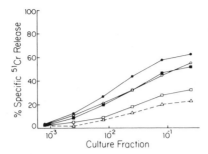

FIGURE 3. Augmentation of CTL development by IL-2 and IL-4. PBM from freshly drawn blood were prepared as described. 10^6 responder cells together with 10^6 irradiated (3000 R) stimulator cells were cultured for 4 or 7 days in a 2 ml volume. Lymphokines were added to a final concentration of 10 ng/ml at the times shown. Target cells for assessment of specific cytotoxicity were 3 day PHA (1%) blasts from the same donor whose cells were used as stimulator cells. Only day 7 CTL data are shown in this figure. See TABLE 2 for day 4 CTL activity and percent recovery per culture. △—△, no lymphokines added; ○—○, 10 ng/ml IL-2 added day 0; ●—●, 10 ng/ml IL-2 added day 3; □—□, 10 ng/ml IL-4 added day 0; ■—■, 10 ng/ml IL-4 added day 3.

PBM with IL-2 or IL-4. The results are shown in TABLE 2. Although LAK activity in response to IL-2 was detectable on day 3 and increased on days 5 and 7, very little LAK activity in response to IL-4 was detectable at any of these time points.

Augmentation of Antigen-Specific CTL Development in Response to IL-4

Freshly prepared PBM from a single donor were stimulated for seven days with irradiated PBM (3000 R) from an allogeneic donor in MLC. Lymphokines were added either at initiation of culture or after 3 days of culture. The results of CTL analysis after 7 days of culture are shown in FIGURE 3. As expected, IL-2 augmented the development of allospecific CTL when added at the initiation of culture (day 0) or halfway through the culture period (day 3). By contrast, the

TABLE 3. Kinetics of CTL Development[a]

Lymphokine Added	Time of Lymphokine Addition	Day of CTL Assessment	CTL Activity (LU_{25}/Culture)	Percent Cell Recovery
0	—	4	<1	62
0	—	7	~5	110
IL-2	day 0	4	<1	60
IL-2	day 3	4	<1	60
IL-2	day 0	7	80	192
IL-2	day 3	7	143	160
IL-4	day 0	4	<1	76
IL-4	day 3	4	<1	80
IL-4	day 0	7	18	149
IL-4	day 3	7	74	124

[a] Cells prepared, cultured, and assessed for CTL activity as described for FIGURE 3.

addition of IL-4 at culture initiation had little effect on CTL development, but was very effective if added on day 3.

Additional experiments demonstrate that IL-4 added at time 0 does not cause an earlier peak in CTL activity (TABLE 3). These data show that IL-4, unlike IL-2 is unable to induce LAK development, but like IL-2 is able to augment antigen-specific CTL development if it is added to mixed leukocyte cultures several days after culture initiation. Also unlike IL-2, IL-4 has not been observed to augment the generation of CTL, which will lyse autologous PHA blast target cells (data not shown).

CONCLUSIONS

We have shown that mitogen-activated primary human T cells, as well as antigen and IL-2-activated human T cells taken from continuous culture, will proliferate in response to human recombinant IL-4. Peripheral blood T cells proliferated optimally in response to IL-4 only after an initial period of activation, in this case by the mitogen PHA. Stimulation with Con A also rendered PBM responsive to IL-4 (data not shown). Previous work with antigen-specific, murine T-cell clones and polyclonal populations has shown that they too can be activated to proliferate in response to a subsequent exposure to IL-4.[2]

We have shown that IL-4 can participate in regulating development of cytotoxic T cells. IL-4, like IL-2, was found to augment CTL development in MLC. Augmentation of CTL development by IL-4, as with proliferation, however, depended upon prestimulation of the responding population. The inability of IL-4 to augment CTL development when added at culture initiation may reflect the requirement of T cells to be previously activated in order to proliferate in response to IL-4, or that IL-2 and IL-4 act on different populations of cells or different stages during CTL differentiation. Alternatively, it is possible that earlier addition of IL-4 activates a regulatory cell population. This hypothesis is currently under investigation.

A screen of several donors indicated that cells from most donors do not show an increase in generation of specific CTL activity if IL-4 is added early, but that CTL activity is increased significantly if IL-4 is added on day 3 or 4 of culture.[6] There is some variation among individuals in responsiveness to IL-4 as opposed to that to IL-2, but on average, IL-4 added on day 3 or 4 is as effective as IL-2 at boosting the antigen-specific CTL response.

IL-4, like IL-2, augments the generation of specific CTL, but does not appear to induce LAK activity. Cellular populations exposed to IL-2 *in vitro* have proven to be effective in the treatment of some forms of cancer, although the exact effector cell type has not been identified. Because IL-4 may well be able to enhance tumor-specific CTL, without generating nonspecific lytic activity associated with LAK, IL-4, either alone or in combination with IL-2, may prove to be a useful immunotherapeutic agent.

REFERENCES

1. GRABSTEIN, K. H., J. EISENMAN, C. MARCH & S. GILLIS. 1986. Purification to homogeneity of B-cell stimulating factor. J. Exp. Med. **163:** 1405.
2. GRABSTEIN, K. H., L. S. PARK, P. J. MORRISSEY, V. PRICE, D. L. URDAL & M. B. WIDMER. 1987. Regulation of murine T-cell proliferation by B-cell stimulatory factor-1. J. Immunol. **139:** 1148.

3. LEE, F., T. YOKOTA, T. OTSUKA, P. MEYERSON, D. VILLARET, R. COFFMAN, T. MOSMANN, D. RENNICK, N. ROEHM, C. SMITH, A. ZLOTNICK & K. ARAI. 1986. Isolation and characterization of a mouse interleukin cDNA clone that expresses B-cell stimulating factor 1 activates and T-cell and mast cell stimulating activities. Proc. Natl. Acad. Sci. USA **83:** 2061.
4. WIDMER, M. B. & K. H. GRABSTEIN. 1987. B-cell stimulating factor regulates the generation of cytolytic T-lymphocytes. Nature (London) **326:** 795.
5. URDAL, D. L., D. Y. MOCHIZUKI, P. J. CONLON, C. J. MARCH, M. L. REMEROWSKI, J. EISENMAN, C. RAMTHUN & S. GILLIS. 1984. Lymphokine purification by reversed phase high performance liquid chromatography. J. Chromatogr. **296:** 171.
6. WIDMER, M. B., R. B. ACRES, H. M. SASSENFELD & K. H. GRABSTEIN. 1987. Regulation of cytolytic cell populations from human peripheral blood by B-cell stimulatory factor-1 (Interleukin-4). J. Exp. Med. **166:** 1447–1455.
7. DOWER, S. K., S. H. HEFENEIDER, A. R. ALPERT & D. L. URDAL. 1985. Quantitative measurement of human interleukin-2 receptor levels with intact and detergent solubilized human T-cells. Mol. Immunol. **22:** 937.
8. ACRES, R. B., P. J. CONLON, D. Y. MOCHIZUKI & B. GALLIS. 1987. Phosphorylation of the CD8 antigen on cytotoxic human T-cells in response to phorbol myristate acetate or antigen presenting B-cells. J. Immunol. **139:** 2268–2274.
9. GRIMM, E. A., A. MAZUMDER, H. Z. ZHANG & S. A. ROSENBERG. 1982. Lymphokine-activated killer cell phenomenon: lysis of natural killer-resistant fresh solid tumor cells by interleukin-2 activated autologous human peripheral blood lymphocytes. J. Exp. Med. **155:** 1823.
10. ROSENBERG, S. A., M. T. LOTZE, L. M. MUUL, S. LEITMAN, A. E. CHANG, S. E. ETTINGHAUSEN, Y. L. MATORY, J. M. SKIBBER, E. SHILINI, J. T. VETTO, C. A. SEIPP, C. SIMPSON & C. M. REICHART. 1985. Observation on the systemic administration of autologous lymphokine activated killer cells and recombinant interleukin-2 to patients with metastatic cancer. N. Engl. J. Med. **313:** 1485.

Expression of T-Cell Receptors by Functionally Distinct Subsets of Immature Adult Thymocytes

GUIDO C. MIESCHER, RAWLEIGH C. HOWE,
RALPH C. BUDD, AND H. ROBSON MacDONALD

Ludwig Institute for Cancer Research
Lausanne Branch
1066 Epalinges, Switzerland

INTRODUCTION

During the intrathymic differentiation of CD4$^+$ CD8$^-$ and CD4$^-$ CD8$^+$ T cells, the genes encoding heterodimeric α/β T-cell receptors (R) undergo rearrangement, expression, and selection.[1] Recently, a population of so-called double negative (DN), that is CD4$^-$ CD8$^-$, thymocytes has been described, which reconstitute *in vivo* all other thymocyte subsets.[2] The majority of adult thymocytes, essentially most cortical thymocytes, coexpress both CD4 and CD8. About half of these cells also express CD3-associated α/β T-cell R,[3] generally at lower intensity than medullary thymocytes, which are the most mature population and presumably seed peripheral lymphoid organs. Nearly all CD4$^+$ CD8$^+$ thymocytes, however, die *in situ*.[4] Accumulating evidence indicates that CD4 and CD8 enhance T-cell recognition of MHC class II and class I molecules, respectively,[5,6] and because of this, it is thought that selective events in the thymus involve CD4 and/or CD8. Recent experiments have demonstrated clearly that negative selection occurs by clonal elimination of self-reactive cells,[7-9] although the role of positive selection or "education" for self-MHC restriction elements is still controversial.

Our laboratory has primarily studied the DN thymocyte subsets. Analysis of DN cells by several criteria has indicated that this population is itself quite heterogeneous.[10,11] These findings implicate the existence of a number of subpopulations: however, the ontogenic and functional relationships between these subsets is largely unknown. We will summarize in this paper studies that have identified four major phenotypically distinct subsets differing in cell-cycle status and *in vitro* activation requirements. We have further focused biochemical and molecular studies on two subpopulations that have opposing patterns of T-cell R expression. Both γ/δ and α/β CD3-associated T-cell Rs have been recently identified on DN thymocytes.[12,13] Although α/β T-cell Rs are now understood to be triggered by MHC molecules generally associated with antigenic peptides,[14] the specificity of γ/δ T-cell Rs remains unknown. Moreover, the functional role of γ/δ cells and the relationship between the γ/δ and α/β lineages remains unclear.

FOUR MAJOR SUBSETS OF DN THYMOCYTES

The heterogeneity of DN thymocytes is a source of considerable confusion because most phenotypic markers identify partly overlapping subsets. Using two-color flow microfluorometry in extensive cross-correlation experiments, we have identified in the thymus of adult C57BL/6 mice four major populations of DN cells, each of which can be identified in a concordant fashion by a number of discriminating markers.[15] DN thymocytes were prepared by treating thymocytes twice with appropriate anti-CD4 and anti-CD8 monoclonal antibodies (mAb) plus complement. We will consider here two CD3⁻ (A+B) and two CD3⁺ populations (C+D). Population A, 30% of DN, is enriched for large actively cycling cells, which we have identified using the RL-73 mAb. RL-73 detects a 55 kDa glycoprotein of unknown function on activated, but not on resting, lymphocytes.[16] Population B, 45% of DN, expresses the interleukin-2 receptor (IL-2R), but also RL-73, albeit with lesser intensity than A. Population C, 15% of DN, is characterized by bright staining for both CD3 and CD5. It does not contain cells reactive with F23.1, a mAb that identifies α/β T-cell R with β chains belonging to the $V\beta_8$ gene family.[17] We have shown[18] that these CD3-associated T cell–R molecules are of

TABLE 1. Phenotype, Cell-Cycle Status, and Activation Requirements of DN Thymocyte Subsets

Population	A	B	C	D
Percent total DN	30	45	15	10
RL-73[a]	+ +	+	−	−
IL-2 R	−	+	−	−
CD3	−	−	+	+
CD5	−	−	+	+
F23.1	−	−	−	+
B2A2	+	+	+	−
Percent cycling[b]	50	13	7	
PMA IONO, IL-2[c]	+	+	+	+
PMA IONO	−	−	−	+
Con A, IL-2	−	−	+	−

[a] Surface phenotype was determined by cross-correlation analysis of two-color flow microfluorometry experiments. + denotes homogeneous staining of essentially all cells. − implies absence of + staining cells.

[b] Cell-cycle analysis of sorted cells was performed by staining with propidium iodide. Populations C and D were not analyzed separately.

[c] Sorted cells (1000) were placed into microwells with the indicated supplements at the following concentrations: PMA, 5–10 ng/ml; IONO, 250 ng/ml; IL-2, 200 U/ml; Con A, 0.5–1 μg/ml. After 6 days, wells were scored for proliferation by measuring incorporation of [³H]thymidine. + denotes optimal growth. − implies no or only residual proliferation. For complete data see reference 15.

the γ/δ type (see below). These cells are small and have only residual staining with RL-73. Population D, 10% of DN, stains brightly with CD5, whereas CD3 is expressed at a lower intensity than in C. Interestingly, up to 50% of population D could be identified with the F23.1 mAb. These small resting thymocytes do not express RL-73. Analysis of cell-cycle status by staining sorted cell populations with the DNA binding dye propidium iodide was consistent with the pattern of RL-73 expression (see TABLE 1). Another cell-surface marker detected by B2A2[19] and J11d[20] mAb identified populations A, B, and C, but not D. The B2A2 antigen has no known function and is expressed on a number of hematopoietic cells, but not on most mature T cells.

IN VITRO ACTIVATION REQUIREMENTS

The four subpopulations of DN cells defined on the basis of IL-2R, RL-73, and B2A2 expression were also found to have distinct activation requirements. In these studies,[15] we used *in vitro* assays in which proliferation was dependent upon exogenously supplied IL-2, or correlated with the endogenous production of IL-2 by the DN cells. Although the role of IL-2 in the *in vivo* proliferation and/or maturation of DN cells is not clear, our and several previous studies have shown that at least some DN cells have the capacity to both produce IL-2 and proliferate *in vitro* to IL-2 under conditions in which only T cells can respond.[21-23] This suggests that responsiveness reflects characteristics of cells committed to the T lineage. Comparison of activation requirements among different subsets may thus provide important clues as to their functional and ontogenic relationships.

Each of the four populations proliferated well to the combination of phorbol myristate acetate (PMA), ionomycin (IONO), and IL-2. Presumably, the mechanism of IL-2–driven proliferation involves the synergistic effects of protein kinase C activation and calcium mobilization induced by PMA and IONO, respectively, a mechanism hypothesized for the activation of peripheral T cells.[24] Of the four subpopulations, one, namely population D, was capable of proliferation to PMA and IONO alone (TABLE 1). Strikingly, the other three subsets proliferated vigorously if IL-1 was included in the cultures. The proliferative responses of the four subpopulations to PMA plus IONO ($+/-$ IL-1 when required) were in most cases correlated with detectable IL-2 production. A reasonable possibility is that the cells proliferated by an autocrine mechanism, using their own synthesized IL-2. IL-1 is a cytokine with effects on many cell types, both of hemopoetic and nonhemopoetic origin. But it is important to point out that we have found that highly purified CD4$^+$ and CD8$^+$ mature T cells are not IL-1–dependent in this assay, even at suboptimal PMA or IONO concentrations (R. C. Howe and H. R. MacDonald, unpublished observations). It is thus tempting to speculate that the requirement for IL-1 by DN cells in this assay reflects a property of progenitor cells (not yet fully differentiated), and that with further maturation such cells lose IL-1–dependence. According to this view, population D might represent the most fully differentiated DN subset in that its response most closely resembles that of peripheral T cells.

A second discriminatory bioassay was found to be IL-2–dependent responsiveness to Con A and to an anti-Thy-1 mAb(V8) previously defined to be mitogenic for peripheral T cells.[25] Both mature CD8$^+$ and CD4$^+$ T-cell subsets are responsive to Con A and anti-Thy-1 mAb (in the presence of IL-2), but they differ in that the CD4$^+$ population requires an additional signal in the form of PMA or accessory cells.[26] Of the four subpopulations defined in this study, only the two RL-73$^-$ subsets (C,D) were responsive in these assays. The response of population D required IL-1 in addition, but neither IL-1, crude supernatant from Con A–stimulated rat-spleen cultures, nor PMA were capable of improving the poor response of populations A and B. The nature of the difference in lectin or anti-Thy-1 responsiveness between these subsets of DN thymocytes is not yet clear. Studies with peripheral T cell–model systems have implicated an obligatory requirement for cell surface–CD3 expression in anti-Thy-1–induced activation.[27] Indeed, populations A and B are largely CD3$^-$, whereas populations C and D are largely CD3$^+$, but whether CD3 expression alone accounts for differential responsiveness of these subsets is not yet clear.

The culturing conditions we have described were essential to expand populations C and D sufficiently to allow characterization of the CD3-associated molecules or mRNA analysis of T cell–R expression. Indeed, as DN thymocytes represent 3% of cells in the mouse thymus, populations C and D account for only 0.5% and 0.3% of total thymocytes, respectively. Population D was isolated by antibody and complement depletion (2x) for CD4, CD8, and B2A2. After 7 days of culturing in the presence of PMA, IONO, and IL-2, the cells were expanded 10- to 20-fold. Like the freshly isolated cells, they expressed CD3, and to about 50%, they also expressed F23.1 determinants.[12] In order to obtain large amounts of population C, we took advantage of the fact that this is the only subset capable of growing to Con A plus IL-2. In practice, total DN thymocytes stimulated with Con A and cultured for 7 days in the presence of IL-2 resulted consistently in cells expressing uniformly CD3 and lacking F23.1 determinants. These cultured cells were therefore considered to be representative of population C.

Expression of T Cell–R Molecules

By immunoprecipitation with anti-CD3 antibodies of surface iodinated and digitonin solubilized cells, population C could be shown to express two predomi-

TABLE 2. T Cell–R Expression by Peripheral Lymph Node T Cells (LN) and $CD3^+$ Subsets of DN Thymocytes

Population	LN	C	D
mRNA[a]			
C_α 1.6 kb	+		+
C_α 1.1 kb	+/−		+
C_β 1.3 kb	+		+
C_β 1 kb	+/−	+	+/−
C_γ 1.3 kb		+	+
C_δ 2 kb		+	+
Immunoprecipitation[b]			
M_r 37–43,000 α/β			+
M_r 35/45,000 γ/δ		+	+/−

[a] Northern blot analysis of C_α, C_β, C_γ, and C_δ mRNA levels in populations cultured with PMA, IONO + IL-2 (D + LN), and in Con A–stimulated DN thymocytes (C) cultured with IL-2. +/− denote 5- to 10-fold lower mRNA levels than +; no symbol implies undetectable levels.

[b] ^{125}I-surface-labeled cells were solubilized using digitonin precipitated with anti-CD3 antibody 145-2C 11[41] and analyzed under reducing conditions.

nant glycosylated polypeptides forming a disulfide-linked heterodimer of M_r 35,000 and 45,000 typical of a γ/δ T-cell R using a single glycosylated γ chain.[18] Corresponding full-length transcripts for the γ and δ genes could be demonstrated by Northern blot analysis (TABLE 2). RNase protection experiments were also consistent with the previously reported predominant expression by adult DN thymocytes of T cell–R γ chains, consisting of $V_{\gamma2}$, $C_{\gamma1}$ gene products.[13] Population C was further shown to lack T cell–R α mRNA and to express only short T cell–R β transcripts (1 kb) corresponding to DJ_β rearrangements. These findings parallel observations in murine fetal ontogeny of predominantly γ/δ T cell–Rs around day 15 of development[13] together with DJ_β rearrangements.[28,29]

Population D was found to express predominantly CD3-associated proteins of M_r 37–43,000 consistent with α/β T cell–R heterodimers. Northern blot analysis showed similar levels of full-length T cell–R α and β transcripts as in normal lymph node cells (TABLE 2). Surprisingly, population D, unlike mature T cells, expressed comparable levels of full-length T cell–R γ mRNA as found in population C. The high sensitivity of RNase-protection analysis allowed quantitation of mRNA levels in fresh isolates of population D. Both fresh and cultivated cells expressed similar levels of T cell–R α, β, and γ mRNA, thereby confirming the results obtained with cultured cells and, in particular, excluding artifactual induction of T cell–R γ mRNA *in vitro*. Compared to population C, population D expressed similar high levels of $V_{\gamma1.2}$ mRNA, which is generally not expressed as a cell-surface protein. $V_{\gamma2}$ mRNA, however, which codes for the M_r 35,000 protein, was expressed at 5- to 10-fold lower levels in D than in C.

Immunoprecipitation experiments with population D consistently showed faint bands compatible with γ/δ T cell–R proteins. By Northern blot analysis, these cells express over 10 times lower levels of T cell–R δ mRNA than population C. Ongoing experiments using hybridomas derived from population D are compatible with the existence of a γ/δ subset within population D that would be distinct from population C. We could find no evidence yet for the alternative possibility of cells expressing both γ/δ and α/β heterodimers.

Regulation of T cell–R γ mRNA has, however, been reported under different short-term cultivation conditions for DN thymocytes.[30] Using PMA and IL-2 for 7 days (and likewise PMA, IONO, and IL-2, unpublished observations), we have observed a dramatic induction of T cell–R γ mRNA in B6 *lpr/lpr* DN lymph node cells.[31] These cells, like population D, express surface α/β T cell–Rs, but when freshly isolated, express only minimal levels of T cell–R γ mRNA. Although further similarities between the two populations have been noted,[13] it is unclear how the *lpr* mutation may relate to this dysregulation of the T cell–R γ genes in *lpr/lpr* DN T cells. Phenotypically mature *lpr/lpr*, as well as normal C57BL/6 T cells do not show altered T cell–R γ mRNA levels upon similar *in vitro* cultivation.

Overexpression of the $V_{\beta8.2}$ Gene Product by Population D

The expression of F23.1 determinants by up to 50% of cells in population D was unusual insofar as the F23.1 mAb detects $V_{\beta8}$ gene products out of a total V_β gene pool of around 20. Furthermore, RNase protection experiments (FIG. 1) and, more recently, mAb specific for $V_{\beta8.2}$[32] indicate that this $V_{\beta8.2}$ gene product, in particular, is considerably overexpressed in population D.

In pre-B lines, preferential expression of V_H genes has been correlated with proximity to the J_H locus.[33] Such an interpretation is unlikely to be applicable to the $V_{\beta8.2}$ gene, which is situated at a further distance from the $J_{\beta1}$ locus than a number of V_β genes, including $V_{\beta8.1}$.[34] Factors other than chromosomal location, however, could lead to differential expression of V_β genes. Fetal organ culture experiments[35] indicate that precursors of population D are already present in day 14 fetal thymus. Any hypothesis should also take into account the observation that population D accumulates significantly only after birth.[13]

To determine whether a putative developmental block would precede or follow the stage of repertoire selection, we examined in a number of different H-2 haplotypes the frequency of cells from population D expressing $V_{\beta8}$ gene products. The lack of major histocompatibility complex (MHC) association we found for $V_{\beta8.2}$ overexpression by population D[12] would argue strongly against a simple positive (or negative) selection of these cells based on reactivity to polymorphic self-MHC components. One possibility might be that T cell–R using $V_{\beta 8.2}$ have an intrinsically weak affinity for nonpolymorphic MHC products involved in the putative positive selection process, thus leading to an accumulation of "unselected" cells in population D.

The question of further differentiation by DN subsets has been recently addressed by *in vivo* reconstitution experiments[36,37] that suggest that population B

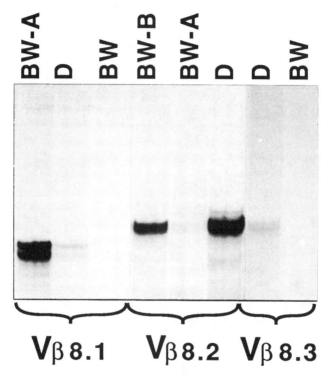

FIGURE 1. RNase protection analysis with $V_{\beta 8}$-specific anti-sense RNA probes. Population D, cultured for 7 days with PMA, IONO, and IL-2 was compared with T-cell hybridomas expressing either $V_{\beta 8.1}$ (BW-A) or $V_{\beta 8.2}$ (BW-B). RNA from thymoma BW5147 (BW) served as the negative control.

had the greatest precursor activity, whereas population D was inactive. DN T cells comparable to population D accumulate in the grotesquely enlarged lymph nodes of *lpr/lpr* mice, and they too have been reported to overexpress $V_{\beta 8.2}$.[38] If indeed population D does not differentiate further nor leave the thymus, it may be conjectured that such a developmental block could be altered in *lpr/lpr* mice.

LINEAGE RELATIONSHIPS OF CD3+ DN THYMOCYTES

The patterns of T cell–R expression that we have described in DN thymocyte subsets are consistent with a dichotomy of α/β and γ/δ T cell–R lineages. The failure of population C to transcribe T cell—R α mRNA or full-length T cell–R β mRNA supports the concept that further rearrangements at these loci are inhibited by productive γ/δ rearrangements. That such cells could, in analogy to immunoglobulin class switching, go on to express α/β T cell-R later in development would seem very unlikely. Rather, these results are compatible with a recently proposed deletional mechanism allowing for mutually exclusive expression of T cell–R α and δ genes.[39]

The *in vivo* differentiation potential of the four major DN populations we have described remains to be clarified. The bulk of the evidence to date, however, would suggest that most progenitor activity for α/β T cells resides in populations

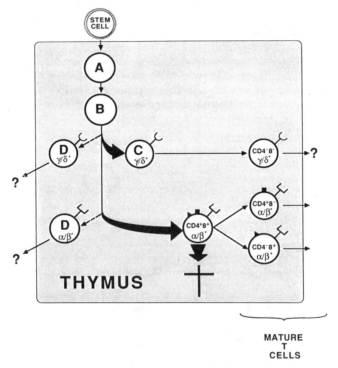

FIGURE 2. Hypothetical model of lineage affiliations of CD3[+] cells (see text).

A and B, but little in population D. In addition, there is no direct evidence that population C would be a precursor of γ/δ T cell–R[+] cells in peripheral lymphoid organs. Whether γ/δ T cell–R[+] DN thymocytes of population D are a significant entity at all is highly questionable. The possibility that at least some CD4[+] CD8[+] cortical thymocytes represent an intermediate stage of differentiation between DN cells and mature T cells is an attractive possibility for which there exists no direct evidence (for discussion see reference 40). It is with such caveats in mind that our working model of the lineage relationships of CD3[+] DN thymocytes should be considered (FIG. 2). It remains to be seen whether either populations A or B give rise to populations C and D.

ACKNOWLEDGMENT

We are indebted to Anne-France Brunet for her patient and cheerful assistance in the preparation of this manuscript.

REFERENCES

1. RAULET, D., R. GARMAN, H. SAITO & S. TONEGAWA. 1985. Developmental regulation of T cell receptor gene expression. Nature **314:** 425.
2. FOWLKES, B. J., L. EDISON, B. J. MATHIESON & T. M. CHUSED. 1985. Early T lymphocytes. Differentiation *in vivo* of adult intrathymic precursor cells. J. Exp. Med. **162:** 802.
3. HAVRAN, W. L., M. POENIE, J. KIMURA, R. TSIEN, A. WEISS & J. P. ALLISON. 1987. Expression and function of the CD3-antigen receptor on murine CD4$^+$8$^+$ thymocytes. Nature **330:** 170.
4. SCOLLAY, R., P. BARTLETT & K. SHORTMAN. 1984. T cell development in the adult murine thymus: Changes in the expression of the surface antigens Ly2, L3T4 and B2A2 during development from early precursor cells to emigrants. Immunol. Rev. **82:** 79.
5. SLECKMAN, BARRY P., A. PETERSON, W. K. JONES, J. A. FORAN, J. L. GREENSTEIN, B. SEED & S. J. BURAKOFF. 1987. Expression and function of CD4 in a murine T-cell hybridoma. Nature **328:** 351.
6. DEMBIC, Z., W. HAAS, R. ZAMOYSKA, J. PARNES, M. STEINMETZ & H. VON BOEHMER. 1987. Transfection of the CD8 gene enhances T-cell recognition. Nature **326:** 510.
7. KAPPLER, J. W., N. ROEHM & P. MARRACK. 1987a. T cell tolerance by clonal elimination in the thymus. Cell **49:** 273.
8. KAPPLER, J. W., T. WADE, J. WHITE, E. KUSHNIR, M. BLACKMAN, J. BILL, N. ROEHM & P. MARRACK. 1987b. A T cell receptor V$_\beta$ segment that imparts reactivity to a class II major histocompatibility complex product. Cell **49:** 263.
9. MACDONALD, H. R., R. SCHNEIDER, R. K. LEES, R. C. HOWE, H. ACHA-ORBEA, H. FESTENSTEIN, R. M. ZINKERNAGEL & H. HENGARTNER. 1988b. T cell receptor V$_\beta$ use predicts reactivity and tolerance to Mls^a-encoded antigens. Nature **332:** 40.
10. FOWLKES, B. J. & B. J. MATHIESON. 1985. Intrathymic differentiation: thymocyte heterogeneity and the characterization of early T-cell precursors. Surv. Immunol. Res. **4:** 96.
11. CEREDIG, R. & H. R. MACDONALD. 1985. Intrathymic differentiation: Some unanswered questions. Surv. Immunol. Res. **4:** 87.
12. BUDD, R. C., G. C. MIESCHER, R. C. HOWE, R. K. LEES, C. BRON & H. R. MACDONALD. 1987b. Developmentally regulated expression of T cell receptor β chain variable domains in immature thymocytes. J. Exp. Med. **166:** 577.
13. PARDOLL, D. M., B. J. FOWLKES, J. A. BLUESTONE, A. M. KRUISBEEK, W. L. MALOY, J. E. COLIGAN & R. H. SCHWARTZ. 1987. Differential expression of two distinct T cell receptors during thymocyte development. Nature **326:** 79.
14. BJORKMAN, P. J., M. A. SAPER, B. SAMRAOUI, W. S. BENNETT, J. L. STROMINGER & D. C. WILEY. 1987. The foreign antigen binding site and T cell recognition regions of class I histocompatibility antigens. Nature **329:** 512.
15. HOWE, R. C. & H. R. MACDONALD. 1988. Heterogeneity of immature (Lyt-2$^-$/L3T4$^-$) thymocytes. Identification of 4 major phenotypically distinct subsets differing in cell cycle status and *in vitro* activation requirements. J. Immunol. **140:** 1047.
16. MACDONALD, H-R., R. K. LEES & C. BRON. 1985. Cell surface glycoproteins involved in the stimulation of interleukin-1–dependent interleukin-2 production by a subline of EL4 thymoma cells. I. Functional characterization by monoclonal antibodies. J. Immunol. **135:** 3944.
17. STAERZ, U. D., H.-G. RAMMENSEE, J. D. BENEDETTO & M. J. BEVAN. 1985. Characterisation of a murine monoclonal antibody specific for an allotypic determinant on T cell antigen receptor. J. Immunol. **134:** 3994.

18. MIESCHER, G. C., R. C. HOWE, R. K. LEES & H. R. MACDONALD. 1988. CD3-associated α/β and γ/δ heterodimeric receptors are expressed by distinct populations of CD4⁻ CD8⁻ thymocytes. J. Immunol. **140:** 1779.

19. CRISPE, I. N. & M. J. BEVAN. 1987. Expression and functional significance of the J11d marker on mouse thymocytes. J. Immunol. **138:** 2013.

20. PALACIOS, R. & H. VON BOEHMER. 1986. Requirements for growth of immature thymocytes from fetal and adult mice *in vitro*. Eur. J. Immunol. **16:** 12.

21. LUGO, J. P., S. N. KRISHNAN, R. D. SAILOR & E. V. ROTHENBERG. 1986. Early precursor thymocytes can produce interleukin 2 upon stimulation with calcium ionophore and phorbol ester. Proc. Natl. Acad. Sci. USA **83:** 1862.

22. TRUNEH, A., F. ALBERT, P. GOLSTEIN & A. SCHMITT-VERHULST. 1985. Early steps of lymphocyte activation bypassed by synergy between calcium ionophore and phorbol ester. Nature **313:** 318.

23. TRUNEH, A., F. ALBERT, P. GOLSTEIN & A.-M. SCHMITT-VERHULST. 1985. Calcium ionophore plus phorbol ester can substitute for antigen in the induction of cytolytic T lymphocytes from specifically primed precursors. J. Immunol. **135:** 2262.

24. KAIBUCHI, K., Y. TAKAI & Y. NISHIZUKA. 1985. Protein kinase C and calcium ion in mitogenic response of macrophage-depleted human peripheral lymphocytes. J. Biol. Chem. **260:** 1366.

25. MACDONALD, H. R., C. BRON, M. ROUSSEAUX, C. HORVATH & J.-C. CEROTTINI. 1985. Production and characterization of monoclonal anti-Thy-1 antibodies that stimulate lymphokine production by cytolytic T cell clones. Eur. J. Immunol. **15:** 495.

26. ERARD, F., M. NABHOLZ, A. DUPUY-D'ANGEAC & H. R. MACDONALD. 1985. Differential requirements for the induction of interleukin 2 responsiveness in L3T4⁺ and Lyt-2⁺ T cell subsets. J. Exp. Med. **162:** 1738.

27. SCHMITT-VERHULST, A.-M., A. GUIMEZANES, C. BOYER, M. POENIE, R. TALEN, M. BUFERNE, C. HUS & L. LESERMAN. 1987. Pleiotropic loss of activation pathways in a T-cell receptor β-chain deletion variant of a cytolytic T-cell clone. Nature **325:** 628.

28. BORN, W., J. YAGUE, E. PALMER, J. KAPPLER & P. MARRACK. 1985. Rearrangement of T-cell receptor β-chain genes during T-cell development. Proc. Natl. Acad. Sci. USA **82:** 2925.

29. BORN, W., G. RATHBUN, P. TUCKER, P. MARRACK & J. KAPPLER. 1986. Synchronized rearrangement of T-cell γ and β chain genes in fetal thymocyte development. Science **234:** 479.

30. KINNON, C., K. L. MCGUIRE & E. V. ROTHENBERG. 1987. Differential regulation of T cell receptor gamma genes in immature thymocyte populations. Eur. J. Immunol. **17:** 1265.

31. MIESCHER, G. C., R. C. BUDD, R. K. LEES & H. R. MACDONALD. 1987. Abnormal expression of T cell receptor genes in Lyt-2⁻ L3T4⁻ lymphocytes of *lpr* mice: Comparison with normal immature thymocytes. J. Immunol. **138:** 1959.

32. FOWLKES, B. J., A. M. KRUISBEEK, H. TON-HAT, M. A. WESTON, J. E. COLIGAN, R. H. SCHWARTZ & D. M. PARDOLL. 1987. A novel population of T-cell receptor $\alpha\beta$-bearing thymocytes which predominantly express a single V_β gene family. Nature **329:** 251.

33. YANCOPOULOS, G. D. & F. W. ALT. 1986. Regulation of the assembly and expression of variable-region genes. Ann. Rev. Immunol. **4:** 339.

34. CHOU, H. S., C. A. NELSON, S. A. GODAMBE, D. D. CHAPLIN & D. Y. LOH. 1987. Germline organization of the murine T cell receptor β-chain genes. Science **238:** 545.

35. CEREDIG, R., F. LYNCH & P. NEWMAN. 1987. Phenotypic properties, interleukin 2 production, and developmental origin of a "mature" subpopulation of Lyt-2⁻/L3T4⁻ mouse thymocytes. Proc. Natl. Acad. Sci. USA. **84:** 8578.

36. SHIMONKEVITZ, R. P., L. A. HUSMANN, M. J. BEVAN & I. N. CRISPE. 1987. Transient expression of IL-2 receptor precedes the differentiation of immature thymocytes. Nature **329:** 157.

37. CRISPE, I. N., M. W. MOORE, L. A. HUSMANN, L. SMITH, M. J. BEVAN & R. P. SHIMONKEVITZ. 1987b. Differentiation potential of subsets of CD4⁻8⁻ thymocytes. Nature **329:** 336.

38. SINGER, P. A., R. J. MCEVILLY, D. J. NOONAN, F. J. DIXON & A. N. THEOFILO-POULOS. 1986. Clonal diversity and T-cell receptor β-chain variable gene expression in enlarged lymph nodes of MRL-lpr/lpr lupus mice. Proc. Natl. Acad. Sci. USA **83:** 7018.

39. CHIEN, Y., M. IWASHIMA, K. B. KAPLAN, J. F. ELLIOT & M. DAVIS. 1987. A new T-cell receptor gene located with the alpha locus and expressed early in T-cell differentiation. Nature **327:** 677.

40. MACDONALD, H. R., R. C. HOWE, T. PEDRAZZINI *et al.* 1988. T cell lineages, repertoire selection and tolerance induction. Immunol. Rev. **104.**

41. LEO, O., M. FOO, D. H. SACHS, L. E. SAMELSON & J. A. BLUESTONE. 1987. Identification of a monoclonal antibody specific for a murine T3 polypeptide. Proc. Natl. Acad. Sci. USA **84:** 1374.

The Influence of MHC Gene Products on the Generation of an Antigen-Specific T-Cell Repertoire[a]

SIMONA B. SORGER, LOUIS A. MATIS,[b] ISAAC ENGEL,
DAVID L. McELLIGOTT, PAMELA J. FINK, AND
STEPHEN M. HEDRICK

Department of Biology
The Cancer Center
University of California, San Diego
La Jolla, California 92093
and
[b]*Medicine Branch*
National Cancer Institute
Bethesda, Maryland 20892

INTRODUCTION

The development and selection of the cells in the immune system has been studied by analyzing the specificity of T-cell populations for the recognition of self-encoded major histocompatibility complex (MHC) molecules. In radiation bone marrow chimeras,[1-4] thymic chimeras,[5-8] allophenic mice,[9] and transgenic mice,[10,11] T cells arise that preferentially respond to antigen in association with the allelic forms of the MHC molecules expressed in the thymus during T-cell maturation. This selection of the näive T-cell population would appear to affect the repertoire of immunologically competent T cells, and an example of the effects of this selection may be manifested in the phenomenon termed immune response (Ir) gene control. For many specific antigens, there is a polymorphism in the ability of mice to respond immunologically, and this polymorphism maps to genes within the MHC.[12-14] In fact, the same genes that control the response to antigen also encode the MHC molecules recognized in association with antigen.[14-16] One hypothesis is that, in nonresponsive mouse strains, selection of the T-cell population in the thymus eliminates or fails to expand the T cells that would respond to antigen in association with the allelic forms of the MHC molecules present.[17-25] Whether this selection process is wholly positive for self-recognition, negative for self-tolerance, or a combination of both is entirely uncertain.

In order to further understand the processes of T-cell selection, we were interested in determining whether the selection mechanisms operating during intrathymic development simply expand all T cells with the ability to recognize self-MHC molecules, or whether these selection mechanisms skew the repertoire of T cells based on additional more complex interactions. One way of addressing this

[a] This work was supported by USPHS Grants AI 21372, GM 35880, and NSF DCB-8452023 (to S. M. Hedrick). S. B. Sorger and I. Engel are supported by USPHS training Grant CA 09174, and S. M. Hedrick is supported by Research Career Development Award AI 00662. P. J. Fink is a senior fellow of the California Division of the American Cancer Society (Ordway Fellowship S-14).

question is to determine whether T cells with the same specificity for antigen and MHC molecules can be commonly found in different MHC congenic strains of mice, or whether each MHC congenic strain has a unique repertoire of T cells.

In this report, we have addressed the question of the development and selection of the T cells specific for pigeon cytochrome *c* in three MHC-congenic stains of mice. In each strain, there are T-cell clones that respond to antigen in association with the MHC molecules from one or two of the other strains.[26-28] Experiments were directed at determining whether the clones in each strain were related not only by specificity, but by the expression of similar α- and β-chain genes encoding the T-cell receptor (TcR). A comparison of the receptor genes expressed indicated that two of the strains appear to express the same genes, whereas the third strain appears to express a different repertoire of receptors. These results have implications for the influence of MHC on the generation of immune response polymorphisms.

MATERIAL AND METHODS

Animals

B10.A and B10.A(5R) mice were obtained from the Jackson Laboratory, Bar Harbor, ME. B10.S(9R) mice were bred at the National Institutes of Health (NIH), Bethesda, MD. Mice of either sex from 6 to 12 weeks of age were used for experiments.

T-Cell Lines and Clones

T-cell lines were established as previously described.[29] T-cell clones were derived by limiting dilution as described.[28] The B10.S(9R) T-cell clones 6.9R.E1 and 6.9R.D6 were derived from the 6.9R.1 line (see text). The 1B6 hybridoma was cloned from an independent line.

Southern Hybridization

High molecular weight DNA was prepared as previously described.[29] DNA was digested to completion with *Hind* III according to manufacturer's specifications and electrophoresed on 0.8% agarose gels at 25 V for 36 hours. The DNA was transferred to nitrocellulose by the method of Southern[30] and hybridized as described.[29]

DNA Probes

The probes for the D and J regions of the β chain and the $V_\beta B10$, $V_\beta 2B4$, $V_\beta C8$, and $V_\alpha 2B4.2$ probes were described in detail in a previous paper.[29] (V, variable region; D, diversity region; J, joining region.) The $V_\beta 86T1$ probe was subcloned from a thymus-derived cDNA clone 86T1.[31] The $V_\beta 86T1$ probe spans a 330 basepair (BP) *Bam* HI-*Eco* RI fragment.

RESULTS

The Comparison of B10.A and B10.A(5R) Antigen-Specific Repertoires

The predominant pigeon cytochrome c–specific T-cell clone in B10.A mice responds to pigeon and moth cytochrome c in association with B10.A antigen-presenting cells (APCs), but only to moth cytochrome c in association with B10.A(5R) APCs (designated phenotype I in reference 29). Interestingly, B10.A(5R) mice do not respond to pigeon cytochrome c, but do respond to immunization with moth cytochrome c. T cells from mice so immunized can be restimulated with moth cytochrome c in association with B10.A(5R) APCs, and can also be restimulated with pigeon or moth cytochrome c in association with B10.A APCs. Consequently, it has been speculated that the B10.A and B10.A(5R) strains produce exactly the same cytochrome c–specific T-cell clones.[32]

To analyze this prediction, DNA from a moth cytochrome c–specific B10.A(5R) hybridoma clone 4.11, which exhibits phenotype I,[26,33] was analyzed for gene rearrangements using α- and β-chain variable region probes derived from B10.A pigeon cytochrome c–specific T-cell clones. As depicted in FIGURE 1, 4.11

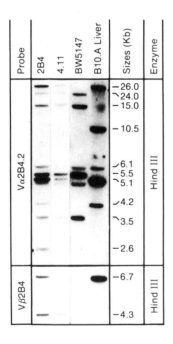

FIGURE 1. Southern blot analyses of DNA from two pigeon cytochrome c–specific hybridomas. 2B4 was derived from a B10.A mouse, whereas 4.11 was derived from a B10.A(5R) mouse. The hybridoma fusion partner, BW5147, and B10.A liver DNA were provided as controls. All the lanes were run on the same agarose gel with irrelevant lanes removed from the final FIGURE. The same blot was used for hybridization with the $V_\alpha 2B4.2$ and $V_\beta 2B4$ probes (see MATERIAL AND METHODS).

has a rearranged 4.3 kb *Hind* III band that hybridized to $V_\beta 2B4$, and thus appears to express the same V_β-J_β combination as the B10.A hybridoma 2B4 and three other previously described B10.A clones, D4, E2, and 2C2.[29] In addition, hybridization with $V_\alpha 2B4.2$ revealed a rearranged 2.6 kb *Hind* III band, again identical to that of the T-cell hybridoma 2B4 from the B10.A strain. Thus, these two clones with identical specificities, although derived from two different mouse strains, apparently rearrange the same V_β-J_β and V_α-J_α gene segments and, therefore, express very similar receptors.

The 2B4 hybridoma was used to generate an anti-idiotypic monoclonal antibody,[34] and this antibody was tested for reactivity on a variety of other pigeon cytochrome *c*–specific clones generated at the same time. Consistent with the results of others,[35] little or no apparent cross-reactivity was seen (L. E. Samelson, personal communication). This is not surprising because phenotype I clones express two slightly different members of the $V_{\alpha}2B4$ gene family,[36] as many as five different $J_{\alpha}s$, and two different $J_{\beta}s$.[29] Given the above data indicating the similarity of the receptor gene elements expressed by 2B4 and 4.11, we would speculate that these clones would be likely candidates for the unusual property of shared idiotypy.

The Comparison of B10.A and B10.S(9R) Antigen-Specific Repertoires

Although the majority of pigeon cytochrome *c*–specific clones in B10.A mice exhibit phenotype I, there exists a percentage of T cells that responds to antigen presented on B10.S(9R), but not B10.A(5R), APCs (phenotype III in reference 29). Previous work has shown that pigeon cytochrome *c*–specific hybridomas and normal T-cell clones isolated from B10.S(9R) mice can be grouped into two different phenotypes.[27,28] Clones of the first phenotype respond to pigeon but not to moth cytochrome *c* on B10.S(9R) APCs and do not respond to pigeon cytochrome *c* on B10.A APCs. T-cell clones typical of the second phenotype respond to pigeon as well as moth cytochrome *c* in the context of B10.S(9R) or B10.A APCs, and all of the MHC specificities map to the I-E_{β} and I-E_{α} genes.[27,28] B10.S(9R) clones of this second phenotype, which we have designated phenotype V, exhibit a reactivity pattern nominally similar to phenotype IIIB B10.A clones (phenotype IIIA and IIIB clones differ only in junctional sequences[29,36]). A comparison of the dose-response curves of phenotype IIIB and phenotype V clones is provided in FIGURE 2. A very important point to note in comparing these dose-response curves is that the antigens used in the experiments were the 81-103,4 fragments of cytochrome *c* because of the unavailability of whole-moth cytochrome *c*. The importance is that the immunogen, whole pigeon cytochrome *c*, elicits a response in phenotype III clones when presented by B10.S(9R) APCs of the same magnitude as that obtained with B10.A APCs, although with possibly a tenfold shift in the dose-response curve to higher concentrations of antigen.[29,36] Thus, although the cross-reaction to cytochrome *c* fragments in association B10.S(9R) APCs appears low, it is really a poorly understood difference between the antigenicity of native and fragmented pigeon cytochrome *c*. Nonetheless, although the dose-response curves of phenotype III and V clones are similar, a comparison of the fine specificities of these two phenotypes revealed several differences. Probably the most striking difference is that phenotype V clones also responded to 10–20% of the maximum when cultured with B10.A APCs in the absence of antigen. This alloreactivity maps to the I-E^k-encoded Ia molecule, the same Ia molecule recognized in association with antigen.[27,28] Thus, phenotype III B10.A clones are similar to phenotype V B10.S(9R) clones, but they are not identical as in the case of phenotype I B10.A and B10.A(5R) clones. We would, therefore, not expect to see identical receptors used by the B10.A and B10.S(9R) strains, but specificity similarities suggested a possible overlap in the use of gene elements. Because B10.A clones of phenotype IV[29] also respond to pigeon cytochrome *c* on B10.A and to some degree on B10.S(9R) APCs, the possibility existed that clones similar to these are present in the B10.S(9R) strain as well (FIG. 2).

In an earlier report,[29] we analyzed the heterogeneity of TcR rearrangements within a population of B10.A pigeon cytochrome *c*–reactive T cells. Using probes

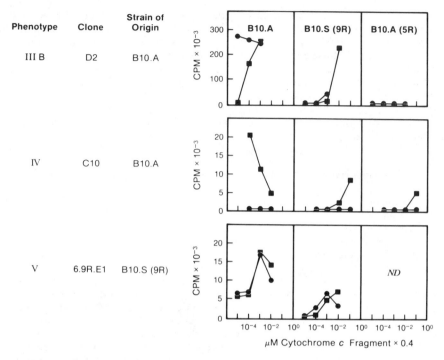

FIGURE 2. Proliferative responses of three prototypic pigeon cytochrome c–specific T-cell clones. Proliferation was measured as cpm of [³H]thymidine incorporated as described previously.[29] Pigeon fragment 81-104 (■) and moth fragment 81-103 (●) were used as antigens with APCs derived from B10.A, B10.S(9R), or B10.A(5R) mice as indicated in the top panel. Each clone exemplifies a phenotype that cross-reacts on B10.A and B10.S(9R) APCs.

that hybridized to the two J_β region clusters, we were able to detect all the β-chain rearrangements that were later found to be represented in T-cell clones of phenotypes I, II, and III derived by limiting dilution. Previously described "D probes" were used to differentiate between DJ and complete VDJ rearrangements.[29] The T-cell lines could be further analyzed with probes to V regions isolated from pigeon cytochrome c–specific clones. The α chain locus was analyzed using V region probes only, because the large introns between J_α regions make it difficult to analyze in a manner similar to the β chain. Using these probes, rearrangements indicative of four separate clonotypes were observed in one T-cell line, and these clonotypes were later cloned from this line or from two other B10.A pigeon cytochrome c–specific lines.[29]

In order to determine the heterogeneity and gene expression of cytochrome c–specific T cells in B10.S(9R) mice, we performed the same type of analysis on a B10.S(9R) T-cell line. Three heterogeneous T-cell lines specific for pigeon cytochrome c were examined: two lines from a B10.A mouse and one line from a B.10S(9R) mouse. Line 5.A.1 was derived from a B10.A mouse immunized with pigeon cytochrome c and was stimulated six times *in vitro* with pigeon cytochrome c on B10.A APCs. Line 5.A.3 was derived from line 5.A.1 at the second *in vitro* stimulation and was stimulated four times with pigeon cytochrome c on

B10.S(9R) APCs. Line 6.9R.1 was derived from a B10.S(9R) mouse immunized with pigeon cytochrome *c*. This line was stimulated five times *in vitro* with pigeon cytochrome *c* on B10.S(9R) APCs. Southern blot data from lines 5.A.1 and 5.A.3 were presented in a previous paper[29] and are provided in FIGURE 3 for comparison. Using the probes to the two J_β clusters, it is immediately apparent that none of the detectable VDJ rearranged bands in line 6.9R.1 were shared by the B10.A lines, 5.A.1 and 5.A.3. Line 6.9R.1 has one prominent VDJ rearrangement when probed with the two J_β probes. This band is a 4.0 kb *Eco* RI fragment that hybridized to the $J_\beta 1$ genomic probe, and is distinct from any of the predominantly rearranged bands observed in either of the B10.A pigeon cytochrome *c*–specific lines. Several minor VDJ rearrangements could be seen with the $J_\beta 2$ probe in the B10.S(9R) line; however, there was no evidence of the predominant 6.0 kb *Eco* RI band characteristic of phenotype III B10.A T-cell clones and line 5.A.3.[29] The 6.0 kb band has been determined to be $V_\beta B10$ rearranging to $J_\beta 2.1$,[29] and this was confirmed when the DNA from the 5.A.3 line was reprobed with $V_\beta B10$ (FIG. 4). The $V_\beta B10$ probe also hybridized to a less intense band in the 5.A.1 lane but not to any of the rearranged bands in the 6.9R.1 lane (FIG. 4 and bands labeled 2 in FIG. 3). Similarly, the $V_\beta 2B4$ probe, which detects phenotype I clones, such as the 2B4

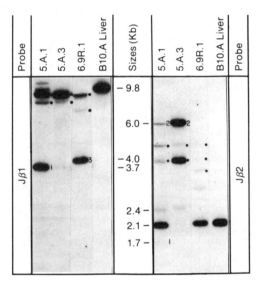

FIGURE 3. Southern blot analyses of three pigeon cytochrome *c*–reactive T-cell lines. As described in the text, line 5.A.1 was derived from a B10.A mouse and was stimulated with antigen on B10.A APCs. Line 5.A.3 was derived from line 5.A.1 and was stimulated with antigen on B10.S(9R) APCs. Line 6.9R.1 was derived from a B10.S(9R) mouse and cultured with B10.S(9R) APCs and antigen. The DNA from these lines and B10.A liver was digested with *Eco* RI, and the two blots represent duplicate samples run on the same agarose gel with only irrelevant lanes removed. The blots were hybridized with probes to the two J_β clusters, $J_\beta 1$ and $J_\beta 2$ probes (see MATERIAL AND METHODS). The germ line bands observed in B10.A liver DNA were identical to those seen in B10.S(9R) liver DNA. The blots were then reprobed with V_β and D_β probes (see MATERIAL AND METHODS; data not shown). The bands that also hybridized to one of the D probes, and therefore represent aberrant DJ rearrangements, are marked with a dot (•). Bands that subsequently hybridized to $V_\beta 2B4$ (1), $V_\beta B10$(2), and $V_\beta 86T1$ (3) are also marked.

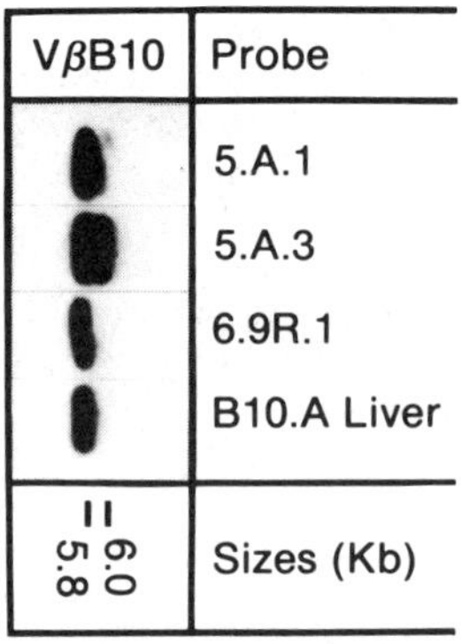

VβB10
Probe
5.A.1
5.A.3
6.9R.1
B10.A Liver
6.0
5.8
Sizes (Kb)

FIGURE 4. Analysis of $V_{\beta}B10$ rearrangements in three pigeon cytochrome *c*–reactive T-cell lines. The Southern blot used for hybridization with the $J_{\beta}1$ probe in FIGURE 3 is shown after removal of this first probe and hybridization to the $V_{\beta}B10$ probe.

hybridoma, hybridized to a rearranged band in the 5.A.1 lane (labeled 1 in FIG. 3), but not to any of the rearranged bands in the 6.9R.1 lane (data not shown). When this Southern blot was probed with $V_{\beta}C8$, which was rearranged in phenotype IV clones,[29] no rearranged bands were detected in any of the lanes (data not shown). Because phenotype IV clones appear to compose only a minor portion of the B10.A pigeon cytochrome *c*–specific repertoire, it is not surprising that they were not detected in these B10.A lines.

Using a probe for the $V_{\alpha}2B4$ gene family, several rearranged bands were detected in both of the B10.A lines (FIG. 5), whereas no rearranged bands hybridized to this probe in the B10.S(9R) line, lane 6.9R.1 (FIGURES 5 and 6). It is interesting to note, however, that two of the germline bands of the $V_{\alpha}2B4$ gene family were deleted in the 6.9R.1 lane. All of the above data indicate that the predominantly represented T cells in the B10.S(9R) line, 6.9R.1, do not use any gene elements that we have characterized for the B10.A lines and clones.

Probe
5.A.1
5.A.3
6.9R.1
B10.A Liver
Sizes (Kb)
Vα2B4.2
26.0
10.5
6.1
5.1
4.2
3.7
3.5
2.6
2.4

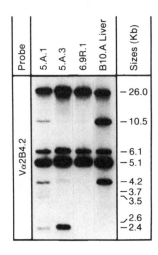

FIGURE 5. Alpha-chain gene rearrangements in pigeon cytochrome *c*–specific T-cell lines. DNA from the same T-cell lines as in FIGURES 3 and 4 was digested with *Hind* III and analyzed on a Southern blot with the $V_{\alpha}2B4.2$ probe as described in MATERIAL AND METHODS.

The β-chain genes of two B10.S(9R) pigeon cytochrome c–specific T-cell hybridomas (designated 9R-1 and 9R-2 in reference 27), which correspond to the two phenotypes identified in the B10.S(9R) mouse, have been isolated from genomic libraries and sequenced. Both hybridomas use the same β-chain rearrangement, namely $V_\beta 86T1^{31}$ rearranged to $J_\beta 1.2$, and differ only in the D_β regions (I. Engel and S. M. Hedrick, unpublished results). This rearrangement results in a 4.0 kb *Eco* RI fragment identical to that observed in the uncloned B10.S(9R)-derived T-cell line 6.9R.1 made several years subsequent to the hybridomas. Therefore, the Southern blot in FIGURE 3 was rehybridized with a probe for $V_\beta 86T1$. The prominent VDJ rearrangement (labeled 3 in FIG. 3) in the 6.9R.1 lane hybridized to the $V_\beta 86T1$ probe, whereas the minor VDJ rearrangements, seen with the $J_\beta 2$ probe, were $V_\beta 86T1$ negative (data not shown). These bands may represent the use of other V_β genes by more rarely expressed clones or nonproductive VDJ rearrange-

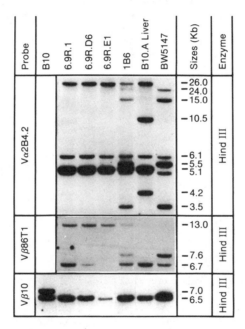

FIGURE 6. Southern blot analyses of α- and β-chain rearrangements in a pigeon cytochrome c–specific B10.S(9R) line and three B10.S(9R) clones. DNA from the 6.9R.1 line, two clones derived from the 6.9R.1 line, and an independently derived hybridoma were digested with *Hind* III. All the lanes in each panel were from the same blot with the exception of B10, which was added to indicate the expected rearrangement. The hybridoma fusion partner, BW5147, and B10.A liver DNA (which exhibits the same germ line bands as B10.S(9R) liver DNA for all three probes), were included as controls. The same blot was used for the $V_\alpha 2B4.2$ and $V_\beta 86T1$ hybridizations. A separate blot was hybridized with $V_\beta B10$. All the probes are described in MATERIAL AND METHODS.

ments in clones with the 4.0 kb *Eco* RI rearrangement. None of the rearranged bands in lanes 5.A.1 and 5.A.3 hybridized to the $V_\beta 86T1$ probe.

Further analyses of the B10.S(9R) line and two phenotype V normal B10.S(9R) T-cell clones (labeled 6.9R.E1 and 6.9R.D6), cloned by limiting dilution from line 6.9R.1, are shown in FIGURE 6. Included in the figure is the independently derived B10.S(9R) hybridoma 1B6 (designated 9R-2 in reference 27), which also exhibits phenotype V. The line and clones examined have the same rearranged 13.0 kb *Hind* III band when probed with $V_\beta 86T1$ corresponding to the 4.0 kb *Eco* RI band observed in line 6.9R.1 (FIG. 6). Hybridization with $V_\beta B10$ expressed by phenotype III B10.A T-cell clones showed no detectable rearranged bands (FIG. 6). In addition, the $V_\beta C8$ gene used by phenotype IV clones also showed no detectable rearranged bands (data not shown).

The B10.S(9R) T-cell clones, as well as the line 6.9R.1, display an identical pattern of bands with the $V_\alpha 2B4.2$ probe (FIGURES 5 and 6). In each case, the same two bands were deleted, whereas the remaining three bands were in germ line configuration. A second, independently derived B10.S(9R) line exhibited this same pattern of bands (data not shown). Southern blot analyses of the B10.S(9R) T-cell line and clones using two other restriction enzymes did not detect any rearranged bands of the $V_\alpha 2B4$ gene family (data not shown). Inasmuch as there is a deletion of germ line bands without rearrangement, the data indicate that the $V_\alpha 2B4$ gene family may not be organized in one continuous cluster, but is interrupted by at least the V_α gene expressed by the B10.S(9R) clones. Nonetheless, the $V_\alpha 2B4$ gene family is not rearranged in cytochrome c–specific B10.S(9R) clones, although every B10.A clone thus far examined rearranges a member of this V_α gene family.[29]

DISCUSSION

From previous analyses of the pigeon cytochrome c–specific T-cell response in B10.A mice, there appears to be a limited number of clonal phenotypes present, and each phenotype is characterized by the rearrangement and expression of a limited set of overlapping TcR gene elements. It was of interest to determine if these were the only TcRs from the available mouse germline repertoire capable of responding to pigeon cytochrome c, or whether the genes expressed in the B10.A strain were only a subset of the total possible response repertoire. Certainly, a comparison of the response to the same nominal antigen in different strains would not be very informative, because evidence indicates that T-cell specificities are a composite of antigen in association with allelic MHC determinants. Therefore, a comparison of receptors expressed in different strains requires that the antigen-specific T-cell clones be degenerate or cross-reactive for at least two allelic MHC molecules.

B10.A pigeon cytochrome c–specific clones have been identified that cross-react on the E_β^k and E_β^b, or E_β^k and E_β^s Ia molecule. This prevalence of cross-reactivities may result in part from the similarity of the three MHC-encoded molecules in question: all three are identical with respect to the alpha chains, and there is a high degree of sequence homology in the beta chains.[37-39] Proliferation data from the B10.A(5R) mouse strain[32,40] revealed a response pattern identical to the majority of the B10.A response to pigeon cytochrome c. Analysis of one B10.A(5R) clone, the T-cell hybridoma 4.11, which exhibited the phenotype of the majority of the T-cell response in this mouse strain (phenotype I), revealed identical gene rearrangements as the B10.A hybridoma 2B4, a clone representative of phenotype I in the B10.A response (see TABLE 1). Therefore, by the analysis of the fine specificity and the expressed TcR gene elements, the repertoire of the B10.A and B10.A(5R) cytochrome c–specific T-cell clones overlaps to the extent that each strain predominantly produced phenotype I clones. A comparison of the cytochrome *c*–specific T cells in B10.A and B10.S(9R) mice revealed a different result. Although each strain produced cross-reacting clones, similar in phenotype, these clones were entirely different with respect to α- and β-chain gene expression. These results do not indicate that phenotype III clones were absolutely not present in B10.S(9R) mice and phenotype V clones are likewise absent from B10.A mice, but the results do argue that their frequency of expression must be very different in the two different strains. Because all three mouse strains are congenic, they presumably possess the same pool of T-cell receptor genes and differ only at the MHC locus. The implication of these results is that the MHC genes influence the selection of the T-cell repertoire such that certain clones are expanded and others are deleted. In the B10.A(5R) strain, the majority of the clones selected were identical to one of the phenotypes present in the B10.A strain, and in B10.S(9R) mice a very different set of clones predominated.

There are several possibilities other than actual repertoire differences that could explain the difference in T-cell clones expressed in the B10.A and B10.S(9R) strains. First, clones similar to phenotype V could be missing in the

TABLE 1. The TcR Gene Rearrangements in Pigeon Cytochrome *c*–Specific T-Cell Clones from Three Congenic Mouse Strains[a]

Cell Type	Name	$V_\beta 2B4$	$V_\beta B10$	$V_\beta C8$	$V_\beta 86T1$	$V_\alpha 2B4.2$	Pheno-type
B10.A hybridoma	2B4	4.3 kb[b]	—	—	N.D.[c]	2.6 kb	I
B10.A(5R) hybridoma	4.11	4.3 kb	—	—	N.D.	2.6 kb	I
B10.A clone	B10	—	7.0 kb	—	N.D.	2.4 kb	III
B10.A clone	C8	—	—	3.1 kb	N.D.	8.4 kb	IV
B10.S(9R) hybridoma	1B6	N.D.	—	—	13.0 kb	—	V
B10.S(9R) clone	D6	N.D.	—	—	13.0 kb	—	V
B10.S(9R) clone	6.9R.E1	N.D.	—	—	13.0 kb	—	V

[a] All sizes represent rearranged *Hind* III restriction fragments, whereas dashes indicate that no rearranged band was seen.

[b] kb, kilobase.

[c] N.D., not done.

B10.A strain because of the I-E^k–specific alloreactivity. In an extensive comparison, however, of pigeon cytochrome *c*–specific T-cell clones with and without alloreactivity, the differences were always found to be attributable to a difference in the J-region in either the α or the β chain.[47] Furthermore, we have recently found clones in $F_1 \rightarrow$ B10.S(9R) radiation chimeras that respond to pigeon cytochrome *c* in association with both B10.A and B10.S(9R) APCs, that lack I-E^k alloreactivity, and that express $V_\beta 86T1$ (P. J. Fink, L. A. Matis, and S. M. Hedrick, unpublished observation). This type of clone should, therefore, be present in a B10.A mouse with an unlimited repertoire. Second, the selection of the T-cell repertoire could be influenced by the MHC antigens expressed on APCs at the time of antigen priming such that the association of each MHC molecule with antigen would form a distinct set of immunodominant epitopes. Thus, the actual recognition sites on the antigen-MHC complex could be different in the two mouse strains causing the expansion of distinctly different T-cell clones. Because we have isolated several clones that respond to antigen on B10.A and B10.S(9R) APCs,[29] however, the recognition sites in these strains must be quite similar.

Third, repertoire differences could be simply due to the fact that although the clones are cross-reactive, they are not sufficiently responsive on the heterologous APCs to be induced during immunization *in vivo*. We think this is not the case because the antigen dose response curves for all of the phenotype V B10.S(9R) clones are virtually identical in the presence of B10.A and B10.S(9R) APCs. Thus, on the basis of affinity, there is no reason for these clones to be absent in the B10.A strain. Clones of phenotype III respond to antigen on B10.S(9R) APCs at a tenfold higher concentration than on B10.A APCs, but this amount of variation is well within the range of the dose response curves exhibited by B10.A clones on autologous APCs.[29,36] As described in the results, we have presented the antigen dose response curves for these clones using cytochrome *c* fragments, although these data do not reflect the true extent of cross-reactivity observed when the immunogen, whole pigeon cytochrome *c*, is used. From these observations, we contend that the paucity of phenotype III clones in the B10.S(9R) strain and a similar lack of phenotype V clones in the B10.A strain are both due to a difference in the repertoire of the two strains, and not simply due to affinity differences.

The possibility exists that these two congenic strains do not, in fact, possess identical V_β gene elements. Southern blot analyses indicate that both strains have germ line bands for $V_\beta B10$ and $V_\beta 86T1$ with no restriction length polymorphisms using two restriction endonucleases, arguing against the possibility of deletion or gross mutation of these V_β regions in either strain. Minor mutations could alter the function or reading frame, however, of these gene segments and would not alter the size of the germ line restriction fragment. To entirely account for the differences in gene expression, two such mutations would have had to occur, one in the $V_\beta B10$ region of the B10.S(9R) strain and one in the $V_\beta 86T1$ region of the B10.A strain, and this possibility seems unlikely.

The data presented in this report imply that the T-cell repertoire in each strain of mice is limited according to the allelic variants of the MHC genes expressed. This limitation may create "holes" in the repertoire, which could account for some, though not necessarily all, of the cytochrome *c* immune response polymorphisms that map to the MHC genes.[13,23,25] Additionally, differences in the association of antigen and MHC molecules, termed determinant selection, may cause MHC-linked nonresponsiveness.[40-43] A comparison of the cytochrome *c*–specific responses in B10.A, B10.A(5R), and B10.S(9R) mice indicates that each of these two mechanisms may contribute to the Ir gene defects observed in this system.

B10.A(5R) mice exhibit an Ir gene defect by not responding to pigeon cytochrome *c*,[32] and this defect might be explained by their limited T-cell repertoire. In addition, the majority of the B10.A clones also exhibit an inability to respond to the pigeon peptide when presented on B10.A(5R) APCs. A minor population of B10.A T cells can respond to pigeon cytochrome *c* on B10.A(5R) APCs, but this response occurs only at the highest concentration of antigen (see phenotype IV in FIG. 2). Inasmuch as neither the B10.A nor B10.A(5R) strains produced clones reactive to pigeon cytochrome *c* and B10.A(5R) APCs, we would have to conclude that, coincidentally both strains have the same repertoire defect. Perhaps a more likely possibility is that the nonresponsiveness of B10.A(5R) mice results from a low-affinity interaction between antigen and Ia molecule, and such affinity differences have now been demonstrated in this and several other systems under Ir gene control.[42,43,44]

Clear differences exist in the pigeon cytochrome *c*–specific repertoires of B10.A and B10.S(9R) mice. B10.A clones, known to react with antigen in association with B10.S(9R) APCs (phenotype III), are not present in the B10.S(9R) strain, whereas similar clones from B10.S(9R) mice (phenotype V) are not present in the B10.A strain. The limitation in the B10.S(9R) T-cell repertoire may cause the Ir gene defect observed in this strain, which is the absence of response to tuna cytochrome c.[27] Functional data show that phenotype III T cells respond to tuna cytochrome c in association with B10.A and B10.S(9R) APCs with equal efficiency,[27] indicating that tuna cytochrome c has a similar affinity for the two Ia molecules. Therefore, the inability of B10.S(9R) mice to respond to tuna cytochrome c does not appear to be caused by an ineffectual antigen-Ia interaction, but may rather be due to a hole in the T-cell repertoire. The two major clonal phenotypes in the B10.S(9R) strain simply do not respond to tuna cytochrome c. For instance, if clones of phenotype III were present in B10.S(9R) mice at the levels found in B10.A mice, this Ir gene defect would not exist, and B10.S(9R) mice would be responders.

Considering all these data, the T-cell repertoire appears to be selected for more than simply the restricted recognition of MHC molecules. Tolerance, positive selection, and antigen presentation are three selective processes that could affect the expressed T-cell repertoire and alter the responder status of an animal.[13,18,45,46] The influence of thymic selection and tolerance on the T-cell repertoire can be studied separately from the effect of differences in antigen presentation by using radiation chimeras. Experiments with [B10.A × B10.S(9R)]F$_1$, F$_1$ → parent and allogeneic bone marrow chimeric animals are underway, to further assess the selective role of the thymus and APCs in TcR α- and β-chain expression.

SUMMARY

We have previously described[29] the B10.A pigeon cytochrome c–specific response in terms of clonal phenotypes and T-cell receptor (TcR) gene usage. All B10.A T-cell clones studied respond to antigen in association with syngeneic B10.A APCs and cross-react to antigen in association with one or two allogeneic variants of the I-E–encoded MHC molecules. In congenic strains of mice expressing these allogeneic MHC alleles [B10.A(5R) and B10.S(9R)], pigeon cytochrome c–specific T cells exhibit very similar MHC cross-reactivities. Our goal was to determine whether the same MHC cross-reactive T-cell clones were expressed in each appropriate strain, or whether each T-cell repertoire was unique. The results indicate that identical V_α-J_α and V_β-J_β combinations were expressed by the major pigeon cytochrome c–specific response phenotype in B10.A and B10.A(5R) mice. Previous functional data supports this overlap in expressed T-cell clones. B10.A and B10.S(9R) mice exhibit similar response phenotypes to pigeon cytochrome c but express distinctly different TcR genes. The results of these studies support the existence of at least two different mechanisms in determining MHC-linked immune response polymorphisms.

REFERENCES

1. VON BOEHMER, H., J. SPRENT & M. NABHOLZ. 1975. Tolerance to histocompatibility determinants in tetraparental bone marrow chimeras. J. Exp. Med. **141:** 322–334.
2. BEVAN, M. J. 1977. In a radiation chimera, host H-2 antigens determine immune responsiveness of donor cytotoxic cells. Nature (London) **269:** 417–418.
3. ZINKERNAGEL, R. M., G. N. CALLAHAN, A. ALTHAGE, S. COOPER, P. A. KLEIN & J. KLEIN. 1978. On the thymus in the differentiation of "H-2 self-recognition" by T cells: evidence for dual recognition? J. Exp. Med. **147:** 882–896.

4. SPRENT, J. 1978. Role of the H-2 complex in induction of T helper cells *in vivo* I. Antigen-specific selection of donor T cells to sheep erythrocytes in irradiated mice dependent upon sharing of H-2 determinants between donor and host. J. Exp. Med. **148:** 478–489.

5. ZINKERNAGEL, R. M., G. N. CALLAHAN, A. ALTHAGE, S. COOPER, J. W. STREILEIN & J. KLEIN. 1978. The lymphoreticular system in triggering virus plus self-specific cytotoxic T cells: evidence for T help. J. Exp. Med. **147:** 897–911.

6. MILLER, J. F. A. P. 1978. Restrictions imposed on T lymphocyte reactivities by the major histocompatibility complex: implications for T cell repertoire selection. Immunol. Rev. **42:** 76–107.

7. BEVAN, M. J. & P. J. FINK. 1978. The influence of thymus H-2 antigens on the specificity of maturing killer and helper cells. Immunol. Rev. **42:** 3–19.

8. WALDMANN, H., H. POPE, C. PETTLES & A. J. S. DAVIES. 1978. The influence of the thymus on the development of MHC restrictions exhibited by T helper cells. Nature (London) **277:** 137–138.

9. BECHTOL, K. B. & H. O. MCDEVITT. 1976. Antibody response of C3H↔(CKB × CWB)F$_1$ tetraparental mice to poly-L(tyr, glu)-poly-D,L-ala-poly-L-lys immunization. J. Exp. Med. **144:** 123–144.

10. LE MEUR, M., P. GERLINGER, C. BENOIST & D. MATHIS. 1985. Correcting an immune-response deficiency by creating E$_\alpha$ gene transgenic mice. Nature (London) **316:** 38–42.

11. YAMAMURA, K.-I., H. KIKUTANI, V. FOLSOM, L. CLAYTON, M. KIMOTO, S. AKIRA, S.-I. KASHIWAMURA, S. TONEGAWA & T. KISHIMOTO. 1985. Functional expression of a microinjected E$_\alpha^d$ gene in C57BL/6 transgenic mice. Nature (London) **316:** 67–69.

12. BENACERRAF, B. & R. W. GERMAIN. 1978. The immune response genes of the major histocompatibility complex. Immunol. Rev. **38:** 70–119.

13. SCHWARTZ, R. H. 1978. A clonal deletion model for Ir gene control of the immune response. Scand. J. Immunol. **7:** 3–10.

14. ZINKERNAGEL, R. M., A. ALTHAGE, S. COOPER, G. KREEB, P. A. KLEIN, B. SEFTON, L. FLAHERTY, J. STIMPFLING, D. SHREFFLER & J. KLEIN. Ir-genes in H-2 regulate generation of anti-viral cytotoxic T cells. J. Exp. Med. **148:** 592–606.

15. LERNER, E. A., L. A. MATIS, C. A. JANEWAY, JR., P. P. JONES, R. H. SCHWARTZ & D. B. MURPHY. 1980. Monoclonal antibody against an Ir gene product? J. Exp. Med. **152:** 1085–1101.

16. MICHEALIDES, M., M. SANDRIN, G. MORGAN, I. F. C. MCKENZIE, R. ASHMAN & R. W. MELVOLD. 1981. Ir gene function in an I-A subregion mutant B6.C-H-2^{bm12}. J. Exp. Med. **153:** 464–469.

17. KAPPLER, J. W. & P. MARRACK. 1978. The role of H-2 linked genes in helper T-cell function. IV. Importance of T-cell genotype and host environment in I-region and Ir gene expression. J. Exp. Med. **148:** 1510–1522.

18. VON BOEHMER, H., W. HAAS & N. K. JERNE. 1978. Major histocompatibility complex-linked immune-responsiveness is acquired by lymphocytes of low-responder mice differentiating in the thymus of high-responder mice. Proc. Natl. Acad. Sci. USA **75:** 2439–2442.

19. HEDRICK, S. M. & J. WATSON. 1979. Genetic control of the immune response to collagen. II. Antibody responses produced in fetal liver restored radiation chimeras and thymus reconstituted F$_1$ hybrid nude mice. J. Exp. Med. **150:** 646–652.

20. ZINKERNAGEL, R. M., A. ALTHAGE, S. COOPER, G. CALLAHAN & J. KLEIN. 1978. In irradiation chimeras, K or D regions of the chimeric host, not of the donor lymphocytes, determine immune responsiveness of antiviral cytotoxic T cells. J. Exp. Med. **148:** 805–810.

21. PIERCE, S. K., N. R. KLINEMAN, P. H. MAURER & C. F. MERRYMAN. 1980. Role of the major histocompatibility gene products in regulating the antibody response to dinitrophenylated poly(L-Glu^{55},L-Ala^{35},L-Phe^9)$_n$. J. Exp. Med. **152:** 336–349.

22. KIMOTO, M., T. J. KRENZ & C. G. FATHMAN. 1981. Antigen-reactive T cell clones. III. Low responder antigen-presenting cells function effectively to present antigen to

selected T cell clones derived from (high responder × low responder)F$_1$ mice. J. Exp. Med. **154:** 883–891.

23. CLARK, R. B. & E. M. SHEVACH. 1982. Generation of T cell colonies from responder 2 guinea pigs that recognize the copolymer L-glutamic acid, L-lysine in association with nonresponder strain 13 Ia antigens. J. Exp. Med. **155:** 635–640.

24. ISHII, N., Z. A. NAGY & J. KLEIN. 1982. Absence of Ir gene control of T cells recognizing foreign antigen in the context of allogeneic MHC molecules. Nature (London) **295:** 531–533.

25. ISHII, N., Z. A. NAGY & J. KLEIN. 1983. *In vitro* correlate for a clonal deletion mechanism of immune response gene-controlled nonresponsiveness. J. Exp. Med. **157:** 998–1005.

26. HEBER-KATZ, E., R. H. SCHWARTZ, L. A. MATIS, C. HANNUM, T. FAIRWELL, E. APPELLA & D. HANSBURG. 1982. Contribution of antigen-presenting cell major histocompatibility complex gene products to the specificity of antigen-induced T cell activation. J. Exp. Med. **155:** 1086–1099.

27. HEDRICK, S. M., L. A. MATIS, T. T. HECHT, L. E. SAMELSON, D. L. LONGO, E. HEBER-KATZ & R. H. SCHWARTZ. 1982. The fine specificity of antigen and Ia determinant recognition by T cell hybridoma clones specific for pigeon cytochrome *c*. Cell **30:** 141–152.

28. MATIS, L. A., D. L. LONGO, S. M. HEDRICK, C. HANNUM, E. MARGOLIASH & R. H. SCHWARTZ. 1983. Clonal analysis of the major histocompatibility complex restriction and the fine specificity of antigen recognition in the T cell proliferative response to cytochrome *c*. J. Immunol. **130:** 1527–1535.

29. SORGER, S. B., S. M. HEDRICK, P. J. FINK, M. A. BOOKMAN & L. A. MATIS. 1986. The generation of diversity in the T cell receptor repertoire specific for pigeon cytochrome *c*. J. Exp. Med. **165:** 279–301.

30. SOUTHERN, E. M. 1975. Detection of specific sequences among DNA fragments separated by gel electrophoresis. J. Mol. Biol. **98:** 503.

31. HEDRICK, S. M., E. A. NIELSEN, J. KAVALER, D. I. COHEN & M. M. DAVIS. 1984. Sequence relationships between putative T-cell receptor polypeptides and immunoglobins. Nature (London) **308:** 153–158.

32. HEBER-KATZ, E., D. HANSBURG & R. H. SCHWARTZ. 1983. The Ia molecule of the antigen-presenting cell plays a critical role in immune response gene regulation of T cell activation. J. Mol. Cell. Immunol. **1:** 3–14.

33. HEDRICK, S. M. *et al.* 1985. Rearrangement and transcription of a T-cell receptor β-chain gene in different T-cell subsets. Proc. Natl. Acad. Sci. USA **82:** 531–535.

34. SAMELSON, L. E., R. GERMAIN & R. H. SCHWARTZ. 1983. Monoclonal antibodies against the antigen receptor on a cloned T-cell hybrid. Proc. Natl. Acad. Sci. USA **80:** 6972–6976.

35. MARRACK, P., R. SHIMONKEVITZ, C. HANNUM, K. HASKINS & J. KAPPLER. 1983. The major histocompatibility complex-restricted antigen receptor on T cells. IV. An antiidiotypic antibody predicts both antigen and I-specificity. J. Exp. Med. **158:** 1635–1646.

36. FINK, P. J., L. A. MATIS, D. L. MCELLIGOTT, M. BOOKMAN & S. M. HEDRICK. 1986. Correlations between T-cell specificity and the structure of the antigen receptor. Nature (London) **321:** 219–226.

37. MENGLE-GAW, L. & H. O. MCDEVITT. 1983. Isolation and characterization of a cDNA clone for the murine I-E$_\beta$ polypeptide chain. Proc. Natl. Acad. Sci. USA **80:** 7621–7625.

38. MENGLE-GAW, L., S. CONNER, H. O. MCDEVITT & C. G. FATHMAN. 1984. Gene conversion between murine class II major histocompatibility complex loci. Functional and molecular evidence from the bm12 mutant. J. Exp. Med. **160:** 1184–1194.

39. MENGLE-GAW, L. & H. O. MCDEVITT. 1985. Predicted protein sequence of the murine I-E$_\beta$ polypeptide chain from cDNA and genomic clones. Proc. Natl. Acad. Sci. USA **82:** 2910–2914.

40. HANSBURG, D., E. HEBER-KATZ, T. FAIRWELL & E. APELLA. 1983. Major histocompatibility complex-controlled, antigen-presenting cell-expressed specificity of T cell

antigen recognition: Identification of a site of interaction and its relationship to Ir genes. J. Exp. Med. **158:** 25–39.

41. HANSBURG, D., C. HANNUM, J. K. INMAN, E. APPELLA, E. MARGOLIASH & R. H. SCHWARTZ. 1981. Parallel cross-reactivity patterns of 2 sets of antigenically distinct cytochrome *c* peptides: possible evidence for a presentational model of Ir gene function. J. Immunol. **127:** 1844–1851.

42. BABBIT, B. P., P. M. ALLEN, G. MATSUEDA, E. HABER & E. R. UNANUE. 1985. Binding of immunogenic peptides to Ia histocompatibility molecules. Nature (London) **317:** 359–361.

43. BUUS, S., S. COLON, C. SMITH, J. H. FREED, C. MILES & H. M. GREY. 1986. Interaction between a "processed" ovalbumin peptide and Ia molecules. Proc. Natl. Acad. Sci. USA **83:** 3968–3971.

44. BUUS, S., A. SETTE, S. M. COLON, C. MILES & H. M. GREY. 1987. The relation between major histocompatibility complex (MHC) restriction and the capacity of Ia to bind immunogenic peptides. Science **235:** 1353–1358.

45. LANGMAN, R. E. 1977. Cell-mediated immunity and the major histocompatibility complex. Rev. Physiol. Biochem. Pharmacol. **81:** 1–37.

46. COHN, M. & R. EPSTEIN. 1978. T-cell inhibition of humoral responsiveness. II. Theory on the role of restrictive recognition in immune regulation. Cell. Immunol. **39:** 125–153.

47. MATIS, L.A., S. B. SORGER, D. L. McELLIGOTT, P. J. FINK & S. M. HEDRICK. 1987. The molecular basis of alloreactivity in antigen-specific, major histocompatibility complex–restricted T cell clones. Cell **51:** 59–69.

Role of Ti/CD3, Thy-1, and Ly-6 in Cytolytic T-Cell Activation Analyzed with Ti Loss Variants[a]

CLAIRE LANGLET,[b] ANNICK GUIMEZANES,[b]
PIERRE KALDY,[b] CLAUDE BOYER,[b]
MICHEL BUFERNE,[b] MARTIN POENIE,[c] ROGER TSIEN,[c]
OBERDAN LEO,[d] JEFFREY BLUESTONE,[d]
LEE LESERMAN,[b] AND
ANNE-MARIE SCHMITT-VERHULST[b]

[b]Centre d'Immunologie INSERM-CNRS de Marseille-Luminy
13288 Marseille Cedex 9, France

[c]Department of Physiology
University of California
Berkeley, California

[d]Immunology Branch
National Cancer Institute
National Institutes of Health
Bethesda, Maryland 20892

INTRODUCTION

Cytolytic T cells (CTL) are among the best studied elements of the immune system because of the development of reagents permitting analysis of the molecular basis of their action, and the sensitivity of target cell lysis assays. The use of T-cell growth factor (interleukin-2 (IL-2)) has allowed the maintenance in long-term culture of CTL clones with defined antigen specificity and stable function. Monoclonal antibodies (mAb) against human and mouse CTL helped define the antigen receptor (Ti),[1,2–5] and the associated CD3 (T3) structures[6,7] involved in antigen-dependent activation of the CTL. Similarly, antigen-independent activation pathways such as CD2 (T11)[8] and T44[9,10] in humans, and Thy-1[11–14] and Ly-6[15–18] in mice are also known. Cell-surface structures such as LFA-1 are involved in cell adhesion, in a Ti/CD3-independent fashion.[19] The CD8 (T8, Lyt-2) and CD4 (T4) structures, generally expressed, respectively, on CTL specific for class I major histocompatibility complex (MHC) products, and on T-helper cells (T$_h$) specific for class II MHC products, appear implicated in recognition/activation involving MHC, either alone or in association with a non-MHC antigen (for review, see references 20 and 21).

We have studied a mouse CTL clone specific for the H-2K^b alloantigen, which is inhibited by Lyt-2–specific mAb in its H-2K^b–mediated activation, but not in activation involving anti-Ti mAb.[5] We recently demonstrated, by gene transfection experiments, that inhibition of this clone observed with mAb correlated with the requirement for expression of the Lyt-2 structure in recognition/activation

[a] This research was supported by institutional Grants from INSERM and CNRS.

involving the class I MHC product, but not in recognition/activation by way of anti-Ti mAb.[22]

Data presented in this publication are aimed at defining the role of the Ti/CD3, Thy-1, and Ly-6 structures of mouse CTL clones for two measurable activation-dependent effector functions: target-cell killing and production of g-interferon (g-IFN). The killing function is not dependent on protein synthesis and can be measured within minutes of CTL–target-cell interaction, as recently shown using digital imaging of changes in intracytoplasmic Ca^{++} concentration ($[Ca^{++}]i$) in effector and target cells loaded with the Ca^{++} sensitive dye Fura-2.[23] g-IFN synthesis is dependent on transcriptional activation and is optimally measured in supernatants around 20 h after CTL–target-cell interaction or after binding of anti-Ti mAb. We previously showed that activation for killing and activation for g-IFN production were obtained in conditions leading to phosphorylation of distinct CD3 components.[24] Here, the role of the Ti/CD3 complex in activation mediated by lectins or by two phosphatidylinositol-anchored differentiation antigens, Thy-1[25] and Ly-6,[26] was evaluated on normal cells and on variants of a CTL clone, which had lost cell-surface expression of the Ti/CD3 complex.[27] Results obtained with a series of Ti⁻ variants indicate that absence of the Ti α or β chain prevents surface expression of the Ti/CD3 complex and that Ti⁻ variants could no longer be activated either for killing or g-IFN production with lectins, anti-Thy-1 or anti-Ly-6 mAb. These results raise the following questions: What is the molecular basis for the dependence of activation mediated by Thy-1 and Ly-6 upon surface expression of the Ti/CD3 complex? Is this dependence specific for activation by phosphatidylinositol membrane-anchored structures? Is this dependence absolute or could the same structures signal in a Ti/CD3-independent fashion on immature precursors of CTL and/or on cells of a distinct lineage? Experimental results will be discussed that give some clues as to the response to the first question, whereas the second and third questions remain unanswered as yet, to the best of our knowledge.

MATERIAL AND METHODS

T-Cell Clone: Origin and Culture Conditions

KB5.C20 is an H-2K^b–specific CTL clone of B10.BR origin,[28] maintained in culture by weekly restimulation with irradiated C57BL/6 spleen cells and IL-2–containing supernatant from phorbol myristic acetate (PMA)–stimulated EL4.c16 cells (SC16).[28,29]

Selection of Ti⁻ Variants of Clone KB5.C20

Negative selection using methotrexate (MTX)-containing, protein A–coupled liposomes (MTX-lip-PA) was adapted from Machy and Leserman[30] as described.[27] Variant KB5.C20.lip.A.2 was obtained from normal KB5.C20 cells, whereas variants Ti⁻.x were selected from KB5.C20 cells that had previously been treated with the mutagen ethyl methyl sulfonate (EMS) at 400 μg/ml. As the Ti⁻ variants can no longer respond to antigen stimulation, their maintenance involves, every other week, a 2 h activation step with ionomycin (iono), 1 μM, and PMA, 1.6 nM, at 37°C, followed by replacement of the medium with 10% SC16 as described.[31]

Reagents

Reagents used were ionomycin (Calbiochem), PMA (Sigma), EMS (Sigma), and acetoxymethyl ester of Fura-2 (Molecular Probes).

Monoclonal Antibodies

The characteristics and origin of the mAb used in this study are summarized in TABLE 1.

Measure of Gamma-Interferon (g-IFN) in Supernatants

g-IFN was measured either by its macrophage-activating factor (MAF) activity as previously described,[32] or by a solid phase radioimmunoassay using two mouse g-IFN–specific hamster mAb, kindly given by Dr. R. D. Schreiber (Washington University, St Louis, MO) adapted from Schreiber *et al.*[33]

TABLE 1. Specificity and Origin of Monoclonal Antibodies Used

mAb	Specificity	Reference
Désiré-1	Ti (KB5.C20)	Hua *et al.* 1986a[34]
H155.124.3	Thy-1(epitope C)	Pont *et al.* 1985[13]
H140.61.2	Thy-1(epitope B)	Pont *et al.* 1985[13]
H129.93.9.1	Thy-1(epitope A)	Pont *et al.* 1985[13]
145.2C.11	CD3 (ε)	Leo *et al.* 1987[7]
143.4.2	Ly-6.2C	Leo *et al.* 1987[37]
19.178	Lyt-2.2	Hämmerling *et al.* 1979[36]
100.5.28	H-2K^k	Lemke *et al.* 1979[35]
20.8.4	H-2K^b	Ozato and Sachs 1981[50]

Measure of CTL Activity

T-cell clones were incubated in V-bottomed microtitre plates with 10^4 ^{51}Cr-labeled target cells as described.[28] ^{51}Cr released in the supernatants of triplicate cultures was measured after a 4 h or 16 h incubation at 37°C as indicated in the TABLES. Percent specific ^{51}Cr released was expressed as [cpm (experimental) − cpm (medium)/cpm maximum (1 N HCl) − cpm (medium)] × 100. Target cells were either H-2^b (EL4.BU) or H-2^k (RDM4) thymomas, or the H-2^d (P388D1) Fc receptor-positive tumor line.

Cytofluorometric Analysis

Immunofluorescence was performed as previously described,[34] except that the fluorescein isothiocyanate (FITC)-labeled reagents were either F(ab')$_2$ rabbit anti-mouse Ig, F(ab')$_2$ goat anti-rat Ig, or goat anti-hamster Ig (all from Cappel), depending on the origin of the first antibody (TABLE 1). Results are expressed as relative fluorescence intensities as described.[34]

Measure of Intracytoplasmic Ca^{++} Concentration [Ca^{++}]i

[Ca^{++}]i was measured using single-cell analysis and digital-image processing of cells loaded with the acetoxymethyl form of the Ca^{++}-sensitive dye, Fura-2 (Molecular Probes), as previously described.[54,27]

RESULTS AND DISCUSSION

Approaches to the Understanding of the Role of Distinct Cell-Surface Structures in the Activation of CTL Effector Functions

Selection of Variants of CTL Clone KB5.C20

KB5.C20 is a CTL clone of B10.BR origin (H-2^k), specific for the H-2K^b alloantigen.[28] It is dependent on antigenic stimulation for efficient IL-2–dependent growth[28] and for activation of its effector functions, target-cell killing and production of g-IFN.[32] These antigen-dependent triggering events can be replaced by an anticlonotypic mAb, Désiré-1,[5,34,32] or by a pulse with a Ca^{++} ionophore such as ionomycin and a protein kinase C activator such as PMA.[31] Selection of variants was based on a negative selection method eliminating cells that bind and internalize liposomes containing the drug methotrexate, specifically targeted to a cell-surface molecule by way of a mAb.[30] Use of the anticlonotypic mAb, Désiré-1, in such a selection on unmutagenized or EMS-treated KB5.C20 cells, led to the isolation of variant cells called KB5.C20.lip.A.2[27] and Ti$^-$.x (this report), respectively. To culture these variants, antigen-specific stimulation was replaced by a pulse with ionomycin (1 μM) and PMA (1.6 nM)[31] every other week, whereas IL-2–containing medium was supplied every 3 or 4 days. We will only consider here variants that have selectively lost cell-surface expression of the Ti and associated CD3 structures (TABLE 2). Among these, some have lost expression of mRNA for the α chain of the T-cell receptor,[27] whereas the defects of others (for example variants Ti$^-$.32, Ti$^-$.33, and Ti$^-$.37) are presently being characterized at the molecular level (P. Kaldy *et al.*, in preparation).

TABLE 2. Selective Loss of Ti and CD3 Expression on Ti$^-$ Variants of Clone KB5.C20

CTL Clone	Relative Fluorescence Intensity after Staining with mAb Specific for:								
	K^b	K^k	Ti(KB5.C20)^a	Lyt-2.2^a	Ly-6.2C^a	—^{b}	Thy-1^b	—^{c}	CD3^c
KB5.C20	3.6	**200.**^{d}	**100.**	**116.**	**33.**	0.	**99.**	0.	**55.**
Ti$^-$.32	3.7	**160.**	3.8	**64.**	**22.**	0.	**84.**	0.	0.
Ti$^-$.33	7.8	**185.**	6.6	**51.**	**29.**	0.	**84.**	0.	0.
Ti$^-$.37	5.4	**139.**	5.8	**42.**	**45.**	0.	**81.**	0.	1.3

^{a} F(ab')$_2$ rabbit anti-mouse Ig-FITC.
^{b} F(ab')$_2$ goat anti-rat Ig-FITC.
^{c} Goat anti-hamster Ig-FITC.
^{d} Bold numbers indicate positive expression of the corresponding marker.

TABLE 3. Loss of Antigen- and Lectin-Mediated Cytolytic Activity by Ti⁻ Variants of Clone KB5.C20

	Percent Specific ^{51}Cr Released from Target Cells[a]					
	EL4.BU		RDM4		P815	
Clone	−[b]	−[c]	−[b]	+ Con A[b]	−[c]	+ Leuco A[c]
KB5.C20	52.[d]	50.	0.2	46.	2.0	55.
KB5.C20.lip.A.2	0.		2.2	6.0		
Ti⁻.32		0.			0.	0.

[a] Effector to target cell ratio = 5 : 1.
[b] Experiment 1.
[c] Experiment 2.
[d] Bold numbers indicate positive responses.

*Cell-Surface Characteristics of Ti-Loss Variants: Selective Loss of
Cell-Surface Expression of Ti and CD3 Components*

As previously described for variant KB5.C20.lip.A.2,[27] the defect in the Ti⁻ variants appeared restricted to cell-surface expression of the Ti and of associated CD3 structures as indicated respectively by lack of staining with mAb Désiré-1 and with mAb 145.2C.11 (specific for the ε chain of the CD3 complex[7]) (TABLE 2). Staining with mAb directed at H-2K^k,[35] Lyt-2.2,[36] Ly-6.2C,[37] and different epitopes of the Thy-1 molecule[13] was positive for the Ti⁻ variants as shown in TABLE 2.

*Functional Analyses of Ti⁻ Variants: Loss of Activation Mediated by Lectins,
by Anti-Thy-1 mAb, and by Anti-Ly-6.2C mAb for Induction of Killing or for
g-IFN Production, but Retention of Killing Capacity and Production of g-IFN
in Response to Ionomycin and PMA*

Activation by Lectins. Lectins bind to a number of cell-surface glycoproteins.[38] If any of these structures were capable of transducing activation signals independently of the Ti/CD3 complex, one would have expected residual lectin-mediated activation of Ti⁻ variants. Results in TABLE 3 indicate that clone KB5.C20 can kill the specific H-2^b target cells (EL4.BU) in the absence of lectin and the H-2^k (RDM4) or H-2^d (P815) targets, provided a lectin such as concanavalin A (Con A) or leucoagglutinin (Leuco A) is present in the ^{51}Cr release assay (by lectin-dependent cell-mediated cytotoxicity (LDCC)). Results, with two Ti⁻ variants (TABLE 3) are shown as an example, which indicate that these variants are incapable of mediating either specific cytotoxicity or LDCC. Results summarized in TABLE 5 indicate that, in addition, Con A and Leuco A could no longer activate production of g-IFN from the Ti⁻ variants. In similar studies, using variants of human IL-2– secreting T-lymphoma cells,[39,40] lack of the Ti/CD3 complex appeared to induce loss of induction by phytohemagglutinin (PHA) of the Jurkat cells,[39] whereas among different Ti⁻/CD3⁻ CD2⁺ variants of the JA3 lymphoma, most but not all had lost the capacity to be stimulated by PHA.[40] Because no reagent to mouse CD2 is yet available, we do not know whether the KB5.C20 clone and its Ti⁻ variants express a similar structure, which appears to constitute a pathway of activation distinct and independent from the Ti/CD3 complex on human lymphoma cells.[40]

Thy-1–Mediated Activation. The Thy-1 molecule, which, in the mouse, is expressed on all cells of T lineage, from embryonic (day 13 thymus) to adult life, has recently been shown to be able to transduce activation signals in T_h,[11–13] T hybridomas,[13] CTL,[14,41] and thymocytes.[42,43] Because of its tissue distribution and potential activating properties, this molecule appeared to be a possible candidate for an activation structure on T-cell precursors before their expression of the Ti/CD3 complex. It was therefore of interest to evaluate the function of this molecule on Ti⁻ variants of mature functional T cells. Results summarized in TABLE 5 indicate that when the appropriate Thy-1–specific mAb[13] are used, clone KB5.C20 is induced to secrete g-IFN upon binding of anti-Thy-1 mAb. This effect is increased upon cross-linking of the Thy-1–specific mAb with mouse anti-rat kappa (MARK) mAb or after binding of two mAb specific for two distinct epitopes of the Thy-1 molecule.[41] As previously described for variant KB5.C20.lip.A.2,[27] it was found that none of the Ti⁻ variants could be induced to produce g-IFN in response to any Thy-1 mAb used alone or in combination with a second Thy-1–specific mAb and/or MARK (reference 41 and TABLE 5). The strong production of g-IFN in response to a pulse with ionomycin and PMA indicated that all Ti⁻ variants tested had retained the capacity to be induced to produce g-IFN.[27,41]

Ly-6–Mediated Activation. Another set of molecules with potential for intracellular signaling are gene products of the Ly-6 locus.[16–18,37] The Ly-6.2C determinant is expressed on a 15 kDa protein[44] on a subpopulation of mouse T cells,[45] 50% of the peripheral Lyt-2 T cells expressing reactivity with mAb 143.4.2.[37] As already indicated (TABLE 2), clone KB5.C20 expresses the Ly-6.2C determinant, which is also present on the Ti⁻ variants of the clone (TABLE 2). In agreement with findings by Leo *et al.*,[37,46] the bridging of Fc receptor-positive target cells (such as P388D1) to CTL through anti-Ly-6.2C IgG₁ mAb 143.4.2 leads to killing of the P388D1 target cells by clone KB5.C20 (TABLE 4). This is similar to previously described Fc receptor-mediated killing of target cells through anti-CD3 mAb[47] or anti-TcR mAb.[48] Similar results were also obtained on the P388D1 target cells following their bridging to KB5.C20 through mAb specific for the Ti (Désiré-1, IgG₂ₐ) or CD3 (145.2C.11, hamster IgG) (TABLE 4). Results in TABLE 4 also show examples of absence of killing when Ti⁻ variants are incubated with Fc receptor-positive target cells P388D1 and anti-Ti mAb Désiré-1 or anti-CD3 mAb 145.2C.11. These results were expected, inasmuch as these mAb do not bind to the Ti⁻ variants. The more surprising result was that the Ti⁻ variants also had lost

TABLE 4. Example of Loss of Ly-6–Mediated Activation for Killing by Ti⁻ Variants of Clone KB5.C20 as Measured by Fc-Mediated Lysis of P388D1 Target Cells

| CTL Clone | Percent Lysis[a] of P388D1 Target Cells in the Presence of mAb to/Reagent: | | | | | | Percent lysis[a] of EL4 Target Cells |
	No	Ti(KB5.C20)	CD3	Ly-6.2C	K^k	Ionomycin + PMA	
KB5.C20	0.	**63.**[b]	**100.**	**42.**	0.	**30.**	**99.**
Ti⁻.32	0.	0.	3.9	0.	0.	**44.**	0.
Ti⁻.33	0.	0.	0.	0.	0.	**25.**	0.

[a] Measured as ⁵¹Cr release at 5 : 1 effector to target cell ratio.
[b] Bold numbers indicate positive responses.

TABLE 5. Summary of Stimuli Leading to Activation for Killing, g-IFN Production, or Increase in [Ca^{++}]i by Clone KB5.C20 (Ti$^+$) and Antigen Receptor Loss Variants (Ti$^-$)

Stimuli	Target Cell Lysis by Clone KB5.C20		g-IFN Production by Clone KB5.C20		Increase in [Ca^{++}]i by Clone KB5.C20	
	Ti$^+$	Ti$^-$	Ti$^+$	Ti$^-$	Ti$^+$	Ti$^-$
H-2K^b cells	+	−	+	−	+	−
Concanavalin A	+	−	+	−	+	−
Leucoagglutinin	+	−	+	−	ND	ND
anti-Ti (Désiré-1)	+	−	+	−	+	−
anti-CD3	+	−	ND	ND	+	−
anti-Thy-1/C	ND^a	ND	+	−	+	−
anti-Ly-6.2C	+	−	+	−	+	−
PMA	+	+	−	−	ND	ND
Ionomycin	−(+)	−(+)	−	−(+)	+	+
PMA + ionomycin	+	+	+	+	ND	ND

^{a} ND = not done.

the capacity to kill the P388D1 target cells through bridging by the anti-Ly-6.2C mAb 143.4.2. (TABLE 4), although PMA-induced[24] or iono plus PMA-induced target-cell killing was as efficient for the Ti$^-$ variants as for clone KB5.C20 (TABLE 4). Results summarized in TABLE 5 indicate that anti-Ly-6.2C mAb also can induce production of g-IFN by clone KB5.C20, but not by the Ti$^-$ variants (Guimezanes *et al.* in preparation).

CONCLUSION

In agreement with recent studies using human Jurkat cells transfected with the murine Thy-1.2 gene,[49] our results using Ti$^-$ variants of a CTL clone had shown that Thy-1–mediated activation is dependent on the expression of the Ti/CD3 complex on mature T cells.[27] Recent work on the stimulation of subpopulations of thymocytes is also compatible with the requirement of CD3 expression associated with a Ti(α/β) or with a Ti(γ/δ) for activation of immature thymocytes.[43] It remains to be established whether, as suggested for human thymocytes[51] and lymphoma cells,[40] a CD2 structure is present and can function as an alternative to the Ti/CD3 system for immature or functional murine T cells. Alternatively, as yet unknown molecules may be involved in signaling in T-cell precursors before their expression of a Ti/CD3 complex. Results presented here indicate that, in addition to the Thy-1 molecule, Ly-6C–mediated activation is similarly dependent on the expression of the Ti/CD3 complex and, therefore, suggest that molecules of the Ly-6 family are not likely candidates for early, CD3-independent activation structures.

The question of the mechanism of signaling through the Thy-1 and Ly-6 molecules, both of which are probably phosphatidylinositol membrane–anchored structures,[25,26] and on the nature of its dependence on elements associated with the Ti/CD3 complex remains to be investigated. Our results have indicated that the Ca^{++} influx, which can be measured after binding of activating mAb to either the Thy-1[27] or the Ly-6C (TABLE 5) molecules of clone KB5.C20, is no longer observed when Ti$^-$ variants of the clone are studied (reference 27 and TABLE 5). If Ca^{++} influx is dependent on a product generated after hydrolysis of phosphatidyl-inositol bisphosphate, as recently suggested (for review, see reference 52), the Thy-1 and Ly-6 activation pathways could depend on an element leading to activation of phospholipase C on the general pathway of protein kinase C-dependent signaling.[53]

ACKNOWLEDGMENT

We thank M. Pierres for antibodies and discussion.

[NOTE ADDED IN PROOF: Northern blot analyses of Ti$^-$ variants used in this study revealed that they had all lost expression of mRNA for the α chain of the Ti (P. Kaldy, unpublished).]

REFERENCES

1. REINHERZ, E. L., S. C. MEUER & S. F. SCHLOSSMAN. 1983. The human T cell receptor: Analysis with cytolytic T cell clones. Immunol. Rev. **74:** 83–112.
2. KRANZ, D. M., D. H. SHERMAN, M. V. SITOVSKY, M. S. PASTERNACK & H. N. EISEN. 1984. Immunoprecipitation of cell surface structures of cloned cytotoxic T lymphocytes by clone-specific antisera. Proc. Natl. Acad. Sci. USA **81:** 573–577.
3. LANCKI, D. W., D. I. MA, W. L. HAVRAN & F. W. FITCH. 1984. Cell surface structures involved in T cell activation. Immunol. Rev. **81:** 65–94.
4. STAERZ, U. D., M. S. PASTERNACK, J. R. KLEIN, J. D. BENEDETTO & M. J. BEVAN. 1984. Monoclonal antibodies specific for a murine cytotoxic T lymphocyte clone. Proc. Natl. Acad. Sci. USA **81:** 1799–1803.
5. HUA, C., M. BUFERNE & A.-M. SCHMITT-VERHULST. 1985. Lysis of hybridoma cells bearing anti-clonotypic surface immunoglobulin by clonotype-expressing alloreactive cytotoxic T cells. Eur. J. Immunol. **15:** 1029–1032.
6. MEUER, S. C., K. A. FITZGERALD, R. E. HUSSEY, J. C. HODGDON, S. F. SCHLOSSMAN & E. L. REINHERZ. 1983. Clonotypic structures involved in antigen-specific human T cell function. Relationship to the T3 molecular complex. J. Exp. Med. **157:** 705–719.
7. LEO, O., M. FOO, D. H. SACHS, L. E. SAMELSON & J. A. BLUESTONE. 1987. Identification of a monoclonal antibody specific for murine T3. Proc. Natl. Acad. Sci. USA **84:** 1374–1378.
8. MEUER, S. C., R. E. HUSSEY, M. FABBI, D. FOX, O. ACUTO, K. A. FITZGERALD, J. C. HODGDON, J. P. PROTENTIS, S. F. SCHLOSSMAN & E. L. REINHERZ. 1984. An alternative pathway of T-cell activation: a functional role for the 50 KD T11 sheep erythrocyte receptor protein. Cell **36:** 897–906.
9. HARA, T., S. M. FU & J. A. HANSEN. 1985. Human T cell activation. II. A new activation pathway used by a major T cell population via a disulfide-bonded dimer of a 44 KD polypeptide (9.3 antigen). J. Exp. Med. **161:** 1513–1524.
10. MORETTA, A., G. PANTALEO, M. LOPEZ-BOTET & L. MORETTA. 1985. Involvement of the T44 molecules in an antigen-independent pathway of T cell activation. Analysis of the correlations to the T cell antigen-receptor complex. J. Exp. Med. **162:** 823–838.
11. KONAKA, Y., M. A. NORCROSS, V. C. MAINO & R. T. SMITH. 1981. Anti-Thy-1 mediated T cell activation. Role of soluble factors and expression of interleukin-2 receptors on T cells. Eur. J. Immunol. **11:** 445–450.
12. GUNTER, K. C., T. R. MALEK & E. M. SHEVACH. 1984. T cell-activating properties of an anti-Thy-1 monoclonal antibody. J. Exp. Med. **159:** 716–730.

13. PONT, S., A. RÉGNIER-VIGOUROUX, P. NAQUET, D. BLANC, A. PIERRES, S. MAR-CHETTO & M. PIERRES. 1985. Analysis of the Thy-1 pathway of T cell hybridoma activation using 17 rat monoclonal antibodies reactive with distinct Thy-1 epitopes. Eur. J. Immunol. **15:** 1222–1228.

14. MACDONALD, H. R., C. BRON, M. ROUSSEAUX, C. HORVATH & J. C. CEROTTINI. 1985. Production and characterization of monoclonal anti-Thy-1 antibodies that stimulate lymphokine production by cytolytic T cell clones. Eur. J. Immunol. **15:** 495–501.

15. ROCK, K. L., E. T. H. YEH, C. F. GRAMM, S. I. HABER, H. REISER & B. BENACER-RAF. 1986. TAP, a novel T cell-activating protein involved in the stimulation of MHC-restricted T lymphocytes. J. Exp. Med. **163:** 315–333.

16. REISER, H., E. T. H. YEH, C. F. GRAMM, B. BENACERRAF & K. L. ROCK. 1986. Gene encoding T-cell-activating protein TAP maps to the Ly-6 locus. Proc. Natl. Acad. Sci. USA **83:** 2954–2958.

17. MALEK, T. R., G. ORTEGA, C. CHAN, R. A. KROCZEK & E. M. SHEVACH. 1986. Role of Ly-6 in lymphocyte activation. II. Induction of T cell activation by monoclonal anti-Ly-6 antibodies. J. Exp. Med. **164:** 709–722.

18. DUMONT, F. 1987. Ly-6C-mediated T cell activation in normal, *lpr/lpr* and *gld/gld* mice. J. Immunol. **138:** 4106–4113.

19. SHAW, S., G. E. GINTHER LUCE, R. QUINONES, R. E. GRESS, T. A. SPRINGER & D. E. SANDERS. 1986. Two antigen-independent adhesion pathways used by human cytotoxic T cell clones. Nature (London) **323:** 262–264.

20. MÖLLER, G., Ed. 1982. Immunol. Rev. **68:** 1–218.

21. BURAKOFF, S. J., organizer, 16th Forum in Immunol. 1987. The role of the CD4(L3T4) molecule in T cell activation. Ann. Inst. Pasteur/Immunol. **138:** 125–169.

22. GABERT, J., C. LANGLET, R. ZAMOYSKA, J. R. PARNES, A.-M. SCHMITT-VERHULST & B. MALISSEN. 1987. Reconstitution of MHC-class I specificity by T-cell receptor and Lyt-2 gene transfer. Cell. **50:** 545–554.

23. POENIE, M., R. Y. TSIEN & A.-M. SCHMITT-VERHULST. 1987. Sequential activation and lethal hit measured by [Ca^{++}]i in individual cytolytic T cells and targets. EMBO J. **6:** 2223–2232.

24. BOYER, C., C. LANGLET, A. GUIMEZANES, M. BUFERNE, C. HUA & A.-M. SCHMITT-VERHULST. 1987. Phosphorylation of T-cell antigen receptor-associated proteins: correlation with activation for killing and/or for gamma-interferon production by a cytolytic T-cell clone. Ann. Inst. Pasteur/Immunol. **138:** 65–82.

25. TSE, A. G. D., A. N. BARCLAY, A. WATTS & A. WILLIAMS. 1985. A glycophospholipid tail at the carboxyl terminus of the Thy-1 glycoprotein of neurons and thymocytes. Science **230:** 1003–1008.

26. REISER, H., H. OETTGEN, E. T. H. YEH, C. TERHORST, M. G. LOW, B. BENACERRAF & K. L. ROCK. 1986. Structural characterization of the TAP molecule: a phosphatidylinositol-linked glycoprotein distinct from the T cell receptor/T3 complex and Thy-1. Cell **47:** 365–370.

27. SCHMITT-VERHULST, A.-M., A. GUIMEZANES, C. BOYER, M. POENIE, R. Y. TSIEN, M. BUFERNE, C. HUA & L. D. LESERMAN. 1987. Pleiotropic loss of activation pathways in a T-cell receptor α-chain deletion variant of a cytolytic T-cell clone. Nature (London) **325:** 628–631.

28. ALBERT, F., M. BUFERNE, C. BOYER & A.-M. SCHMITT-VERHULST. 1982. Interactions between MHC-encoded products and cloned T-cells. I. Fine specificity of induction of proliferation and lysis. Immunogenetics **16:** 533–549.

29. ALBERT, F., C. BOYER, M. BUFERNE & A.-M. SCHMITT-VERHULST. 1984. Interactions between MHC-encoded products and cloned T-cells. II. Analysis of physiological requirements indicates two different pathways of stimulation by class I alloantigens. Immunogenetics **19:** 279–294.

30. MACHY, P. & L. D. LESERMAN. 1984. Elimination or rescue of cells in culture by specifically targeted liposomes containing methotrexate or formyl-tetrahydrofolate. EMBO J. **3:** 1971–1977.

31. ALBERT, F., C. HUA, A. TRUNEH, M. PIERRES & A.-M. SCHMITT-VERHULST. 1985. Distinction between antigen receptor and Il-2 receptor triggering events in the activa-

tion of alloreactive T-cell clones with calcium ionophore and phorbol esters. J. Immunol. **134:** 3649–3655.

32. HUA, C., C. BOYER, A. GUIMEZANES, F. ALBERT & A.-M. SCHMITT-VERHULST. 1986b. Analysis of T cell activation requirements with the use of alloantigens or anti-clonotypic monoclonal antibody. J. Immunol. **136:** 1927–1936.

33. SCHREIBER, R. D., L. J. HICKS, A. CELADA, N. A. BUCHMEIER & P. W. GRAY. 1985. Monoclonal antibodies to murine gamma-interferon which differentially modulate macrophage activation and anti-viral activity. J. Immunol. **134:** 1609–1618.

34. HUA, C., C. BOYER, M. BUFERNE & A.-M. SCHMITT-VERHULST. 1986a. Monoclonal antibodies against an H-2K^b-specific cytotoxic T cell clone detect several clone-specific molecules. J. Immunol. **136:** 1937–1944.

35. LEMKE, H., G. J. HÄMMERLING & U. HÄMMERLING. 1979. Fine specificity analysis with monoclonal antibodies of antigens controlled by the major histocompatibility complex and by the Qa/TL region in mice. Immunol. Rev. **47:** 175–206.

36. HÄMMERLING, G. J., U. HÄMMERLING & L. FLAHERTY. 1979. Qat-4 and Qat-5, new murine T-cell antigens governed by the Tla region and identified by monoclonal antibodies. J. Exp. Med. **150:** 108–116.

37. LEO, O., M. FOO, D. M. SEGAL, E. SHEVACH & J. A. BLUESTONE. 1987. Activation of murine T lymphocytes with monoclonal antibodies: detection on Lyt-2$^+$ cells of an activation antigen not associated with the T cell receptor complex. J. Immunol. **139:** 1214–1222.

38. SITKOVSKY, M. V., M. S. PASTERNACK, J. P. LUGO, J. KLEIN & H. N. EISEN. 1984. Isolation and partial characterization of concanavalin A receptors on cloned cytotoxic T lymphocytes. Proc. Natl. Acad. Sci. USA **81:** 1519–1523.

39. WEISS, A. & J. D. STOBO. 1984. Requirement for the coexpression of T3 and the T cell antigen receptor of a malignant human T cell line. J. Exp. Med. **160:** 1284–1299.

40. MORETTA, A., A. POGGI, D. OLIVE, C. BOTTINO, C. FORTIS, G. PANTALEO & L. MORETTA. 1987. Selection and characterization of T-cell variants lacking molecules involved in T-cell activation (T3 T-cell receptor, T44, and T11): analysis of the functional relationship among different pathways of activation. Proc. Natl. Acad. Sci. USA **84:** 1654–1658.

41. GUIMEZANES, A., M. BUFERNE, S. PONT, M. PIERRES & A.-M. SCHMITT-VERHULST. 1988. Interactions between the Thy-1 and T cell antigen receptor pathways in the activation of cytotoxic T cells: evidence from synergistic effects, loss variants and anti-CD8 antibody mediated inhibition. Cell Immunol. In press.

42. PONT, S., A. RÉGNIER-VIGOUROUX, S. MARCHETTO & M. PIERRES. 1987. A Thy-1.1-specific monoclonal alloantibody activates both mouse and rat T cells. Cell. Immunol. **107:** 64–68.

43. HOWE, R. C. & H. R. MACDONALD. 1988. Heterogeneity of immature (Lyt-2$^-$ 163T4$^-$) thymocytes. J. Immunol. **140:** 1047–1055.

44. TAKEI, F. 1982. Biochemical characterization of H9/25, an allospecificity encoded by the Ly-6 region. Immunogenetics **16:** 201–208.

45. KIMURA, S., N. TADA, Y. LIU-LAM & U. HÄMMERLING. 1984. Studies of the mouse Ly-6 alloantigen system. II. Complexities of the Ly-6 region. Immunogenetics **20:** 47–56.

46. LEO, O., D. H. SACHS, L. E. SAMELSON, M. FOO, R. QUINONES, R. GRESS & J. A. BLUESTONE. 1986. Identification of monoclonal antibodies specific for the T cell receptor complex by Fc receptor-mediated CTL lysis. J. Immunol. **137:** 3874–3880.

47. SPITS, H., H. YSSEL, J. LEEUWENBERG & J. E. DE VRIES. 1985. Antigen-specific cytotoxic T cell and antigen-specific proliferating T cell clones can be induced to cytolytic activity by monoclonal antibodies against T3. Eur. J. Immunol. **15:** 88–91.

48. STAERZ, U. D. & M. J. BEVAN. 1985. Cytotoxic T lymphocyte-mediated lysis via the Fc receptor of target cells. Eur. J. Immunol. **15:** 1172–1177.

49. GUNTER, K. C., R. N. GERMAIN, R. A. KROCZEK, T. SAITO, W. M. YOKOYAMA, C. CHAN, A. WEISS & E. M. SHEVACH. 1987. Thy-1-mediated T-cell activation requires co-expression of CD3/Ti complex. Nature (London) **326:** 505–507.

50. OZATO, K. & D. H. SACHS. 1981. Monoclonal antibodies to mouse MHC antigens. III. Hybridoma antibodies reacting to antigens of the H-2^b haplotype reveal genetic control of isotype expression. J. Immunol. **126:** 317–320.

51. FOX, D. A., R. E. HUSSEY, K. A. FITZGERALD, A. BENSUSSAN, J. F. DALEY, S. F. SCHLOSSMAN & E. L. REINHERZ. 1985. Activation of human thymocytes via the 50 KD T11 sheep erythrocyte binding protein induces the expression of interleukin 2 receptors on both T3$^+$ and T3$^-$ populations. J. Immunol. **134:** 330–335.

52. HOUSLAY, M. D. 1987. Egg activation unscrambles a potential role for IP4. Trends Biochem. Sci. **12:** 1–2.

53. NISHIZUKA, Y. 1984. The role of protein kinase C in cell surface signal transduction and tumour promotion. Nature (London) **308:** 693–698.

54. POENIE, M., J. ALDERTON, R. A. STEINHARDT & R. Y. TSIEN. 1986. Calcium rises abruptly and briefly throughout the cell at the onset of anaphase. Science **233:** 886–889.

Murine Graft-versus-Host Disease as a Model for the Development of Autoimmunity

Relevance of Cytotoxic T Lymphocytes

CHARLES S. VIA AND GENE M. SHEARER

Immunology Branch
National Cancer Institute
National Institutes of Health
Bethesda, Maryland 20892

INTRODUCTION

Murine models of spontaneously occurring lupus-like disease have been described for several strains of mice (reviewed in reference 1). As in human systemic lupus erythematosus, elevated serum levels of anti-DNA antibodies and the subsequent development of an immune complex glomerulonephritis are features common to the MRL, NZBxW, and BXSB models of murine lupus. Although multiple immunological abnormalities have been described in these strains of mice, it is unclear which of these abnormalities are central to the onset of lupus and which abnormalities are merely epiphenomena.

Lupus-like disease has also been described for the parent-into-F_1 model of murine graft-versus-host disease (GVHD). In this model, the intravenous injection of parental spleen cells into healthy, unirradiated F_1 mice results in GVH-induced immune abnormalities due to T cells in the donor inoculum that recognize and respond to the H-2 alloantigens of the opposite parent that are expressed by the F_1.[2-4] Because the F_1 also express H-2 antigens identical to those expressed by the donor, rejection of donor cells by the F_1 host does not occur. A unique feature of this model is that lupus-like disease (*i.e.,* anti-DNA antibody formation and immune-complex glomerulonephritis) can be induced in an immunologically normal strain of F_1 mice that would not spontaneously develop these features otherwise.

Of further note is the observation that the injection of F_1 mice with spleen cells from one parent may result in autoimmune phenomena, whereas injection of the same F_1 mice with spleen cells from the opposite parent results in immunosuppressive phenomena. For example, Gleichman and co-workers have shown that using the $(B10 \times DBA/2)F_1$, the injection of DBA/2 parental cells results in autoimmunity and a lupus-like disease, whereas the injection of B10 parental cells results in anemia, hypogammaglobulinemia, and an increased mortality.[4] This latter outcome (also termed an immunosuppressive GVH), was shown by these workers to occur whenever donor cells differ from the F_1 host by both a class I and class II MHC difference. Autoimmune phenomena (also termed an immunostimulatory GVH) was shown to occur when donor cells differ from the F_1 by a class II major histocompatibility complex (MHC) difference only.[5] A paradox thus arises, because in the $B10 \times DBA/2$ F_1 combination, both the B10 and

DBA/2 donor cells differ from the F_1 by a class I plus II MHC difference, yet the injection of DBA/2 parental cells mimics the results seen when only a class II MHC difference is present. The purpose of the present study was to compare the cellular interactions that occur early in both of these forms of GVH and to delineate the mechanisms that determine whether autoimmune or suppressive phenomena will occur. In the following studies, we have replaced the B10 parent with a C57BL/6 parent, inasmuch as similar outcomes are observed.

MATERIAL AND METHODS

Mice

C57BL/6, DBA/2, and (C57BL/6 × DBA/2)F_1 male mice (B6D2F$_1$) were obtained from the DCT Animal Program, NCI, NIH.

Induction of GVH

Cell suspensions were prepared in Hanks' balanced salt solution from the spleen cells of normal parental donors or syngeneic F_1 controls. The suspensions were filtered through nylon mesh, adjusted to the desired concentration, and injected into the tail vein of normal F_1 mice.

In vitro *Generation and Assay for Cell-Mediated Lympholysis*

Spleen cells from F_1 mice injected with either parental spleen cells or syngeneic F_1 spleen cells two weeks prior, were tested for their ability to generate *in vitro* cell-mediated lympholysis of F_1 target cells. Briefly, cells were cultured with RPMI 1640 with 10% fetal calf serum, penicillin, streptomycin, nonessential amino acids, sodium pyruvate, 2-mercaptoethanol, and L-glutamine in 7% CO_2 humidified air mixture at 37°C. Four × 10^6 responder cells were cultured with 2 × 10^6 irradiated (2000R) F_1 stimulator cells for five days, after which the effectors were harvested and cytolytic activity was assessed as the ability to lyse ^{51}Cr-labeled, three day concanavalin A spleen-cell blasts in a 4 hour assay. Results are expressed as percent specific lysis and are calculated as follows: (experimental release − spontaneous release)/(maximal release − spontaneous release) × 100 = % specific lysis. Each value represents the mean percent ^{51}Cr release from three replicate wells. Standard errors were consistently <5% of the mean value and are omitted.

Immunofluorescence Staining and Flow Cytometry Analysis

Cells suspensions were prepared in Hanks' balanced salt solution (without phenol red) containing 10% fetal calf serum and 0.1% sodium azide. One million cells were incubated with anti-Fc receptor antibody (2.4G2) for 10 minutes at 4°C, incubated with fluorescein-conjugated antibody for 30 minutes, washed twice, and incubated for 30 minutes with Texas red streptavidin. Cells were then washed twice, resuspended and analyzed for fluorescence. All incubations were performed at 4°C and involved saturating levels of reagents as determined by previous experiments.

Fluorescein-conjugated anti-mouse Thy-1.2 and anti-Lyt-2 antibodies were purchased from Becton-Dickinson Immunocytometry Systems (Mountain View, CA). Fluorescein-conjugated MT-4 (anti-L3T4),[6] biotin labeled 34-5-8 (anti-H-2D^d),[7] and 2.4G2 (anti-Fc receptor)[8] were kindly provided by J. Titus and D. Sachs, NIH. Biotin-labeled 5F1 (anti-H-2K^b)[9] was provided by J. Bluestone, NIH. Multicolor flow cytometry was performed as previously described.[10]

All of the anti-T-cell reagents used in these analyses gave clearly distinguishable positive and negative peaks of fluorescence intensity. Channel numbers for integration of data were chosen on the basis of staining on normal spleen cells. Staining of normal F_1 spleen cells with anti-MHC reagents resulted in unimodal positive profiles when compared to negative controls. Channel numbers for integration of anti-MHC data were chosen using these normal spleen cell profiles such that $\geq 90\%$ of the F_1 cells were positive. When donor parental cells were detected in GVH animals, these cells were seen as subpopulations clearly negative (equivalent to nonspecific binding) for F_1-specific MHC.

Anti-DNA Antibodies

Antibodies to ssDNA were determined by ELISA. Plates were coated with ssDNA and test serum added as previously described.[11] Fifty μl of a 1/250 dilution of peroxidase-labeled, affinity-purified goat anti-mouse IgG was added to each well, and the remainder of the assay was performed as previously described.[12] Results are expressed as the optical density (OD) at a final serum dilution of 1 : 32.

RESULTS

Autoimmune Phenomena

TABLE 1 demonstrates that using the B6D2F$_1$, only mice injected with DBA/2 donor cells (DBA GVH) develop elevated serum levels of anti-DNA antibodies when compared to the syngeneic-injected control mice. Additionally, in the DBA GVH group, anti-DNA antibody levels are higher at 4 weeks postspleen cell injection compared to 2 weeks postinjection for both the 100×10^6 and the $50 \times$

TABLE 1. IgG Antibodies to ssDNA in B6D2F$_1$ Mice Injected with Donor Spleen Cells

Number and Type of Donor Cells	Day 14[a]	Day 28
50×10^6 B6D2F$_1$	.05[b]	.04
100×10^6 B6	.05	.04
50×10^6 B6	.10	.03
5×10^6 B6	.01	.06
100×10 DBA/2	.51	.64
50×10^6 DBA/2	.20	.31
5×10^6 DBA/2	.05	.05
Positive control (NZB female)	.96	

[a] Time after injection of donor cells.

[b] OD at a final serum dilution of 1 : 32. Results are from pooled serum of two mice in each group.

TABLE 2. Presence of Parent Anti-F_1 Cytolytic Activity in the Spleens of GVH Mice

Responder cells[a]	Stimulator cells	Targets[b]		
		F_1	DBA/2	B6
F_1 injected F_1 controls	F_1	0	0	0
DBA GVH	F_1	0	0	0
B6 GVH	F_1	22	39	0

[a] B6D2F_1 mice were injected with 60×10^6 syngeneic F_1, DBA/2, or B6 spleen cells two weeks prior to testing.

[b] Percent lysis of designated target at an effector:target of 40:1.

10^6 donor cell doses. Also, at both the 2 week and 4 week time points, higher numbers of donor cells results in higher serum levels of anti-DNA antibodies. In an effort to determine the earliest events in this model, we have chosen to study mice 2 weeks after the injection of $50–60 \times 10^6$ donor cells, because this combination approaches the threshold for induction of autoimmunity.

Presence of Parental Cells with Anti-F_1 Cytotoxic T Lymphocyte (CTL) Activity in GVH Mice

It is possible that in the parent-into-F_1 model of GVHD there is the development of parental cells with cytolytic activity towards F_1 host cells. Such cells could be important in the subsequent development of chimerism. By eliminating F_1 cells, parent anti-F_1 CTL may facilitate donor repopulation of the F_1 host. We therefore tested for the presence of such cells in the spleens of either B6-injected F_1 mice (B6 GVH) or DBA GVH mice. As seen in TABLE 2, lysis of F_1 targets was observed only by B6 GVH mice. As expected, this activity was directed towards H-2D and not towards H-2B. No cytolytic activity toward either target was detected in either DBA GVH mice or syngeneic-injected control mice.

To further clarify the observed differences in the development of parent anti-F_1 CTL in these two models of GVH, two-color flow cytometry was performed. In this way, T-cell subpopulations of both donor and host origin could be quantified. As shown in TABLE 3, B6 GVH is characterized by a reduction in total spleen cells recovered, a reduction in the number of host T cells (shown here as a reduction in host L3T4 cells), and donor T-cell chimerism of approximately 22 percent. Although both donor Lyt-2$^+$ and L3T4$^+$ cells are present, donor Lyt-2$^+$ cells are the predominant T-cell phenotype present. By contrast, the DBA GVH is characterized by an increase in total spleen cells recovered, normal to increased numbers of host T cells (shown as host L3T4$^+$ cells), and donor T-cell chimerism of approximately 2% and comprised almost exclusively of L3T4$^+$ cells. Thus, a striking difference between these two types of GVH is the almost complete absence of donor Lyt-2$^+$ cells in the DBA GVH.

Because in the B6 GVH, donor T cells are predominantly Lyt-2$^+$, and in the DBA GVH, donor Lyt-2$^+$ cells are virtually absent, it is not surprising that parent anti-F_1 CTL activity is present in B6 GVH mice and not observed for DBA GVH mice (TABLE 2). It should be emphasized that despite the almost 10-fold difference in the relative frequency of donor T-cell chimerism in these two types of GVH, because of the reduced spleen-cell recovery in B6 GVH mice and the increased recovery in DBA GVH mice, the actual numbers of donor L3T4$^+$ cells is compa-

TABLE 3. Parental T-Cell Chimerism in the Spleens of GVH Mice

Group	Cells/spleen ($\times 10^{-6}$)	Host[a] L3T4 cells/ spleen[c] ($\times 10^{-6}$)	Donor[b] Percent Thy-1.2[d]	L3T4/spleen[e] ($\times 10^{-6}$)	L3T4 : Lyt2[f]
Normal B6D2F$_1$[g]	86	13.5	0	0	0
B6 GVH	26	4.6	23	2.0	.48

		Host L3T4 cells/ spleen	Donor Percent Thy-1.2	L3T4/spleen ($\times 10^{-6}$)	L3T4 : Lyt-2
Normal B6D2F$_1$	65	13	0	0	0
DBA GVH	130	20	2	2.6	14.4

[a] Host cells are defined as staining positively with antibody specific for the MHC of the F$_1$. For B6 (K^{b}D^b)-injected mice (B6 GVH), anti-D^d was used to detect F$_1$ (K^b/K^d, D^b/D^d) cells. For DBA/2-injected mice (DBA GVH), anti-K^b was used to detect F$_1$ cells.

[b] Donor cells are defined as staining negatively with antibody specific for the MHC of the F$_1$.

[c] Cells staining positively with both anti-L3T4 and anti-MHC antibody.

[d] Cells staining positively with anti-Thy-1.2 and negatively with anti-MHC antibody.

[e] Cells staining positively with anti-L3T4 and negatively with anti-MHC antibody.

[f] L3T4 : Lyt-2 of cells staining negatively with anti-MHC antibody.

[g] Normal F$_1$ mice or GVH mice were tested two weeks after donor-cell injection. Results are expressed as the mean values of two mice tested individually.

rable for both groups, that is, approximately 2×10^6 donor L3T4$^+$ cells/spleen. Thus, the profound reduction in donor Lyt-2 cells seen for DBA GVH mice cannot be attributed to differences in donor-cell engraftment.

Why then do DBA GVH mice fail to exhibit appreciable numbers of donor Lyt-2$^+$ cells, and how does this failure relate to the development of autoimmunity? To address this question, we compared the *in vitro* anti-F$_1$ precursor CTL (pCTL) frequency for both B6 and DBA/2 donor spleen cells. Surprisingly the anti-F$_1$ pCTL frequency for DBA mice was approximately 9-fold less than the anti-F$_1$ pCTL frequency of B6 mice.[13] Thus, the defective development of parent anti-F$_1$ CTL and the virtual absence of donor Lyt-2$^+$ cells in DBA GVH mice appears due to a naturally occurring deficit in anti-F$_1$ pCTL in the DBA/2 donor inoculum.

DISCUSSION

Based on the foregoing data, we have constructed a model for the early immunologic events that occur in these two forms of GVH. FIGURE 1 (parts 3–4) illustrates the sequence of events following the injection of B6 spleen cells into B6D2F$_1$ hosts. Initially, donor-derived B6 L3T4$^+$ T-helper cells (T$_h$) recognize Ia^d on F$_1$ class II expressing cells (B cells and APCs). This initial step involves recognition of allogeneic Ia by donor L3T4$^+$ cells and is a feature common to both types of GVH. The finding of the present study that donor L3T4$^+$ cells are present equally in spleens of mice with both types of GVH is consistent with this interpretation. In the present model, however, we suggest that as a result of this recognition, donor L3T4$^+$ T$_h$ respond by making lymphokines that allow the maturation of donor-derived precursor CTLs specific for H-2^d. These effectors then eliminate F$_1$ cells (FIG. 1, part 4), and the resulting expansion of donor cells leads to significant levels of parental T-cell chimerism to include both donor Lyt-2$^+$ and L3T4$^+$ cells. In the spleen, this cytolytic activity would be directed mainly towards F$_1$ B cells, which are the predominant cell type present. The finding of the present study that B6 GVH spleens contain donor Lyt-2$^+$ cells (cytotoxic phenotype) and are depleted of host cells, particularly host Thy-1.2$^-$ cells, supports this interpretation. Additionally, we have observed that the frequency of Fc receptor-positive cells in spleens of B6 GVH mice is reduced to approximately 30–35% of normal levels at two weeks after the induction of GVH (data not shown).

Following the injection of DBA/2 spleen cells (FIG. 1, part 1), the initial event would be similar to that in the B6-GVH, that is, donor-derived L3T4$^+$ T-helper cell recognition of Ia^b on F$_1$ class II-expressing cells that leads to the production of lymphokines. In this scenario, due to a naturally occurring reduction in the number of anti-F$_1$ pCTL, defective development of parental anti-H-2^b CTL activity fails to reduce the number of F$_1$ B cells. Parental T-cell chimerism is limited to L3T4$^+$ cells, which provide help to F$_1$ B cells in the form of an allogeneic effect (Fig. 1, part 2). Polyclonal activation of B cells and subsequent autoantibody formation would result as previously described by Gleichmann et al.[4] In contrast to the Gleichmann model, however, we propose that it is the lack of development

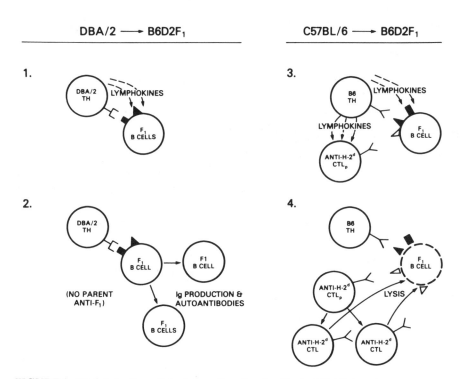

FIGURE 1. Models for the cellular interactions involved in the DBA/2-into-F$_1$ murine GVH (1, 2) and the B6-into-F$_1$ murine GVH (3, 4).

of DBA/2 parental CTL specific for F_1 cells that is the permissive defect in the development of autoimmunity in this form of GVH, because similar T-cell help to F_1 B cells (allogeneic effect) occurs in the B6 GVH. In the B6-induced GVH, however, activated F_1 B cells would be eliminated by B6 donor CTLs.

Thus, in this murine model of GVH, the development of autoimmunity is not solely the result of excessive or inappropriate T-helper cell activity, but rather, is associated with a deficient effector arm of T-cell immunity (CTL) that fails to efficiently remove the source of antigenic stimulation. Thus, a heretofore unrecognized function of CTLs may be to remove the source of continued antigenic stimulation, thereby reducing the likelihood of humoral autoimmunity. Therapeutic strategies for the treatment of SLE should consider the possibility that the primary defect may involve defective effector function instead of, or in addition to, excessive T-helper cell activity.

REFERENCES

1. THEOFILOPOULOS, A. N. & F. J. DIXON. 1985. Murine models of systemic lupus erythematosus. Adv. Immunol. **37:** 269–390.
2. SHEARER, G. M. & R. P. POLISSON. 1980. Mutual recognition of parental F_1 lymphocytes. J. Exp. Med. **151:** 20–31.
3. PICKEL, K. & M. K. HOFFMANN. 1977. Suppressor T cells arising in mice undergoing a graft-vs-host response. J. Immunol. **118:** 653–656.
4. GLEICHMANN, E., S. T. PALS, A. G. ROLINK et al. 1984. Graft-vs-host reactions: clues to the etiopathology of a spectrum of immunological diseases. Immunology Today **5:** 324–332.
5. ROLINK, A. G., S. PALS & E. GLEICHMANN. 1983. Allosuppressor and allohelper T cells in acute and chronic graft-vs-host disease. II. F_1 recipients carrying mutations at H-2K and/or I-A. J. Exp. Med. **157:** 755–767.
6. PIERRES, A., P. NUQUET, A. VAN AGTHOVEN et al. 1984. A rat anti-mouse T4 monoclonal antibody (H129.19) inhibits proliferation of Ia reactive T cell clones. J. Immunol. **132:** 2775–2782.
7. OZATO, K., N. M. MAYER & D. H. SACHS. 1982. Monoclonal antibodies to mouse MHC antigens. IV. A series of hybridoma clones producing anti-H-2^d antibodies. Transplantation **34:** 113–120.
8. UNKELESS, J. C. 1979. Characterization of a monoclonal antibody directed against mouse macrophage and lymphocyte Fc receptors. J. Exp. Med. **150:** 580–596.
9. SHERMAN, L. A. & C. P. RANDOLPH. 1981. Monoclonal anti-H-$2K^b$ antibodies detect serological differences between H-$2K^b$ mutants. Immunogenetics **12:** 183–186.
10. SEGAL, D. M., S. O. SHARROW, J. F. JONES et al. 1981. Fc (IgG) receptors on rat basophilic leukemia cells. J. Immunol. **138:** 126–133.
11. REEVES, J. P. & A. D. STEINBERG. 1985. Effect of xid gene on graft-vs-host induced autoantibody production in nonautoimmune mice. Clin. Immunol. Immunopathol. **36:** 320–329.
12. HATHCOCK, K. S., J. J. KENNY & R. J. HODES. 1985. Helper T cell requirements for T15 idiotype expression on phosphorylcholine-specific antibodies. Eur. J. Immunol. **15:** 564–569.
13. VIA, C. S., S. O. SHARROW & G. M. SHEARER. 1987. Role of cytotoxic T lymphocytes in the prevention of lupus-like disease occurring in a murine model of graft-vs-host disease. J. Immunol. **139:**1840–1849.

Linked Recognition of Helper and Cytotoxic Antigenic Determinants for the Generation of Cytotoxic T Lymphocytes[a]

DELANIE CASSELL AND JAMES FORMAN

Immunology Program and the Department of Microbiology
University of Texas Health Science Center at Dallas
Dallas, Texas 75235

INTRODUCTION

Many cytotoxic T lymphocyte (CTL) responses require helper activity provided by L3T4 T cells.[1] Removal of L3T4 cells from *in vitro* cultures prevents the generation of CTL, and addition of interleukin-2 (IL-2) reconstitutes this activity.[2-4] Although helper molecules in addition to IL-2 may play a role in CTL generation, a simple model to explain T-cell help consists of the following: 1) L3T4 cells recognize antigen and secrete IL-2; 2) CTL precursors recognize antigen and express IL-2 receptors; and 3) the binding of L3T4 cell-derived IL-2 to the IL-2 receptor on CTL precursors permits their proliferation and differentiation leading to CTL effector activity (FIG. 1). T-B cell collaboration was originally postulated to occur by linked recognition through an antigen bridge allowing for close approximation of these two cell types.[5] This concept has recently been modified by the finding that B cells can present antigen in the context of class II molecules in a manner similar to other antigen-presenting cells (APC).[6-8] Thus, T-B collaboration occurs by linked recognition in which T-helper cells (T_h) see antigen in the context of Ia on the B cell without the need for an antigen bridge. In the mouse, it is difficult to demonstrate expression of conventional class II molecules on T cells. CTL activity can be readily demonstrated in bone marrow radiation chimeras where T_h are restricted to an Ia phenotype that differs from the Ia genotype of the CTL.[9] Therefore, models of T-B collaboration do not appear to explain T-T interactions between L3T4 and Lyt-2 cells.

B6.Tla (Qa-1^a) mice do not generate a primary *in vitro* CTL response against cells from the Qa-1 congenic strain C57BL/6 (Qa-1^b).[10] Female B6.Tla^a mice do generate an *in vitro* response if previously primed *in vivo* with male but not female (sex-matched) B6 cells. We previously postulated that the B6 male cells provide a helper antigen, H-Y, in addition to Qa-1, which allows for anti-H-Y–specific helper cells to activate Qa-1–specific CTL precursors. In this report we provide further evidence to support this concept and relate these findings to a physiologic model for T-T collaboration, which requires linked recognition.

[a] This work was supported by NIH Grants AI11851 and CA41099 and the Texas Department of the Ladies Auxiliary, Veterans of Foreign Wars.

METHODS

Animals

Mice were bred and maintained in our animal colony at the University of Texas Health Science Center at Dallas. The strains used were C57BL/6 (abbreviated B6) (Qa-1^b) and its Qa-1/Tla congenic pair B6.Tl^a (Qa-1^a).

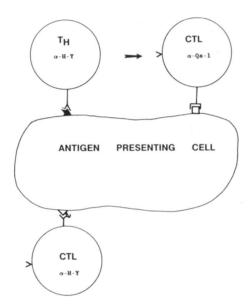

FIGURE 1. Model for T-T collaboration between T_h and CTL.P. An APC must display determinants recognized by both CTL.P and T_h. In the system described here, B6.Tla^a mice lack T_h for Qa-1.^{b} Effective priming occurs when APC express Qa-1^b together with a helper antigen to which the mice can respond. In this case the T_h-recognized antigen is H-Y and is presented in the context of I-A^b. The close proximity between the two T cells is postulated to allow for a high local concentration of T_h-secreted lymphokines (presumably IL-2) that can bind to receptors on the CTL.P. Also shown is an anti-H-Y CTL.P, which would be induced by the same T_h. □, Qa-1^b; ▲, IA^b; △, H-2D^b; ●, H-Y; →, lymphokines; >, lymphokine receptor.

Monoclonal Antibodies

Two non-cross-reactive monoclonal antibodies (mAb) to various surface markers were employed; the first mAb was used with guinea pig complement for depletion of T-cell subsets, and the second mAb was used to monitor depletion by flow cytofluorimetry with fluoresceinated mouse anti-rat κ as a secondary reagent. Anti-Thy-1.2 mAb was obtained from New England Nuclear Products (Boston, MA) as an ascites, and 30H12 is an affinity-purified rat IgG$_{2b}$ mAb. Anti-

L3T4 mAbs were 2B6 (rat μ ascites was a gift of Dr. Ethan Shevach, NIH) and GK1.5 (rat IgG$_{2b}$, affinity purified). Anti-Lyt-2 mAbs were H02.2 (mouse μ ascites) and 2.43 (rat IgG$_{2b}$, supernatant).

Concanavalin A Supernatant and Interleukin-2

Recombinant (r) IL-2 obtained from yeast cultures was kindly provided by Dr. Philip J. Barr from Chiron (Emeryville, CA). Concanavalin A (Con A)-induced supernatants were collected after 24 hr incubation of Fisher rat spleen cells with 3 μg/ml Con A and used in cultures at a final concentration of 25 percent.

In Vivo Inoculation of Anti-L3T4 Antibody

One hundred μg of affinity-purified GK1.5 was injected i.p. on days 0, 3, 6, and 9, and priming was carried out with 30×10^6 spleen cells administered i.p. on day seven.

In Vivo Inoculation of rIL-2

A total dose of 80,000 U of rIL-2 was administered i.p. twice a day for 7 days beginning at the time of priming with spleen cells.

Generation of Anti-Qa-1 CTL in Vitro

Anti-Qa-1 CTL were generated as previously described.[10] Briefly, 5×10^6 responder cells were cocultured with 5×10^6 irradiated (2000R) stimulator cells in RPMI 1640 with 10% fetal bovine serum in a volume of 2.0 ml in 24-well plates. After 5 days of culture, the plates were harvested and dilutions of cultures were tested for cytolytic activity against target cells in a 4 hr ^{51}Cr release assay.

Target Cells

Target cells were spleen cells cultured for 2–3 days with 5 μg/ml of concanavalin A (Con A). The lymphoblasts were spun through a lymphoprep gradient to remove dead cells prior to labeling with isotope.

Calculations

Specific release (experimental release − spontaneous release/total release − spontaneous release) was determined for serial dilutions of each culture, and from this release, linear regression was calculated. One lytic unit (LU) equals the fraction of culture required for 40% specific release. Data is expressed as the reciprocal of LU or LU/culture. In most experiments, the effector to target ratio required for 40% specific release was ~50–100, and this comprised approximately $\frac{1}{14}$ of the culture.

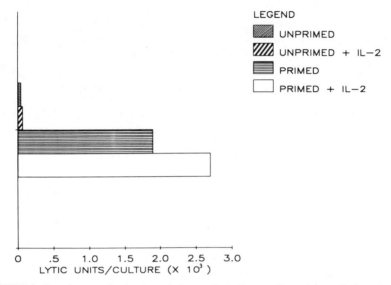

FIGURE 2. Requirement for *in vivo* priming to Qa-1. Responding spleen cells from B6.Tla female mice either unprimed or primed with B6 male spleen cells were cultured with B6 female splenic stimulators in the presence of 100 U/ml rIL-2. Cytolytic activity was assayed against Con A-induced splenic blasts from B6 and B6.Tla^a female mice. No activity was detected against B6.Tla^a targets. The 95% confidence intervals (CI) for LU values are as follows: unprimed (0–75), unprimed + IL-2 (3–24), primed (561–1.6 × 10^4), and primed + IL-2 (720–8.8 × 10^4).

RESULTS

Unprimed B6.Tla^a Animals Do Not Generate a Primary in Vitro *Response to Qa-1^b in the Presence of Helper Activity*

The purpose of these experiments is to analyze the role of helper activity *in vivo* for the generation of CTL activity. Although primed B6.Tla^a (Qa-1^a) anti-B6 (Qa-1^b) (anti-Qa-1^b) spleen cells give rise to Qa-1^b–specific CTL, unprimed B6.Tla^a spleen cells do not generate activity against Qa-1^b when cocultured with Qa-1 congenic B6 stimulator cells (FIG. 2). This nonresponsiveness is not due to a deficiency of T-helper activity because the addition of rIL-2 (FIG. 2) or Con A supernatant (not shown) does not reveal latent CTL activity in unprimed animals. This supernatant does, however, reconstitute CTL activity in L3T4 cell-depleted cultures containing primed anti-Qa-1 CTL precursors (P) (data not shown). Thus, *in vivo* inoculation of B6.Tla^a mice with B6 spleen cells is required for the generation of primed anti-Qa-1 CTL.P that can be detected after *in vitro* culture. This finding allowed us to dissect the role of helper activity *in vivo* for the generation of primed CTL.P.

H-Y and Qa-1 Must be Expressed on the Same Antigen-Presenting Cell for Successful Priming in Vivo

We previously showed that B6.Tla^a animals cannot be successfully primed *in vivo* to Qa-1 using sex-matched B6 cells as the immunogen.[11] Inoculating female

B6.Tla[a] mice with male B6 cells, however, did allow for successful priming. We postulated that the male (H-Y) antigen provided helper determinants that allowed for the generation of helper activity and that B6 animals were deficient in specific helper activity directed against Qa-1. A model to explain this data is presented in FIGURE 1. This model indicates that two different determinants, one recognized by a CTL (anti-Qa-1) and the other recognized by a L3T4-helper cell (anti-H-Y) must be presented on the same APC for priming to occur. This model was first tested by showing that mice primed with these two antigens on separate cells did not lead to effective sensitization. Thus, spleen cells from B6.Tla[a] female mice primed with a mixture of B6.Tla[a] male cells (H-Y) and B6 (Qa-1[b]) female cells fail to generate anti-Qa-1[b] CTL activity when challenged *in vitro* (FIG. 3). This confirms our previous results indicating that the two antigens need to be on the same APC.

IL-2 Replaces the Need for H-Y in Priming for the Qa-1 CTL Response

If H-Y serves to activate T_h to elaborate IL-2, then inoculation of mice with Qa-1 in the absence of H-Y should lead to priming of anti-Qa-1 CTL.P if mice are coinjected with IL-2. Accordingly female B6.Tla[a] mice were inoculated with either female or male B6 cells in the presence or absence of rIL-2. A total of 80,000 U of rIL-2 was inoculated over a period of 7 days. The results of this protocol demonstrate that rIL-2 can substitute for H-Y in allowing for successful priming for anti-Qa-1 CTL activity (FIG. 4). In some cases, the activity generated from rIL-2 inoculation is greater than the control group (as seen in FIG. 4), whereas in other cases, it is less (not shown). In other experiments, rIL-2 did not lead to

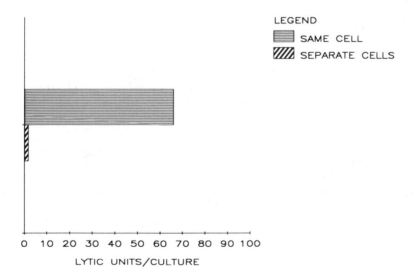

FIGURE 3. B6.Tla[a] female mice were primed with either B6 male cells (both antigens on the same cell) or with a combination of B6 female and B6.Tla[a] male cells (antigens on separate cells). Spleen cells from primed B6.Tla[a] animals were cultured with B6 female stimulators. No cytolytic activity was detected against B6.Tla targets. The 95% CI are as follows: same cell (0), separate cells (45–91).

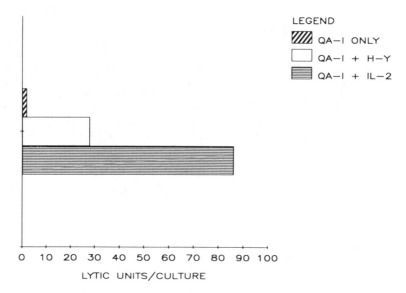

FIGURE 4. IL-2 substitutes for H-Y *in vivo*. B6.Tla females were primed with B6 female cells (Qa-1 only), B6 male cells (Qa-1 + H-Y), or with B6 female cells and 80,000 U rIL-2 (Qa-1 + IL-2). Spleen cells from these animals were restimulated *in vitro* with B6 female cells. No cytolytic activity was detected against B6.Tla targets. The 95% CI are as follows: Qa-1 only (0), Qa-1 + H-Y (14–49), Qa-1 + IL-2 (40–170).

successful priming, which may suggest that either local delivery of IL-2 is somewhat variable when inoculated parenterally or that factors in addition to IL-2 may sometimes play a role in the priming process.

Removal of L3T4 Cells Prevents Priming for an Anti-Qa-1 CTL Response

According to the model presented (FIG. 1), removal of L3T4 cells should prevent successful priming even in the presence of the H-Y antigen. Accordingly, B6 mice were treated with 100 μg of anti-L3T4 (GK1.5) on days 0, 3, 6, and 9. On day 8 these mice were primed with B6.Tla[a] spleen cells and subsequently tested (on day 27) *in vitro* for Qa-1 CTL activity. Treatment with GK1.5 abrogated the detection of anti-Qa-1 CTL activity (FIG. 5). Thus, these data show that even in the presence of the H-Y helper antigen, priming cannot occur *in vivo* in L3T4-deficient mice.

DISCUSSION

The data presented supports a model for T-T collaboration for the generation of CTL activity *in vivo*. According to the model, L3T4-helper cells assist in the activation of CTL by secreting an antigen nonspecific lymphokine, IL-2, which binds to IL-2 receptors on CTL.P. In order for this mediator to act, both T_h and CTL need to be in close proximity. This proximity is accomplished by the presence of an APC, which forms a three-cell complex and approximates the T_h and CTL through an intermolecular form of linked recognition. We previously showed and demonstrate here that both the H-Y and Qa-1 antigen need to be on the same APC in order for effective priming to occur,[10] a finding also confirmed by others.[11,12] In this study we have tested two other predictions of this model. First, we show that in the absence of the helper antigen, H-Y, mice can be successfully primed if inoculated with rIL-2. Thus, a primary function of the L3T4 cell is to secrete this lymphokine, which allows for CTL activation. Several studies indicate that factors in addition to IL-2 are required for CTL differentiation *in vitro*,[13–16] although other evidence suggests that IL-2 alone can serve this function.[2] It is possible that IL-2 promotes the elaboration of additional factors by CTL themselves, or that *in vivo* IL-2 secondarily allows for other cell types to secrete additional helper factors. Nevertheless, the minimal model we present relates primarily to the cell types involved in the cooperative response rather than their factors or lymphokines. We have noted that in some experiments coinoculation of rIL-2 together with sex-matched Qa-1 disparate cells did not lead to effective priming. This could relate to a need for additional factors. It is difficult, however, to know whether the IL-2 concentration is appropriate at the site of priming, making the interpretation of such negative results difficult.

It is important to note that although B6.Tla[a] animals fail to generate an anti-Qa-1[b] response, A and (B6.Tla[a] × A)F₁ mice do. Further, this responsiveness is due to an H-2–linked immune response gene.[10,17] Thus, these data demonstrate that animals unable to mount a CTL response due to a lack of helper activity can be converted to responder status by *in vivo* administration of IL-2.

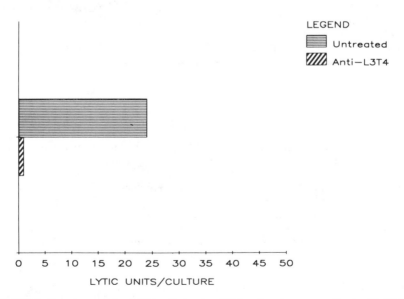

FIGURE 5. Requirement for L3T4 cells *in vivo*. B6 female mice were primed with B6.Tla[a] male cells without (untreated) or with the concomitant administration of GK1.5. Spleen cells from these animals were subsequently restimulated *in vitro* with B6.Tla female cells. No cytolytic activity was detected against B6 targets. The 95% CI are as follows: untreated (15–36) and anti L3T4 (0).

A second prediction, *viz.*, in the presence of the helper antigen H-Y, priming should not occur in animals depleted of L3T4 cells by *in vivo* inoculation of anti-L3T4 antibody, was also borne out. This protocol has been used by others to show that helper activity can be ablated. For example, Coulie *et al.*[18] have noted that help for primary and secondary T-dependent antibody responses is completely abrogated by administration of smaller amounts of GK1.5 than are used in this report. Waldor *et al.*[19] have reported similar findings and noted both the prevention and reversal of experimental allergic encephalomyelitis in susceptible mice as a result of *in vivo* treatment with GK1.5. In this latter report, the extent of depletion of peripheral L3T4 cells is well-documented.

Although the model we present accounts for T-T collaboration for a specific CTL response, two issues are not readily understood. First, there is no requirement for the L3T4 and Lyt-2 cell to be specific for the same antigen, as is readily illustrated in the immune response studied here. Whereas this may yield promiscuous interactions, two different antigens need to be concentrated on the same APC for priming to occur. In this system, we readily accomplish this by using a minor H (H-Y) and class I antigen (Qa-1) intrinsic to the inoculated cells. In a viral infection, it would be predicted that an efficient response would only be generated if the virus infected an Ia$^+$ APC. Because antigen reprocessing can occur for class I responses,[20] infection of Ia$^-$ cells may lead to shedding of antigenic components that are re-presented by APC, which can sensitize both CTL.P and T_h. We would suggest that it is unlikely that two different antigens are shed and re-presented by an APC at a concentration high enough to activate both T_h and CTL.

The second issue raised by the model that requires explanation is that a three rather than two-cell interaction is required for T-cell activation. This would imply that T-T collaboration represents a very rare event. It is possible that very few APC function in a lymphoid organ *in vivo* and that most APC express high levels of both antigens shortly after antigen exposure. Although this would limit the time frame of T-T cooperation, it would increase the probability for successful interaction. A better understanding of T-cell trafficking and APC function *in vivo* is required for further analysis of this issue.

SUMMARY

These studies present a model for T-T collaboration for the generation of cytotoxic T lymphocytes. The *in vitro* CTL response against Qa-1 alloantigens in B6 Qa-1 congenic mice requires that animals are first primed *in vivo* with Qa-1 together with a second (helper) antigen. Both the antigen recognized by CTL (Qa-1) and T_h (H-Y) must be presented on the same APC for successful priming. This finding is consistent with a linked recognition model whereby both molecules are presented on the same APC in order to accomplish close proximity between the two T cells. To further test this model, we demonstrated that in the absence of the helper antigen, H-Y, mice could be successfully primed against Qa-1 if coinoculated with a product of a T_h, IL-2. We further showed that mice treated with anti-L3T4 antibodies could not be primed to Qa-1 even though the cells used for immunization expressed the H-Y helper antigen. Taken together, these results lend further support to a model of linked recognition between T_h and CTL.P where close proximity allows for the lymphokine IL-2 to bind to its receptor on the CTL allowing for the successful induction of CTL.P.

REFERENCES

1. PILARSKI, L. M. & J. F. KROWKA. 1985. Regulation of the induction of cytotoxic T cells by antigen-specific regulatory T cells and by antigen-specific T cell factors. *In* Recognition and Regulation in CMI. J. Watson & J. Marbrook, Eds. Marcel Dekker, Inc.

2. ERARD, F., P. CORTHESY, M. NABHOLZ, J. W. LOWENTHAL, P. ZAECH, P. PLAETINCK & H. R. MACDONALD. 1985. Interleukin 2 is both necessary and sufficient for the growth and differentiation of lectin-stimulated cytolytic T lymphocyte precursors. J. Immunol. **134:** 1644–1652.

3. KERN, D. E., S. GILLIS, M. OKADA & C. S. HENNEY. 1981. The role of interleukin 2 (IL2) in the differentiation of cytotoxic T cells: the effect of monoclonal anti-IL-2 antibody and adsorption with IL-2 dependent T cell lines. J. Immunol. **127:** 1323–1328.

4. MIZOUCHI, T., H. GOLDING, A. S. ROSENBERG, L. H. GLIMCHER, T. R. MALEK & A. SINGER. 1985. Both L3T4$^+$ and Lyt-2$^+$ helper T cells initiate cytotoxic T lymphocyte responses against allogeneic major histocompatibility antigens but not against trinitrophenyl-modified self. J. Exp. Med. **162:** 427–443.

5. MITCHISON, N. A. 1971. The carrier effect in the secondary response to hapten protein conjugates. II. Cellular cooperation. Eur. J. Immunol. **1:** 18–28.

6. KAKIUCHI, T., R. W. CHESNUT & H. M. GREY. 1983. B cells as antigen-presenting cells: the requirement for B cell activation. J. Immunol. **131:** 109–114.

7. ASHWELL, J. D., A. L. DEFRANCO, W. E. PAUL & R. H. SCHWARTZ. 1984. Antigen presentation by resting B cells. Radiosensitivity of the antigen-presentation function and two distinct pathways of T cell activation. J. Exp. Med. **159:** 881–905.

8. LANZAVECCHIA, A. 1985. Antigen-specific interaction between T and B cells. Nature (London) **314:** 537–539.

9. FINK, P. J. & M. J. BEVAN. 1981. Influence of H-2 antigen expression on killer T cell specificity, differentiation, and induction. Proc. Natl. Acad. Sci. USA **78:** 6401–6405.

10. KEENE, J. A. & J. FORMAN. 1982. Helper activity is required for the *in vivo* generation of cytotoxic T lymphocytes. J. Exp. Med. **155:** 768–782.

11. KROWKA, J. F., B. SINGH, A. FOTEDAR, T. MOSMANN, M. A. GIEDLIN & L. M. PILARSKI. 1986. A requirement for physical linkage between determinants recognized by helper molecules and cytotoxic T cell precursors in the induction of cytotoxic T cell responses. J. Immunol. **136:** 3561–3566.

12. JURETIC, A., B. MALENICA, E. JURETIC, J. KLEIN & Z. A. NAGY. 1985. Helper effects required during *in vivo* priming for a cytotoxic response to the H-Y antigen in nonresponder mice. J. Immunol. **134:** 1408–1414.

13. RAULET, D. H. & M. J. BEVAN. 1982. A differentiation factor required for the expression of cytotoxic T cell function. Nature (London) **296:** 754–756.

14. WAGNER, H., C. HARDT, B. T. ROUSE, M. ROLLINGHOFF, P. SCHEURICH & K. PFIZENMAIER. 1982. Dissection of the proliferative and differentiative signals controlling murine cytotoxic T lymphocyte responses. J. Exp. Med. **155:** 1876–1881.

15. FALK, W., D. N. MANNEL, B. KATZER, B. KALTMANN, P. H. KRAMMER, T. DIAMANSTSTEIN & W. DROGE. 1985. Induction of IL 2 receptor expression and cytotoxicity of thymocytes by stimulation with TCF1. J. Immunol. **135:** 1160–1164.

16. TAKAI, Y., S. H. HERRMANN, J. L. GRENSTEIN, G. L. SPITALNY & S. J. BURAKOFF. 1986. Requirement for three distinct lymphokines for the induction of cytotoxic T lymphocytes from thymocytes. J. Immunol. **137:** 3494–3500.

17. KEENE, J-A. & J. FORMAN. 1983. H-2 linked IR gene control of H-2 unrestricted cytotoxic T lymphocytes. *In* IR genes, past, present, and future. C. W. Pierce, S. E. Cullen, J. A. Kapp, B. D. Schwartz & D. C. Shreffler. Ed. 355–359. The Humana Press. Clinton, N.J.

18. COULIE, P. G., J-P COUTELIER, C. UYTTENHOVE, P. LAMBOTTE & J. VAN SNICK. 1985. *In vivo* suppression of T-dependent antibody responses by treatment with a monoclonal anti-L3T4 antibody. Eur. J. Immunol. **15:** 638–640.
19. WALDOR, M. K., S. SRIRAM, R. HARDY, L. A. HERZENBERG, L. A. HERZENBERG, L. LANIER, M. LIM & L. STEINMAN. 1985. Reversal of experimental allergic encephalomyelitis with monoclonal antibody to a T-cell subset marker. Science **227:** 415–417.
20. BEVAN, M. J. 1976. Cross priming for a secondary cytotoxic response to minor H antigens with H-2 congenic cells which do not cross-react in the cytotoxic assay. J. Exp. Med. **143:** 1283–1288.

The Mls Reaction

A Regulatory Phenomenon

ULRICH HAMMERLING, ROGER PALFREE,
MAUREEN TOULON, AND MICHAEL HOFFMANN

Memorial Sloan-Kettering Cancer Center
New York, New York 10021

Mls REACTIVITY AND SELF-Ia RECOGNITION

Mixed-lymphocyte stimulation (Mls) was first observed by Festenstein in 1973.[1] The basic observation was that coculturing of spleen cells of DBA/2 and BALB/c mice leads to vigorous proliferation. The proliferating cells were shown to be T-helper cells[2] (T_h) derived from the BALB/c but not from the DBA/2 strains; in other words, the reaction was unilateral. A second important fact emerged when the major histocompatibility complex (MHC) types of these two strains were found to be identical, thus setting Mls reactivity apart from alloreactivity, which by definition occurs between lymphocytes of different MHC types. Furthermore, alloreactivity is always bidirectional, whereas Mls reactivity, of which further examples in combinations other than DBA/2 → BALB/c soon emerged, are rarely bidirectional. The genetic analysis of Mls revealed that the reaction was governed by a single, dominant locus on chromosome 1, the Mls locus. To date, five alleles have been identified.[1,3]

The mechanism of the Mls reaction is still controversial. It was originally thought that the reaction was due to recognition by the T_h cell of a minor antigen expressed on the genetically mismatched antigen-presenting cell.[1,4] This model would explain the apparent MHC-restricted recognition of the "foreign Mls antigen." Several key findings, however, are incompatible with this view. First, the magnitude of the Mls response often exceeds that of an alloreactive response. Limiting dilution assays have revealed that 1/30 of spleen cells can be activated.[5] Thus the repertoire set aside by responder strains to recognize Mls exceeds by far what could reasonably be expected for a moderately polymorphic "foreign antigen." Second, antigen-specific or alloreactive T_h-cell clones have frequently been found to become Mls-reactive.[6-8] As these cell lines have a defined antigen specificity, it is difficult to imagine that the clonotypic receptor would also see the Mls "antigen." Third, studies with dual-reactive T-cell hybridomas (Mls and alloreactive) that segregate chromosomes have demonstrated that the recognition structures responsible for alloreactivity and for Mls are encoded by different chromosomes.[9]

On the basis of these observations it seems likely that the primary recognition of the Mls product occurs by a receptor structure distinct from the T-cell receptor. Nevertheless, the participation of the clonotypic receptor is essential. In its absence, Mls reactions are not elicited. This follows from the observation by Janeway and Katz[3] for one ovalbumin and Mls dual-reaction T-cell clone in which blockade of the clonotypic receptor with antireceptor antibody leads to abrogation of Mls responsiveness. As Mls responsiveness is also suppressed when the presenting cells are treated with anti-class II antibodies,[2,10] it is likely that recognition of class II antigen by the clonotypic receptor is an essential prerequisite for the Mls reaction to proceed. In other words, the autologous mixed-lymphocyte reaction (AMLR) is an essential component of the Mls reaction.

One objection to autorecognition has been the observation that many Mls reactive clones, in contrast to T-cell populations, are not strictly class II-haplotype-restricted,[11] although they are clearly class II antigen-dependent. It is conceivable, however, that cross-reactive epitopes of different haplotypes are sufficient to provide the autorecognition signal, even if recognition should be of low affinity.

If the Mls reaction requires an autorecognition signal and a second signal generated through interaction of the Mls product with a ligand of the T_h cells, which is separate from the clonotypic receptor, then the Mls is fundamentally different, not only from the allogenic MLR but also from antigen-specific T-cell stimulation: Mls looks more like a regulatory phenomenon.

MODELS TO EXPLAIN Mls

Two models have been proposed with the common basis of an AMLR. Janeway and colleagues[7] have suggested that Mls could be understood as a device for stabilization of class II antigen T-cell receptor (TcR) interactions. In a situation where Mls^b T_h cells are exposed to class II antigen on Mls^a APC, the disparate Mls product might either enhance the availability of Ia antigen for the T cell, or enhance the complex formation between TcR and Ia. In either case, an amplification of the autorecognition signal would result in activation of a proportion of T_h cells.

A second model has been proposed by us.[12] We suggest that the control of the autologous MLR (i.e., the effective restraint of T_h cells, which are subject to constant autostimulation by class II antigen), and the Mls reaction are consequences of the same regulatory principle. T_h cells are positively selected in the thymus for their ability to recognize individual class II antigen epitopes, and as mature cells they retain the TcR specificity according to which they were recruited.[13] Despite this affinity for Ia, peripheral T_h cells do not react spontaneously with MHC class II antigen. As we do not believe the TcR changes its specificity, we postulate a control system that down-regulates T_h cells. We attribute this task to the Mls system by suggesting that the Mls receptor expressed on APC normally delivers a down-regulatory signal to the syngeneic T_h cell by way of an as yet unidentified ligand on the T_h-cell surface. Auto-Ia stimulation and the Mls interaction signals are a balanced antagonistic pair keeping the overall T_h-cell stimulus below a threshold required for response.

It follows from these considerations that activation of T_h cells could occur when they encounter auto-MHC antigen alone on APC in the absence of a proper down-regulating signal. This situation, in our opinion, is the case in the Mls response. Here, T_h cells are artificially mixed with APC, which are syngeneic at the MHC locus but are allogeneic at the Mls locus. Because the Mls product is polymorphic, the situation may arise that a mismatch of APC and T_h cell leads to inadequate down-regulatory control with consequential autoactivation of a proportion of T_h cells. Therefore, the Mls reaction essentially can be regarded as a decontrolled AMLR.

Neither the structural product nor the nature of the functional polymorphism controlled by the Mls locus is known. The best assumption to date is that the Mls encodes a cell-interaction molecule. Such a receptor-like molecule expressed on

APC would have a corresponding ligand molecule on the T_h cell. A first guess that Mls polymorphism may affect the receptor-ligand specificity itself is attractive in the context of our down-regulation molecule, as a failure of a receptor to engage properly with a genetically mismatched ligand would be a straightforward explanation for lack of down-regulation. The observed unidirectionality of Mls reactions, however, would be difficult to reconcile with this view. Moreover, if sets of receptor-ligand pairs coevolve in different mouse strains, both entities must be polymorphic, requiring two-gene control for Mls. This is not the case. The available evidence suggests that Mls activation is controlled by a single, dominant gene.[1] These considerations have led us to seek an explanation that invokes polymorphism only for the Mls product. We postulate that polymorphism does not influence receptor-binding properties but affects the strength of signal transmission. What is genetically inherited is the efficiency of down-regulation controlled by the Mls locus, and as a consequence, the range of auto-reactive strength within the thymically selected T_h population (see below). Considering for the moment only two Mls alleles, a and b, we propose that Mls[b] strains are strong down-regulators relative to Mls[a] strains, which are weak down-regulators.

Mls AND ADAPTIVE DIFFERENTIATION IN THE THYMUS

The requirement for recognition of both specific antigen and of MHC antigen sets T-cell immunity fundamentally apart from B-cell immunity. It is becoming increasingly clear that a single receptor is responsible for this dual recognition. The observations by Zinkernagel and Doherty[14] first established MHC restriction for cytotoxic T cells, and the principle of genetic restriction has been extended to T cells in general.[15] MHC restriction is learned by T_h cells in the thymus. This was gleaned from experiments with bone marrow chimeras, in which bone marrow cells were transferred into lethally irradiated hosts differing from the donor at MHC (review in reference 13). Maturing T_h cells are recruited in the thymus, and the MHC antigens expressed by the thymic epithelium determine their MHC reactivity.[16,17] One may envision this adaptive differentiation as a selection process entailing an active recruitment of those T_h cells that happen to recognize an epitope of class II antigen, at the expense of those T_h-precursor cells that have no specificity for class II antigen. In other words, T_h cells are actively selected and eventually allowed to enter the pool of immunocompetent postthymic cells because they recognize Ia antigenic determinants.

Recognition of self-Ia antigen puts T_h cells at odds with the tenet of immunology that prohibits reactivity to self. To avoid this conflict, a second selection process is necessary in which the T_h cells with the highest affinity range to self are removed, leaving intact and available for further maturation[18,19] only the second tier of cells with intermediate affinities to self-Ia. One has to realize that after removal of the overtly self-reactive cells, the remaining T cells are also autoreactive, in a latent form. The essence of our Mls model is that latent autoreactivity and down-regulation by the Mls product keep the T_h cells in dynamic balance. A consequence of this concept is that the level of permissible autoreactivity in thymus development is influenced by the extant Mls phenotype. As the thymus can be regarded as a self-adjusting system, it follows that T cells, maturing under a highly down-regulating Mls influence (such as Mls[b]), can attain a higher upper limit of autoreactivity than the same pool of cells would acquire when maturing in the same MHC environment, but under control of a different Mls allele, (*e.g.*,

Mls^a) with a relatively lower down-regulation strength. The level of maximally permissible autoreactivity would be lower in the second instance. Thus, Mls reactivity, as measured in the mixed lymphocyte cultures (MLC), is not only governed by the Mls allele expressed on the antigen-presenting cells (APC), but is also a reflection of the level of autoreactivity the responding T$_h$ cells have "learned" in the thymus. The overt proliferative reaction of an Mls^b T$_h$ cell exposed to an Mls^a APC is a consequence of failed regulation because a cell of high internal auto-Ia reactivity is inadequately balanced by APC with a low down-regulatory potential.

An interesting prediction can be made concerning the activation of T$_h$ cells of Mls^a strains in context of Mls^b APC, that is, in reverse Mls direction. In this instance, relatively low autoreactive T$_h$ cells are paired with APC of high negative influence and are down-regulated below the level they are normally attuned to. Under these circumstances of reverse Mls, T$_h$-cell activation should be more difficult and require more upward stimulation by antigen or mitogen to compensate for the inordinately high negative influence.

We have tested our hypothesis, using concanavalin A (Con A), a Ia-dependent mitogen, as a stimulant. We find that BALB/c T$_h$ cells experience a synergistic effect when activated by Con A in context with DBA/2 APC. This synergistic effect is measurable as a shift of the Con A dose response curve to lower concentrations (see FIG. 1, panel A). The fact that use of DBA/2 APC results in synergistic, not additive effects, is a sure indication that the entire T$_h$-cell population is affected and that the Mls effect works by regulation. Reversing the Mls direction and testing the influence of BALB/c (Mls^b) APC on DBA/2 (Mls^a) T$_h$ cells, we find that the activation by Con A is impeded as demonstrated by the shift of the dose-response curve to higher Con A concentrations in reference to the dose requirement of DBA/2 T$_h$ cells with completely syngeneic APC. Thus, the predicted bidirectionality of Mls reactions, eliciting synergy in the direction Mls^a → Mls^b and antagonism in the reverse direction, was upheld. We have mapped this regulatory influence to the Mls locus, using APC of BALB/c.Mls^a congenic mice as stimulator cells in Con A-dependent T$_h$-cell activation. The results show that BALB.Mls^a APC behave in all respects like DBA/2; that is, they exert a synergistic effect in Con A activation of BALB/c T$_h$ cells.

Differences in the activation potential of APC from different strains in antigen-specific responses of T$_h$-cell clones have been attributed to Mls differences before. Janeway *et al.* have published evidence that activation of conalbumin-specific T$_h$ clones of BALB/c mice is facilitated by DBA/2 APC.[20] The same report presents evidence that one AKR (Mls^a) T$_h$-cell clone is more difficult to activate with B10.BR APC than with AKR APC. We have repeated this experiment and confirm the results. Assays with ten cloned cell lines, including antigen-specific hybridomas, have consistently shown that irrespective of the Mls genotype of the cell line, the antigen-dependent activation requires less antigen concentration or fewer cell numbers with Mls^a APC as compared to Mls^b APC. This is in accord with our assumption that the Mls^b allele determines higher down-regulation than Mls^a.

Our explanation of the Mls reaction as a deregulated auto-MLR is consistent with most observations, with one important exception: the genetics of the Mls indicate control by a dominant gene of chromosome one.[21] Our model at first glance would be more in tune with recessive control, as its basic premise is a suboptimal interaction in the Mls-mismatched situation. An APC heterozygous at Mls could be expected to provide adequate regulation for the homozygous T$_h$ cells, as it possesses a set of "correct" receptor molecules. In codominant ex-

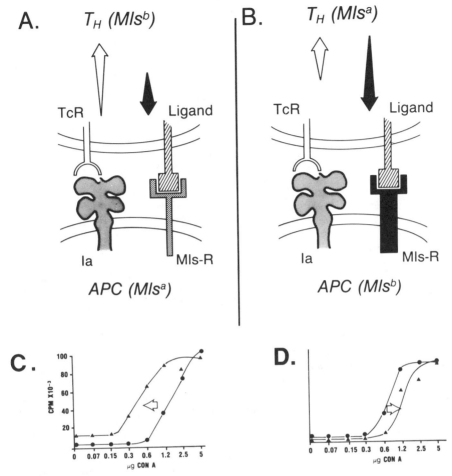

FIGURE 1. Panel **A** depicts T_h cells of Mls^b genotype interacting with Ia-matched APC of Mls^a type. The up-regulating signal generated by self-Ia recognition is symbolized by an open arrow. This signal is a variable entity within the T_h-cell population, and for individual cells depends on the TcR affinity for the respective Ia epitope used in the selection process in the thymus. The interaction of the Mls receptor with an unknown ligand on the T_h cell generates a down-regulation signal (solid arrow), which counteracts up-regulation. The strength of the Mls signal is genetically determined as high (Mls^b) or low (Mls^a). When interacting cells are of the same genotype, up-regulation would be adequately compensated, but, in the case depicted, the genetic mismatch causes insufficient down-regulation, allowing a proportion of cells to become activated in an overt proliferative response. In the $Mls^a \rightarrow Mls^b$ direction, the entire T_h- cell population is positively affected, as demonstrated by a shift of the Con A dose-response curve of BALB/c (Mls^b) thymocytes activated in context with DBA/2 (Mls^a) APC (▲—▲) to lower Con A concentrations as compared to activation with syngenic APC (●—●) (panel **C**). Panel **B** shows the reverse Mls effect. Here, T_h cells are exposed to APC in the Mls^b allele, which have a high (genetically fixed) down-regulation potential. As argued in the text, Mls^a T_h cells have a lower permissible autoreactivity (symbolized by a shorter open arrow). The resulting mismatch of Mls^a T_h cells with Mls^b APC is measurable as a suppression of activation. This reverse Mls effect is demonstrable as a shift in the Con A dose-response curve to higher Con A concentrations. A comparison of two sets of dose response curves for DBA/2 Mls^a thymocytes activated with Mls^a APC (●—●) or Mls^b APC (▲—▲) is shown (panel **D**).

pression, however, only half the receptor molecules are of the correct type, and therefore regulation may remain defective on stoichiometric grounds.

CONCLUSIONS

Whether T_h cells are maturing in the thymus or whether they are engaged in an immune response, they operate under the principle of selection. In both instances, the criterion for selection is an appropriate fit to class II antigen epitopes. Consequentially, the function of T_h cells is inseparably linked with reactivity to autologous class II antigen. In other words, autoreactivity is the central feature around which T_h-cell function revolves. Autoreactivity can be modulated in several ways. It is ordinarily down-regulated to prevent precocious activation of mature T_h cells. In the event of an immune response, the synergistic recognition of foreign antigen and class II antigen will up-regulate the T_h cell and counteract negative control influences to a point where activation becomes irreversible. *In vitro*, mitogens such as Con A can substitute for foreign antigen, and would initiate the polyclonal immune response to the extent that this is Ia-dependent.

Of special interest are *in vitro* situations where the down-regulation of the auto-MLR is perturbed. One major mode of control of the auto-MLR has been attributed by us to the Mls receptor, which interacts with an as yet unidentified ligand on the syngeneic T_h cell to transmit a down-regulatory signal. Genetic mismatching of APC and T_h at the Mls locus would interfere with this control signal, and a consequence of defective down-regulation would be activation by auto-Ia recognition, whereas supranormal down-regulation would impede T_h activation.

REFERENCES

1. FESTENSTEIN, H. 1973. Immunogenetic and biological aspects of *in vitro* lymphocyte allotransformation (MLR) in the mouse. Transplant. Rev. **15:** 62–68.
2. JANEWAY, C. A., P. LERNER, J. M. JASON & B. JONES. 1980. T lymphocytes responding to Mls locus antigens are Lyt 1+, 2− and I-A restricted. Immunogenetics **10:** 461–497.
3. JANEWAY, C. A. & M. E. KATZ. 1985. The immunobiology of T cell responses to Mls locus disparate stimulator cells. I. Unidirectionality, new strain combinations and the role of Ia antigens. J. Immunol. **134:** 2057–2063.
4. MACPHAIL, S. & O. STUTMAN. 1985. H-2-linked genes determine Mls stimulatory capacity. Fed. Proc. Fed. Am. Soc. Exp. Biol. **44:** 969.
5. MACPHAIL, S., S. T. ISHIZAKA, M. M. BYKOWSKY, E. C. LATTIME & O. STUTMAN. Specific neonatally induced tolerance to Mls locus determinants. J. Immunol. **135:** 2967–2974.
6. BRACIALE, V. L. & T. J. BRACIALE. 1981. Mls-locus recognition by a cloned line of H-2 restricted influenza virus-specific cytotoxic T lymphocytes. J. Immunol. **127:** 859–862.
7. KATZ, M. E. & C. A. JANEWAY. 1985. The immunobiology of T cell responses to Mls locus disparate stimulator cells. Effects of Mls-disparate stimulator cells on cloned, protein antigen-specific, Ia restricted T cell lines. J. Immunol. **134:** 2064–2078.
8. WEBB, S. R., J. HU, I. MACNEIL, J. SPRENT & D. B. WILSON. 1984. T cell hybridomas with dual specificity for Mls and H-2 determinants: selective loss of one specificity. J. Cell Biochem. **8A**(Supp.): 160.
9. WEBB, S. R., J. HU, I. MACNEIL, P. MARRACK, J. SPRENT & D. B. WILSON. 1985. T cell receptors for responses to Mls determinants and allo-H-2 determinants appear to be encoded on different chromosomes. J. Exp. Med. **161:** 269–274.

10. MacPhail, S. & O. Stutman. 1984. Independent inhibition of IL-2 synthesis and cell proliferation by anti-Ia antibodies in mixed lymphocyte responses to Mls. Eur. J. Immunol. **14:** 318–324.
11. Molnar-Kimber, K. & J. Sprent. 1980. Absence of H-2 restriction in primary and secondary mixed-lymphocyte reactions to strong Mls determinants. J. Exp. Med. **151:** 407–417.
12. Hämmerling, U. & M. K. Hoffmann. 1986. The role of the Fc receptor in T cell activation. Scand. J. Immunol. **24:** 621–624.
13. Longo, D. L., L. A. Matis & R. H. Schwartz. 1981. Insight into autoimmune response gene function from experiments with chimeric animals. CRC Crit. Rev. Immunol. **2:** 83.
14. Zinkernagel, R. M. & P. C. Doherty. 1975. H-2 compatibility requirement for T cell mediated lysis of target cells infected with lymphocyte choriomeningitis virus. J. Exp. Med. **141:** 1427–1436.
15. Bevan, M. J. 1975. The major histocompatibility complex determines susceptibility to cytotoxic T cells directed against minor histocompatibility antigens. J. Exp. Med. **142:** 1349–1364.
16. Singer, A., K. S. Hathcock & R. J. Hodes. 1982. Self-recognition in allogenic thymic chimeras. Self-recognition by T helper cells from thymus-engrafted nude mice is restricted to the thymic H-2 haplotype. J. Exp. Med. **155:** 339–344.
17. Sprent, J. 1978. Restricted helper function of F1 parent bone marrow chimeras controlled by K-end of H-2 complex. J. Exp. Med. **147:** 1838–1842.
18. Hoffmann, M. K. 1984. T cell antigen receptor function: the concept of autoaggression. Immunology Today **5**(1): 10–13.
19. Kappler, J. W., N. Roehm & P. Marrack. 1987. T cell tolerance by clonal elimination in the thymus. Cell **49:** 273–280.
20. Janeway, C. A., P. J. Conrad, J. Tite, B. Jones & D. B. Murphy. 1983. Efficiency of antigen presentation differs in mice differing at the Mls locus. Nature (London) **306:** 80–82.
21. Festenstein, H., C. Bishop & B. A. Taylor. 1977. Location of Mls locus on mouse chromosome 1. Immunogenetics **5:** 357–361.

Phenotypic Identification of Memory Cytolytic T Lymphocytes in a Subset of Lyt-2+ Cells

JEAN-CHARLES CEROTTINI, RALPH C. BUDD,[a] AND
H. ROBSON MacDONALD

Ludwig Institute for Cancer Research
Lausanne Branch
1066 Epalinges, Switzerland

INTRODUCTION

It is generally accepted that the primary immune response to an antigen includes the formation of long-lived, antigen-specific memory cells, in addition to effector cells. These memory cells are thought to be responsible for the heightened immune response that follows secondary exposure to an antigen. As the secondary antibody response is generally characterized by the production of increased levels of antibodies having higher avidity for antigen, it has been proposed that immunologic memory at the B-cell level includes both an increased frequency of antigen-reactive lymphocytes and a greater mean avidity of their antigen receptors.[1-4] In the case of T-cell responses, little is known about the formation of memory helper cells during immunization. By contrast, there is evidence that the frequency of cytolytic T-lymphocyte precursors (CTL-P) may increase after immunization.[5] In addition, indirect evidence has been provided that cytolytic T lymphocytes (CTL) bearing high avidity antigen receptors are augmented in immunized animals compared with CTL from normal animals.[6-8] Detailed analysis of memory CTL, however, has been hampered by the lack of suitable surface markers allowing identification and isolation of these cells. As discussed below, recent studies from our laboratory indicate that murine memory CTL-P can be identified phenotypically in a minor subpopulation of Lyt-2+ cells defined by the surface marker Pgp-1.

THE Pgp-1 ANTIGEN

This antigen was originally described as a major cell membrane glycoprotein on murine cultured fibroblasts and peritoneal phagocytic cells (hence its designation phagocyte glycoprotein 1).[9,10] Also designated Ly24, Pgp-1 has a M_r of 80–95,000 and is encoded by a locus on chromosome two.[11] It has been identified in a wide variety of tissues including brain, liver, kidney, and lung.[12] In hematopoietic tissues, Pgp-1 is found in highest amounts in the bone marrow.[9,12] Although it is expressed in most prothymocytes, only about 5% of adult thymocytes are Pgp-1+.[12,13] The vast majority of these Pgp-1+ thymocytes are confined to the minor (Lyt-2− L3T4−) subset known to contain immature thymocytes.[14] Unlike adult

[a] Present address: Department of Medicine, Division of Immunology, Stanford University, School of Medicine, Stanford, CA 94305.

thymocytes, the great majority of fetal thymocytes are Pgp-1$^+$ at day 13–14 of gestation.[15] Thereafter, the proportion of Pgp-1$^+$ thymocytes declines, reaching adult levels by day 19 of gestation. On the basis of these findings, it has been proposed that at least some of the Pgp-1$^+$ cells within the thymus are progenitors of mature thymocytes.[15]

In contrast to mature (Lyt-2$^+$ L3T4$^-$ and Lyt-2$^-$ L3T4$^+$) thymocytes, peripheral T cells contain a significant proportion of Pgp-1$^+$ cells.[16] FIGURE 1 shows a comparison of Pgp-1 expression in Lyt-2$^+$ cells from cortisone-resistant thymocytes (which are representative of mature thymocytes) and from peripheral blood of C57BL/6 mice. It can be seen that blood Lyt-2$^+$ lymphocytes are separated by Pgp-1 into well-defined dull (Pgp-1$^-$) and bright (Pgp-1$^+$) subpopulations, whereas the vast majority of cortisone-resistant Lyt-2$^+$ thymocytes express the Pgp-1$^-$ phenotype. In the example shown in FIGURE 1, 40% of blood Lyt-2$^+$ lymphocytes

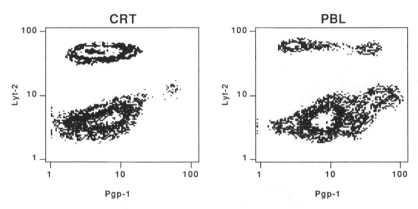

FIGURE 1. Difference in surface Pgp-1 expression by Lyt-2$^+$ cells of cortisone-resistant thymocytes (CRT) or peripheral blood lymphocytes (PBL). Cells were stained sequentially with anti-Pgp-1 rat monoclonal antibody (mAb), FITC-labeled goat anti-rat IgG, biotin-labeled anti-Lyt-2 mAb, and avidin-phycoerythrin as described in ref. 17. Samples were passed on a flow microfluorometer gated to exclude nonviable cells. At least 10^5 cells were accumulated for analysis.

are Pgp-1$^+$, as compared to only 5% of cortisone-resistant Lyt-2$^+$ thymocytes. A similar difference in Pgp-1 expression is observed between blood and cortisone-resistant thymic L3T4$^+$ lymphocytes. In peripheral lymphoid organs, Pgp-1 expression by Lyt-2$^+$ or L3T4$^+$ cells is also heterogeneous. For example, about 38% and 29%, respectively, of Lyt-2$^+$ and L3T4$^+$ splenic cells are Pgp-1$^+$ in young adult C57BL/6 mice.[17] Similar, although slightly lower, percentages of Pgp-1$^+$ cells are found within lymph node Lyt-2$^+$ and L3T4$^+$ subpopulations. Interestingly, the percentages of Pgp-1$^+$ cells in both subpopulations increase progressively between one week of age and adult life. Moreover, these percentages increase further after adult thymectomy.[17]

As there is evidence that the cells that migrate from the thymus to the peripheral T-cell compartment emerge from the pool of mature thymocytes, it is likely that most, if not all, thymus migrants are Pgp-1$^-$. It is therefore conceivable that the thymus is responsible for the continued renewal of peripheral T cells lacking

Pgp-1. Changes in Pgp-1 expression by peripheral T cells as a function of age or thymectomy are consistent with this interpretation.

What is then the origin of the peripheral Lyt-2[+] or L3T4[+] cells expressing the Pgp-1 phenotype? One possibility is that these cells arise from Pgp-1[+] precursor cells by an extrathymic pathway. In support of this possibility is the fact that the Thy-1[+] lymphocytes that are found in aged congenitally athymic nude mice are all Pgp-1[+].[17] Alternatively, Pgp-1[+] T cells may arise from peripheral Pgp-1[−] T cells as a result of immunization. The latter hypothesis is supported by the demonstration that Pgp-1[−] Lyt-2[+] lymph node cells become Pgp-1[+] after mitogenic or antigenic stimulation *in vitro*.[17,18] Moreover, expression of Pgp-1 by these stimulated cells is stable, even when they revert to small-sized quiescent lymphocytes in long-term cultures.[17] In this respect, Pgp-1 is distinct from other surface markers, which are only transiently expressed on T cells during activation.

MEMORY AT THE CTL LEVEL

One approach used to assess memory at the CTL level is to determine the changes in the frequency of antigen-specific CTL-P caused by immunization.[5] Examples of such changes are shown in TABLE 1. It can be seen that the degree of increase in CTL-P frequency, resulting from immunization, may vary from one antigenic system to another. Minor transplantation antigens, such as the male H-Y antigen, represent systems in which quantitative differences in CTL-P frequencies between normal and immunized mice are quite large (20-fold). In some viral systems in which antigen-specific CTL-P are detectable in normal mice, immunization leads normally to a 10-fold increase in CTL-P frequencies. By contrast, immunization against major histocompatibility complex (MHC) alloantigens results in a very modest (3-fold) increase in CTL-P frequencies.

Another characteristic of immunologic memory is the enrichment for responding lymphocytes with high avidity antigen receptors. At present, there is no direct way to measure the avidity of CTL antigen receptors. An indirect approach is to determine the susceptibility of CTL to inhibition of cytolytic activity by anti-Lyt-2 antibodies. It is well-documented that such a susceptibility varies drastically among individual CTL clones.[6,7] Neither the amount of Lyt-2 expressed by CTL clones nor the magnitude of their lytic activity correlates with susceptibility to inhibition by anti-Lyt-2 antibody. By contrast, the susceptibility of CTL clones to anti-Lyt-2 inhibition varies inversely with the level of target-cell antigen expression.[19] Moreover, the proportion of CTL clones that are susceptible to inhibition by anti-Lyt-2 antibodies decreases after immunization.[7] Taken together, these findings have led to the concept that the major role of Lyt-2 molecules is to

TABLE 1. Effect of Priming on the Frequency of Antigen-Specific CTL-P in C57BL/6 Spleen Cells[a]

Antigen	Mean Frequency (Reciprocal)	
	Primed	Unprimed
H-Y	3,631	>100,000
MSV	475	7,388
H-2[d]	154	399

[a] Based on data published in MacDonald *et al.*[5]

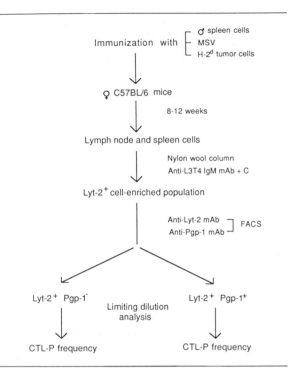

FIGURE 2. Quantitation assessment of the Pgp-1 subset distribution of memory CTL-P. Experimental protocol used for the analysis of the distribution of antigen-specific memory CTL-P in the Pgp-1⁻ and Pgp-1⁺ subsets of Lyt-2⁺ spleen cells from immunized C57BL/6 mice. For details, see ref. 17. C = complement; FACS = fluorescence-activated cell sorter.

stabilize antigen binding by CTL bearing low avidity receptors. Consequently, measurement of resistance to anti-Lyt-2 inhibition at the clonal level provides a way to assess the frequency of CTL with high-avidity antigen receptors.

Pgp-1 EXPRESSION BY MEMORY CTL

As mentioned above, Pgp-1⁻ Lyt-2⁺ lymphocytes express Pgp-1 after mitogenic or antigenic stimulation *in vitro*. Moreover, a recent study from our laboratory has demonstrated that virtually all the CTL that are generated in mice injected with allogeneic tumor cells are Pgp-1⁺ Lyt-2⁺,[17] thus suggesting that a similar transition from Pgp-1⁻ to Pgp-1⁺ may occur in Lyt-2⁺ cells stimulated *in vivo*.

To test further this concept, we have recently analyzed the distribution of antigen-specific memory CTL-P in the Pgp-1⁻ and Pgp-1⁺ subsets of Lyt-2⁺ spleen cells from mice immunized with either H-Y, Moloney sarcoma virus (MSV), or MHC (H-2ᵈ) alloantigen.[16,17] The experimental protocol used in this study is shown in FIGURE 2.

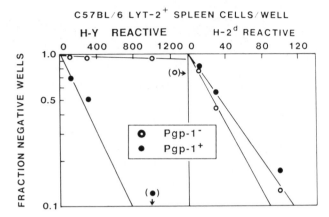

FIGURE 3. Comparison of the frequencies of H-Y–specific (left panel) and allospecific (right panel) CTL-P in Pgp-1⁻ Lyt-2⁺ (O) and Pgp-1⁺ Lyt-2⁺ (●) subpopulations obtained from H-Y–immune C57BL/6 mice. (Budd *et al.*[16] With permission from the *Journal of Immunology*.)

In all three cases, the frequency of antigen-specific CTL-P was enhanced in the Pgp-1⁺ subset. For example, the Pgp-1⁺ subset was enriched 30-fold for anti-H-Y CTL-P compared to the Pgp-1⁻ subset (FIG. 3). The specificity of this enrichment was demonstrated by the fact that the frequencies of CTL-P for an unrelated antigen (the H-2^d alloantigen) were nearly identical in the Pgp-1⁻ and Pgp-1⁺ subsets of Lyt-2⁺ spleen cells in mice immunized against the H-Y antigen. Similarly, the Pgp-1⁺ Lyt-2⁺ subset was enriched 8-fold for anti-MSV CTL-P compared to the Pgp-1⁻ Lyt-2⁺ subset in spleens of mice immunized against this virus.

In spleens of mice immunized with H-2^d alloantigen, the frequency of antigen-specific CTL-P was only enriched 3-fold in the Pgp-1⁺ Lyt-2⁺ subpopulation compared to the Pgp-1⁻ Lyt-2⁺ subpopulation. This agrees with the above-mentioned modest increase in the frequency of antigen-specific CTL-P following immunization with MHC alloantigens. By contrast, a marked difference between the Pgp-1⁺ and Pgp-1⁻ subsets was observed when the frequency of CTL-P with high-avidity antigen receptors was determined by the method described above. As shown in TABLE 2, the Pgp-1⁺ subset was highly enriched for such cells (68%) compared to the Pgp-1⁻ subset (3%). Moreover, it is noteworthy that the Pgp-1⁻ subset in immune mice had fewer CTL-P with high-avidity antigen receptors than

TABLE 2. Frequency of Anti-Lyt-2 Resistant CTL-P in Pgp-1 Subsets of Lyt-2⁺ Spleen Cells from Normal or Alloimmune C57BL/6 Mice[a]

		Frequency (Reciprocal)	
Immunization	Subset	Total	Resistant (%)
None	Pgp-1⁻	41	242 (17)
	Pgp-1⁺	49	221 (22)
H-2^d	Pgp-1⁻	49	1,649 (3)
	Pgp-1⁺	15	22 (68)

[a] Based on data published in Budd *et al.*[17]

the corresponding subset in normal mice. These data would be consistent with the hypothesis that at least some anti-Lyt-2 resistant CTL-P that were originally Pgp-1⁻ became Pgp-1⁺ during the course of immunization *in vivo*.

CONCLUDING REMARKS

Taken together, the results discussed in the previous sections indicate that expression of Pgp-1 identifies a discrete subset of Lyt-2⁺ cells that have both the quantitative and qualitative properties of memory CTL-P. Accordingly, the following model of Pgp-1 expression in cells of the CTL lineage should be considered (FIG. 4). Mature CTL-P in the thymus lack detectable surface Pgp-1. Subsequent

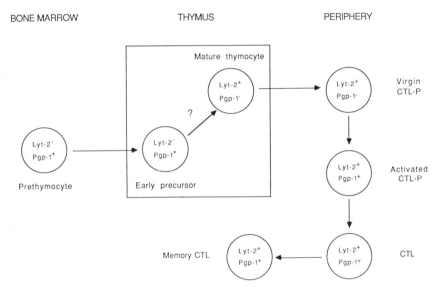

FIGURE 4. Model of Pgp-1 surface expression in cells of the CTL lineage. For explanation, see text.

to migration in peripheral tissues, these mature CTL-P express Pgp-1 when they are activated by antigen during primary immunization. The resulting CTL are therefore Pgp-1⁺. Once acquired, surface Pgp-1 is constitutively expressed thereafter, hence memory CTL-P are Pgp-1⁺.

Because Pgp-1 appears to identify two subpopulations within peripheral L3T4⁺ cells, it is likely that the model of Pgp-1 expression described above also applies to these cells. Further work, however, is needed to define immunologic memory at the level of L3T4⁺ cells.

A prediction of the model of antigen-stimulated acquisition of surface Pgp-1 by peripheral T cells is that the Pgp-1⁺ subset should include recently activated lymphocytes as well as memory cells. In this respect, it is noteworthy that 10–20% of Pgp-1⁺ T cells are medium- to large-sized lymphocytes, whereas the vast majority of Pgp-1$^-$ T cells are small.[16] Whether these large Pgp-1$^+$ cells represent recently activated T cells has yet to be determined.

As mentioned previously, a significant proportion of immature (Lyt-2$^-$ L3T4$^-$) thymocytes is Pgp-1$^+$. Although there is evidence that this subset contains cells that give rise to mature T cells, a direct precursor-product relationship between Pgp-1$^+$ and Pgp-1$^-$ cells in the thymus has not yet been established. If such a relationship does exist, this would mean that Pgp-1 expression by cells of the T lineage is concomitant with distinct stages of maturation or differentiation. As no definite function has been attributed to Pgp-1 so far, it is difficult to speculate about the biological significance of Pgp-1 expression (or lack thereof) by T cells. Whatever the functional role of Pgp-1 may be, it is evident that this marker is extremely useful in identifying peripheral T cells that have been previously activated *in vivo*.

REFERENCES

1. EISEN, H. N. & G. W. SISKIND. 1964. Variations in affinities of antibodies during the immune response. Biochemistry **3:** 996–1008.
2. ANDERSSON, B. 1970. Studies of the regulation of avidity at the level of the single antibody-forming cell. The effect of antigen dose and time after immunization. J. Exp. Med. **132:** 77–88.
3. CELADA, F. 1971. The cellular basis of the immunologic memory. Prog. Allergy **15:** 223–267.
4. DAVIE, J. M. & W. E. PAUL. 1972. Receptors on immunocompetent cells. V. Cellular correlations of the "maturation" of the immune response. J. Exp. Med. **135:** 660–674.
5. MACDONALD, H. R., J.-C. CEROTTINI, J.-E. RYSER, J. L. MARYANSKI, C. TASWELL, M. B. WIDMER & K. T. BRUNNER. 1980. Quantitation and cloning of cytolytic T lymphocytes and their precursors. Immunol. Rev. **51:** 93–123.
6. MACDONALD, H. R., N. THIERNESSE & J.-C. CEROTTINI. 1981. Inhibition of T cell-mediated cytolysis by monoclonal antibodies against Lyt-2: heterogeneity of inhibition at the clonal level. J. Immunol. **126:** 1671–1675.
7. MACDONALD, H. R., A. L. GLASEBROOK, C. BRON, A. KELSO & J.-C. CEROTTINI. 1982. Clonal heterogeneity in the functional requirement for Lyt-2/3 molecules on cytolytic T lymphocytes (CTL): possible implications for the affinity of CTL antigen receptors. Immunol. Rev. **68:** 89–115.
8. MALISSEN, B., N. REBAI, A. LIABEUF & C. MAWAS. 1982. Human cytolytic T cell structures associated with expression of cytolysis. I. Analysis at the clonal level of the cytolysis inhibiting effect of 7 monoclonal antibodies. Eur. J. Immunol. **12:** 739–747.
9. HUGHES, E. N., G. MENGOD & J. T. AUGUST. 1981. Murine cell surface glycoproteins. Characterization of a major component of 80,000 daltons as a polymorphic differentiation antigen of mesenchymal cells. J. Biol. Chem. **256:** 7023–7027.
10. HUGHES, E. N., A. COLOMBATTI & J. T. AUGUST. 1983. Murine cell surface glycoproteins. Purification of the polymorphic Pgp-1 antigen and analysis of its expression on macrophages and other myeloid cells. J. Biol. Chem. **258:** 1014–1021.
11. COLOMBATTI, A., E. N. HUGHES, B. A. TAYLOR & J. T. AUGUST. 1982. Gene for a major cell surface glycoprotein of mouse macrophages and other phagocytic cells is on chromosome 12. Proc. Natl. Acad. Sci. USA **79:** 1926–1929.
12. TROWBRIDGE, I. S., J. LESLEY, R. SCHULTE, R. HYMAN & J. TROTTER. 1982. Biochemical characterization and cellular distribution of a polymorphic, murine cell-surface glycoprotein expressed on lymphoid cells. Immunogenetics **15:** 299–312.
13. LESLEY, J., R. HYMAN & R. SCHULTE. 1985. Evidence that the Pgp-1 glycoprotein is expressed on thymus-homing progenitor cells of the thymus. Cell. Immunol. **91:** 397–403.

14. TROWBRIDGE, I. S., J. LESLEY, J. TROTTER & R. HYMAN. 1985. Thymocyte subpopulation enriched for progenitors with an unrearranged T-cell receptor α-chain gene. Nature (London) **315:** 666–669.
15. LESLEY, J., J. TROTTER & R. HYMAN. 1985. The Pgp-1 antigen is expressed on early fetal thymocytes. Immunogenetics **22:** 149–157.
16. BUDD, R. C., J.-C. CEROTTINI & H. R. MACDONALD. 1987. Phenotypic identification of memory cytolytic T lymphocytes in a subset of Lyt-2$^+$ cells. J. Immunol. **138:** 1009–1013.
17. BUDD, R. C., J.-C. CEROTTINI, C. HORVATH, C. BRON, T. PEDRAZZINI, R. C. HOWE & H. R. MACDONALD. 1987. Distinction of virgin and memory T lymphocytes. Stable acquisition of the Pgp-1 glycoprotein concomitant with antigenic stimulation. J. Immunol. **138:** 3120–3129.
18. LYNCH, F., G. CHAUDHRI, J. E. ALLAN, P. C. DOHERTY & RH. CEREDIG. 1987. Expression of Pgp-1 (or Ly24) by subpopulations of mouse thymocytes and activated peripheral T lymphocytes. Eur. J. Immunol. **17:**137–140.
19. SHIMONKEVITZ, R., B. LUESCHER, J.-C. CEROTTINI & H. R. MACDONALD. 1985. Clonal analysis of cytolytic T lymphocyte-mediated lysis of target cells with inducible antigen expression: correlation between antigen density and requirement for Lyt-2/3 function. J. Immunol. **135:** 892–899.

Cellular Interactions Resulting in Skin-Allograft Rejection

AMY S. ROSENBERG,[a,b] TOSHIAKI MIZUOCHI, AND
ALFRED SINGER

Immunology Branch
National Cancer Institute
National Institutes of Health
Bethesda, Maryland 20892

INTRODUCTION

The mechanisms by which cells effecting the rejection of tissue allografts are activated have not been clearly delineated.[1,2] Even the most basic issues remain unresolved: the precise nature of the effector function responsible for allograft rejection (cytotoxic T lymphocytes (CTL) versus delayed-type hypersensitivity (DTH)),[3–5] the dependence or independence of the putative-effector cell on other cellular functions,[6–8] and whether rejection is mediated by one cellular population or by interactions between discrete cellular populations.[9,10] The complexity is further compounded by the cellular diversity of the tissues transplanted. Thus, the variability of antigen-presenting cell (APC) function found in different tissues,[11–14] whether grafts are directly vascularized (organ grafts) as opposed to indirectly vascularized (skin and endocrine tissue grafts),[15] the varied expression and inducibility of MHC class I and class II determinants from tissue to tissue[16–20] and from species to species,[21] present formidable factors in attempts to reconcile the data.

In an attempt to better understand the mechanisms of allograft rejection, we have focused on the antigen specificities and functional characteristics of phenotypically distinct T-cell populations, as described *in vitro,* and assayed their *in vivo* ability to mediate the rejection of skin allografts. Previously, we identified the class I-specific Lyt-2$^+$ T-helper (T$_h$) cell as the cell type determining the rate at which class I disparate, K^b mutant skin grafts are rejected.[22] In this report, we present results demonstrating that skin allograft rejection can result from interactions between T$_h$ and T-effector cells and that these two interacting populations need not be phenotypically identical, nor express the same antigen specificity.

MATERIAL AND METHODS

Mice

B10 nu/nu female mice were obtained from the Small Animal Section, Research Service, National Institutes of Health, Bethesda, MD. C57BL/6 mice were obtained from the Jackson Laboratory, Bar Harbor, ME. In some protocols,

[a] To whom correspondence should be addressed: Immunology Branch, National Cancer Institute, Bldg. 10 Rm. 4B-17, Bethesda, MD 20892.
[b] Recipient of the American Society of Transplant Physicians-Sandoz Fellowship 1986.

C57BL/6 mice came from the Charles River Laboratories, Charles River, NY. B6.T1a[a] mice[23] were bred in our own animal facility and were a generous gift of Dr. L. Flaherty. BALB.B mice were bred in our own animal facility. B10 nude mice were 6–14 weeks at the time of engraftment and adoptive transfer. B6 mice were 13–16 weeks of age at the time of engraftment.

Monoclonal Antibodies

Anti-L3T4 monoclonal antibody was either a culture supernatant of the hybridoma cell line GK1.5,[24] generously provided by Dr. Frank Fitch, University of Chicago, Chicago, IL, or came from ascitic fluid of the hybridoma cell line RL-172/4,[25] generously provided by Dr. Ada Kruisbeek, National Institutes of Health, Bethesda, MD. Anti-Lyt-2.2 monoclonal antibody was a culture supernatant of the hybridoma cell line 83-12-5, generously provided by Dr. Jeffrey Bluestone, National Institutes of Health, Bethesda, MD.

Isolation of T-Cell Subpopulations

Depletion of L3T4[+] T cells or Lyt-2[+] T cells was accomplished by incubating spleen cells at a density of 10^7 cells/ml with anti-L3T4 (1 : 2 dilution of GK1.5 or a 1 : 100 dilution of RL-172/4) or anti-Lyt-2.2 (1 : 5 dilution) monoclonal antibodies for 30 minutes at 37° C. Cells were then pelleted, resuspended, and incubated with complement for 50 minutes at 37° C. The cells treated with GK1.5 were resuspended at 10^7 per ml in low toxicity rabbit complement (Cedar Lane, Ontario, Canada) diluted 1 : 10. The cells treated with RL-172/4 and 83-12-5 were resuspended at 10^8 per ml in guinea pig complement (Gibco Laboratories, Chagrin Falls, OH) diluted 1 : 3. Treated cells were washed three times before injection into experimental animals.

Skin Grafting of Normal B6 Mice

B6 mice were engrafted either on the left thorax alone or on both thoraxes, with tailskin grafts, according to an adaptation of the method of Billingham and Medawar.[26] Bandages were removed on day 7, and the grafts were scored daily until rejection or the end point of the experiment.

Skin Grafting and Adoptive Transfer

Female B10 nude mice were engrafted on the thorax on day 0 with tailskin allografts from female mice according to an adaptation of the method of Billingham and Medawar.[26] On day 1, the mice were injected intravenously with 5–7 $\times 10^7$ spleen cells from unprimed B6 mice that had been 1) untreated, 2) treated with anti-L3T4 antibody and complement (C) *in vitro,* or 3) treated with anti-Lyt-2 and C *in vitro* according to the protocols mentioned above. In one protocol, mice received 3.5×10^7 of each isolated population. Bandages were removed on day 7 and the grafts scored daily until rejection or the end point of the experiment.

RESULTS

Rejection of Multiple Minor-H Disparate Skin Grafts

We used an adoptive transfer model in an attempt to elucidate the cellular mechanisms involved in the rejection of skin allografts. B10 nude mice were engrafted with tailskin grafts on day 0 and the following day were reconstituted with $50–70 \times 10^6$ syngeneic $H-2^b$ spleen cells that were unfractionated or separated into phenotypically distinct populations by negative selection (FIG. 1). Using this system, we first studied the response to multiple minor-H antigens. We found that both untreated T-cell populations and $L3T4^+$ T-cell populations efficiently reject BALB.B skin grafts, whereas the isolated $Lyt-2^+$ population fails to do so (FIG. 2). Thus, the $L3T4^+$ minor-H specific population possesses the requisite cellular functions to mediate the rejection of minor-H disparate grafts, whereas the $Lyt-2^+$ population is deficient. Of interest, however, is the enhanced rejection of these grafts by T-cell populations containing both $Lyt-2^+$ and $L3T4^+$ T cells (FIG. 2, unt), indicating that collaboration between $Lyt-2^+$ and $L3T4^+$ T cells augment the rejection of these grafts.

PROTOCOL

Mice: B10 ♀ nude

Grafts: tailskin grafts

Cells: B6 ♀ spleen cells or negatively
selected spleen cell subpopulations

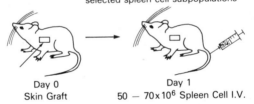

Day 0   Day 1
Skin Graft $50 - 70 \times 10^6$ Spleen Cell I.V.

FIGURE 1. Adoptive transfer system. Female B10 nu/nu mice were engrafted with tailskin grafts on day 0, per MATERIAL AND METHODS. On day 1, they were reconstituted with $5–7 \times 10^7$ spleen cells or negatively selected spleen-cell subpopulations (see MATERIAL AND METHODS for cell treatments) from normal B6 female mice.

Rejection of H-Y Disparate Skin Grafts

To investigate the hypothesis that collaboration *in vivo* between cellular populations expressing T_h and T-killer (T_k) functions could mediate skin allograft rejection, we turned to a system in which antigen-specific T_h cells could be clearly distinguished from antigen-specific T_k cells. As the *in vitro* cytotoxic response to the male-specific H-Y antigen is mediated by interactions between $L3T4^+$, H-Y–specific T_h and $Lyt-2^+$, H-Y–specific T_k,[27] we examined the *in vivo* rejection of H-Y disparate skin allografts.

Accordingly, female B10 nu/nu mice were engrafted with B6 male tailskin grafts and reconstituted with female $H-2^b$ spleen cell populations or subpopulations. As can be seen in TABLE 1, neither isolated $Lyt-2^+$ nor $L3T4^+$ T cells

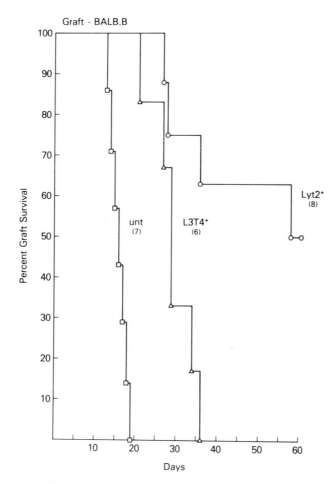

FIGURE 2. Ability of unseparated and phenotypically distinct T-cell populations to mediate the rejection of multiple minor-H disparate grafts. B10 nu/nu mice were engrafted with multiple minor-H disparate BALB.B skin grafts and reconstituted with T-cell populations that were unfractionated, L3T4+ by negative selection with anti-Lyt-2 +C, or Lyt-2+ by negative selection with anti-L3T4 +C. Number of mice in each group is shown in parentheses. Grafts were scored daily until rejection or day 81.

TABLE 1. Rejection of H-Y Disparate Skin Grafts by Nude Mice Reconstituted with Unseparated or Phenotypically Distinct T-Cell Populations

Host	Graft	Antigen Disparity	Reconstituting B6 Female Spleen-Cell Population	Day of Reconsti- tution	No. Rejected	MST (Days)
1 B10nu/nu F	B6M	H-Y	Unfractionated	1	12/14	46.5
2 B10nu/nu F	B6M	H-Y	L3T4+	1	1/16	>81
3 B10nu/nu F	B6M	H-Y	Lyt-2+	1	2/23	>81
4 B10nu/nu F	B6M	H-Y	L3T4+ + Lyt-2+	1	6/9	69

79

mediate the rejection of H-Y disparate skin grafts. Mice reconstituted, however, with cell populations containing both L3T4$^+$ and Lyt-2$^+$ T-cell populations (TA-BLE 1, groups 1 and 4) rejected their H-Y disparate grafts. Thus, populations deficient in either antigen-specific T_h or T_k function fail to reject these grafts. As a different way of testing whether both phenotypically distinct subsets were requisite for the rejection of H-Y disparate skin grafts, we engrafted B10 nude mice with H-Y disparate skin grafts and initially reconstituted them with L3T4$^+$ T cells alone. Such mice failed to reject their H-Y disparate grafts. The phenotypes of the splenic T cells of these reconstituted mice were investigated by fluorescence-activated cell sorter (FACS) analysis on day 58 and shown to be overwhelmingly L3T4$^+$ with less than 0.5% Lyt-2$^+$ T cells. The mice were then given, on day 60, a second reconstitution of isolated Lyt-2$^+$ T cells; the mice subsequently rejected their H-Y disparate skin grafts with a median survival time (MST) = 36 days (data not shown), following the addition of Lyt-2$^+$ T cells. Thus, the necessity for both H-Y–specific T_h cellular function and H-Y–specific T_k cellular function to mediate the rejection of H-Y disparate skin grafts is reflected by the requirement for both L3T4$^+$- and Lyt-2$^+$-positive T cells *in vivo*. Having shown the requirement for collaboration between phenotypically and functionally distinct T-cell subsets to reject H-Y–disparate skin grafts in the adoptive transfer model, we investigated whether such collaborations could be demonstrated in normal mice.

Rejection of Qa-1 Disparate Skin Grafts

As can be seen in FIGURE 3, normal B6 mice fail to reject their Qa-1 disparate B6.T1a^a tailskin grafts. This system was investigated because it afforded an opportunity to test further whether interactions between antigen-specific T_h and T_k cells were essential for skin allograft rejection. Thus, limiting amounts of antigen-specific T_h, T effector, or both cellular functions could potentially be causal in the failure of normal mice to reject these grafts. We first investigated the possibility that the failure of normal B6 mice to reject Qa-1 disparate tailskin grafts was secondary to a deficiency in Qa-1–specific T-cell help. To do so, we assessed whether Qa-1–specific effector cells, capable of rejecting skin allografts, could function if a proven source of T-cell help were provided. To stimulate T-cell help, we used the T-helper response to H-Y antigens. Accordingly, B6 mice were engrafted with two skin grafts (TABLE 2): on the left flank, an "inducer" graft was placed, which expressed determinants designed to trigger T_h cells; and on the right flank, an "indicator" graft was placed, expressing only the target Qa-1 antigen. As can be seen in TABLE 2, group 1, when the inducer graft expressed only a Qa-1 disparity, neither graft was rejected. An inducer graft expressing both H-Y and Qa-1 determinants (group 2), induced prompt rejection of the B6.T1a^a indicator graft in female mice, whereas an inducer graft expressing only an H-Y disparity failed to trigger rejection of the indicator graft. That the rejection of the Qa-1 disparate indicator graft was contingent upon the activation of H-Y–specific T cells is shown by the failure of the Qa-1 + H-Y–inducer graft (which triggered the rejection of the indicator graft in female mice) to trigger rejection of the indicator graft in male mice (TABLE 2, group 4), which cannot respond against H-Y determinants.

That the H-Y–specific T cells involved in the rejection of the Qa-1 disparate indicator grafts were T_h cells, as opposed to T_k cells, is shown by the failure of H-Y–specific effector cells, generated in the response to the inducer graft in group 3, to cross-reactively reject the indicator B6.T1a^a graft. Thus, from these data, it is clear that Qa-1 effector cells capable of rejecting Qa-1 disparate skin grafts are present in normal B6 mice, and B6 mice retain Qa-1 disparate grafts because they are deficient in Qa-1–specific T-cell help.

DISCUSSION

The cellular mechanisms by which skin allografts are rejected are likely to be diverse and dependent on the antigenic determinants expressed by the graft. Whether rejection proceeds exclusively by way of the activity of dual function cells[9] or can proceed by way of interactions between discrete T-cell subsets, each of which possesses a requisite function, has been unclear. What we have demonstrated in these studies is that collaboration between two discrete T-cell popula-

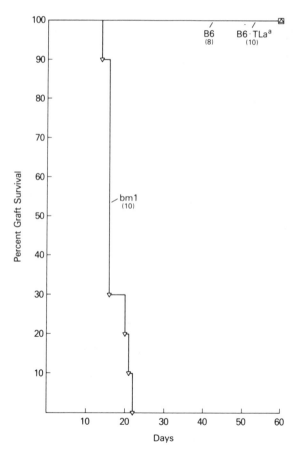

FIGURE 3. Rejection of Qa-1 disparate B6.TLa[a] skin grafts by normal B6 mice. B6 mice were engrafted with tailskin grafts as specified in MATERIAL AND METHODS. The grafts were scored daily until rejection or day 60.

TABLE 2. Rejection of Qa-1^a Skin Allografts Induced by H-Y Carrier Determinants

		Left (Inducer) Graft					Right (Indicator) Graft				
gp	Host	Strain	Sex	Antigenic Disparity	MST (Days)	Fraction Rejecting	Strain	Sex	Antigenic Disparity	MST (Days)	Fraction Rejecting
1	B6 F	B6.T1a^a	F	Qa-1^a	>83	0/4	B6.T1a^a	F	Qa-1^a	>83	0/4
2	B6 F	B6.T1a^a	M	Qa-1^a + H-Y	21	9/9	B6.T1a^a	F	Qa-1^a	23	9/9
3	B6 F	B6	M	H-Y	25	9/9	B6.T1a^a	F	Qa-1^a	>83	3/9
4	B6 M	B6.T1a^a	M	Qa-1^a	>83	0/3	B6.T1a^a	F	Qa-1^a	>83	0/3

tions is the mechanism by which some grafts are normally rejected and is a mechanism by which graft rejection can be induced.

To facilitate our investigation of the mechanisms of allograft rejection, we used an adoptive transfer model, the T-cell reconstituted nude mouse. In previous studies of this model, we addressed the concern that the rejection observed in adoptively transferred mice was not solely mediated by the adoptively transferred cells but was contributed to by cells of nude host origin, and that T cells of the reciprocal phenotype, present as contaminants in the original donor inoculum, had expanded *in vivo* and were contributing to graft rejection. Investigation of these concerns showed that, to the best of our technical ability, the rejection specificities of the reconstituted nude mice reflected those of the cells with which they were reconstituted and not contaminants in the original donor inoculum or mature T cells of nude host origin.[10]

In our studies of graft rejection, using this system, there was evident synergy between phenotypically distinct T-cell populations in mediating the rejection of skin grafts bearing multiple minor-H and H-Y disparities. Though not possible to assess directly whether T_h cells as defined *in vitro* are the same as the T-inducer cells active in graft rejection, the fact that their Ly phenotypes, antigen specificities, and ability to trigger effector cells are the same would speak for identity. Similarly, *in vitro*-defined T_k cells may well be identical to T-effector cells that function in graft rejection on the basis of the similarity of their Ly phenotypes, antigen specificities, and T_h requirements. The strongest evidence implicating the cytotoxic T cell's role in effecting graft rejection derives from the ability of cytotoxic cells cloned either *in vitro* or from rejecting grafts to mediate graft rejection[28–30] or tissue destruction, even with low cell numbers.[31] Whether populations of T_h and T_k interact by way of the secretion of soluble mediators or do so through activated macrophages is unclear. Reports of prolongation of skin and cardiac allograft survival across major histocompatibility complex (MHC) barriers by *in vivo* treatment with anti-IL-2 receptor monoclonal antibody (mAb), however, would favor some role for soluble mediators.[32] That the mechanism by which this interaction proceeds may not always be between two discrete populations of cells, one with T_h and one with T_k function, is shown by the ability of one distinct cellular population with both functions (dual function cells) to effect graft rejection.[9] Indeed, the ability of dual function cells to mediate tissue allograft rejection is consistent with the rejection of MHC class I and MHC class II disparate grafts by isolated populations of Lyt-2$^+$ and L3T4$^+$ T cells.[10,33]

The studies done in normal B6 mice, which fail to reject Qa-1 disparate tailskin grafts, significantly extend the findings derived from the nude mouse model by revealing that an antigen-specific deficiency of T_h function in normal mice leads to long-term maintenance of skin grafts, and that the cellular populations interacting to mediate skin allograft rejection need neither be phenotypically identical, nor possess the same antigen specificity. Thus, H-Y–specific T_h cells that are L3T4$^+$ collaborate with Qa-1–specific effector cells in mediating the rejection of Qa-1 disparate grafts. Further, the positive correlation we have shown between the ability to generate a CTL response *in vitro* and the generation of a graft-rejection response *in vivo*[10] is highlighted by the Qa-1 system in which the failure of normal B6 mice to generate a cytotoxic response *in vitro* to Qa-1 determinants has been shown secondary to a lack of antigen-specific T_h.[34] Additionally, the ability of H-Y to function as a helper antigen that triggers Qa-1–specific effector cells to reject Qa-1 disparate grafts *in vivo* is paralleled by its ability to prime Qa-1–specific CTL *in vivo*.[35] Lastly, the generation of effector cells capable of rejecting the Qa-1 disparate indicator graft was contingent on the helper and effector determinants being physically present on the same graft (TABLE 2, groups II and III) and is similar to the requirement for these determinants to be present on the same stimulator cell during the *in vivo* priming phase of a cytotoxic response.[35] Thus, it is conceivable that in cases of clinical transplantation, graft rejection could potentially be triggered by the expression of viral determinants on the graft that act as "carriers" and so trigger a vigorous helper response.

In summary, this work shows that the rejection of skin allografts can be mediated by interactions between both T-helper/inducer and T-killer/effector cells and that an isolated deficiency in T_h function can lead to long-term retention of selected allografts.

REFERENCES

1. MASON, D. W. & P. J. MORRIS. 1986. Effector mechanisms in allograft rejection. Annu. Rev. Immunol. **4:** 119.
2. STEINMULLER, D. 1985. Which T cells mediate allograft rejection? Transplantation **40:** 229.
3. BRENT, L., J. B. BROWN & P. B. MEDAWAR. 1962. Quantitative studies on tissue transplantation immunity. VI. Hypersensitivity reactions associated with the rejection of homografts. Proc. R. Soc. Lond. Ser. B **156:** 187.
4. CEROTTINI, J.-C. & K. T. BRUNNER. 1974. Cell mediated cytotoxicity, allograft rejection, and tumour immunity. Adv. Immunol. **18:** 67.
5. CANTY, T. G. & J. R. WUNDERLICH. 1971. Quantitative assessment of cellular and humoral responses to skin and tumor allografts. Transplantation **11:** 111.
6. LOVELAND, B. E., P. M. HOGARTH, R. CEREDIG & I. F. C. McKENZIE. 1981. Cells mediating graft rejection in the mouse: I. Lyt-1 cells mediate skin graft rejection. J. Exp. Med. **153:** 1044.
7. LeFRANCOIS, L. & M. J. BEVAN. 1984. A reexamination of the role of Lyt-2 positive T cells in murine skin graft rejection. J. Exp. Med. **159:** 57.
8. HALL, B. M. & S. E. DORSCH. 1985. Do helper-inducer cells mediate rejection without T cytotoxic-suppressor cells. Transplant. Proc. **17:** 233.5.
9. ISAKOV, N., L. N. BIEL & F. H. BACH. 1985. Induction of class I antigen-disparate pancreatic islet graft rejection by *in vivo* administration of cloned helper cell-independent cytolytic T lymphocytes. Transplant. Proc. **17:** 727.
10. ROSENBERG, A. S., T. MIZUOCHI, S. O. SHARROW & A. SINGER. 1987. Phenotype specificity and function of T cell subsets and T cell interactions involved in skin allograft rejection. J. Exp. Med. **165:** 1296–1315.
11. SNELL, G. D. 1957. The homograft reaction. Ann. Rev. Microbiol. **11:**439.
12. LAFFERTY, K. J., A. BOOTES, G. DART & D. W. TALMAGE. 1976. Effect of organ culture on the survival of thyroid allografts in mice. Transplantation. **22:** 138.
13. LECHLER, R. I. & J. R. BATCHELOR. 1982. Restoration of immunogenicity to passenger cell-depleted kidney allografts by the addition of donor strain dendritic cells. J. Exp. Med. **155:** 31.
14. LAFFERTY, K. J., S. J. PROWSE & C. J. SIMEONOVIC. 1983. Immunobiology of tissue transplantation: a return to the passenger leukocyte concept. Ann. Rev. Immunol. **1:** 143.
15. TALMAGE, D. & F. G. LaROSA. 1987. Transplantation. *In* Immunological Diseases. M. Samter, Ed. Little Brown. Boston. In press.
16. MILTON, A. D. & J. W. FABRE. 1985. Massive induction of donor-type class I and class II major histocompatibility complex antigens in rejecting cardiac allografts in the rat. J. Exp. Med. **161:** 98.
17. DE WAAL, R. M. W., M. J. J. BOGMAN, C. N. MAASS, L. M. H. CORNELISSEN, W. J. M. TAX & R. A. P. KOENE. 1983. Variable expression of Ia antigens on the vascular endothelium of mouse skin allografts. Nature (London) **303:** 426.

18. HART, D. N. J., S. V. FUGGLE, K. A. WILLIAMS, J. W. FABRE, A. TING & P. J. MORRIS. 1981. Localization of HLA-ABC and DR antigens in human kidney. Transplantation **31:** 428.

19. DAAR, A. S., S. V. FUGGLE, J. W. GABRE, A. TING & P. J. MORRIS. 1984. The detailed distribution of MHC class II antigens in normal human organs. Transplantation **38:** 293.

20. CAUGHMAN, S. W., S. O. SHARROW, S. SHIMADA, D. STEPHANY, T. MIZUOCHI, A. S. ROSENBERG, S. I. KATZ & A. SINGER. 1986. Ia^+ murine epidermal Langerhans cells are deficient in surface expression of class I MHC. Proc. Natl. Acad. Sci. USA **83:** 7348.

21. FABRE, J. W. 1982. Rat kidney allograft model: Was it all too good to be true? Transplantation **34:** 223.

22. ROSENBERG, A. S., T. MIZUOCHI & A. SINGER. 1986. Analysis of T-cell subsets in rejection of K^b mutant skin allografts differing at class I MHC. Nature (London) **322:** 829.

23. BOYSE, E. A., L. J. OLD & E. STOCKERT. 1965. The TL (Thymus Leukemia) antigen: A review. P. Grabar & P. A. Miescher, Eds. Fourth International Symposium on Immunopathology. Grune and Stratton, New York.

24. DIALYNAS, D. P., Z. S. QUAN, K. A. WALL, A. PIERRES, J. QUINTANS, M. R. LOKEN, M. PIERRES & F. W. FITCH. 1984. Characterization of the murine T cell surface molecule, designated L3T4, identified by monoclonal antibody GK1.5: similarity of L3T4 to the human Leu3/T4 molecule. J. Immunol. **131:** 2445.

25. CEREDIG, R., J. W. LOWENTHAL, M. NABHOLZ & H. R. MACDONALD. 1985. Expression of interleukin-2 receptors as a differentiation marker on intrathymic stem cells. Nature (London) **314:** 98.

26. BILLINGHAM, R. E. & P. B. MEDWAR. 1951. The technique of free skin grafting in mammals. J. Exp. Biol. **28:** 385.

27. BOOG, C. J. P., W. M. KAST, H. TH. MARC TIMMERS, J. BOES, L. P. DEWAAL & C. J. M. MELIEF. 1985. Abolition of specific immune response defect by immunization with dendritic cells. Nature (London) **318:** 59.

28. ENGERS, H. D., A. L. GLASEBROOK & G. D. SORENSON. Allogeneic tumor rejection induced by the intravenous injection of $Lyt2^+$ cytotoxic T lymphocyte clones. J. Exp. Med. **159:** 234.

29. SNIDER, M. E., L. ARMSTRONG, J. L. HUDSON & D. STEINMULLER. 1986. *In vitro* and *in vivo* cytotoxicity of T cells cloned from rejecting allografts. Transplantation **42:** 171.

30. OROSZ, C. G., N. E. ZINN, L. SIRINEK & R. M. FERGUSON. 1986. *In vivo* mechanisms of alloreactivity. Transplantation **41:** 75.

31. TYLER, J. D., S. J. GALLI, M. E. SNIDER, A. M. DVORAK & D. STEINMULLER. 1984. Cloned $Lyt2^+$ cytotoxic T lymphocytes destroy allogeneic tissue *in vivo*. J. Exp. Med. **139:** 234.27.

32. KIRKMAN, R. L., L. V. BARRETT, G. N. GAULTON, V. E. KELLEY, W. A. KOLTUN, F. J. SCHOEN, A. YTHIER & T. B. STROM. 1985. The effect of anti-interleukin-2 receptor monoclonal antibody on allograft rejection. Transplantation **40:** 719.

33. SPRENT, J., M. SCHAEFER, D. LO & R. KORNGOLD. 1986. Properties of purified T cell subsets II. *In vivo* responses to class I vs class II H-2 differences. J. Exp. Med. **163:** 998.

34. KEENE, J.-A. N. 1983. "Cell surface-associated" carrier effect for cytotoxic T lymphocyte induction. Ph.D. Thesis. The University of Texas Health Science Center, Dallas, TX. p. 374.

35. KEENE, J. & J. FORMAN. 1982. Helper activity is required for the *in vivo* generation of cytotoxic T lymphocytes. J. Exp. Med. **155:** 768.

Donor-Directed Cytotoxic T Cells and Other Inflammatory Components of Acute Allograft Rejection[a]

PEKKA HÄYRY,[b] DARIUSZ LESZCZYNSKI,
ARTO NEMLANDER, BERNADETTE FERRY,
RISTO RENKONEN, EEVA VON WILLEBRAND, AND
JORMA HALTTUNEN

Transplantation Laboratory and Fourth Department of Surgery
University of Helsinki
Helsinki, Finland

INTRODUCTION

In organ transplants, mixed lymphocyte culture (MLC)-primed T cells kill specifically stimulator-strain target cells *in vitro*.[1] Moreover, high numbers of donor-directed cytotoxic T cells (CTL) have been demonstrated *in situ*, at the site of rejecting graft.[2–5] Consequently the role of donor-specific CTL in the process of rejection has been emphasized.

The purpose of this communication is to reconsider the role of CTL in acute allograft rejection, compare the frequency of donor-specific components to other inflammatory components *in situ*, and place the donor-specific CTL in proper perspective in the rejection process.

A PRIMARILY VASCULARIZED ORGAN ALLOGRAFT

When vascular supply is connected to the recipient, sensitization occurs, if immunosuppression is not adequate. In the past, a fair amount of debate existed between the relative role of central (meaning the recipient lymphoid system) and peripheral (meaning the allograft itself) sensitization. Both venues are obviously operative.

After transplantation, physiological recirculation of recipient white cells from blood to lymph resumes. During their transit through the allograft, the recirculating leukocytes get in contact with graft antigen-presenting cells (APC). The graft also sheds alloantigens that make contact with and are processed by the recipient APC; further immunological stimuli is thereby provided.[6]

At least two types of APC exist in the allograft: donor-derived graft passenger macrophages (dendritic cells) and graft vascular endothelial cells. Both cell types are able to present alloantigens and release at least one of the stimulatory signals, namely interleukin-1 (IL-1).

[a] This study was supported by Grants from the Academy of Finland, the Sigrid Juselius Foundation, and the Kidney Foundation, Helsinki, Finland, and by Grants 1RO1AM26882-03-06 and 37130-01-03 from the National Institutes of Health, Bethesda, Maryland.

[b] Address all correspondence to P. Häyry, Transplantation Laboratory, University of Helsinki, Haartmaninkatu 3, SF 00290 Helsinki, Finland.

According to a formal concept of the rejection response, both CD4 (helper) and CD8 (cytotoxic) antigen-responding cells participate in the response. This results in the generation of T-helper cells, cytotoxic T cells, and their end products.[7,8] Consequently, as stated, the lymphoid cells are often regarded as (prime) mediators of rejection.

The APC–T-cell interactions have been investigated in detail in the test tube, in the mixed-lymphocyte culture–cell-mediated lympholysis (MLC-CML) assay.[1] As these interactions are widely covered by other presentations in this volume (H. Wagner), they will not be dealt with here.

STRUCTURE OF INFLAMMATION

A different view is obtained if one investigates the inflammatory cell contents in a rejecting allograft. Several groups of investigators,[9–15] including us,[16] have isolated these inflammatory cells and defined them by morphology and/or by using modern immunological markers.[17]

The graft always undergoes an inflammatory response, even after syngeneic transplantation. Compared to a syngeneic graft, in a drug-unmodified rat renal allograft, the inflammatory response is approximately one log order stronger in magnitude and also qualitatively different.[17] The same applies to human renal allografts undergoing episodes of rejection.[18]

The first inflammatory cells recovered from a rejecting allograft are lymphoid cells, followed by mononuclear phagocytes. At the peak of rejection, mononuclear phagocytes are more numerous than all lymphoid cell types together. The appearance of granulocytes is a late phenomenon and linked with graft necrosis (FIG. 1A).

The lymphoid components of inflammation may be split further by using monoclonal antibodies directed to lymphoid cell subsets.[17] The major lymphoid cell components invading a rejecting renal allograft in a nonimmunosuppressed rat are shown in FIGURE 1B. As seen in the FIGURE, CD8 cytotoxic lymphocytes are more numerous than CD4 helper lymphocytes. Considering only the activated (blastogenic) component of the lymphoid compartment, the CD4 blasts are more numerous than CD8 blasts at very early stages of inflammation, although later on, the CD8 blasts take over the CD4 blasts. Interesting is that also Ig-positive (B) cells participate actively in inflammation. Although this compartment is numerically small, many of the intragraft B cells undergo blastogenesis; hence the Ig-positive (B) blasts in the inflammatory infiltrate are even more numerous than the CD4 (T) blasts.

FUNCTIONS OF INFLAMMATORY CELLS *IN SITU*

The functions of inflammatory cells have been investigated *in vitro* after enzymatic digestion of the graft and isolation of the inflammatory component. The first cytotoxic cells appearing in a rejecting renal allograft in nonimmunosuppressed rats (FIG. 2A) are the so-called natural killer (NK) effector cells, mediating lytic activity towards the characteristic target cells.[19] At this stage, lymphoid cells performing antibody-dependent cellular cytotoxicity (ADCC) with added relevant antibody are also frequent. The frequency of both these cell types peaks on days 3–4 and declines rapidly thereafter. Cytotoxic T cells with target specificity to the

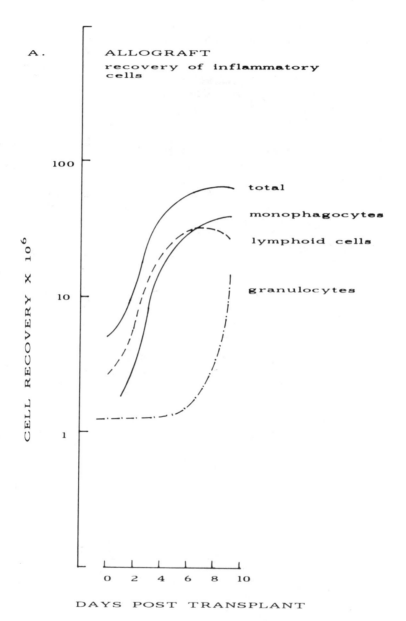

FIGURE 1A. Generation of inflammation in drug-unmodified rat renal allograft rejection. Recovery of major inflammatory cell types by way of enzymatic digestion. Solid lines: total number of inflammatory cells and recovery of inflammatory mononuclear phagocytes. Dashed line: recovery of inflammatory lymphoid cells. Dotted and dashed line: recovery of granulocytes.[17]

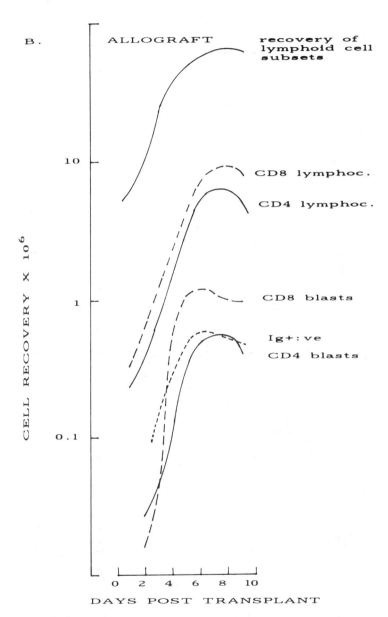

FIGURE 1B. Generation of inflammation in drug-unmodified rat renal allograft rejection. Recovery of lymphoid-cell subsets in the same experiment. Solid line: CD4-expressing lymphocytes and blast cells. Dashed line: CD8-expressing lymphoid cells and blast cells. Short dashed line: recovery of immunoglobulin-containing lymphoid cells.[17]

donor, defined by affinity chromatography and by a target-cell panel, appear
somewhat later, peak around day 7, and disappear from the graft after it has been
destroyed. Concomitantly and shortly thereafter, cells with high plasminogen
activator (PA) activity appear in the graft. Most of these cells are obviously
activated mononuclear phagocytes (FIG. 2A).

When the humoral component of the response[20] is studied, numerous IgG- and
IgM-containing lymphoid cells are seen in the allograft during all stages of rejection (FIG. 2B). In the indirect hemolytic plaque assay, however, only approximately 1 : 10–1 : 3 of the IgG- and very few IgM-expressing lymphoid cells release
the antibody of the same isotype. The B-cell response in the allograft occurs much

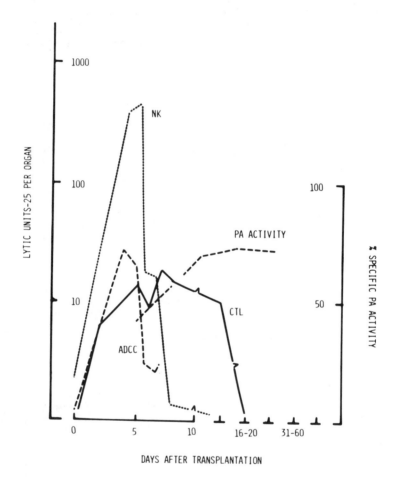

FIGURE 2A. Functions of the inflammatory lymphoid cells. Cellular response. Recovery
(in lytic units) of NK-effector cells, effector cells mediating ADCC after addition of relevant
antibody and recovery of CTL during the course of drug-unmodified rat renal allograft
rejection. The dashed line peaking on day 16–20 indicates plasminogen activator (PA) activity in the inflammatory cell population.[19,20]

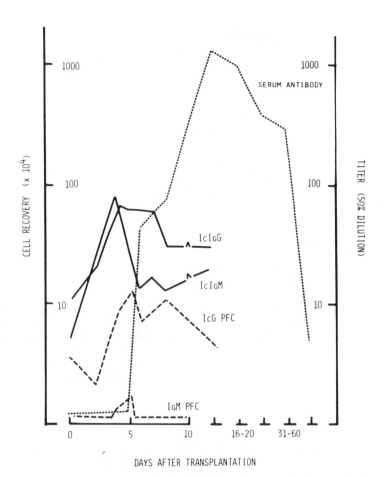

FIGURE 2B. Functions of the inflammatory lymphoid cells. Humoral response. Intracellular IgG- and IgM- (IcIgG and IcIgM) containing cells and cells releasing IgG and IgM in indirect plaque assay in the graft-infiltrating inflammatory population are shown. For comparison (dashed line), the serum antibody titer against class I plus class II in complement-dependent cytolysis is also demonstrated.[19,20]

earlier than any detectable serum antibody to the graft donor appears in the circulation (FIG. 2B).

FREQUENCY OF DONOR-DIRECTED T CELLS *IN SITU*

The frequencies of donor-specific T-helper cells (T_h) and CTL and their precursors (pT_h and pCTL) in the inflammatory population have been defined recently by at least three independent groups of investigators. These data are summarized in TABLE 1. In a limiting-dilution assay, the peak frequency of

TABLE 1. Frequency of Donor MHC-Directed T_h/pT_h and CTL/pCTL in the Graft and in the Recipient Spleen during Rejection

		Relative frequency of donor-reactive cells in limited dilution assay	
		Early	Peak
T_h/pT_h	graft[a]	1 : 3100	1 : 670
	spleen[a]	1 : 1300	1 : 180
CTL/pCTL	graft[b]	—	1 : 500
	graft[c]	—	1 : 1000

[a] Congeneic LBN (RTI[n]) renal allograft to Lew (RTI[l]) strain.[21]
[b] Major plus minor incompatible mouse sponge-matrix (SM) allografts.[22]
[c] Dog renal allografts by fine-needle aspiration biopsy (FNAB).[23]

donor-directed T_h/pT_h in the graft was about 1 : 600.[21] The peak frequency of CTL/pCTL was of the same order of magnitude, 1 : 500–1 : 1000.[22,23]

Considering inflammatory B cells with specificity to the graft donor, we have recently hybridized LBN strain to Lewis strain renal allograft-infiltrating inflammatory cells with X63-Ag-8.653 myeloma line under limiting dilution conditions (unpublished). The clone frequency producing specific anti-LBN antibodies was even smaller, of the order of 1 : 700,000. If corrected to inflammatory B-blast cells, the frequency of donor-directed B-cell clones was approximately 1 : 700.

Taken together, the frequencies of specific donor-directed T and B cells, if correct, are very low and represent at the most 0.5–1% of the inflammatory cell population. It is thus rather inconceivable that donor-directed lymphoid cells alone could bring about graft rejection; a major role should be anticipated to the remaining of the inflammatory components.

WHICH GRAFT CELLULAR COMPONENTS ARE SENSITIVE TO INFLAMMATORY DAMAGE?

Unfortunately very little information is available on the relative sensitivity of various graft cellular components to the host immune/inflammatory attack. The work performed by Deziel and Guttmann[24] in Canada and one earlier study of ours[25] suggest that the graft vascular endothelial component is particularly sensitive.

Recently, Leszczynski et al.[26] have analyzed, by using various histochemical methods, the relative sensitivity of rat renal allograft components to rejection. These findings are summarized in TABLE 2. Supposing that the decline in the enzyme activity is proportional to the extent of target-cell damage, they suggested—by comparison to a syngeneic graft—that the most sensitive component in a renal allograft is the vascular endothelium, in particular the intertubular capillary endothelium. Very dramatic declines in the adenosine-3-phosphatase activity were recorded in the allograft intertubular capillary endothelium compared to a syngeneic graft. The loss of enzyme activity was considerably smaller in glomerular, arterial, and venous endothelium. The tubular cells were obviously even less sensitive, and only a moderate decline in the activities of alkaline phosphatase (AP), isocitrate dehydrogenase (IDH), and lactate dehydrogenase (LDH) was recorded in the tubular compartment of the renal allograft.

As yet, practically no experiments have been carried out, for example, *in vitro,* to investigate the sensitivity of, for example, renal allograft endothelial, glomerular, and tubular cells to cytotoxic T cells invading the transplant. Neither has it been adequately established whether the high NK activity and the large granular lymphocytes (LGL), invading the allograft at early stages of rejection, carry any cytotoxic potential to the graft cellular components.

We have recently evaluated[27] the second possibility by isolating the inflammatory leukocytes from a rat renal allograft on day 3, when there is only incipient or no donor-directed CTL activity, but a very high NK activity (FIG. 3) in the graft. When the inflammatory cells were tested for cytotoxicity against donor vascular endothelial cells, to donor peritoneal exudate cells (relevant target) and to YAC (NK target; positive control), the inflammatory cells were lytic to YAC, but incapable of killing either the vascular endothelial cells or the specific donor target cells. This indicates that the inflammatory NK cells may not carry significant cytotoxic functions towards the donor vascular endothelium. The result does not rule out the possibility that upon further activation *in situ* by the inflammatory lymphokines they later become cytotoxic to graft components.

ARE CTL NECESSARY FOR REJECTION TO OCCUR?

Adoptive transfer of CD4 (T helper) cells to adult thymectomized, irradiated, bone-marrow reconstituted (ATxBM) B rats or mice is usually far more effective for restoring the ability to reject than transfer of CD8 (cytotoxic) cells. These experiments have recently been summarized by Steinmuller.[28] This is, however, only a relative argument: the ATxBM procedure does not entirely eliminate the CTL precursor pool and, in fact, in most cases, recipient CTL are present in the grafts of T_h-reconstituted rodents at the time of rejection.[28]

On the other hand, donor-specific CTL have repeatedly been isolated from allografts, rendered enhanced or tolerant by various treatment modalities, in spite of the fact that these allografts (undergoing also an inflammatory response) are not

TABLE 2. Damage of DA to WF Strain Rat Renal Allograft Components during Rejection: A Histochemical Study[a]

	Percent of enzyme activity in allograft compared to syngeneic graft[b]			
	ATP	AT	IDH	LDH
Endothelial cells				
intertubular	13	—	—	—
glomerular	74	—	—	—
arterial	83	—	—	—
venous	90	—	—	—
Tubular cells				
proximal	—	78	59	70
distal	—	—	85	64

[a] Leszczynski *et al.*[26]

[b] ATP = adenosine triphosphatase; AP = alkaline phosphatase; IDH = isocitrate dehydrogenase; LDH = lactate dehydrogenase.

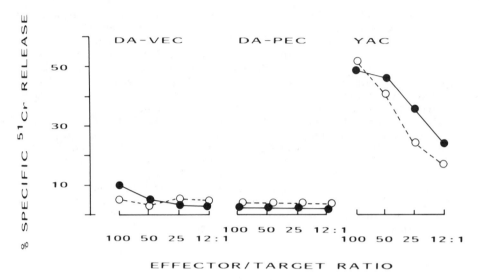

FIGURE 3. Lytic activity of DA to WF renal allograft-infiltrating inflammatory leukocytes on day 3 after transplantation towards NK target cells (YAC), donor-derived peritoneal exudate cells (PEC) and donor-derived vascular endothelial cells (VEC). At this stage of rejection, high NK activity is present in the graft, whereas no donor-directed CTL activity is demonstrable against the specific target. Neither do the inflammatory cells kill donor-derived VEC at this time point. (Häyry et al.[27] With permission from Plenum Publishing Co.)

permanently rejected (P. Morris, personal communication). This is also the case with ATxBM recipients, which were transplanted without transfer of lymphoid cells, that is, under conditions where the recipient accepts a kidney allograft.[29] As seen in FIGURE 4, equal numbers of donor-specific CTL were isolated from these grafts, compared to ordinary rejecting allografts, although in the B rats the intragraft CTL peaked later.

Taken together, these results do not convincingly show that the donor-specific CTL in the graft are necessary for the rejection to occur. In fact, some of these results speak against this possibility.

AMPLIFICATION OF INFLAMMATION AND THE "VASCULAR GATE"

The extensive damage of the allograft in context of acute cellular rejection, though often reversible with drugs, suggests that the remaining inflammatory components in addition to the donor-specific CTL are also of relevance. This brings about the questions, How and whereby are these inflammatory components generated? and How are they regulated?

During rejection, concomitantly with the generation of the inflammatory response, the inflammatory (white) cell traffic through the allograft increases in magnitude by at least one log order. In a study of Nemlander et al.,[30] the proliferating white cells were labeled separately in the graft or in the recipient, and the type and localization of the labeled cells was tracked down by autoradiography 18 h later. The authors demonstrated (TABLE 3) that at the beginning of rejection, very few labeled cells migrated from the donor to the allograft, whereas at the peak of rejection, nearly half of the labeled white cells of the recipient spleen moved into the graft within an 18 h period. The traffic in the vice versa direction was equally impressive. These data are in agreement with the many previous

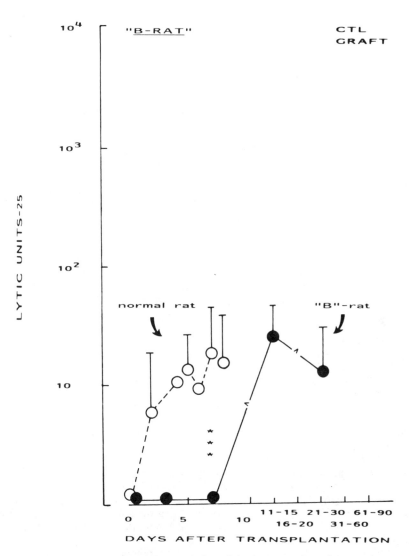

FIGURE 4. Generation of donor-directed lytic activity in a normal, nonimmunosuppressed rat and in the inflammatory population of adult thymectomized, irradiated, bone-marrow reconstituted B rats. In terms of recovery of lytic units per organ, the CTL activity in the B rats is equally high as in a normal rat, although it peaks approximately one week later.[29]

TABLE 3. Migration of Rat Renal Allograft-Responding (Proliferating) White Blood Cells (WBC) between the Host and the Graft

Labeled compartment	Site of assay	Number of labeled cells ($\times 10^6$) recovered from the site of labeling and/or from a distant site 18 h after injection of [^{3}H]TdR[b]	
		day 1 (early)	day 4 (peak)
Host-labeled cells	remaining in spleen	15.0	30.0
	migrating to graft	0.25	18.0
Graft-labeled cells	remaining in graft	0.4	15.0
	migrating to spleen	1.6	30.0

[a] From Nemlander et al.[30]

[b] Proliferating cells were selectively labeled in the graft and in the host by tritiated thymidine ([^{3}H]TdR); the label was neutralized with cold thymidine, and the number of labeled cells in the graft and recipient spleen was quantitated 18 h later.

results, for example, those of Pedersen and Morris,[31] tracking the exit of white cells to the lymphatics draining sheep renal allografts.

Concomitantly with the generation of inflammation, several changes take place in the graft vascular endothelium that are possibly relevant to increased leukocyte diapedesis. One of these is increased expression of class II antigens on the endothelial (and other parenchymal) cells (FIG. 5).[32–34]

Evidence exists that increased Ia expression and increased leukocyte diapedesis (and thereby inflammation) are regulated by the inflammatory cells themselves: if two allografts are provided simultaneously from the same donor, such as heart and lung,[35] they are frequently rejected independently of each other. Thus inflammatory lymphokines, provided by the inflammatory leukocytes, are proper candidates to regulate leukocyte diapedesis and Ia antigen re-expression in the graft.

Attachment of white cells to vascular endothelium is the necessary first step for their immigration into tissue. In a recent study, Leszczysnki and I[36] investigated whether and to what extent inflammatory lymphokines, provided in nature by inflammatory cells and in our study by gene technology, could facilitate Ia expression and leukocyte binding by isolated, cultured vascular endothelial cells (TABLE 4). We found that a wide variety of inflammatory lymphokines, including recombinant IL-1, IL-2, and gamma-interferon at a concentration range of 10–1000 U/ml, upregulated Ia expression on isolated endothelial cells *in vitro* and facilitated the binding of both allogeneic and syngeneic leukocytes to the endothelial cells.[36]

Whether these two phenomena, Ia expression and leukocyte binding to endothelium, are interrelated, was investigated further by applying gamma-interferon and drugs known to inhibit either one. In such an experiment (TABLE 5), methylprednisolone (MP) at a concentration of 1 μg/ml did not inhibit the gamma-interferon-induced class II antigen upregulation *in vitro* (or, in fact, enhance it), but entirely inhibited the leukocyte binding. On the other hand, prostaglandin E2 (PGE2), at a concentration of 10^{-7} M, entirely inhibited Ia-expression but did not inhibit the binding of leukocytes.[36] Thus these two phenomena, though anatomically and functionally closely related, seem not to be regulated by the same vectors.

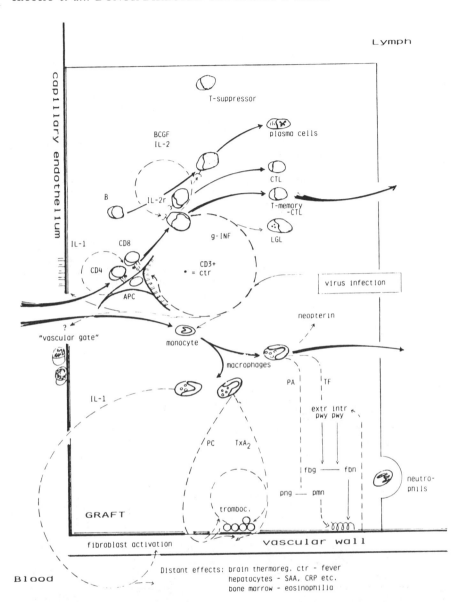

FIGURE 5. Some cellular and molecular pathways involved in immune recognition and generation of inflammation in primarily vascularized organ allografts. The rectangular section in the middle indicates the allograft, the section below, the vascular supply; the section to the left indicates the capillary network, and the section to the right and to the top, the lymphatic drainage. Abbreviations: CD4 and CD8, lymphoid subsets corresponding to T4 and T8 in humans; APC, antigen-presenting cell; IL-2r, IL-2 receptor; SAA, serum amyloid protein A; CRP, C-reactive protein; PC, prostacyclin; TxA$_2$, thromboxane A$_2$; PA, plasminogen activator; TF, tissue factor; extr pwy and intr pwy, extrinsic and intrinsic pathway of blood coagulation; fbg, fibrinogen; fbn, fibrin; png, plasminogen; pmn, plasmin.[37]

TABLE 4. Effect of Various Lymphokines on Ia Expression and Binding of Allogeneic WF Leukocytes by Cultured DA Rat Endothelial Cells (EC)[a]

Lymphokine	Concentration	Percent of Ia expressing EC[b]		Binding of allogeneic leukocytes (percent of EC)[c]		
		24 h	72 h	2 h	24 h	72 h
None		1	1	1	1	1
rIL-1	1000 U/ml	3	22	22	7	5
	100 U/ml	3	17	14	3	5
	10 U/ml	2	10	9	2	2
rIL-2	1000 U/ml	3	21	ND	3	10
	100 U/ml	2	15	ND	3	13
	10 U/ml	1	15	ND	1	9
rIFN	1000 U/ml	10	44	ND	20	61
	100 U/ml	4	18	ND	11	30
	10 U/ml	2	10	ND	2	12

[a] From Leszczynski and Häyry.[36]
[b] After stimulation of cultured EC for indicated times; immunohistochemical assay.
[c] After stimulation of cultured EC for indicated times; 30 min binding assay for the WBC.
A similar pattern was obtained with syngeneic leukocytes (not shown).

GENERATION OF A VICIOUS CYCLE

We believe, furthermore, that the host-graft interaction is not a one-way switch-on/switch-off interaction, but the graft participates by several positive, and possibly also negative (feedback), mechanisms in the generation of the rejection response. Furthermore, it is likely that the inflammatory response is amplified (and becomes self-supportive) by the generation of a vicious cycle inside the allograft during rejection (FIG. 6). The prime components of this cycle are recognition of the graft alloantigens by the host recirculating leukocytes, increased leukocyte diapedesis to the graft, and increased expression of major histocompatibility locus antigens in (and on) the graft cells.[37]

The generation of such a cycle is supported by the following experiment of Ferry et al.[38] DA rat heart endothelial cells were isolated and cultured to purity in vitro. In resting state, they expressed class I, but not substantially class II, alloantigens of the cell surface. When the endothelial cells were stimulated with gamma-

TABLE 5. Inhibition of gIFN-Induced Ia Expression and Leukocyte Binding by Prostaglandin E2 and Methylprednisolone

Lympho-kine	Concen-tration	Drug	Concen-tration	Percent of Ia expressing EC	Binding of allogeneic leukocytes (percent of EC)[a]
none	—			1	2
rIFN	100 U/ml		—	23	20
rIFN	100 U/ml	MP	1 μg/ml	58	2
rIFN	100 U/ml	PGE2	10^{-7} M	3	19

[a] A similar pattern was obtained with syngeneic leukocytes (not shown).[36]

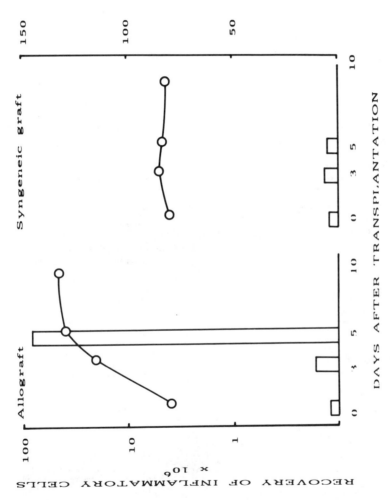

FIGURE 6. Generation of inflammation (circles), and expression of class II MHC antigens (columns) in nonimmunosuppressed DA to WF renal allografts and in DA to DA syngeneic grafts after transplantation. (Leszczynski *et al.*[26] With permission from Springer-Verlag.)

TABLE 6. Priming of a WF (RTI^v) Recipient by Isolated Cells of DA (RTI^a) Origin[a]

Priming cell type	Number of cells required to reduce DA heart allograft survival by 50%[b]
Spleen DC	10^4
Endothelial cells, class II (+++)	10^3
Endothelial cells, class II (+/−)	10^7

[a] From Ferry *et al.*[38]
[b] The recipient rat was challenged with a relevant heart allograft 72 h after priming of the recipient by isolated cells.

interferon, they expressed strongly also class II. When the two types of endothelial cells, class II-negative and class II-positive, were compared for their immunogenic potency in a "primed rejection assay," four log orders more class II-negative endothelial cells than class II-positive endothelial cells were required to reduce the survival of a challenging heart allograft by 50 percent. In fact, the class II-positive endothelial cells in this assay were as immunogenic as isolated, allogeneic spleen dendritic cells (TABLE 6).

It is also possible that this vicious cycle may be generated in well-functioning grafts by exogenous lymphokine stimulation, for example, in context of a viral infection. In this context, we must sidestep from rat experiments to clinical data using FNAB. Approximately 200 renal allograft recipients were aspiration-biopsied during the postoperative period by FNAB. Class II expression, inflammation, and serum creatinine were recorded in these patients.[39] As seen in TABLE 7, the well-functioning grafts (approx. 1–3 months after the operation) did not substantially display class II, there was practically no inflammation in these grafts, and

TABLE 7. Class II Expression, Inflammation, and Level of Serum Creatinine in Fourteen Patients with Proven CMV Disease

	Patients with proven CMV disease[a] (n = 14)		
Prior to disease (days −1 . . . −16)			
class II expression (% positive PC)		7.5 ± 1.8	
inflammation			
blasts		0 ± 0	
TCI		3.0 ± 1.9	
serum creatinine (μmol)		124 ± 85	
At the onset of disease (days +1 . . . +4)	no rejection (n = 2)	reversible rejection (n = 10)	irreversible rejection (n = 2)
class II expression (% positive PC)	50 ± 0	66 ± 12	57 ± 15
inflammation			
blasts	0 ± 0	1.4 ± 1.9	0 ± 0
TCI	2.9 ± 2.3	6.1 ± 1.9	4.0 ± 3.0
serum creatinine (μmol/l)	173 ± 97	308 ± 186	334 ± 181

[a] ±SD.

the serum creatinine of these patients was near to normal. The slight elevation in serum creatinine levels may be attributed to cyclosporine. Fourteen of these patients underwent a proven cytomegalovirus (CMV) infection within 6 months after transplantation. In the context of CMV infection, the class II antigen expression in all grafts was sharply upregulated, and 12 of 14 grafts underwent, thereafter, a classical cellular rejection. A plausible explanation is that gamma-interferon and/or other lymphokines, generated in the context of the CMV infection, provoked the rejection episode, after depletion of the passenger dendritic cells, by way of the up-regulation of class II antigens on the endothelial cells.[39,40]

ACTIVATION OF THE MONONUCLEAR PHAGOCYTES

A final and probably just as important component of inflammation, is the mononuclear phagocytes. This inflammatory component of rejection has not been dealt with very precisely in the past, although many investigators including Mason *et al.*,[13] Forbes *et al.*,[41] and Lowry and co-workers[42] have stressed the importance of the "delayed hypersensitivity" responses in a rejecting allograft.

TABLE 8. Thy 1$^+$ (Pluripotent Precursor) Cells in the DA to WF Renal Allograft and in the WF Recipient during Rejection

	Percent of Thy 1$^+$ cells			
	Renal allograft	Recipient spleen	Recipient blood	Recipient bone marrow
Allograft				
day 0		11.8	12.6	36.2
1	<1	7.0	8.6	22.6
3	29.0	24.0	21.5	19.0
5	2.8	8.4	8.8	15.4
Syngeneic Graft				
day 4	2.4	14.2	12.2	27.3

At later stages of rejection, mononuclear phagocytes are the largest single inflammatory component of the inflammatory response. An intriguing finding by Nemlander[30] was that when the graft was selectively labeled with tritiated thymidine, 18 hours after labeling, very large numbers of graft inflammatory macrophages had incorporated tritiated thymidine. It is not entirely uncommon to find either erythroid or myeloid precursor cells (erythroblasts, monoblasts) in the inflammatory population. This suggests that dividing macrophage precursors (possibly even pluripotent stem cells) are present in the graft.

This possibility has been recently investigated by Leszczynski and Häyry (unpublished) by using Thy-1 (theta) antibody, known in the rat to selectively label the pluripotent precursor cells.[43] We found (TABLE 8) that during rejection, nearly one-third of the inflammatory cells in the graft were Thy-1 positive. Most of these cells were morphologically "lymphocytes," indistinguishable from the remaining "lymphoid" elements. Concomitantly there was a depletion of the Thy-1 positive cells in the recipient bone marrow and an influx of Thy-1 positive cells to the circulation and to the recipient spleen. These results, though preliminary, suggest that pluripotent stem cells may be one relevant component of the inflammatory response, and that these cells are able to generate and mature to different lineages under the influence of the inflammatory lymphokines (J. Ihle, personal communication).

CONSEQUENCES OF MONONUCLEAR PHAGOCYTE ACTIVATION

The consequences of mononuclear phagocyte activation in the graft may be exemplified with three major venues, probably of importance in context of acute rejection (FIG. 6).

The first one is the release of IL-1 (and related monokines) from activated mononuclear phagocytes. This brings about many of the clinical symptoms of acute rejection. These include fever, through stimulation of the brain thermoregulatory center;[44] release of acute-phase proteins, such as serum amyloid protein A and C-reactive protein[45] from recipient hepatocytes; and eosinophilia as a consequence of bone marrow stimulation.[44] IL-1 and related monokines may also be partially responsible for fibroblast activation, graft atherosclerosis, and graft fibrosis.

The second venue is generated by arachidonic acid metabolites, as exemplified in FIGURE 5 by prostacyclin and thromboxane A2. Thromboxane A2 generates vasoconstriction and thrombocyte adhesion, and prostacyclin opposes these effects. Investigators have documented a relative surplus of TxB2, compared to 6-keto-PG in a rejecting allograft,[46] and release of TxB2 during rejection in urine,[47] which support this concept. Furthermore, many studies have demonstrated that during rejection, thrombocytes accumulate into the graft, and can be traced down, for example, by using [111]Indium. In a recent study by von Willebrand, Zola, and Häyry,[48] we found that the accumulation of thrombocytes into the graft is a two-stage phenomenon: there is an accumulation of thrombocytes into the graft over the blood background level in all rejections. On most occasions the thrombocytes occurring in the graft, as demonstrable by FNAB and relevant antithrombocyte monoclonal antibodies, appear as loose aggregates, intravascular and often in close proximity to blood granulocytes. In severe and irreversible rejections, however, the thrombocytes have a tendency to agglutinate to the graft endothelium.[48]

A final pathway, and probably a very late one, is linked to the activation of the coagulation mechanism. Here, tissue factor released by activated macrophages, and responsible for the activation of the extrinsic pathway, may represent a key molecule.[11]

CONCLUSIONS

During acute cellular rejection, an allograft is infiltrated by several types of lymphoid and nonlymphoid cells. In addition, deposits of antibody and complement are frequently encountered.

Adoptive transfer studies of T-cell depleted B rats suggest that the CD4-expressing T-helper cells are crucial for the initiation of the response, whereas the CD8-expressing T-cytotoxic cells are of less importance.

Immunologically specific components of the inflammatory response, T-helper and cytotoxic cells and immunoglobulin-producing B cells with products directed to the graft donor, are only a minority of the inflammatory population. Together they seem to represent less than one percent of all inflammatory cell types. It is therefore conceivable that a major part of tissue damage is produced by the remaining inflammatory components lacking target specificity. Such cell types in the inflammatory infiltrate include lymphoid cells lacking target specificity (the NK-effector cells), possibly lymphokine-activated killer (LAK) cells, and mononuclear phagocytes.

So far, experimental evidence has produced no demonstrable function for the inflammatory NK cells. Neither elimination of the NK cells by asialo-GM-1 antibody significantly delays rat allograft rejection. Another possible pathway, still unexplored, is based on lymphokine-activated LAK cells. Such cells are most likely generated in situ due to a high local concentration of lymphokines in the graft.

Many significant functions have been attributed to the inflammatory macrophages. These effects, mediated by IL-1 or related monokines, include fever, eosinophilia, and generation of acute phase proteins by recipient hepatocytes. IL-1 and related lymphokines may also be partially responsible for the activation of fibroblasts in the graft. Many arachidonic acid metabolites, released in particular by activated macrophages, also seem to affect graft function. Thromboxane A2, inducing vasoconstriction and platelet aggregation over opposing prostacyclin seems to be especially important. Finally, activation of the extrinsic coagulation pathway by tissue factor, released also by inflammatory macrophages, may be linked with graft thrombosis and necrosis.

Taken together, it seems obvious that several cell types, in addition to the immunologically specific ones and donor-directed CTL, participate in acute cellular rejection. It is therefore plausible to assume that all these various inflammatory cascades are of importance and that rejection is a summation of these effects.

The different components of inflammation seem to be linked by a vicious cycle, generated in the allograft during rejection. The essential components of this cycle are recognition of graft antigens by host immunocompetent cells, increased leukocyte diapedesis to the graft, and increased MHC (in particular class II) antigen expression in the graft.

REFERENCES

1. HÄYRY, P. & V. DEFENDI. 1970. Mixed lymphocyte cultures produce effector cells: Model in vitro for allograft rejection. Science **168:** 133–135.
2. STROM, T. B., N. L. TILNEY, J. M. PARADYSZ, J. BANCEWICZ & C. B. CARPENTER. 1977. Cellular components of allograft rejection: Identity, specificity and cytotoxic function of cells infiltrating acutely rejecting allografts. J. Immunol. **118:** 2020–2026.
3. ROBERTS, P. J. & P. HÄYRY. 1977. Effector mechanisms in allograft rejection. II. Density, electrophoresis and size fractionation of allograft-infiltrating cells demonstrating several classes of killer cells. Cell. Immunol. **30:** 236–253.
4. VON WILLEBRAND, E., A. SOOTS & P. HÄYRY. 1979. In situ effector mechanisms in rat kidney allograft rejection. II. Heterogenicity of the effector cells in the inflammatory infiltrate vs that in the spleen of the recipient rat. Cell. Immunol. **46:** 327–336.
5. ASCHER, N. L., R. M. FERGUSON, R. HOFFMAN & R. SIMMONS. 1979. Partial characterization of cytotoxic cells infiltrating sponge-matrix allografts. Transplantation **27:** 254–259.
6. BATCHELOR, J. R. & R. I. LECHLER. 1982. Why MHC incompatible grafts induce strong primary alloimmunity. Transplant. Proc. **XIV:** 535–537.
7. LAFFERTY, K. J. 1980. Immunogenicity of foreign tissues. Transplantation **29:** 179–183.

8. WAGNER, H., C. HARDT, K. HEEG, K. PFIZENMAIER, W. SOLBACH, R. BARTLETT, H. STOCKINGER & M. RÖLLINGHOFF. 1980. T-T cell interactions during cytotoxic T-lymphocyte (CTL) responses: T-cell-derived helper factor (interleukin 2) as a probe to analyze CTL responsiveness and thymic maturation of CTL progenitors. Immunol. Rev. **51:** 215–221.

9. FORBES, R. D. C. & R. D. GUTTMANN. 1984. Pathogenetic studies of cardiac allograft rejection using inbred rat models. Immunol. Rev. **77:** 5–29.

10. HALL, B. M. & S. E. DORSCH. 1984. Cells mediating allograft rejection. Immunol. Rev. **77:** 31–59.

11. HANCOCK, W. W. 1984. Analysis of intragraft effector mechanisms associated with human renal allograft rejection: Immunohistological studies with monoclonal antibodies. Immunol. Rev. **77:** 61–84.

12. MACPHERSON, G. G. & S. E. CHRISTMAS. 1984. The role of the macrophage in cardiac allograft rejection in the rat. Immunol. Rev. **77:** 143–166.

13. MASON, D. W., M. J. DALLMAN, R. P. ARTHUR & P. J. MORRIS. 1984. Mechanisms of allograft rejection: The roles of cytotoxic T-cells and delayed-type hypersensitivity. Immunol. Rev. **77:** 167–184.

14. TILNEY, N. L., J. W. KUPIEC-WEGLINSKI, C. D. HEIDECKE, P. A. LEAR & T. B. STROM. 1984. Mechanisms of rejection and prolongation of vascularized organ allografts. Immunol. Rev. **77:** 185–216.

15. ASCHER, N. L., R. A. HOFFMAN, D. W. HANTO & R. L. SIMMONS. 1984. Cellular basis of allograft rejection. Immunol. Rev. **77:** 217–232.

16. HÄYRY, P., E. VON WILLEBRAND, E. PARTHENAIS, A. NEMLANDER, A. SOOTS, I. LAUTENSCHLAGER, P. ALFOLDY & R. RENKONEN. 1984. The inflammatory mechanisms of allograft rejection. Immunol. Rev. **77:** 85–142.

17. RENKONEN, R., A. SOOTS, E. VON WILLEBRAND & P. HÄYRY. 1983. Lymphoid cell subclasses in rejecting renal allograft in the rat. Cell. Immunol. **77:** 187–195.

18. HÄYRY, P. & E. VON WILLEBRAND. 1981. Monitoring of human renal allograft rejection with fine needle aspiration cytology. Scand. J. Immunol. **13:** 87–97.

19. NEMLANDER, A., A. SOOTS & P. HÄYRY. 1984. In situ effector pathways of allograft destruction. 1. Generation of the "cellular" effector response in the graft and the graft recipient. Cell. Immunol. **89:** 409–419.

20. NEMLANDER, A., T. PAAVONEN, A. SOOTS & P. HÄYRY. 1984. In situ effector pathways of allograft destruction. 2. Generation of the "humoral" response in the graft and the graft recipient. Cell. Immunol. **89:** 420–426.

21. MANCA, F., B. FERRY, M. JAAKKOLA, J. HALTTUNEN, L. HORSMANHEIMO & P. HÄYRY. 1987. Frequency and functional characterization of specific T-helper cells infiltrating rat kidney allografts during acute rejection. Scand. J. Immunol. **25:** 255–264.

22. OROSZ, C. G., E. N. ZINN, L. P. SIRINEK & R. M. FERGUSON. 1986. In vivo mechanisms of alloreactivity. I. Frequency of donor-reactive cytotoxic T-lymphocytes in sponge matrix allografts. Transplantation **41:** 75–83.

23. DOVEREN, R. F. C., C. J. VAN DER LINDEN, W. A. BUURMAN & E. E. M. SPRONKEN. 1986. Analysis of cytotoxic T-lymphocyte response in rejecting allografted canine kidneys. Transplantation **41:** 33–38.

24. DEZIEL, C. & R. D. GUTTMANN. 1980. Differential susceptibility of cardiac cell populations to in vitro immune injury. Transplantation **30:** 52–54.

25. PARTHENAIS, E., A. SOOTS & P. HÄYRY. 1979. Sensitivity of rat heart endothelial and myocardial cells to alloimmune lymphocytes and to alloantibody-dependent cellular cytotoxicity. Cell. Immunol. **48:** 375–382.

26. LESZCZYNSKI, D., M. LASZCZYNSKA, J. HALTTUNEN & P. HÄYRY. 1987. Renal target structures in acute allograft rejection. A histochemical study. Kidney Int. **31:** 1311–1316.

27. HÄYRY, P., A. NEMLANDER, J. TARKKANEN, B. FERRY, M. JAAKKOLA, Y. NIETOSVAARA & J. USTINOV. 1988. Natural cytotoxicity and allograft rejection. In Functions of the natural immune system. C. W. Reynolds & R. H. Wiltrout, Eds. Plenum. New York. In press.

28. STEINMULLER, D. 1985. Which T cells mediate allograft rejection? Transplantation **40:** 229–233.
29. NEMLANDER, A., D. LESZCZYNSKI, J. HALTTUNEN, R. RENKONEN, A. SOOTS & P. HÄYRY. 1987. Evidence that thymectomized, bone-marrow-reconstituted rats do not reject their allografts. Transplantation **44:** 662–668.
30. NEMLANDER, A., A. SOOTS, E. VON WILLEBRAND, B. HUSBERG & P. HÄYRY. 1982. Redistribution of renal allograft responding leukocytes during rejection. 2. Kinetics and specificity. J. Exp. Med. **156:** 1087–1100.
31. PEDERSEN, N. C. & B. MORRIS. 1970. The role of the lymphatic system in the rejection of homografts: A study of lymph from renal transplants. J. Exp. Med. **131:** 936–947.
32. HÄYRY, P., E. VON WILLEBRAND, J. AHONEN & B. EKLUND. 1981. Are transplantation antigens stable constituents on human renal allografts? Proc. Eur. Dial. Transplant Assoc. **18:** 367–374.
33. DE WAAL, R. M. W., M. J. J. BOGMAN, C. N. MAASS, L. M. H. CORNELISSEN, W. J. M. TAX & R. A. P. KOENE. 1983. Variable expression of Ia antigens on the vascular endothelium of mouse skin allografts. Nature **303:** 426–429.
34. HALL, B. M., G. G. DUGGIN, J. PHILIPS, G. A. BISHOP, J. S. HORVATH & D. J. TILLER. 1984. Increased expression of HLA-DR antigens on renal tubular cells in renal transplants: Relevance to the rejection response. Lancet **2:** 247–251.
35. COOPER, D. K. C., D. NOVITZKY, A. G. ROSE & B. A. REICHART. 1986. Acute pulmonary rejection precedes cardiac rejection following heart-lung transplantation in a primate model. J. Heart Transplant. **5:** 29–32.
36. LESZCZYNSKI, D. & P. HÄYRY. Effects of various lymphokines on Ia-expression and lymphocyte binding to vascular endothelium. Submitted.
37. HÄYRY, P., B. FERRY, D. LESZCZYNSKI, F. MANCA, M. JAAKKOLA, J. HALTTUNEN, E. VON WILLEBRAND, H. SCHELLEKENS & P. V.D. MEIDE. 1986. Generation and breakdown of a vicious cycle in context of acute allograft rejection. Transplant. Proc. **XVIII** Suppl. **4:** 52–62.
38. FERRY, B., J. HALTTUNEN, D. LESZCZYNSKI, H. SCHELLEKENS, P. V.D. MEIDE & P. HÄYRY. 1987. Impact of class II MHC antigen expression on the immunogenic potential of rat vascular endothelial cells. Transplantation **44:** 499–503.
39. VON WILLEBRAND, E., E. PETTERSSON, J. AHONEN & P. HÄYRY. 1986. CMV infection, class II antigen expression, and human kidney allograft rejection. Transplantation **42:** 364–367.
40. POBER, J. S., T. COLLINS, M. A. GIMBORNE, JR., P. LIBBY & C. S. REISS. 1986. Inducible expression of class II major histocompatibility complex antigens and the immunogenicity of vascular endothelium. Transplantation **41:** 141–146.
41. FORBES, R. D. C., R. P. LOWRY, M. GOMERSALL & J. BLACKBURN. 1985. Comparative immunohistologic studies in an adoptive transfer model of acute rat cardiac allograft rejection. Transplant. Proc. **17:** 869–871.
42. GURLEY, K. E., R. P. LOWRY, R. D. C. FOBERS. 1983. Immune mechanisms in organ allograft rejection. II. T helper cells, delayed-type hypersensitivity, and rejection of renal allografts. Transplantation **36:** 401–405.
43. THIERFELDER, S. 1977. Haemopoietic stem cells of rats but not of mice express Th-1.1 alloantigen. Nature **269:** 691–693.
44. LAUTENSCHLAGER, I., E. VON WILLEBRAND & P. HÄYRY. 1985. Blood eosinophilia, steroids and rejection. Transplantation **40:** 354–357.
45. MAURY, C. P. J., A. M. TEPPO, B. EKLUND, P. HÄYRY & J. AHONEN. 1983. Serum amyloid A levels in human renal allograft rejection. Clin. Sci. **65:** 547–550.
46. TANNENBAUM, J. S., C. B. ANDERSON, G. A. SICARD, D. W. MCKEEL & E. E. ETHEREDGE. 1984. Prostaglandin synthesis associated with renal allograft rejection in the dog. Transplantation **37:** 438–446.
47. FOEGH, M., B. KHIRABADI & P. W. RAMWELL. 1985. Prolongation of experimental cardiac allograft survival with thromboxane-related drugs. Transplantation **40:** 124–125.
48. VON WILLEBRAND, E., H. ZOLA & P. HÄYRY. 1985. Thrombocyte aggregates in renal allografts. Analysis by the fine needle aspiration biopsy and monoclonal anti-thrombocyte antibodies. Transplantation **39:** 258–262.

Tissue Destruction Resulting from the Interaction of Cytotoxic T Cells and Their Targets[a]

DAVID STEINMULLER,[b,c] JOHN D. TYLER,[d]
MARY ELLEN SNIDER,[b,e] ROGER L. NOBLE,[b]
BRUCE L. RISER,[f] HUNEIN F. MAASSAB,[g] AND
STEPHEN J. GALLI[h]

[b]Department of Surgery
University of Michigan Medical School
Ann Arbor, Michigan 48109

[d]Department of Surgery and Medical Biology
University of Tennessee Medical Center
Knoxville, Tennessee 37920

[f]Department of Pathology
University of Michigan Medical School

[g]Department of Epidemiology
University of Michigan School of Public Health
Ann Arbor, Michigan 48109

[h]Department of Pathology
Beth Israel Hospital and Harvard Medical School
The Charles A. Dana Research Institute
Beth Israel Hospital
Boston, Massachusetts 02215

The work reviewed here began as an attempt to examine the *in vivo* relevance of a group of cytotoxic T lymphocyte (CTL) clones directed against the then newly described histocompatibility (H) antigen, epidermal alloantigen-1 (Epa-1).[1] Because, as its name implies, Epa-1 is preferentially expressed on epidermal cells (EC), as determined in cell-mediated cytotoxicity assays *in vitro*,[2] we were particularly interested in determining whether Epa-1–specific CTL would attack allogeneic skin cells *in vivo*. Thus, we were gratified to find that relatively small numbers of clone 21-4, one of our most reliable Epa-1–specific clones, evoked full-thickness skin necrosis in an immunologically specific, major histocompatibility complex (MHC)–restricted, dose-dependent fashion upon intradermal inoculation into appropriate allogeneic hosts.[3,4]

The necrotic skin lesions that we initially evoked with clone 21-4,[4] and subsequently with several other Epa-1–specific CTL clones generated entirely *in vivo*,[5] represent an intense form of the "immune lymphocyte transfer reaction." This reaction was first described in 1958 by Brent *et al.*[6] in the guinea pig and then

[a] This work was supported by U.S.P.H.S. Research Grants AI21208, AI23653, AI22674, and AI23990 from the National Institutes of Health.
[c] Present address: Dr. David Steinmuller, 352C Medical Laboratories, The University of Iowa, Iowa City, IA 52242.
[e] Present affiliation: T Cell Sciences, Inc., Cambridge, MA 02139.

subsequently described by them[7] and others[8,9] in the rabbit. Billingham and Streilein's laboratory described this reaction in the hamster,[10-12] rat,[13] mouse,[14,15] and dog.[16] At the time of these reports, the effector cells for transfer reactions were crude suspensions of lymph node cells (LNC) and spleen cells (SC) from animals sensitized with a skin allograft, without any subsequent *in vitro* manipulation to boost alloimmunity. Consequently, reactions elicited with such cells rarely progressed beyond induration. By contrast, in our studies the lesions progressed to full-thickness necrosis. To determine whether this intense reaction reflected our use of cloned or *in vitro*-selected CTL, we tested the ability of cells sensitized in a classic or contemporary fashion to evoke transfer reactions in parallel in two inbred mouse strain combinations. For the classic test, we immunized hosts with

TABLE 1. Classic versus Contemporary Immune Lymphocyte Transfer Reactions

	Reactions Grades[a]										
	C3H/He Anti-CBA				C3H/He Anti-BALB/c						
Day	LNC[b]		CTL[c]		LNC			CTL			
1	1+	1+	3+	3+	1+[d]	1+	1+	3+[d]	3+	3+	3+
2	2+	3+	3+	3+	2+	2+	2+	4+	3+	3+	5+
3	2+	4+	4+	5+	2+	1+	2+	5+	4+	4+	5+
4	2+	4+	5+	5+	1+	1+	1+	5+	4+	5+	5+
5	2+	4+	5+	5+	0	0	0	5+	5+	5+	5+
6	1+	5+	5+	5+	0	0	0	5+	5+	5+	5+
7	4+	5+	5+	5+							
8	5+	5+	5+	5+							
CMC[e]	0		61%		0			91%			

[a] 0, no perceptible response; 1+, barely perceptible swelling; 2+, swelling 3–4 mm in diameter, site soft; 3+, swelling ≥5 mm in diameter, site firm; 4+, large reaction with indurated core; 5+, site ulcerated or necrotic. Grades shown are the highest of three injection sites per host, except for the two hosts that received 2.5×10^7 cells at a single site. Grading was performed daily 1–8 days after injection of LNC or CTL.

[b] Draining lymph node cells (LNC) from skin-grafted hosts (classic test).

[c] *In vitro*-generated cytotoxic T lymphocytes (contemporary test).

[d] These two hosts received 2.5×10^7 cells; all others, 1×10^7 cells per site.

[e] Percent specific lysis of host-strain splenic lymphoblasts by effector LNC or CTL in 3 hr chromium-release cytotoxicity assays at an effector-to-target–cell ratio of 25 : 1.

a single skin allograft and harvested LNC from draining lymph nodes;[14] for the contemporary test, we primed hosts with an intraperitoneal inoculation of 1×10^7 allogeneic SC and then generated CTL from host SC *in vitro* in one-way mixed lymphocyte cultures.[2]

As seen in TABLE 1, the CTL evoked earlier and more intense transfer reactions than the LNC in both the H-2–compatible C3H/He anti-CBA and the H-2–incompatible C3H/He anti-BALB/c strain combinations. The differences in the effectiveness of the CTL and LNC were particularly apparent in the latter combination, where the reactions evoked by the LNC never even became indurated, whereas all the reactions evoked by the CTL developed ulceration. In fact, we were surprised to find that the reactions induced by LNC in the C3H/He anti-CBA strain combination eventually ulcerated, inasmuch as Streilein *et al.*[13-15] did not observe reactions of this intensity in their original descriptions of murine transfer reactions. We used LNC obtained exclusively, however, from lymph nodes, draining the site of the sensitizing skin allograft, whereas Streilein et al. pooled LNC from draining and contralateral nodes (J. W. Streilein, personal communication). Regardless, our observations on the ability of allospecific CTL—particularly those cloned from rejecting allografts and draining lymph nodes[5]—to induce ulcerative transfer reactions demonstrate that allogeneic tissue can be destroyed through the direct mediation of CTL. This finding has clear relevance to the question of which T cells mediate allograft rejection.[17,18]

More recently, we discovered that in certain contexts CTL also can mediate destruction of syngeneic tissue,[19] apparently by initiating events that lead to an intense inflammatory reaction on the part of the host itself. This observation also has a precedent in the early work of Brent et al.[7] They were interested in establishing that transfer reactions were provoked "by a local engagement of sensitized cells with antigen." To do this, they used normal hosts as "neutral soil for the interaction of antigen with sensitized cells," a principle previously established by those investigating the tuberculin reaction in the guinea pig.[7] Thus, Brent et al. mixed sensitized A anti-B lymphoid cells (LC) with B cells and injected the mixtures into A hosts—hosts syngeneic to the effector cells; they reported feeble though significant cutaneous inflammatory reactions. Stronger reactions of this nature were described by Ramseier and Streilein,[11] who injected mixtures of sensitized host-strain LC and allogeneic LC or EC into the skin of irradiated hamsters. Once more, however, the reactions were never scored as necrotic, again presumably reflecting the use of unselected effector cell populations with a low frequency of specifically sensitized CTL.

We first evoked "innocent bystander" reactions with CTL directed against Epa-1, the previously mentioned tissue-restricted, non-H-2 H antigen, well expressed on EC, fibroblasts, and activated macrophages, but poorly expressed, if at all, on LC.[20] Mixtures of Epa-1–specific bulk-culture or cloned CTL of strain C3H/He origin and Epa-1[+] strain CBA EC evoked grossly observable skin ulceration 3–5 days after injection into the skin of syngeneic C3H/He hosts.[19] As seen in FIGURE 1, as few as 5×10^6 cloned CTL, mixed with an equal number of allogeneic EC, evokes an intense inflammatory reaction, with tissue necrosis extending from the panniculus carnosus to the epidermal surface. Clone NR46, which produced the lesion shown in the FIGURE, was derived from CTL generated entirely *in vivo* in EC-impregnated sponge-matrix allografts.[5] These Epa-1–specific clones are Lyt-2[+] and L3T4[−], as determined by flow cytometry[5]—they express the classic phenotype of MHC class I–directed mouse CTL—and they lyse EC *in vitro* in an antigen-specific, H-2–restricted, dose-dependent fashion.[4,5]

The transfer and bystander reactions in the Epa-1 and other CTL–target-cell systems we have studied to date have virtually the same kinetics. But as seen in FIGURE 2, the latter reactions are not as consistent as the former. For example, all of the Epa-1 transfer reactions ulcerated compared to 82% of the bystander reactions. Moreover, in contrast to transfer-reaction ulcers, which often exceed 5 mm in diameter, bystander-reaction ulcers are rarely more than 2 mm across, though the swelling and induration at the site often exceed 10 mm. Nevertheless, the degree of tissue necrosis seen in bystander-reaction lesions (FIG. 1) is remarkable considering that the only source of specific antigen for the CTL are several million admixed target cells. Both transfer and bystander reactions are self-limiting, and the incidence of ulcerative lesions usually does not increase after five days. In the usual experiment, the ulcers heal within ten days after injection. Ulcers, however, may persist up to 15 days if the hosts are supplied with exogenous T-cell growth

FIGURE 1. C3H/He mouse skin at the site of an intradermal injection three days earlier of 5×10^6 C3H/He clone NR46 cytotoxic T lymphocytes (CTL) together with 5×10^6 CBA epidermal cells (1 μm, Epon-embedded, Giemsa-stained sections). **a:** The solid arrow indicates the border between viable epidermis (extending to the right of the arrow) and necrotic epidermis (extending to the left of the arrow). The open arrowhead indicates a hair follicle within the region of necrotic dermis. Two viable hair follicles within the area of unaffected dermis are indicated by solid arrowheads ($\times 100$). **b:** Site of injection of clone NR46 CTL and keratinocytes (some of the latter indicated by solid arrowheads) in the deep dermis. There is extensive inflammation. In addition, a skeletal muscle fiber of the panniculus carnosus exhibits focal necrosis (open arrowhead) as well as a region that appears viable (solid arrow) ($\times 250$).

factor in the form of interleukin-2 (IL-2)–rich culture supernatants (data now shown). The dependence of the reactions on IL-2 is also evident from the finding that 1×10^6 Epa-1–specific CTL, which normally are too few to evoke ulcerative transfer reactions, do so when they are injected suspended in IL-2–rich supernatant fluid instead of conventional medium (data not shown).

FIGURE 2 also illustrates the specificity of the transfer and bystander reactions. Epa-1–specific CTL produce ulcerative transfer reactions in allogeneic CBA but not in syngeneic C3H/He hosts, and the same CTL evoke ulcerative bystander reactions when admixed with allogeneic CBA EC but not syngeneic C3H/He EC. CBA EC targets alone evoked grade 2+ and 3+ reactions that were most intense during the first day after injection. These transient reactions probably resulted from inflammation caused by stratum corneum antigens,[21] because reactions of the same intensity were evoked by syngeneic C3H/He EC, and reactions evoked by injections of CBA LC alone were barely perceptible (data not shown).

Although we first described ulcerative transfer reactions with Epa-1 CTL,[3-5] they are by no means limited to this H-antigen system, but are evoked almost invariably by CTL directed against a variety of non-H-2 and H-2 antigens, as seen in TABLE 2. Surprisingly, bystander reactions with alloreactive CTL are evoked much more readily against non-H-2 than against H-2 antigens: we evoked ulcerative bystander lesions in only one of ten H-2 incompatible compared to four of five H-2–compatible strain combinations. The lack of bystander reactivity of most of

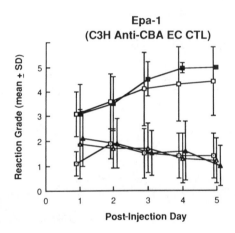

FIGURE 2. Kinetics of immune lymphocyte transfer and bystander reactions in the Epa-1 histocompatibility system. For reaction grades, see TABLE 1. CTL (C3H/He anti-CBA epidermal cells, EC) to CBA hosts (–■–, n = 26); CTL to C3H/He hosts (–⊡–, n = 26); CTL plus CBA EC to C3H/He hosts (–□–, n = 33); CTL plus C3H/He EC to C3H/He hosts (–▲–, n = 8); CBA EC alone to C3H/He hosts (–△–, n = 12).

the H-2–specific CTL was unexpected given that these same CTL invariably produced H-2–specific ulcerative transfer reactions. The defect does not seem to be due to an H-2 Ir gene effect,[22] because the incidence of ulcerative bystander lesions evoked by DBA/2 and BALB/c CTL—both H-2^d—directed against the same C57BL/6 targets was 64% and 0%, respectively. Nor can it simply be due to non-H-2 Ir gene effects:[22] the incidence of ulcerative bystander lesions evoked by DBA/2 CTL directed against C57BL/6, BALB/c, and CBA targets was 64%, 23%, and 0%, respectively (TABLE 2).

We think that mechanisms similar to those activated during intense delayed-type hypersensitivity (DTH) reactions may be responsible for the tissue destruction seen in bystander reactions (see below). If this is so, then the difficulty in evoking ulcerative bystander lesions with H-2–specific CTL may reflect the well-established, though not well-appreciated, fact that non-H-2 antigens are actually

TABLE 2. Incidence of Ulcerative Skin Lesions Evoked by Bulk-Culture CTL in Immune Lymphocyte Transfer and Bystander Reactions in Various Inbred Mouse Strain Combinations

Target Antigen(s)	Strain Combination (Donor Anti-Host)	H-2 Haplotype (Donor/Host)	Transfer Reactions[a]		Bystander Reactions[b]	
			No./No. Tested	Percent	No./No. Tested	Percent
Epa-1	C3H/He anti-CBA[c]	k/k	26/26	100	27/33	82
H-Y	C57BL/6 female anti-C57BL/6 male	b/b	8/9	89	7/11	64
Multiple	C3H/He anti-CBA	k/k	9/10	90	12/16	75
Non-H-2	CBA anti-C3H/He	k/k	9/9	100	2/6	33
	DBA/2 anti-BALB/c	d/d	8/9	89	3/13	23
	BALB/c anti-DBA/2	d/d	4/4	100	0/4	0
H-2	C57BL/6 anti-A/J	b/a	7/7	100	0/8	0
	C57BL/6 anti-BALB/c	b/d	5/5	100	0/10	0
	C57BL/6 anti-DBA/2	b/d	4/4	100	0/4	0
	C57BL/6 anti-CBA	b/k	2/2	100	0/7	0
	BALB/c anti-C57BL/6	d/b	7/7	100	0/12	0
	DBA/2 anti-C57BL/6	d/b	11/11	100	9/14	64
	DBA/2 anti-CBA	d/k	4/4	100	0/4	0
	CBA anti-C57BL/6	k/b	3/3	100	0/6	0
	C3H/He anti-C57BL/6	k/b	4/4	100	0/9	0
	C3H/He anti-BALB/c	k/d	9/9	100	0/4	0
TNP	CBA anti-TNP-CBA[d]	k/k	NA[e]		27/42	64
Influenza A	DBA/2 anti-flu-DBA/2[f]	d/d	NA		18/29	62

[a] Evoked with an intradermal inoculation of 25×10^6 CTL.
[b] Evoked with an intradermal inoculation of a mixture of 25×10^6 CTL and 5×10^6 epidermal or spleen cell targets.
[c] Epidermal cell immunogens and targets; the tests with all other strain combinations involved spleen cell immunogens and targets.
[d] 2,4,6-trinitrophenyl-conjugated syngeneic CBA spleen cells.
[e] Not applicable.
[f] Influenza A virus-infected syngeneic DBA/2 spleen cells.

more effective than H-2 antigens in evoking DTH.[23-27] To explain this, Ohori *et al.*[26] proposed that although H-2 antigens represent a stronger stimulus, they also may provoke "a negative regulatory response, which the minor antigens escape." This could be the induction of suppressor T cells (T_s). It is important to reemphasize, however, that the same H-2–specific CTL consistently evoke ulcerative transfer reactions in H-2–incompatible strain combinations where they fail to evoke bystander reactions. But, in contrast to the latter reactions, where the admixed target cells represent a very limited source of alloantigen, in transfer reactions, where CTL are injected directly into allogeneic skin, alloantigen essentially is unlimited. The latter situation may result in much less pervasive downregulation by T_s. The hypothesis that T_s dominate bystander reactions in H-2 but not in non-H-2 antigen systems is testable, and experiments along these lines currently are in progress. For example, we are determining the effect of combining H-2 and non-H-2 CTL–target-cell mixtures in the same inoculum and whether T_s actually are present in strain combinations where CTL–target-cell mixtures fail to evoke bystander reactions.

The capacity to initiate ulcerative bystander reactions is not limited to alloreactive CTL but also is a characteristic of CTL directed against hapten-modified and virus-infected target cells in totally syngeneic systems. Our observations in these systems, fully described elsewhere,[28] are summarized at the bottom of TABLE 2. Mixtures of specifically sensitized CTL and trinitrophenyl-modified or influenza A virus-infected syngeneic SC evoked necrotic, ulcerative bystander lesions in the skin of syngeneic hosts with a similar incidence to those evoked by alloreactive CTL directed against non-H-2 antigens. Thus, bystander reactions are not peculiar to CTL specific for H antigens but appear to be a general manifestation of CTL–target-cell interactions in non-MHC systems.

A fundamental characteristic of the T-cell receptor is its ability to recognize antigen only when the antigen is associated on the cell surface with a molecule encoded by the MHC,[29] the H-2K^k gene product in the case of Epa-1.[30] Thus, we previously established that the capacity of both bulk-culture and cloned Epa-1–specific CTL to lyse EC *in vitro* and to evoke transfer reactions *in vivo* shows the identical H-2 restriction specificity.[3-5] For example, clone 21-4 CTL evoke ulcerative lesions in the skin of H-2K^k B10.A and B10.BR hosts but not in the skin of H-2K^b B10.MBR and H-2K^d B10.OL hosts,[4] even though all of these H-2 congenic and recombinant strains on the C57BL/10 background are Epa-1$^+$.[31] Therefore, we were fascinated to observe that the capacity of Epa-1–specific CTL to evoke ulcerative bystander lesions is apparently not H-2–restricted.[19] For example, mixtures of H-2^k C3H/He CTL and CBA EC evoke ulcerative lesions in Epa-1$^-$, H-2^b C3H.SW hosts as well as they do in C3H/He hosts, and C3H/He CTL are just as capable of evoking ulcerative bystander reactions in syngeneic hosts when they are injected together with Epa-1$^+$, H-2^b C57BL/6 EC as with Epa-1$^+$, H-2^k CBA EC.[28] In fact, as seen in TABLE 3, the current overall incidence of ulcerative bystander reactions evoked with H-2–incompatible and –compatible target cells and hosts is virtually identical, whereas there is a marked difference in the incidence of transfer reactions in H-2–compatible and –incompatible hosts in the Epa-1 system. The substitution of H-2–incompatible for H-2–compatible hapten-modified target cells did not significantly reduce the incidence of ulcerative bystander reactions in the trinitrophenyl (TNP) system, although the substitution of H-2–incompatible hosts did (TABLE 3). By contrast, although the data are incomplete, it appears that bystander reactions in the influenza A system do follow the rules of MHC restriction (TABLE 3).

Because the associative recognition of antigen with an MHC gene product is such an important feature of the T-cell receptor,[29] we are examining the apparent disregard for this in our bystander-reaction systems very critically. For example, the use of H-2–incompatible target cells and hosts in bystander-reaction systems runs the risk of stimulating local cutaneous host-versus-graft reactions against the foreign H-2 antigens expressed by the CTL or admixed target cells, and we have preliminary evidence that such reactions apparently can give rise to ulcerative skin lesions in certain strain combinations (data not shown). In addition to this relatively trivial explanation of the nonrestricted appearance of bystander reactions, we also are examining the possibility that H-2–compatible antigen-presenting cells (APC) in the host or in the cell inoculum might circumvent MHC restriction by presenting antigen shed from the admixed allogeneic target cells to the CTL. For example, when ulcerative skin lesions are evoked in C3H/He (H-2^k) hosts by mixing C57BL/6 (H-2^b) instead of CBA (H-2^k) EC with C3H/He anti-

TABLE 3. Major Histocompatibility Complex (H-2) Restriction Tests of Transfer and Bystander Reactions

Non-H-2 Antigen System	Reaction System	No. of Ulcerative Skin Lesions/No. Tested (Percent)		
		H-2–Compatible[a] Target Cells and Hosts	H-2–Incompatible[a]	
			Target Cells[b]	Hosts[c]
Epa-1	Transfer	26/26 (100)	NA[d]	2/27 (7)
	Bystander	27/33 (82)	10/14[e] (71)	12/15 (80)
TNP[f]	Bystander	27/42 (64)	6/12[g] (50)	3/13[h] (23)
Flu[i]	Bystander	18/29 (62)	3/13[j] (23)	0/3

[a] In relation to the injected bulk-culture cytotoxic T lymphocytes (CTL).
[b] Hosts H-2–compatible in relation to the CTL.
[c] Admixed target cells (in bystander reactions) H-2–compatible in relation to the CTL.
[d] Not applicable.
[e] .7 > p > .5 versus 27/33 (all p values from chi square tests with Yates' correction).
[f] 2,4,6-trinitrophenyl modified cells.
[g] .7 > p > .5 versus 27/42.
[h] .05 > p > .02 versus 27/42.
[i] Influenza A-virus infected cells.
[j] .05 > p > .02 versus 18/29.

Epa-1 CTL, Epa-1 antigen shed by the C57BL/6 EC might be presented to the CTL by syngeneic APC. The fact that ulcerative bystander reactions in the Epa-1 system are evoked with syngeneic CTL–target-cell mixtures in H-2–incompatible hosts (TABLE 3) indicates that if presentation of Epa-1 by host APC occurs, it occurs in nonrestricted fashion. Ulcerative bystander reactions, however, are usually not evoked in H-2–incompatible hosts in the TNP-hapten and influenza-virus systems (TABLE 3). Moreover, although we have evoked ulcerative bystander reactions with cloned Epa-1–specific CTL, all of the H-2–restriction tests of bystander reactivity in this antigen system were conducted with unpurified, bulk CTL populations that might have included macrophages or other APC. Thus, currently we also cannot dismiss the possibility that H-2–compatible donor APC in bystander-reaction inocula present antigen shed from the admixed allogeneic target cell to the CTL. Van Loveren et al.,[32] however, described a nonadherent

Lyt-1[+] mouse T-cell population that mediates an obligatory early component of DTH in non-MHC restricted fashion. If, as we suspect, mechanisms similar to those evoked in DTH are critical components of bystander reactions, lymphokines released during the initial CTL–target-cell interaction might activate these nonrestricted helper T cells, which in turn might release a cascade of cellular reactions[33] that eventuate in tissue destruction. Currently, we are investigating all of these possible explanations (which unfortunately are not mutually exclusive) of the apparent lack of MHC restriction of bystander reactions in some of the antigen systems we have studied. (Both cloned[4,5] and bulk-culture[30] Epa-1–specific CTL are H-2–restricted in their ability to evoke transfer reactions.)

Regardless of whether they truly defy MHC restriction, bystander reactions, as well as transfer reactions, are quite relevant to the theme of this volume, the biology of cytotoxic T cells and their role in disease. The destruction of allogeneic tissue in transfer reactions is clear evidence of the capacity of CTL to mediate allograft rejection. Thus, our demonstration that CTL, extracted and cloned from skin-cell–impregnated sponge-matrix allografts and from lymph nodes draining the sites of real skin allografts, destroy allogeneic skin[5] fulfills a form of Koch's postulates regarding CTL as mediators of allograft immunity[17] and adds to the growing evidence that CTL with the murine equivalent of the CD8 phenotype effect the acute rejection of allografts by sensitized hosts.[34,35] Our results should not be construed, however, as disputing a role in allograft rejection for other functionally distinct T lymphocytes, such as those with the CD4 (helper) phenotype that lyse target cells expressing class II MHC antigens and that mediate DTH.[17,18]

As already indicated, the tissue destruction seen in transfer reactions appears to result directly from an attack by CTL upon the allogeneic tissue into which they are inoculated: the capacity of CTL to mediate an ulcerative transfer reaction is dose-dependent, antigen-specific, and MHC-restricted.[3-5] By contrast, the destruction of "innocent cells" in bystander reactions appears to be mediated through nonspecific inflammatory cells and factors of host origin activated by the initial antigen-specific CTL–target-cell interaction. The evidence for this is twofold. First, there is no detectable nonspecific cytotoxicity by Epa-1–specific CTL *in vitro* (the only CTL we have tested so far in this regard): the addition of increasing numbers of unlabeled ("cold") Epa-1[+] EC target to cocultures of Epa-1–specific CTL and ^{51}Cr-labeled Epa-1[-] EC targets in reverse competitive ("cold-target") inhibition assays does not increase the release of ^{51}Cr above the background for the latter targets.[28] Second, supernatant fluid concentrated from cocultures of Epa-1–specific CTL and Epa-1[+] targets has no detectable cytotoxic effect on Epa-1[-] targets *in vitro* or when injected into the skin of Epa-1[-] hosts.[28] Although based on negative data, these findings suggest that soluble factors generated by the interaction of anti-Epa-1 CTL and their antigen-specific targets apparently are not directly responsible for the destruction of bystander cells. Thus, we feel that the bystander phenomenon more likely reflects the contribution of host regulatory and inflammatory cells not present in the artificial microenvironment of *in vitro* cell-mediated cytotoxicity assays,[27] which are activated and/or recruited at the site of inoculation of the CTL–target-cell mixture. These cells may in turn mediate nonspecific tissue destruction themselves, as would be expected of activated macrophages and natural killer cells, or indirectly, through the release of factors such as lymphotoxin, tumor necrosis factor, or toxic lysosomal enzymes. We suggest that this entire cascade of events might be triggered by lymphokine(s) released during the initial antigen-specific CTL–target-cell interaction.[32,33] Presumably, the same series of events occurs in transfer reactions, raising the interesting question of the extent to which the nonspecific mechanisms activated in bystander reactions normally contribute to the tissue destruction observed in such settings as allograft rejection, tumor immunity, and viral infections.

The concept that innocent bystander cells and tissue can be damaged as a consequence of an immune response activated by the recognition of a specific antigen, although not widely appreciated, is not new. Thus, Mintz and Silvers'[36] elegant demonstration of the focal rejection of chimeric skin grafts from allophenic (tetraparental) donors composed of mixtures of syngeneic and allogeneic cells is generally regarded as definitive evidence of the specificity of allograft rejection. The evidence of nonspecific rejection in their study, however, is often overlooked: when the majority of the cells in the chimeric grafts were allogeneic, the entire grafts were rejected. In Mintz and Silvers' own words, "nonspecific necrosis can sometimes contribute to the death of the neighboring cells if enough target cells are originally implicated in the rejection."[36]

But the latter findings do not constitute proof that the syngeneic elements of the grafts were rejected in an antigenically nonspecific manner. Dvorak *et al.*[37] showed that the vasculature of split-thickness human skin allografts represents a critical target of the first-set rejection response. One might therefore postulate, as suggested by Dr. Don W. Mason (personal communication), that if the microvasculature of a chimeric graft was predominantly allogeneic, then the apparently "nonspecific" rejection seen in the Mintz and Silvers study[36] might have been caused by an antigenically specific attack on the composite grafts' vasculature. On the other hand, Dvorak *et al.*[37] also showed that the rejection of first-set human skin allografts is preceded by widespread damage of venules and arterioles in both the allograft itself and in the underlying recipient tissue, the latter certainly constituting an antigenetically nonspecific effect of the graft-rejection process. One of us observed very significantly increased contraction (presumably, a manifestation of tissue necrosis) of skin isografts taken from bone marrow chimeras, where the only targets of rejection were allogeneic "passenger leukocytes" (D. Steinmuller, unpublished observations). Similarly, Stuart *et al.*[38] observed unremitting, fatal uremia in bilaterally nephrectomized rats that received kidney isografts from allogeneic bone marrow chimeras.

Innocent bystander reactions are undisputed components of certain destructive graft-versus-host reactions in the skin,[39] kidney,[40] and small intestine[41,42] and of intense DTH reactions to tuberculin and purified proteins.[43,44] For example, Holoshitz *et al.*[44] reported that injections of T-cell lines specifically reactive with myelin basic protein or with purified-protein derivative evoked bystander encephalitis and arthritis, respectively, in mice. Niederkorn *et al.* observed that certain genetic disparities,[45] and certain tumors,[46] allogeneic or syngeneic tumors, respectively, transplanted to the anterior chamber of the mouse eye were rejected with minimal nonspecific damage to the globe; with others, acute inflammatory reactions produced massive bystander destruction of ocular tissue, resulting in blindness. The catastrophic, nonspecific form of rejection seemed to occur only when DTH was a prominent part of the immune response.[46] Bystander damage also can account for the rejection of mixtures of two syngeneic tumors, only one of which elicits a strong cell-mediated immune response.[47] In this model system, morphologic analysis indicates that rejection depends on bystander damage to the composite tumors' common vasculature.[47]

Our observation that ulcerative bystander reactions frequently occur when CTL interact with virus-infected target cells in syngeneic hosts also has clear implications for the histopathology of viral infections. For example, the widespread and frequently life-threatening results of cytomegalovirus (CMV) infection in transplant patients are well-known.[48] Patients with the lethal CMV syndrome develop gastrointestinal hemorrhages, and CMV can be isolated from the sites of ulceration producing the hemorrhages. It is generally thought that a cytolytic effect of the virus itself causes the ulceration.[48] Our findings suggest, however, that intense inflammatory reactions triggered when the host's own CTL destroy virus-infected autochthonous cells may contribute to the tissue damage.

SUMMARY

In vitro- and *in vivo*-generated cytotoxic T lymphocytes (CTL) specific for major and minor histocompatibility antigens evoked antigen-specific full-thickness skin necrosis when injected intradermally into allogeneic mice in a variety of strain combinations. In addition, CTL–target-cell mixtures injected intradermally into hosts syngeneic to the CTL also evoked destruction of host tissue. These "innocent bystander" reactions were evoked with alloreactive CTL as well as with CTL directed against hapten (TNP)-modified and virus (influenza A)-infected target cells. Unlike the direct reactions, the bystander reactions in histocompatibility-antigen systems occurred in spite of H-2 incompatibility of the CTL, admixed target cells, and the hosts. One explanation for these results, currently under investigation, is that some bystander reactions may occur without MHC restriction. In aggregate, our findings indicate that nonspecific as well as antigen-specific reactions initiated by CTL–target-cell interactions may contribute to tissue destruction in allograft rejection, in severe forms of delayed-type hypersensitivity, and in certain viral infections.

ACKNOWLEDGMENTS

We are grateful to Kathryn A. Aker, James J. Camilleri, Laura B. Campolito, Ane K. Gardner, and Gina M. Toth for technical assistance and to Marjorie M. Fisher and Terry P. Calhoun for help in preparing the manuscript.

REFERENCES

1. TYLER, J. D. & D. STEINMULLER. 1982. Establishment of cytolytic T lymphocyte clones to epidermal alloantigen Epa-1. Transplantation 34: 140–143.
2. TYLER, J. D. & D. STEINMULLER. 1981. Cell-mediated cytotoxicity to non-MHC alloantigens on mouse epidermal cells. III. Epidermal-cell specific cytotoxic T lymphocytes. J. Immunol. 126: 1759–1763.
3. TYLER, J. D., D. STEINMULLER, S. J. GALLI & K. G. WADDICK. 1983. Allospecific graft-versus-host lesions mediated in MHC-restricted fashion by cloned cytolytic T lymphocytes. Transplant. Proc. 15: 1441–1445.
4. TYLER, J. D., S. J. GALLI, M. E. SNIDER, A. M. DVORAK & D. STEINMULLER. 1984. Cloned Lyt-2+ cytolytic T lymphocytes destroy allogeneic tissue *in vivo*. J. Exp. Med. 159: 234–243.
5. SNIDER, M. E., L. ARMSTRONG, J. L. HUDSON & D. STEINMULLER. 1986. *In vitro* and *in vivo* cytotoxicity of T cells cloned from rejecting allografts. Transplantation 42: 171–177.
6. BRENT, L., J. BROWN & P. B. MEDAWAR. 1958. Skin transplantation immunity in relation to hypersensitivity. Lancet 2: 562–564.

7. BRENT, L., J. BROWN & P. B. MEDAWAR. 1962. Quantitative studies on tissue transplantation immunity. VI. Hypersensitivity reactions associated with the rejection of homografts. Proc. R. Soc. London, Series B. **156:** 187–209.
8. MANNICK, J. A. & R. H. EGDAHL. 1962. Transformation of nonimmune lymph nodes cells to state of transplantation immunity by RNA. Ann. Surg. **156:** 156–366.
9. DVORAK, H. F., A. B. T. U. KOSUNEN & B. H. WAKSMAN. 1963. The "transfer reaction" in the rabbit. Lab. Invest. **12:** 58–68.
10. RAMSEIER, H. & R. E. BILLINGHAM. 1964. Delayed hypersensitivity reactions and transplantation immunity in Syrian hamsters. Ann. N.Y. Acad. Sci. **120:** 379–392.
11. RAMSEIER, H. & J. W. STREILEIN. 1965. Homograft sensitivity reactions in irradiated hamsters. Lancet **1:** 622–624.
12. RAMSEIER, H. & R. E. BILLINGHAM. 1966. Studies on delayed cutaneous inflammatory reactions elicited by inoculation of homologous cells into hamsters' skin. J. Exp. Med. **123:** 629–656.
13. STREILEIN, J. W. & R. E. BILLINGHAM. 1967. Cutaneous hypersensitivity reactions to cellular isoantigens in rats. J. Exp. Med. **126:** 455–473.
14. STREILEIN, J. W. & R. E. BILLINGHAM. 1970. An analysis of the genetic requirements for delayed cutaneous hypersensitivity reactions to transplantation antigens in mice. J. Exp. Med. **131:** 409–427.
15. STREILEIN, J. W., I. ZEISS & D. STEINMULLER. 1970. Studies on immune lymphocyte transfer reactions in murine homologous cell chimeras. Transplantation **10:** 403–410.
16. STREILEIN, J. W. & C. F. BARKER. 1966. Transplantation immunity and delayed cutaneous hypersensitivity reactions in dogs. J. Immunol. **98:** 601–608.
17. STEINMULLER, D. 1985. Which T cells mediate allograft rejection? Transplantation **40:** 229–233.
18. MASON, D. W. & P. J. MORRIS. 1986. Effector mechanisms in allograft rejection. Annu. Rev. Immunol. **4:** 119–45.
19. SNIDER, M. E. & D. STEINMULLER. 1987. Nonspecific tissue destruction as a consequence of cytotoxic T lymphocyte interaction with antigen-specific target cells. Transplant. Proc. **19:** 421–423.
20. BURLINGHAM, W. J., M. E. SNIDER, J. D. TYLER & D. STEINMULLER. 1984. Lysis of mouse macrophages, fibroblasts and epidermal cells by epidermal alloantigen-specific CTL. Effect of culture and inflammatory agents on Epa-1 expression. Cell. Immunol. **87:** 553–565.
21. MARX, R., K. DALZIEL & P. J. DYKES. 1984. Inflammation caused by intracutaneous implantation of stratum corneum. Br. J. Dermatol. **27,** Suppl. 3: 109–113.
22. SIMPSON, E. 1984. H-2 and non-H-2 Ir genes. Ann. Immunol. **135C:** 410–413.
23. KON, N. D. & P. A. KLEIN. 1976. Measurement of H-2 and non-H-2 antigens in the mouse with the footpad swelling test. J. Immunol. **117:** 413–415.
24. SMITH, F. I. & J. F. A. P. MILLER. 1979. Delayed-type hypersensitivity to allogeneic cells in mice. III. Sensitivity to cell-surface antigens coded by the major histocompatibility complex and by other genes. J. Exp. Med. **150:** 965–976.
25. LA ROSA, G. & D. W. TALMAGE. 1985. Synergism between minor and major histocompatibility antigens in the rejection of cultured allografts. Transplantation **39:** 480–485.
26. OHORI, P., S. NADAL & J. F. BURDICK. 1983. Strong stimulation of two aspects of delayed-type hypersensitivity by minor antigens. Transplantation **36:** 581–583.
27. BURDICK, J. F. 1986. Strong cellular immune response induced *in vivo* against minor antigens in the mouse. Immunology **58:** 615–620.
28. STEINMULLER, D., M. E. SNIDER, R. L. NOBLE, H. F. MAASSAB & S. J. GALLI. 1987. Nonspecific tissue destruction resulting from cytotoxic T cell-target cell interactions. Manuscript in preparation.
29. ROBERTSON, M. 1986. T-cell receptor: gamma gene product surfaces. Nature (London) **322:** 110–111.
30. STEINMULLER, D., J. D. TYLER & C. S. DAVID. 1981. Cell-mediated cytotoxicity to non-MHC alloantigens on mouse epidermal cells. I. H-2 restricted reactions among strains sharing the H-2^k haplotype. J. Immunol. **126:** 1747–1753.

31. STEINMULLER, D., J. D. TYLER & A. R. ZINSMEISTER. 1985. Strain distribution of the new tissue-restricted alloantigen Epa-1. Transplant. Proc. **17:** 749–753.
32. VAN LOVEREN, H., K. KATO, R. MEADE, R. GREEN, M. HOROWITZ, W. PTAK & P. W. ASKENASE. 1984. Characterization of two different Ly-1$^+$ T cell populations that mediate delayed-type hypersensitivity. J. Immunol. **133:** 4202–4211.
33. BRETSCHER, P. A. 1986. A cascade of T-T interactions, mediated by the linked recognition of antigen, in the induction of T cells able to help delayed-type hypersensitivity responses. J. Immunol. **137:** 3726–3735.
34. COBBOLD, S. & H. WALDMANN. 1986. Skin allograft rejection by L3/T4$^+$ and Lyt-2$^+$ T cell subsets. Transplantation **41:** 634–639.
35. GURLEY, K. E., B. M. HALL & S. E. DORSCH. 1986. "The factor of immunization" in allograft rejection: carried by cytotoxic T cells, not helper-inducer T cells. Transplant. Proc. **18:** 307–309.
36. MINTZ, B. & W. K. SILVERS. 1970. Histocompatibility antigens on melanoblasts and hair follicle cells. Cell-localized homograft rejection in allophenic skin grafts. Transplantation **9:** 497–505.
37. DVORAK, H. F., M. C. MIHM, A. M. DVORAK, B. A. BARNES, E. J. MANSEAU & S. J. GALLI. 1979. Rejection of first-set skin allografts in man. The microvasculature is the critical target of the immune response. J. Exp. Med. **150:** 322–337.
38. STUART, F. P., E. BASTIEN, A. HOLTER, F. W. FITCH & W. L. ELKINS. 1971. Role of passenger leukocytes in the rejection of renal allografts. Transplant. Proc. **3:** 461–464.
39. STREILEIN, J. W. 1972. Pathologic lesions of GVH disease in hamsters: Antigenic target versus "innocent bystander." Prog. Exp. Tumor Res. **16:** 396–408.
40. ELKINS, W. L. & R. D. GUTTMANN. 1968. Pathogenesis of a local graft versus host reaction: immunogenicity of circulating host leukocytes. Science **159:** 1250–1251.
41. ELSON, C. O., R. W. REILLY & I. H. ROSENBERG. 1977. Small intestinal injury in the graft versus host reaction: an innocent bystander phenomenon. Gastroenterology **72:** 886–889.
42. MOWAT, A. McI. 1986. Evidence that Ia$^+$ bone-marrow-derived cells are the stimulus for the intestinal phase of the murine graft-versus-host reaction. Transplantation **42:** 141–143.
43. WAKSMAN, BYRON H. 1962. Tissue damage in the "delayed" (cellular) type of hypersensitivity. *In* Mechanisms of Cell and Tissue Damage Produced by Immune Reactions (Second International Symposium on Immunopathology). B. Schwabe, Ed.: 154–166. Grune & Stratton. New York.
44. HOLOSHITZ, J., Y. NAPARSTEK, A. BEN-NUN, P. MARQUARDT & I. R. COHEN. 1984. T lymphocyte lines induce autoimmune encephalomyelitis, delayed hypersensitivity and bystander encephalitis or arthritis. Eur. J. Immunol. **14:** 729–734.
45. NIEDERKORN, J. Y., J. A. SHADDUCK & J. W. STREILEIN. 1981. Immunogenetic basis of immunologic privilege in the anterior chamber of the eye. Immunogenetics **13:** 227–236.
46. KNISELY, T. L., M. W. LUCKENBACH, B. J. FISCHER & J. Y. NIEDERKORN. 1987. Destructive and nondestructive patterns of immune rejection of syngeneic intraocular tumors. J. Immunol. **138:** 4515–4523.
47. GALLI, S. J., R. C. BAST JR., B. S. BAST, T. ISOMURA, B. ZBAR, H. J. RAPP & H. F. DVORAK. 1982. Bystander suppression of tumor growth: Evidence that specific targets and bystanders are damaged by injury to a common microvasculature. J. Immunol. **129:** 1790–1799.
48. RUBIN, R. H. & N. E. TOLKOFF-RUBIN. 1984. The problem of cytomegalovirus infection in transplantation. Prog. Transplant. **1:** 89–114.

Influence of Cyclosporine on CTL Behavior *in Vitro* and *in Vivo*[a]

C. G. OROSZ,[b,c] N. E. ZINN,[b] P. W. ADAMS,[b]
M. B. WIDMER,[d] AND R. M. FERGUSON[b]

[b]*Therapeutic Immunology Laboratories*
Department of Surgery
College of Medicine
The Ohio State University
Columbus, Ohio 43210

[c]*Comprehensive Cancer Care Center*
The Ohio State University
Columbus, Ohio 43210

[d]*Immunex Corporation*
51 University Street
Seattle, Washington 98101

INTRODUCTION

Historically, cytolytic T lymphocytes (CTL) have been promoted as an integral component of organ allograft rejection. *In vitro* studies have shown that the functional activation of CTL by allogeneic cells is a complex process that requires two initiating signals: contact with appropriate alloantigens and contact with appropriate lymphokines. These lymphokines can be produced either by the CTL themselves,[1] or by other antigen-activated T lymphocytes.[2,3]

Many immunosuppressive drugs used clinically to control allograft rejection have been shown to interfere *in vitro* with normal T-cell behavior. Among these drugs is the widely used immunosuppressant, cyclosporine (CsA), which can interfere with lymphokine production and the development of cytolytic activity in mixed lymphocyte cultures.[4–8] Because the suppressive effects of CsA can be reversed if exogenous lymphokines are added to CsA-suppressed mixed lymphocyte cultures (MLC),[4,5] and because CsA does not interfere with the expression of preformed CTL activity,[7,8] it is generally believed that CsA influences CTL only indirectly, by blocking the production of lymphokines requisite for CTL maturation. Our investigations in several different experimental systems suggest that CsA may also have direct effects on CTL behavior *in vitro,* and that CsA can influence *in vivo* CTL behavior in ways that were not predicted by previous *in vitro* studies.

[a] This work was supported in part by an Ohio State University Seed Grant, by a Grant from the Kidney Foundation of Central Ohio, by a Grant from the Department of Surgery Medical Research and Development Fund, by PHS Grant number P30 CA 16058 13 awarded by the National Cancer Institute, DHHS, and by NIH Grants AI20851 and AI34774.

CsA EFFECTS IN LIMITING-DILUTION MICROCULTURES

Limiting dilution analysis has been used to quantitate CTL populations in both mouse and humans.[9-11] We designed limiting-dilution analysis (LDA) studies to monitor donor-specific CTL populations in the peripheral blood of renal allograft recipients on CsA therapy. In initial experiments, we studied the influence of CsA on CTL development in limiting-dilution microcultures, primarily to evaluate the effects of CsA that may be inadvertently carried over from the patient into the experimental system. We found that addition of CsA to limiting-dilution microcultures severely depresses CTL frequency estimates. This was unexpected, inasmuch as limiting-dilution microcultures are routinely supplemented with excess exogenous interleukin 2 (IL-2), which is thought to be necessary and sufficient for CTL generation under these culture conditions. If CsA affects CTL development solely by eliminating the endogenous production of requisite lymphokines, then CTL behavior in limiting-dilution microcultures should be insensitive to the presence of CsA.

For these studies, various dilutions of Ficoll-Hypaque purified human peripheral blood mononuclear cells (PBMC) were cocultured in replicate microwells with a fixed number of irradiated (2000 R) allogeneic PBMC plus 10 units/ml of IL-2 (Cellular Products, Inc., Buffalo, NY). After seven days of incubation, the microwells were tested for alloreactive CTL activity by ^{51}Cr release, and the pattern of cytolytic activity was analyzed for CTL frequency in the initial PBMC population by the method of chi square minimization.[12] As shown in TABLE 1, the presence of 1–1000 ng/ml CsA in the limiting-dilution microcultures during incubation decreases subsequent CTL frequency estimates by 30 to 90 percent. Addition of the CsA at the end of the incubation period has little effect on the CTL frequency estimates (data not shown). In subsequent experiments, we observed that supplementation with additional human recombinant IL-2 (up to 600 units/ml), human recombinant gamma-interferon (IFN) (up to 500 units/ml), or various concentrations of human MLC supernatants (used as a source of multiple lympho-

TABLE 1. Influence of CsA on Estimates of Human Alloantigen-Reactive CTL Frequency[a]

	CO Anti-JG			DW Anti-PN		
CsA (ng/ml)	No. of CTL per 10^6 PBMC	95% Confidence Range	Percent Residual Response	No. of CTL per 10^6 PBMC	95% Confidence Range	Percent Residual Response
none	351	243–459	100	101	77–126	100
1000	11	4–19	3	7	2–12	7
100	64	32–97	18	39	23–54	39
10	95	71–119	27	64	46–82	63
1	224	182–267	64	72	51–93	71

[a] Various concentrations of CsA were included in limiting-dilution microcultures in these independent, representative experiments. The cytolytic activity that subsequently developed was analyzed for apparent CTL frequency and 95% confidence limits by the method of Chi square minimization. These frequency values have been mathematically converted to the number of CTL/10^6 PBMC, and the percent of control frequency estimate has been provided: for reference, 351 CTL/10^6 PBMC corresponds to a T-cell frequency of 1 cell/2846 PBMC, and 11 CTL/10^6 PBMC corresponds to 1 cell/86,809 PBMC. Shown are the results of two separate LDA experiments using PBMC from donor CO versus donor JG, and from donor DW versus donor PN.

TABLE 2. Influence of CsA on Frequency Estimates of Human Alloreactive CTL and Proliferating Cells[a]

		DS Anti-PN			.	NZ Anti-LT		
CsA (ng/ml)	Anal-ysis	No. of CTL per 10^6 PBMC	95% Confidence Range	Percent Control Response		No. of CTL per 10^6 PBMC	95% Confidence Range	Percent Control Response
none	CTL	169	133–240	—		52	29–76	—
1000	CTL	23	9–37	13.6		<3	—	<5.0
none	PC	1724	1218–2227	—		131	87–174	—
1000	PC	1680	1147–2222	97.4		130	88–172	99.2

[a] CsA was included in limiting-dilution microcultures in these independent, representative experiments. Parallel microcultures were tested for cytolytic activity (CTL) and for [³H]thymidine incorporation (PC). The results were analyzed for apparent CTL and PC frequency by the method of Chi square minimization. These frequencies were mathematically converted to the number of CTL per 10^6 PBMC, and the percent of control frequency estimate has been provided. Shown are the results of two separate LDA experiments using PBMC from donor DS versus donor PN, and from donor NZ versus donor LT.

kine) do not overcome the suppressive activity of CsA in limiting-dilution microcultures (data not shown). In general, we have found no evidence for a limiting cytokine in this experimental system.

Normally, a dense halo of lymphocytes develops in functionally positive (cytolytic) limiting-dilution microwells, and lack of detectable function frequently correlates with lack of cell growth. Prominent cell growth, however, is observed in CsA-supplemented, noncytolytic limiting-dilution microcultures. This is demonstrated in TABLE 2. Parallel limiting-dilution microcultures were used to identify CTL, as detected by ⁵¹Cr release, or to identify proliferating cells (PC), as detected by [³H]thymidine incorporation. The patterns of cytolysis and thymidine incorporation were analyzed to yield estimates of CTL and PC frequencies. CsA decreased CTL frequency estimates by approximately 90%, whereas PC frequency estimates were not significantly affected by CsA. If CsA is influencing CTL by interfering with IL-2 receptor expression (a controversial issue, see references 13–15), then little proliferation would have been expected in the presence of CsA.

One interpretation of this data is that CsA can block terminal CTL differentiation, but not CTL clonal expansion, under limiting-dilution culture conditions. This would suggest that the signaling systems for proliferation and cytolytic function in CTL are separable and differentially sensitive to CsA. This hypothesis would also imply that CsA has an inhibitory effect on CTL, which is independent of helper T-cell dysfunction.

CsA EFFECTS ON CLONED CTL BEHAVIOR

More subtle aspects of CsA's suppressive influence on CTL behavior were revealed during separate studies that involved cloned murine CTL.[16] Characteristically, CTL clones can be made to proliferate by contact with IL-2. Additional proliferation is observed if IL-2 is accompanied by appropriate alloantigen, although alloantigen alone is a poor proliferative stimulus, except for those CTL that can secrete IL-2.[1] FIGURE 1 illustrates the effect of CsA on the alloantigen-

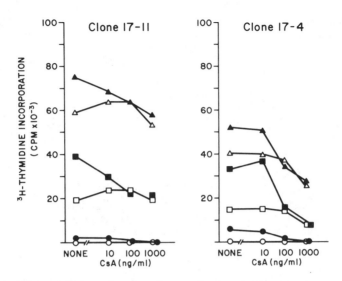

FIGURE 1. Effect of CsA on the alloantigen and/or lymphokine-driven proliferation of murine CTL clones. Clone 17-4 and clone 17-11 cells (1×10^4/well) were incubated in media (○), 2% secondary MLC supernate (□), or 8% secondary MLC supernate (△) in the absence (open symbols) or presence of 1×10^6 DBA/2 splenocytes (solid symbols) plus various concentrations of CsA. Cultures were incubated for 72 hours and harvested after a 6 hour terminal pulse with [^{3}H]thymidine.

driven and/or lymphokine-driven proliferation of murine CTL clones. The two representative clones, 17-11 and 17-4, were derived from C57BL/6 anti-DBA/2 MLCs. Both are cytolytic for H-2^d target cells, but only one (17-4) can secrete IL-2.

Both clones proliferate in a dose-dependent manner when cultured with secondary MLC supernatant, a potent source of exogenous lymphokines. This proliferation was influenced only slightly by CsA, even at concentrations as high as 1000 ng/ml. By contrast, antigen-driven proliferation of these clones was quite sensitive to suppression by CsA. For CTL clones, the influence of alloantigen is best visualized as the synergistic proliferation observed in the presence of both alloantigen and lymphokine. CsA at concentrations of 100 ng/ml completely blocked the component of proliferation that was induced by alloantigen and left the lymphokine-dependent component intact. In FIGURE 1, this phenomenon has been illustrated using [^{3}H]thymidine as an index of clone function. Virtually identical results are obtained when cytolytic activity, rather than [^{3}H]thymidine incorporation, is monitored (data not shown). This underscores the effects of CsA on cloned CTL proliferation, because cytolytic activity observed under these experimental conditions is directly proportional to the size of the CTL population in each microculture.

In general, we have observed that lymphokine-driven proliferation of CTL clones continues in the presence of CsA, but that alloantigen does not synergistically increase lymphokine-driven proliferation if CsA is present.

CsA EFFECT ON LYMPHOCYTE MOBILIZATION *IN VIVO*

In a third series of studies, we investigated the influence of CsA on CTL behavior *in vivo*. These studies used sponge-matrix allografts[17] to induce alloimmunity and to localize alloactivated CTL *in vivo*. In this experimental model, mice are implanted subcutaneously with small polyurethane sponges, which are injected with three million allogeneic splenocytes prior to wound closure. These mice develop intensive cellular and humoral alloimmunity that peaks approximately 10 days after implantation.[17–19] Cellular alloimmunity is evidenced by the accumulation of active, alloreactive CTL in the sponge allografts.[17–19] The advantage of this experimental model is that the sponges can be explanted, and sponge-infiltrating cells can be readily retrieved for further study.

In initial experiments, we treated sponge-allograft recipients daily with CsA and found that donor alloantigen-specific CTL activity (as detected by ^{51}Cr-release assay) of the sponge infiltrating cells was markedly diminished (data not shown). This effect may have resulted from diminished CTL activation, or from diminished CTL accumulation at a graft site. When sponge-allograft infiltrates were subjected to LDA, we found that the number of donor alloantigen-reactive CTL was markedly reduced by CsA in a dose-dependent manner (TABLE 3). Hence, CsA interferes with the accumulation of donor alloantigen-reactive CTL in sponge-matrix allografts. We observed that optimal impairment of CTL accumulation required the daily delivery of approximately 30 mg/kg directly to the graft site. If CsA is delivered to a distant subcutaneous site, 50–70 mg/kg/day are necessary to achieve similar levels of immunosuppression (see TABLE 4). It is interesting to note that CsA impairs accumulation of donor-reactive CTL, but has little detectable effect on the number of cells that infiltrate the graft, or on the percentage of T cells in the graft infiltrate (TABLE 3).

Because peripheral blood is the apparent source of CTL that enter the sponge allografts, we next determined if CsA clears donor-reactive cells from the peripheral blood, making them unavailable to the graft site. To do this, we used LDA to quantitate donor-reactive CTL in peripheral blood and at the graft site in CsA-

TABLE 3. Effect of CsA on Accumulation of Alloreactive CTL in Sponge Matrix Allografts[a]

Daily CsA (ng/ml)	Mean Viable Recovery	Mean Percent of Thy-1.2+ Cells	Mean No. of CTL per Graft	No. of CTL of Percent Control
none	4.3 ± 0.1	25.6 ± 3.5	2483 ± 1232	100
600	3.9 ± 1.0	19.0 ± 2.4	1353 ± 265	54
6,000	3.1 ± 1.3	22.3 ± 12.8	1122 ± 387	45
60,000	4.6 ± 1.8	16.7 ± 3.6	415 ± 155	17
600,000	3.0 ± 0.1	19.4 ± 2.7	103 ± 25	4

[a] C57BL/6 mice (3 per group) were implanted with DBA/2 sponge allografts. These mice were treated daily with subsponge injections of 30 mg/kg CsA. After ten days, the sponges were removed, and the infiltrating cells were counted, analyzed for percent Thy-1.2+ cells by immunofluorescence and visual microscopy, and analyzed for frequency of DBA/2-reactive CTL by limiting-dilution analysis (LDA). These frequencies have been mathematically converted to mean number of CTL/sponge allograft, based on frequency and viable cell recovery.

treated sponge-allograft recipients. As shown in TABLE 4, CsA treatment effectively diminished donor-reactive CTL accumulation at the graft site, but had little detectable influence on the number of donor-reactive CTL in the peripheral blood. Consequently, it appeared that the donor-reactive CTL were available, but were unable to enter the graft site under the influence of CsA. These data suggest that CsA may influence the behavior of the vascular barrier at the graft site, or may affect donor-reactive lymphocytes in such a way as to make them inefficient at tissue infiltration. In any event, it appears that CsA has an effect on *in vivo* CTL behavior that was not predicted on the basis of *in vitro* experimental data.

CONCLUSIONS

It is widely acknowledged that CsA has profound inhibitory effects on helper T-cell function, but that CsA influences cytolytic T cells only indirectly, by de-

TABLE 4. Effect of CsA on Distribution of Alloreactive CTL in Recipients of Sponge-Matrix Allografts[a]

Cell Source	Therapy	CTL Reciprocal Frequency	No. of CTL per 10^6 Cells	Percent Control Response
Sponge	PBS	3,605	277	100
	CsA subsponge	<385,529	<3	<1
	CsA subcutaneous	40,820	24	8
PBL	PBS	4,799	208	100
	CsA subsponge	3,758	266	127
	CsA subcutaneous	5,569	179	86

[a] C57BL/6 mice (3 per group) were implanted with DBA/2 sponge allografts, and treated with daily injections of 30 mg/kg CsA subsponge, an equal volume of CsA diluent subsponge (phosphate-buffered saline, PBS), and 50 mg/kg CsA at a distant subcutaneous site. After 10 days, sponge infiltrating cells and red blood cell-free peripheral blood lymphocytes (PBL) were collected and pooled from similarly treated mice. These pooled cell populations were tested for frequency of DBA/2-reactive CTL by LDA, and the CTL frequencies were mathematically converted to the number of CTL/10^6 cells.

priving them of the helper T lymphocyte products that are required for CTL activation. Indeed, it has been established that CsA has little or no effect on the expression of CTL activity once it has been developed.[7,8] The development of cytolytic activity, however, is but one of several antigen-driven functions displayed by CTL. Other antigen-driven functions include lymphokine secretion[20] and proliferation.

We have shown with CTL clones that CsA can influence CTL proliferation in a manner that is independent of lymphokine availability. Hence, cloned CTL continue to respond to the proliferative stimulus delivered by lymphokines in the presence of CsA, but they fail to respond to the synergistic proliferative stimuli delivered by alloantigen plus lymphokine when CsA is present. These data suggest that the lymphokine-associated and alloantigen-associated components of CTL proliferation are differentially sensitive to CsA. This, in turn, suggests that there is a difference in the metabolic pathways by which these two proliferative stimuli are transmitted through CTL.

It has been shown that CTL secrete a variety of lymphokines, including gamma-IFN,[20] and sometimes IL-2.[1] Herold *et al.*[21] have shown that murine CTL clones with the capacity for gamma-IFN production lose this ability in the presence of CsA, even though they continue to express cytolytic function. In those experiments, a noncellular stimulus was used to initiate CTL function, so the inhibitory effect of CsA resulted from a direct effect of CsA on the CTL, and not from a secondary effect of CsA through a contaminating cell population.

Taken together, these data indicate that active CTL are not insensitive to the immunosuppressive effects of CsA. Rather, only selected CTL functional activities (expression of lytic activity, lymphokine-driven proliferation) are CsA-resistant, whereas other functional activities (lymphokine secretion, alloantigen-driven proliferation) are CsA-sensitive.

There is also some evidence that the acquisition of cytolytic activity by inactive CTL precursors (CTLp) may be sensitive to suppression by CsA. We have shown that human CTLp fail to develop cytolytic activity in limiting-dilution microcultures (TABLE 3). Cytolytic activity remains absent in these microcultures, even if they are supplemented with large concentrations of a variety of different lymphokines known to promote CTL maturation. Others have shown a similar effect of CsA on the development of cytolytic activity in murine limiting-dilution microcultures.[22] Unlike the murine studies, we have found that fresh human PBMC and human primary MLC cells are similarly sensitive to the suppressive effects of CsA in limiting-dilution microcultures (data not shown). These data suggest that CsA may act by impairing the function of CTL precursors, as well as active CTL in a manner that is independent of helper T lymphocyte dysfunction.

During these studies, we observed that CsA-supplemented limiting-dilution microcultures continue to develop proliferative responses, although they fail to develop cytolytic activity. If it is assumed that antigen-reactive CTL are the predominant cell type that proliferates in these microcultures, then it follows that CsA selectively impairs CTL maturation, but spares CTL proliferation triggered by alloantigen plus lymphokine. In turn, this would suggest that the metabolic pathways by which alloantigen plus lymphokine cause CTL proliferation versus CTL maturation may be different. It is probable, however, that other non-CTL cell populations proliferate in limiting-dilution microcultures, and it is not clear if the CTL subpopulation is sufficiently large to detectably alter proliferative cell frequencies, even if the entire alloreactive CTL subpopulation fails to proliferate under the influence of CsA.

Our experimental observations with LDA might also be explained if CsA interfered with the antigen-driven acquisition of IL-2 receptors by human PBMC. The effect of CsA on the alloantigen-induced acquisition of IL-2 receptors by human PBMC remains a matter of debate.[13-15] It would be surprising, however, to find that the prominent proliferative response in CsA-supplemented limiting-dilution microcultures occurred independently of IL-2/IL-2 receptor interactions. Clearly, the effects of CsA on antigen-induced CTL and CTLp function require additional study.

Finally, we have observed that CsA can cause aberrant mobilization of CTL in alloimmunized mice. For example, treatment of sponge-allograft recipients with CsA minimizes the accumulation of allograft-reactive CTL at the graft site. Others have observed an impaired accumulation of activated T cells at graft sites in other experimental models of allograft rejection.[23,24] The mechanism by which CsA influences CTL accumulation at the graft site remains a matter of speculation. It is possible that CsA blocks lymphokine secretion at the graft site. The lymphokine would normally act as a chemoattractant,[25] and would alert the vascular barrier to allow interstitial accumulation of lymphoid cells.[26,27] It is equally possible that CsA blocks alloantigen-driven CTL activation and proliferation in draining lymph nodes, thus depriving graft sites of activated, donor-reactive CTL. Regardless of the mechanism, it is clear that CsA has unanticipated effects on alloantigen-driven CTL mobilization *in vivo.*

In general, it is erroneous to consider that CTL are not susceptible to suppression by CsA. Although CTL-mediated cytolytic activity, once it has been generated, seems relatively insensitive to CsA, CTL appear to be as sensitive to CsA as nonlytic helper T cells with respect to other aspects of CTL behavior, such as alloantigen-induced lymphokine secretion and alloantigen-induced proliferation. Furthermore, aspects of CTL behavior that are manifest *in vivo,* but that are not monitored *in vitro,* such as lymphocyte compartmentalization and mobilization, also appear to be sensitive to CsA.

ACKNOWLEDGMENTS

We wish to thank Ms. Cindy Narcross for her secretarial assistance in the preparation of this manuscript. This is paper #35 from the Therapeutic Immunology Laboratories.

REFERENCES

1. WIDMER, M. & F. BACH. 1981. Nature **294:** 750–752.
2. CANTOR, H. & E. BOYSE. 1975. J. Exp. Med. **141:** 1390–1399.
3. GLASEBROOK, A. & F. FITCH. 1980. J. Exp. Med. **151:** 876–895.
4. BUNJES, D., C. HARDT, H. ROLLINGHOFF & H. WAGNER. 1981. Eur. J. Immunol. **11:** 657–661.
5. HESS, A., P. TUTSCHKA & G. SANTOS. 1982. J. Immunol. **128:** 355–359.
6. HESS, A., P. TUTSCHKA, Z. PU & G. SANTOS. 1982. J. Immunol. **128:** 360–367.
7. PALACIOS, R. 1981. Cell. Immunol. **61:** 453–462.
8. WANG, B., E. HEACOCK, K. COLLINS, I. HUTCHINSON, N. TILNEY & J. MANNICK. 1981. J. Immunol. **127:** 89–93.
9. RYSER, J. E. & H. MACDONALD. 1979. J. Immunol. **122:** 1691–1696.
10. BRYAN, D., C. PINTO & T. FULLER. 1983. Human Immunol. **6:** 876–895.
11. KABELITZ, D., W. R. HERZOG, B. ZANKER & H. WAGNER. 1985. Scand. J. Immunol. **22:** 329–335.
12. TASWELL, C. 1981. J. Immunol. **126:** 1614–1619.
13. REED, J., A. ABIDI, J. ALPERS, R. HOOVER, R. ROBB & P. NOWELL. 1986. J. Immunol. **137:** 150–154.
14. MIYAWAKI, T., A. YACHIE, S. OHZEKI, T. NAGAOKI & N. TANIGUCHI. 1983. J. Immunol. **130:** 2737–2742.
15. GELFAND, E., R. CHEUNG & G. MILLS. 1987. J. Immunol. **138:** 1115–1120.
16. OROSZ, C. G., R. K. FIDELUS, D. C. ROOPENIAN, M. B. WIDMER, R. M. FERGUSON & F. H. BACH. 1982. J. Immunol. **129:** 1865–1868.
17. ROBERTS, P. & P. HAYRY. 1976. Transplantation **21:** 437–445.
18. ASCHER, N., R. FERGUSON, R. HOFFMAN & R. SIMMONS. 1979. Transplantation **27:** 254–259.
19. OROSZ, C., N. ZINN, L. SIRINEK & R. FERGUSON. 1986. Transplantation **41:** 75–83.
20. PRYSTOWSKY, M., J. ELY, D. BELLER *et al.* 1982. J. Immunol. **129:** 2337–2344.
21. HERALD, K., D. LANCKI, R. MOLDWIN & F. FITCH. 1986. J. Immunol. **136:** 1315–1321.

22. HEEG, K., K. DEUSCH, W. SOLBACK, D. BUNJES & H. WAGNER. 1984. Transplantation **38:** 532–536.
23. COX, J., A. FORSYTH, J. DEVILLIERS, M. YACOUB & P. CHISHOLM. 1984. Transplantation **38:** 17–22.
24. MASON, D. & P. MORRIS. 1984. Transplantation **37:** 46–51.
25. ASCHER, N., R. HOFFMAN, D. HANTO & R. SIMMONS. 1984. Immunol. Rev. **77:** 217–232.
26. DUIJVESTIJN, A., M. KERKHOVE, R. BARGATZE & E. BUTCHER. 1987. J. Immunol. **138:** 713–719.
27. DUIJVESTIJN, A., A. SCHREIBER & E. BUTCHER. 1986. Proc. Nat. Acad. Sci. USA **83:** 9114–9118.

Cross-linking of T-Cell Receptors Is Insufficient to Induce IL-2 Responsiveness (Activation) in Resting Lyt-2+ T Cells

IL-4 or RIF Are Essential as Second Signal[a]

HERMANN WAGNER, KLAUS HEEG, AND
CONNY HARDT

Department of Medical Microbiology and Immunology
University of Ulm
D-7900 Ulm, West Germany

INTRODUCTION

Two signals are thought to control activation of resting Lyt-2+ murine T cells. Cross-linking of T-cell receptor structures by antigen recognition is believed to induce expression of functional (high affine) interleukin-2 (IL-2) receptors (*i.e.*, IL-2 responsiveness), whereas autocrine- or paracrine-provided IL-2 is assumed to promote their growth and maturation into cytotoxic effector cells.[1] This view falls short of explaining why *in vivo* and *in vitro* the immunogenicity of constitutively expressed allogeneic MHC antigens is restricted to certain accessory cells such as dendritic cells.[2] In what sense then differ functional effective (immunogenic) stimulator cells from cells that present MHC antigens in a nonimmunogenic form? Is immunogenicity governed by a "costimulator activity" provided as additional signal by antigen-presenting cells (APC)?

In attempts to search for the postulated costimulator activity, we devised an *in vitro* bioassay. This bioassay is based on the experimental finding that high-density (resting) murine Lyt-2+ T cells exposed to the mitogen concanavalin A (Con A) remain refractory to the growth-promoting effect of IL-2, that is, the ligand Con A lacks the ability to induce functional IL-2 receptors.[3] Subsequently, we have extended this finding to high-density Lyt-2+ T cells, the antigen receptors of which were cross-linked by anti-F23 monoclonal antibodies (mAb) covalently bound to sepharose beads, or by exposure to nonimmunogenic allogeneic stimulator cells. Here we describe that in all three systems the costimulator activity provided by the T-helper cell product interleukin-4 (IL-4) or by the macrophage product IL-2 receptor-inducing factor (RIF)[3] restricts the induction of IL-2 responsiveness.

[a] This work was supported by the SFB 322 and the BMFT.

MATERIAL AND METHODS

The mice, culture medium, chemicals used, and the preparation of high-density (resting) Lyt-2$^+$ responder cells has been described in detail.[4] Semipurified RIF was prepared from culture supernatants of P388-D1 cells by batch elution from hydroxylapatite following fractionation on phenyl-sepharose as described.[4] Purified mAb F23.1[5] were covalently coupled to CNBr-activated sepharose 4 B (Pharmacia at 1 mg protein/ml) sepharose beads according to the Pharmacia Handbook for affinity chromatography. Recombinant IL-4 as obtained from producer cells transfected with the pKCR.IL-4.Neo-gene was a kind gift from Dr. W. Müller, Institute for Genetics, Cologne, West Germany. High-density B cells were obtained from splenic lymphocytes by first selecting, by Percoll centrifugation, for high-density cells (p > 1.062), followed by treatment with anti-Thy-1 mAb plus complement and recovering viable cells after a Ficoll centrifugation step. Stimulator cells were treated with mitomycin. The T-cell assays ([^{3}H]thymidine uptake, ^{51}Cr-assay, and the preparation of target cells) have been described.[4]

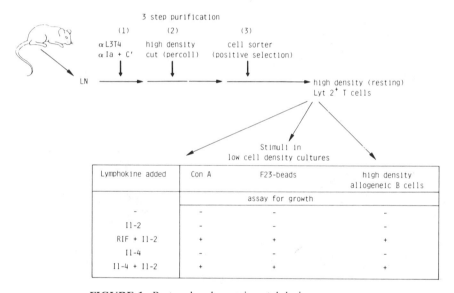

FIGURE 1. Protocol and experimental design.

RESULTS

Technical Aspects

The experimental protocol outlined in FIGURE 1 summarizes our present approach. As detailed, highly purified resting murine Lyt-2$^+$ T cells are prepared from nylon wool nonadherent murine lymph-node (LN) cells according to a three-step procedure. First, a negative selection step, using a mixture of cytotoxic mAb (anti-L3T4, anti-Ia$^+$ plus complement) was used to deplete for Ia$^+$ and L3T4$^+$ cells. This step was followed by a Percoll density centrifugation cut. Finally, out of the high-density LN cells (p = >1.07), Lyt-2$^+$ T cells were positively selected, using an EPIC's V cell sorter.[4]

Cross-linking of T-Cell Receptors (TCR) Is Insufficient To Induce IL-2 Responsiveness in Resting Lyt-2$^+$ T Cells

As detailed elsewhere,[3,4] limited numbers of high-density (resting) Lyt-2$^+$ T cells exposed to the ligand Con A (2 μg/ml) remain refractory to the growth-promoting effect of exogenous IL-2. This state of unresponsiveness can be overcome by adding accessory cells, or the protein kinase C activator phorbol myristic acetate (PMA),[4] or semipurified RIF prepared from the culture supernatant of the macrophage cell line P388-D1. RIF bioactivity is associated with a 44 kDa protein[4] and is shown not to be related to IL-1. The results detailed in TABLE 1 demonstrate that recombinant IL-4 exhibits the same functional activities as RIF. Note

TABLE 1. Recombinant IL-4 as well as RIF Restrict IL-2 Responsiveness of Resting Lyt-2$^+$ Exposed to Con A

Lyt-2$^+$ T Cells (1000/Well) Plus[a]	Proliferative Responses (cpm)
Con A (2 μg/ml)	850
Con A + IL-2 (50 U/ml)	680
Con A + RIF (20% v/v) plus IL-2	55,510
IL-4 (15% v/v)	880
Con A + IL-4	1,060
Con A + IL-4 + IL-2	28,530
IL-4 + IL-2	730

[a] High-density Lyt-2$^+$ T cells (1 $\times$ 10^3/well) were exposed to Con A and to the various reagents listed. Cell proliferation was measured after four days by [^{3}H]thymidine uptake. No proliferative response was observed without addition of Con A. The data are given as the mean of quadruplicate samples.

that the anti-IL-2 receptor mAb effectively inhibits growth of Con A-stimulated Lyt-2$^+$ T cells induced by RIF or IL-4 in response to exogenous IL-2 (TABLE 2). This type of result provides direct evidence that both RIF as well as IL-4 operate by triggering into function the IL-2 receptor pathway required for IL-2–promoted growth.

We assume that in the bioassay used, the function of Con A is to cross-link cell-surface structures including TCR. Therefore we wished to directly demonstrate that cross-linking of the TCR as a signal is insufficient to induce expression of functional IL-2 receptors in resting Lyt-2$^+$ T cells. To this we resorted to the use of insolubilized F23.1 anti-TCR antibodies.[5] F23.1 mAb was covalently bound to sepharose beads, and 0.25 mg of beads were added to high-density Lyt-2$^+$ T cells (1 $\times$ 10^3/well) plus 50 U recombinant IL-2. The data presented in TABLE 3 clearly show that cross-linking of TCR structures per se is insufficient to induce IL-2 responsiveness. As in the case of Con A (TABLE 3), addition of either RIF or IL-4 is required for the expression of functional IL-2 receptors.

TABLE 2. Anti-IL-2R mAb Block Growth of Con A-Stimulated Lyt-2$^+$ Induced by RIF or IL-4 in Response to IL-2

RIF (20% v/v)	IL-4 (20% v/v)	Anti-IL-2R mAb (7D4) (Final Dilution 1 : 80)	Lyt-2$^+$ T Cells (1 × 10^3/Well) Plus Con A (2 μg/ml) and IL-2 (50 U/ml)[a] (cpm)
−	−	−	700
+	−	−	28,000
+	−	+	1,200
−	+	−	35,700
−	+	+	900

[a] The bioassay was performed as described in TABLE 1.

RIF as well as IL-4 Convey Immunogenicity to Nonimmunogenic Stimulator Cells

In vitro the ability of allogeneic stimulator cells to initiate a primary T-cell response is restricted to dendritic-like accessory cells.[2] Resting B cells appear not to be immunogenic, even though they constitutively express the alloantigen in question.[6] Because RIF (as IL-4) triggered resting Lyt-2$^+$ T cells to respond to IL-2, provided their TCR were cross-linked by way of insolubilized F23.1 mAb, we wished to analyze whether RIF (or IL-4) exhibit similar functions in antigen-driven primary Lyt-2$^+$ T-cell responses. Conceivably TCR cross-linking by antigen recognition represents one of the prime events in primary T-cell activation. As detailed in TABLE 4, in the presence of exogenous IL-2, high-density Lyt-2$^+$ T cells respond well towards class I MHC incompatible "accessory cells" enriched for dendritic cells by both cell proliferation and generation of antigen-specific cytotoxic effector cells. Class I disparate high-density B cells, however, are essentially nonimmunogenic. Although addition of recombinant IL-1 does not alter this lack of immunogenicity, RIF conveys immunogenicity to high-density allogeneic B cells, as does recombinant IL-4 (TABLES 3 and 4). Note that anti-IL-2 receptor mAb effectively block this type of response, indicating that again they are triggered through the IL-2 receptor pathway. Essentially similar results were

TABLE 3. IL-4 Receptor Displays RIF Activity

High-Density Lyt-2$^+$ CBA T Cells (10^3/Well) Plus 50 U IL-2 Addition of	Stimulus[a]		
	Con A (2 μg/ml) Proliferative Response (cpm)	F23 Beads Proliferative Response (cpm)	High-Density Allogeneic B Cells (1 × 10^5/Well) Proliferative Response (cpm)
—	1,200	1,900	970
Semipurified RIF (15% v/v)	41,200	34,700	8,600
IL-4 (20% v/v)	23,800	29,114	7,050
TNF	1,500	1,300	840

[a] 5 mg anti-F23 mAb were coupled to 2 gr Sepharose beads. 0.25 mg F23.1 beads were used per well. The bioassay was performed as detailed in TABLE 1.

TABLE 4. RIF Conveys Immunogenicity to Nonimmunogenic Allogeneic Stimulator Cells

Responder Cells (5000/Well) C57BL/6 Lyt-2⁺ Plus 50 U/ml IL-2		Stimulator Cells[a]			
		"High-Density" B Cells (2 × 10⁵/Well)		"Accessory Cells" (1 × 10⁵/Well)	
Addition of	MHC Difference	Prolif- eration (cpm)	Percent Specific Lysis	Prolif- eration (cpm)	Percent Specific Lysis
—	class I (bm1)	470	0	19,700	23
IL-1 (20 U/ml)	class I (bm1)	680	0	31,000	43
RIF (20% v/v)	class I (bm1)	36,225	10	60,200	49
RIF plus anti-IL-2R mAb		1,200	0	3,700	2
	class I + II (BALB/c)	780	0	26,700	42
RIF (20% v/v)	(BALB/c)	42,700	12	51,470	57

[a] Cultures were split at day 7 and assayed for proliferative or cytolytic activity. The data are given as mean of quadruplicate cultures.

obtained in the trinitrophenyl (TNP) system (TABLE 5). Although gamma-interferon (IFN) and recombinant IL-1 proved to be ineffective, it is RIF that clearly conveys immunogenicity to TNP-conjugated allogeneic high-density B cells. Even though antigen recognition on antigen-presenting stimulator cells is clearly more complex compared to mere cross-linking of TCR by immobilized T23.1 antibodies, we conclude that basically, similar events are operating. We suggest that TCR cross-linking of antigen-reactive T cells takes place upon exposure to high-density allogeneic B cells, yet unlike accessory cells, this type of stimulator cell lacks the expression of costimulator activity.[6] Obviously this deficiency is overcome by either RIF or IL-4.

It could be argued that the target of RIF (or IL-4) represents the stimulator cells rather than the responding Lyt-2⁺ T cells, thus rendering high-density B cells

TABLE 5. RIF Triggers Resting Lyt⁺ T Cells to Respond towards Nonimmunogenic TNP-Syngeneic Stimulator Cells

C57BL/6 (5000/Well) Lyt-2⁺ T Cells Plus 50 U/ml IL-2	Stimulator Cells (C57BL/6)[a]				
	High-Density B Cells—TNP			Accessory Cells—TNP	
	Prolif- eration (cpm)	Percent Specific Lysis		Prolif- eration (cpm)	Percent Specific Lysis TNP Blasts
		Blasts	TNP Blasts		
—	1,800	0	0	20,700	18
RIF (20% v/v)	32,800	2	26	48,200	31
IL-1 (50 U/ml)	4,300	3	9	25,800	22
gamma-IFN (20 U/ml)	5,100	1	4	ND	ND
gamma-IFN + IL-1	4,200	0	2	ND	ND

[a] For details, see legend to TABLE 4.

immunogenic. To test this possibility, high-density B cells were first cultured for 24 h in the presence of RIF or IL-4, and subsequently tested for their ability to elicit a primary T-cell response. As shown in TABLE 6, neither RIF nor IL-4 alters the intrinsic lack of immunogenicity of resting B cells. Both agents, however, augment T-cell responsiveness when present during the induction period of a primary Lyt-2$^+$ T-cell response.

DISCUSSION

Primary T-cell activation can be defined rather narrowly as that series of events that is required to induce responsiveness to the growth-promoting effect of IL-2, that is, expression of functional IL-2 receptors. A key step within these events most likely represents cross-linking of T-cell antigen receptor structures (TCR) by presented antigen. To analyze whether cross-linking of TCR per se is

TABLE 6. Lack of IL-4 (or RIF) to Render High-Density B Cells Immunogenic

Preculture[a] of high-density bm1 mouse-derived B cells in the presence of	Addition of lymphokine in the MLR[b]		Proliferative response of high-density C57BL/6 Lyt-2$^+$ T cells (5000/well) (cpm)
	RIF (20% v/v)	IL-4 (20% v/v)	
—	+	−	7,900
—	−	+	11,400
IL-4 (20% v/v)	−	−	640
RIF (20% v/v)	−	−	970
RIF	+	−	9,400

[a] High-density B cells were cultured for 24 h in medium supplemented with IL-4 or RIF. Thereafter cells were washed, mitomycin C-treated, and used as stimulator cells (1 × 10^5 cells/culture).
[b] MLR = mixed lymphocyte reaction.

sufficient to trigger expression of functional IL-2 receptors by antigen-reactive T cells, we used three *in vitro* models experimentally approximating antigen recognition. Thus, we evaluated in the presence of exogenous IL-2 the responsiveness of high-density (resting) Lyt-2$^+$ T cells exposed to the mitogen Con A, or to immobilized F23.1 mAb directed against an allotypic determinant on the TCR, or to high-density allogeneic B cells known[6] to lack immunogenicity. The fact that neither Con A, nor immobilized F23.1 mAb, nor presented alloantigen are capable of inducing IL-2 responsiveness in resting Lyt-2$^+$ T cells strongly suggests that TCR cross-linking per se is insufficient to trigger expression of functional IL-2 receptor expression, that is, T-cell activation.

On the other hand, these observations provided the basis for a bioassay to search for physiological costimulator activities capable of complementing TCR cross-linking, such that expression of functional IL-2 receptors does occur. It is known that costimulator activity is provided physiologically by dendritic stimulator cells[2] or inducer agents mimicking the action of signal transducers such as the phorbolester PMA. It is also known that a variety of accessory molecules besides, the TCR, such as T4, T8, and T11, are involved in the T-cell activation process yielding in expression of functional IL-2 receptors,[7] although the respective mode of action is yet unknown.

The new information detailed here is that in three apparently distinct model systems the macrophage cell line product, RIF, as well as the T-cell product IL-4, induces IL-2 responsiveness in resting Lyt-2$^+$ exposed to either mitogenic lectins, or immobilized F23.1 mAb, or nonimmunogenic allogeneic stimulator cells. The interpretation of the physiological significance is rather complicated in the mitogen system, inasmuch as the target structures of Con A are ill-defined and most likely consist of a complex array of surface molecules including the TCR of resting Lyt-2$^+$ T cells. Conceptually, the interpretation is straightforward in the F23.1 system. The F23.1 mAb recognizes epitopes of the TCR encoded in the three-member Vβ.8 subfamily within the β-chain gene complex, which contains about 20 Vβ-gene segments. Immobilized F23.1 mAb, therefore, will cross-link TCR structures of those T cells that use this particular Vβ.8 gene set in the construction of a specifically reactive TCR. The interpretation of the results obtained using nonimmunogenic allogeneic B cells is again complicated, because the stimulator cells express, besides major histocompatibility complex (MHC) structures, other cell-surface structures, including the acceptor molecule for T11. Because the experimental data obtained in the three model systems appear as equal, however, we assume that indeed we are analyzing identical mechanisms. We therefore conclude that two restricting points are existing during antigen-specific activation of resting Lyt-2$^+$ T cells. The first restricting point represents TCR cross-linking. TCR cross-linking by way of antigen recognition is a signal necessary, but insufficient, to induce IL-2 receptor expression; it renders the cell susceptible to costimulator activity. We show here that either the T-helper cell product, IL-4, or the macrophage product, RIF, exhibit costimulator activity. Thus, the second restricting point during the activation of resting Lyt-2$^+$ T cells can be defined by the functional activity of RIF (or IL-4) on Lyt-2$^+$ T cells, as a consequence of which IL-2 responsiveness becomes induced. In fact, we recently found that resting Lyt-2$^+$ triggered by Con A accumulate an RNA message for the β chain of the IL-2 receptor, provided the cells are exposed to RIF.[8] Thus, in molecular terms, RIF (and presumably also IL-4) appears to be involved in the activation of genes encoding for IL-2 receptors. This interpretation fits the functional data described here.

Two issues raised by our results need to be addressed. First, the demonstration of the existence of two restricting points controlling the activation of resting Lyt-2$^+$ T cells explains to us why class I MHC antigens presented by high-density B cells are nonimmunogenic as opposed to class I MHC antigen presented by accessory cells. Obviously, high-density B cells lack costimulator activity, a characteristic of dendritic-like accessory cells. Second, the availability of lymphokines exhibiting costimulator activity such as IL-4 and semipurified RIF may turn out to be helpful in augmenting the immunogenicity to otherwise nonimmunogenic antigens.

SUMMARY

High-density (resting) murine Lyt-2$^+$ T cells exposed *in vitro* to the ligand concanavalin A (Con A), or immobilized F23.1 monoclonal antibody (mAb) recognizing an allotypic determinant on the T-cell receptor (TCR), or high-density (resting) allogeneic B stimulator cells remain IL-2–unresponsive; such cells do not express functional IL-2 receptors unless reconstituted with accessory cells. We conclude that cross-linking of TCR is insufficient as signal to induce IL-2 responsiveness, that is, activation.

Both the macrophage product RIF and the T-cell product interleukin-4 efficiently induce the IL-2 responsiveness in resting Lyt-2$^+$ T cells exposed *in vitro* either to the ligand Con A, or to immobilized F23 mAb, or to nonimmunogenic allogeneic stimulator cells. We conclude that two restricting points control the induction of IL-2 responsiveness (activation) in antigen-driven Lyt-2$^+$ T-cell responses, that is, cross-linking of TCR by way of presented antigen and "costimulator" activity expressed by accessory cells. Both RIF and IL-4 express costimulator activity, therefore replacing the requirement for accessory cells.

ACKNOWLEDGMENTS

Mrs. R. Schmittberger provided skilled assistance.

REFERENCES

1. SMITH, K. A. 1983. T cell growth factor, a lymphocytotrophic hormone. *In* Genetics of the Immune Response. E. Möller & G. Möller, Eds. Plenum. New York.
2. STEINMAN, R. M., B. GUTCHINOW, M. D. WITMER & M. C. NUSSENZWEIG. 1983. Dendritic cells are the principal stimulators of primary mixed leukocyte reactions in mice. J. Exp. Med. **157**: 613–627.
3. HARDT, C., T. DIAMANTSTEIN & H. WAGNER. 1985. Signal requirements for the *in vitro* differentiation of cytotoxic T lymphocytes: Distinct soluble mediators promote preactivation of CTL-precursors, clonal growth and differentiation into cytotoxic effector cells. Eur. J. Immunol. **15**: 472–478.
4. HARDT, C., N. SATO & H. WAGNER. 1987. Functional and biochemical characteristics of a murine interleukin 2 receptor inducing factor. Eur. J. Immunol. **17**: 209–216.
5. STAERZ, U. D. & M. J. BEVAN. 1986. Activation of resting T lymphocytes by a monoclonal antibody directed against an allotypic determinant on the T cell receptor. Eur. J. Immunol. **16**: 263–270.
6. KRIEGER, J. I., S. F. GRAMMER, H. M. GREY & R. W. CHESNUT. 1985. Antigen presentation by splenic B cells: Resting B cells are ineffective, whereas activated B cells are effective accessory cells for T cell responses. J. Immunol. **135**: 2937–2945.
7. HÜNIG, T., G. TIEFENTHALER, K. M. MEYER ZUM BÜSCHENFELDE & S. C. MEUER. 1987. Alternative pathway activation of T cells by binding of CD2 to its cell-surface ligand. Nature **326**: 298–301.
8. HARDT, C. 1987. Activation of murine CD8$^+$ lymphocytes: two distinct signals regulate c-myc and interleukin 2 receptor RNA expression. Eur. J. Immunol. **17**: 1711–1718.

Soluble Antigen-Specific Helper Molecules Active in the Induction of Cytotoxic T Lymphocytes[a]

LINDA M. PILARSKI, JOHN F. KROWKA, AND
JULIE P. DEANS

Department of Immunology
University of Alberta
Edmonton, Alberta Canada T6G2H7

INTRODUCTION

The inductive events that impinge on a cytotoxic T lymphocyte precursor cell (CTLp) are widely viewed as being fundamentally different from those that control the induction of other types of precursor cell, such as B cells or the T cells that mediate delayed-type hypersensitivity (T-DTH).[1,2] Whereas B cells and T-DTH require interaction with antigen-specific helper T cells brought into close physical contact by way of an antigen bridge, CTLp recognizing antigen *in vitro* appear to require for their induction only those signals provided by non-antigen-specific lymphokines such as IL-2.[3-5] Although antigen-specific helper T cells are essential for the induction of CTLp in the absence of exogenous IL-2, the role played by these helpers is ambiguous and could involve secretion of IL-2, triggered by antigen.[6-10] By contrast, the generation of memory CTLp *in vivo* appears to depend upon close physical proximity of helpers and CTLp, operationally detected as a requirement for linkage of haptenic determinants recognized by the CTLp and carrier determinants seen by the helper,[11,12] to create an antigen bridge.

An experimental approach for defining the requirements for the induction of CTLp and the role, if any, of antigen-specific inductive events has been difficult to design, due mainly to the fact that most populations of helper T cells have the ability to secrete IL-2 upon triggering with antigen. The presence of IL-2 in the cultures being analyzed will obscure any antigen-specific inductive events. This fact, however, does not of itself mean that antigen-specific events do not play a role in the generation of CTL. Because the populations of CTLp responsive to various cell-surface antigens have in all probability experienced antigen prior to intervention by an investigator, the majority are likely to be memory cells that have experienced initial inductive events *in vivo* resulting in expression of IL-2 receptors. In addition, it is likely that populations of CTLp are heterogeneous, including both virgin and experienced precursors. If antigen-specific inductive events are required for the initial signaling mechanisms, then one might reasonably predict that virgin CTLp will require an antigen-specific inductive event before they are able to respond to nonspecific lymphokines such as IL-2, and memory cells might be responsive both to signals delivered by way of antigen-specific events and to those delivered nonspecifically.

It should be emphasized that a requirement for an antigen-specific interaction does not demand that the actual triggering signal be itself antigen-specific. The

[a] This work was funded by the Medical Research Council of Canada.

136

most reasonable explanation for required close physical contact between the cell delivering the signal and the receiving cell postulates that a mediator is involved that acts only at "short range." Short-range effects may occur if the signal involves cell membrane contact or if the mediator involved is labile or needed at very high local concentration. They could also involve directed delivery of a triggering agent(s), achieved through alignment by the trimolecular T-cell receptor (TCR)/antigen/precursor-cell receptor for antigen complex of the secretory apparatus of the helper cell with the "inductive" receptor(s) of the target precursors. The mediators involved are unlikely to be IL-2 or other nonspecific lymphokines, as these act at "long range." We speculate that there exists a signaling mechanism unique to this initial inductive event requiring either a helper T cell or its antigen-specific product for successful signal delivery. It seems likely that antigen-specific events may act in synergy with nonspecifically delivered signals to trigger CTLp, and evidence to support this view has been reported by Kwong *et al.*[13,14]

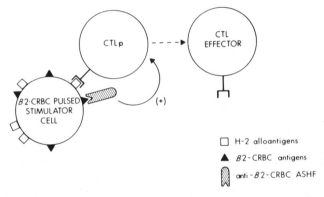

FIGURE 1. Antigen bridging: Linked recognition of alloantigen (hapten) by the CTLp and recognition of carrier by helper molecules.

Thus, in order to dissect the events involved in the induction of CTLp, a system must be designed that is free of IL-2 and the ability to produce IL-2. To achieve this, a source of cell-free help is required. Antigen-specific helper factor (ASHF) produced by helper T-cell clones and lines is a necessary tool for analyzing the induction of CTLp. We have designed an experimental system within which the induction of CTLp is dependent upon ASHF for delivery of inductive signals.[15-18] Thymocytes are used as a source of CTLp deficient in helper activity and therefore dependent upon a source of exogenous help.[6] As a source of both antigen and antigen-presenting cells (APC), adherent irradiated allogeneic stimulator cells are pulsed with a source of carrier antigen, either fragments of chicken red blood cells (CRBC) or a synthetic polypeptide poly18.[16,17,19] In this situation, the intrinsically expressed major histocompatibility (MHC) class I antigens serve as the haptenic determinants to be recognized by the CTLp. The carrier determinants (extrinsic antigen) are presented by these allogeneic APC for recognition by either helper cells[5] or ASHF[16] (FIG. 1).

The relationship between hapten and carrier determinants in this system is analogous to the interaction between MHC class II–specific helpers and class I–

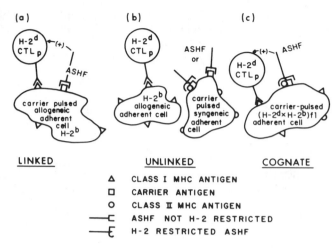

FIGURE 2. Experimental design to determine the type of interaction required between helper molecules and CTLp, involving physically linked or unlinked haptenic and carrier determinants. (Krowka et al.[17] With permission from the *Journal of Immunology*.)

specific CTLp.[20] A similar system for analyzing the induction of B cells has been described in which helper cells and B cells recognize different membrane components present on the same cell surface;[21] this type of hapten carrier linkage has been termed intrastructural in contrast to the classical intramolecular linkage where hapten and carrier are covalently linked.[21] The ability to manipulate hapten and carrier determinants independently is an essential feature of our experimental system because it allows the analysis of CTLp-inductive interactions when hapten and carrier are linked or unlinked, and when carrier is presented in association with appropriate or inappropriate MHC class II molecules (Fig. 2).

PROPERTIES OF ANTIGEN-SPECIFIC HELPER FACTOR

ASHF is derived from culture supernatants of helper T-cell clones, lines, or hybridomas and prepared by enrichment over an antigen affinity column. CRBC-specific ASHF discussed here is produced by concanavalin (Con) A stimulation of antigen and IL-2–dependent T-cell clones, LB19-1 or GK15-1, for 12 hours.[22] Poly18-specific ASHF is constitutively produced by the p18.68 hybridoma[23] by culture of cells for 24–48 hours. From these clones, the amount of ASHF needed for optimal functional activity is that produced by approximately 3×10^3 to 10^4 cells in the time periods indicated. The affinity-enriched ASHF is then added to thymocyte CTLp and carrier-pulsed allogeneic adherent cells, and the generation of alloantigen-specific CTL is assessed five days later (Fig. 3).

ASHF is able to efficiently induce the generation of CTL only when the allogeneic adherent cells are pulsed with an appropriate carrier antigen, indicating the stringent antigen-specificity of the inductive function.[16] In optimal conditions using the T-cell line CHI, the amount of ASHF required for detectable inductive function is that derived from 100–1000 cells over a 24 hour period, suggesting that the assay detects ASHF in physiological concentrations.[16]

The T-cell lines and clones used to produce ASHF were originally selected for their ability to help B-cell responses.[24] Inasmuch as they also were able to help in the generation of CTL, it was of interest to determine whether the same or different forms of ASHF were involved. ASHF derived from a heterogeneous T-cell line, CHI, was fractionated using anion-exchange chromatography and shown to consist of at least two separate forms of ASHF, one of which helped B-cell responses, and one which helped CTL responses.[15] A T-cell clone derived from CHI, produced a form of ASHF only able to induce CTLp but not B cells. These observations can be interpreted to indicate two distinct antigen-specific molecules or two forms of the same antigen-specific molecule. As will be discussed below, ASHF appears to consist of two distinct subunits, and some evidence suggests that the most likely explanation for the above observations involves differential assembly of antigen-specific and -nonspecific subunits to create active AHSF with inductive capacity limited to a particular class of immune precursor.[15]

In indirect assay systems, functional ASHF was shown to consist of two distinct noncovalently linked subunits, one of which was antigen-specific and presumably the product of the antigen-specific helper T cells. The second subunit appeared to include MHC class II determinants and to be produced by an adherent cell type other than the antigen-specific helper cell.[16,24,25] The two subunits appear to be held together by calcium, as dissociation of the subunits is effected by treatment with EGTA followed by affinity chromatography. Functional activity of the eluted antigen-specific molecules is restored by the presence of adherent cells expressing a specific Ia haplotype syngeneic to the cell type producing the ASHF. We have referred to these Ca^{2+}-deficient ASHF preparations as incomplete ASHF. A second source of incomplete ASHF is derived from a T-cell clone that produces the antigen-specific subunit and is deficient in the Ia^+ subunit. Both these incomplete forms of ASHF will help in the induction of a CTLp response but not in a B-cell response.[16,24] Their functional activity in the CTL response is restricted to culture conditions that include adherent cells syngeneic to the source of the ASHF, suggesting that the functional activity, but not the recognition of antigen, is restricted by the Ia region of the MHC. We have speculated that this represents an unconventional type of H-2 restriction operating at the level of

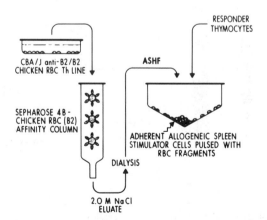

FIGURE 3. Experimental design to analyze the role of helper molecules in the induction of CTLp. (J. D. Watson & J. Marbrook.[29] With permission from Marcel Dekker, Inc.)

subunit assembly, that may be of major importance in MHC-restricted cell inter-actions rather than in the MHC-restricted recognition of antigen.[15,16,18]

A REQUIREMENT FOR PHYSICAL LINKAGE OF HAPTEN AND CARRIER DETERMINANTS IN THE INDUCTION OF CTLp

Because ASHF exhibited stringent specificity in its recognition of carrier and in its subsequent functional activity, it was possible to design experiments to assess the role of antigen-specifically delivered inductive signals in the generation of CTL. Two ASHF were used, LB19-1, specific for CRBC,[22] and p18.68, specific for poly18 and derived from an Ia^d-restricted hybridoma.[23] These were shown to be specific in criss-cross experiments (FIG. 4). LB19-1 was able to help H-2^b–specific CTLp only when stimulator cells were pulsed with CRBC fragments, and not when the carrier was poly18. Similarly, the p18.68 ASHF helped anti-H-2^b CTLp only when the allogeneic adherent stimulator cells were pulsed with poly18, not with CRBC. The responses obtained with ASHF as the source of help were of comparable magnitude to those triggered by IL-2–containing prepara-tions. It is, however, not possible with this type of culture to determine whether the set of CTLp responding to ASHF and antigen is the same as the set of CTLp responding to IL-2 and antigen. The CTL generated in response to ASHF had a comparable specificity pattern to those generated in response to IL-2.[17]

In order to determine the role of antigen bridging in the interaction between ASHF and CTLp, the hapten and carrier were presented in both linked and unlinked form (FIG. 5). BALB/c thymocytes constituted the CTLp population, so BALB/c alloantigens on the various stimulator populations are regarded as self

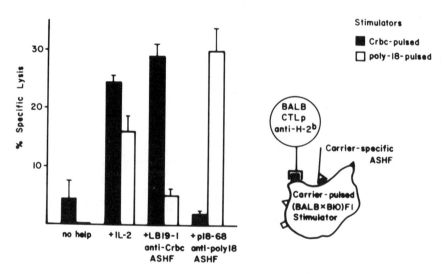

FIGURE 4. Criss-cross specificity control to demonstrate specificity of CRBC-specific and poly18-specific ASHF. BALB/c thymocytes were cultured with (BALB/c × B10)F1 irradi-ated antigen-pulsed adherent cells with or without the appropriate ASHF. Assay was at day 5 on B10 Con A blast cells that had not been pulsed with any type of carrier.

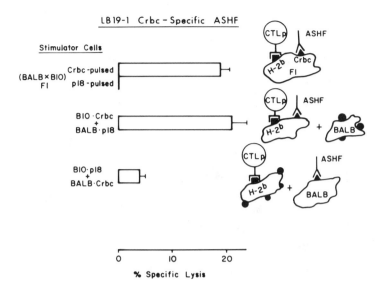

FIGURE 5. ASHF from LB19-1 is able to trigger CTLp only when the haptenic MHC class I antigens are physically linked to the CRBC carrier determinants. BALB/c thymocytes were stimulated with irradiated adherent cells of the type indicated and pulsed with carrier antigen as indicated in the FIGURE.

and do not present intrinsic H-2 class I for recognition by CTLp. (BALB/c × B10)F1 stimulator cells pulsed with CRBC represent physically linked hapten (H-2^b) and carrier (CRBC); an effective CTL response is generated in the presence of LB19-1 CRBC-specific ASHF. Similarly, when B10 adherent cells are pulsed with CRBC and mixed with poly18-pulsed BALB/c cells, both hapten and carrier are physically linked on the same cell surface, and a strong CTL response is generated. When B10 adherent cells, however, are pulsed with poly18 and when BALB/c cells are pulsed with CRBC, the hapten and carrier are presented on different cells and are thus physically unlinked. In this group, there is no effective CTL response generated, indicating a need for an antigen bridge to link ASHF and CTLp.

Inasmuch as LB19-1 is an ASHF of H-2^b origin, it could be argued that the above result represents a need for linkage of carrier/IA^b. If so, then this result could be interpreted as a need for cognate recognition of carrier by the ASHF rather than linked recognition of hapten and carrier. To address this issue, we used ASHF derived from cell line GK15-1 of H-2^k origin. The thymocyte population was also of H-2^k origin. As before, using F1 stimulators, the hapten (H-2^d), the carrier (CRBC), and Ia^k are all physically linked on the same cell surface. With these conditions, an efficient CTL response was generated against H-2^d (FIG. 6). When hapten and carrier were linked on the BALB/c stimulator cell surface and Ia^k was unlinked, an equally strong CTL response was generated, indicating that ASHF did not require presentation of carrier in association with Ia^k for its functional activity. Finally unlinking of hapten (BALB/c) from carrier-Ia^k (CBA cells pulsed with CRBC) resulted in a loss of functional ASHF activity and a subsequent lack of CTL generation.

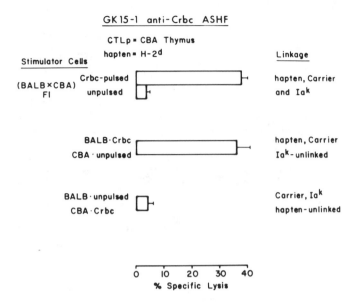

FIGURE 6. CRBC-specific ASHF acts by way of linked associative recognition but has no apparent need for cognate recognition of carrier and MHC class II. CBA thymocytes were stimulated with irradiated adherent cells of the type and carrier-pulsing indicated.

Thus, for these CRBC-specific ASHF, we were unable to detect a requirement for cognate recognition of carrier antigen but observed a stringent requirement for antigen-bridging of CTLp and ASHF. We conclude that the induction of CTLp follows the same rules that operate in the induction of B cells or T-DTH, defined as a need for linked associative recognition of hapten and carrier determinants. Although IL-2 is also able to trigger CTLp resident in the thymocyte population, these experiments demonstrate an alternate mechanism of induction that requires close physical proximity of the collaborating moieties and presumably involves a short range mediator.

POLY18-SPECIFIC ASHF REQUIRES BOTH COGNATE RECOGNITION OF ANTIGEN AND PHYSICAL LINKAGE OF HAPTEN AND CARRIER FOR FUNCTIONAL ACTIVITY

The hybridoma from which poly18-specific ASHF is derived is able to secrete IL-2 only when poly18 is presented on Ia^d APC. This indicates that the TCR for antigen has fine specificity for a determinant composed of poly18 in association with Ia^d.[23] A reasonable working hypothesis regarding the production of an antigen-specific soluble molecule by an antigen-specific T cell predicts that ASHF should share the same fine specificity expressed by the cell surface TCR, analogous to variable region sharing between surface and secreted immunoglobulin produced by B cells.

In the experiment described by FIGURE 7, the effects of unlinking hapten, carrier, and Ia^d are explored. (BALB/c × B10)F1 stimulator cells pulsed with poly18 express all three elements on the same cell surface and are therefore physically linked through an intrastructural linkage. In this group, BALB/c thymocytes mounted a strong CTL response when the stimulator cells were pulsed with poly18 but not with CRBC. No CTL response was detectable, however, when hapten (H-2^b) and carrier were physically linked, but no cognate recognition was possible (Ia^d was unlinked). Neither was a response seen if hapten was unlinked from a cognate poly18-Ia^d complex. Thus, unlike the CRBC-specific ASHF, physical linkage of three elements, hapten, carrier, and Ia^d, was required for functional inductive activity of ASHF in the generation of CTL.

We interpret this to indicate requirements for both cognate recognition of carrier in association with Ia, and physical linkage of ASHF and CTLp by way of an antigen bridge. A further important conclusion from this experiment is that ASHF exhibits the same fine variable-region specificity as does the TCR on the cell that produces ASHF. The fact that ASHF binds sufficiently well to poly18 to allow affinity-enrichment on an antigen column probably reflects differential avidity requirements for binding and for functional activity. Mediating a functional effect is likely to require considerably greater avidity, which would be achieved by recognition of the poly18/Ia^d complex on the surface of an APC.

MONOCLONAL ANTIBODY KJ16.133 SPECIFICALLY PRECIPITATES MOLECULES IN LB19-1 ASHF

If ASHF represents the antigen-specific molecule through which the helper T cell mediates its collaborative interactions, then it is imperative that ASHF and

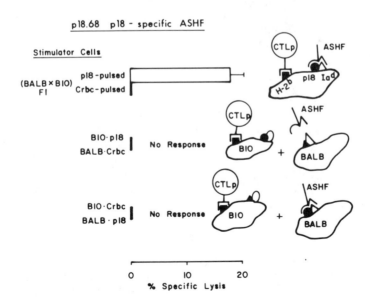

FIGURE 7. Poly18-specific ASHF acts by way of linked associative recognition and sees the carrier antigen only in association with MHC class II. Conditions were same as for FIGURE 5.

the TCR share identical variable-region specificity, although it might reasonably be expected that the constant regions of these two clonotypic molecules would differ. Because the effect of ASHF *in vitro* mimics that seen in the induction of memory CTLp *in vivo*, both in terms of cognate and of linked-associative recognition of antigen,[11,12] it seems likely that ASHF is the T-cell analogue of the immunoglobulin secreted by sIg+ B cells.

Inasmuch as the p18.68 hybridoma expressed KJ16.133+ receptors, we predicted that the poly18-specific ASHF produced by these cells should also express

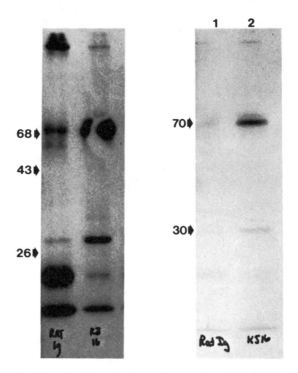

FIGURE 8. SDS-polyacrylamide gel electrophoresis of purified LB19-1 ASHF, immunoprecipitated with KJ16.133 (lane 2) and normal rat immunoglobulins (Ig) (lane 1). The ^{125}I-labeled, 0.25 M NaCl fast-protein liquid chromatography (FPLC-Pharmacia, Piscataway, NJ) anion-exchange fraction of antigen affinity-enriched supernatant of the LB19-1 helper T cell clone was immunoprecipitated overnight at 4°C. Left gel: before absorption with Sepharose-coupled rat Ig; right gel: after absorption with rat Ig Sepharose. Both gels were run under nonreducing conditions.

the determinants recognized by KJ16.133. Immunoprecipitation of labeled p18.68 cell-surface material by KJ16.133 coupled to Sepharose beads, followed by separation on a reducing gel, gave a 40 kDa band, consistent with an identity as the alpha/beta TCR heterodimer (unpublished). KJ16.133 is a monoclonal antibody that detects members of the $V_{beta}8$ gene family.[26] In order to determine the reactivity of KJ16.133 with ASHF, affinity-enriched poly18-specific ASHF was passed over a column of KJ16.133 coupled to Sepharose beads. Essentially all of the antigen-specific inductive capacity was depleted from the column effluent, indicating binding by functional ASHF to the KJ16 column. The functional activity could be eluted from the KJ16 column by high salt, and 50% of the activity originally loaded on the column was recovered in the eluate (data not shown). This strongly suggests that the functional moiety of ASHF bears determinants recognized by KJ16.133 and that the same variable region genes are used to encode both the TCR and ASHF. Similar results have been reported by Kwong and Teh using an ASHF specific for alloantigens.[14]

The use of the $V_{beta}8$ genes by the p18.68 cells is, however, not supported by gene-sequencing data. Kilgannon, Fotedar, and Singh (personal communication) have found that the V gene used by this hybridoma is not $V_{beta}8$, suggesting that a cross-reactive determinant encoded by other V genes is being recognized by KJ16.133 on both the TCR and ASHF. This conclusion is further supported by our observation that the TCR on p18.68 is reactive with KJ16, but not with F23.1, which also recognizes the $V_{beta}8$ family[27] (Deans *et al.*, unpublished). This phenotype has not been previously reported and suggests use of a gene outside the $V_{beta}8$ family.

ASHF derived from the LB19-1 clone appeared to express KJ16.133 determinants as identified in ELISA assays, so affinity-enriched Con A-stimulated supernatant material was further fractionated using a monoQ anion-exchange FPLC column, the relevant fractions pooled, concentrated, and subjected to iodination. The labeled ASHF was then immunoprecipitated, using KJ16.133-coupled Sepharose beads. After separation on nonreducing SDS-PAGE gels, we were able to detect 70 kDa and 30 kDa bands, specifically precipitated by KJ16.133 but not by normal rat immunoglobulin (FIG. 8). The 70 kDa band was still detectable when the immunoprecipitate was run on reducing gels, indicating it did not consist of disulfide-linked subunits (data not shown).

CONCLUSIONS

The results described above clearly indicate that the induction of CTLp can occur through collaboration with the antigen-specific product of an antigen-specific helper T cell. As is the case for the induction of other classes of immune precursors, the generation of CTL requires that the interacting cell types be brought into close physical proximity with an inductive agent by antigen-bridging. This suggests that the signaling mechanism involved in these initial inductive events occurs through mediators that act only within a constrained local environment achieved by linked recognition of antigen. The induction appears to require the presence of either an antigen-specific helper T cell or its antigen-specific product, and thus is not likely to involve nonspecific lymphokines such as IL-2, which are known to act at long range. Because the same heterogeneous population of thymic CTLp is induced to generate CTL by antigen in conjunction with either ASHF or IL-2, a single CTLp may be responsive to both agents, or alternatively, ASHF and IL-2 may act on distinct subsets. Preliminary work has detected subsets of CTLp that are inducible only by ASHF and not by IL-2 (unpublished).

The demonstration of linked recognition of antigen in the induction of a cytotoxic T-cell response raises as many questions as it resolves. The mechanism of action of ASHF in this inductive event and the relationship with IL-2–mediated events are particularly germane. It is reasonable to predict that ASHF-mediated events precede the expression of IL-2 receptors on a virgin precursor and are followed by IL-2–triggered division and differentiation in synergy with other late-acting lymphokines. An alternate hypothesis is that ASHF and IL-2–mediated events represent two distinct nonoverlapping pathways *in vivo,* that direct the responding cells to different functional end points. These are not necessarily mutually exclusive options and could both operate under appropriate immuno-regulatory conditions.

The chain of events leading to induction of the CTLp and to generation of CTL is still unclear. Although some evidence suggests that ASHF interacts with the CTLp itself, this has not yet been unequivocally demonstrated. The possibility exists that ASHF triggers a helper T-cell precursor, specific for either the protein carrier or for alloantigen, to differentiate to helper-effector cells that then help the CTLp.[8] The most likely explanation involves triggering of both T helpers and of CTLp by ASHF; preliminary work indicates that spleen cells depleted of helpers and cultured at limiting dilution are induced by ASHF and antigen to generate CTLp (unpublished). We predict that ASHF is the mediator of positive inductive signaling for all classes of precursor and initiates the regulatory cascade of help and suppression that controls cell-mediated and humoral immunity.

Finally, the question arises concerning the mechanism whereby ASHF signals a CTLp or other precursor. It could act directly on the surface of the CTLp to deliver a positive signal, explaining the need for close antigen-bridging. Alternatively, and perhaps more likely, it may bind to an accessory cell type, conferring passive specificity on that cell that is then responsible for delivering the signal to the CTLp through membrane contact or through short range mediators. An indirect mechanism of action by an antigen-specific helper molecule was initially proposed by Bretscher, on theoretical grounds.[28] If correct, this model predicts that ASHF has constant region domains designed for cytophilic binding and inter-action with an activating receptor complex on the accessory cell surface. The constant regions are therefore likely to be different from those used for the surface TCR, although the variable regions must remain identical for both soluble and surface forms to preserve the specificity of action in the T-helper population. The indirect model also predicts the existence of specialized lineages of accessory cells, programmed to deliver either positive or negative signals; these cells would express surface receptors with affinity for the constant regions of either ASHF or a suppressor molecule, but not for both. It is difficult to conceive of a mechanism whereby an individual accessory cell could differentially deliver either positive or negative signals directed by the diverse collection of antigen-specific molecules that would randomly bind to its surface *in vivo*.

In summary then, we have demonstrated a requirement for linked associative recognition of antigen in the induction of CTLp, indicating that non-antigen-specific lymphokines do not constitute the sole means of signaling for this class of precursor. Antigen-bridging of helper and precursor is essential for induction in cultures depleted of lymphokines. We predict that immature, perhaps virgin CTLp will depend exclusively upon antigen-specific modes of induction, whereas antigen-experienced memory CTLp are triggered by either antigen-specific or nonspecific modes, probably due to the expression of a higher density of lympho-kine receptors. Finally we predict that *in vivo*, the initial event in the induction of a CTLp requires antigen-bridging and a signal delivered only through close physical proximity of helper and CTLp.

REFERENCES

1. BRETSCHER, P. A. 1974. Hypothesis. On the control between cell mediated, IgM and IgG immunity. Cell. Immunol. **13:** 171–195.
2. TUCKER, M. J. & P. A. BRETSCHER. 1982. T cells cooperating in the induction of delayed-type hypersensitivity act via the linked recognition of antigenic determinants. J. Exp. Med. **155:** 1037–1049.

3. WAGNER, H., C. HARDT, K. HEEG, K. PFIZENMAIER, W. SOLBACH, R. BARTLETT, H. STOCKINGER & M. ROLLINGHOFF. 1980. T-T cell interactions during cytotoxic T lymphocyte (CTL) responses: T cell derived helper factor (interleukin 2) as a probe to analyze CTL responsiveness and thymic maturation of CTL progentors. Immunol. Rev. **51:** 215–256.

4. SHAW, J., B. CAPLAN, V. PAETKAU, L. M. PILARSKI, T. L. DELOVITCH & I. F. C. MCKENZIE. 1980. Cellular origins of co-stimulator (IL-2) and its activity in cytotoxic T lymphocyte responses. J. Immunol. **124:** 2231–2239.

5. KROWKA, J. F., C. GUIDOS, A. SINHA, K.-C. LEE, E. DIENER & L. M. PILARSKI. 1987. Comparative functional analysis of helper T lymphocyte responses to soluble and particulate antigens. J. Immunol. **138:** 3114–3119.

6. PILARSKI, L. M. 1977. A requirement for antigen-specific helper T cells in the generation of cytotoxic T cells from thymocyte precursors. J. Exp. Med. **145:** 709–723.

7. BAUM, L. L. & L. M. PILARSKI. 1978. *In vitro* generation of antigen-specific helper T cells that collaborate with cytotoxic T cell precursors. J. Exp. Med. **148:** 1579–1591.

8. PILARSKI, L. M. & I. F. C. MCKENZIE. 1985. Requirement for help in the generation of alloantigen-specific helper T cells. Transplantation **40:** 305–310.

9. ASHMAN, R. B. & A. MULLBACHER. 1979. A T helper cell for anti-viral cytotoxic T-cell responses. J. Exp. Med. **150:** 1277–1282.

10. COOLEY, M. A. & A. SCHMITT-VERHULST. 1979. Specific helper T cells permit differentiation of thymic anti-self-trinitrophenyl cytotoxic precursor cells. J. Immunol. **123:** 2328–2336.

11. KEENE, J. A. & J. FORMAN. 1982. Helper activity is required for the *in vivo* generation of cytotoxic T lymphocytes. J. Exp. Med. **155:** 768–782.

12. JURETIC, A., B. MALENCA, E. JURETIC, J. KLEIN & Z. A. NAGY. 1985. Helper effects required during *in vivo* priming for a cytolytic response to the H-Y antigen in nonresponder mice. J. Immunol. **134:** 1408–1414.

13. KWONG, P. C. & H. S. TEH. 1987. Mechanism of action of a D^b-specific helper clone and factor in cytotoxic responses to alloantigens. Immunology **61:** 151–157.

14. KWONG, P. C. & H. S. TEH. 1987. Characterization of a D^b-specific helper factor required for the induction of cytotoxic responses to alloantigens with the use of monoclonal antibodies specific for the helper factor or the T cell antigen receptor. Immunology. **61:** 143–150.

15. KROWKA, J. F., C. SHIOZAWA, E. DIENER & L. M. PILARSKI. 1986. Functional activity of soluble antigen-specific helper T cell molecules. Requirement for separable entities for the induction of cytotoxic T cell and B cell responses. Transplantation. **42:** 162–167.

16. KROWKA, J. F., C. SHIOZAWA, E. DIENER, V. PAETKAU & L. M. PILARSKI. 1984. Induction of cytotoxic T lymphocyte responses by antigen-specific helper factors. J. Immunol. **133:** 2018–2024.

17. KROWKA, J. F., B. SINGH, A. FOTEDAR, T. MOSMANN, M. GIEDLIN & L. M. PILARSKI. 1986. A requirement for physical linkage between determinants recognized by helper molecules and cytotoxic T cell precursors in the induction of cytotoxic T cell responses by antigen-specific helper T cell molecules. J. Immunol. **136:** 3561–3566.

18. PILARSKI, L. M. & J. F. KROWKA. 1985. Regulation of the induction of cytotoxic T cells. Antigen-specific regulatory T cells and antigen-specific T cell factors. *In* Recognition and Regulation in Cell Mediated Immunity. J. D. Watson & J. Marbrook, Eds.: 367–436. Marcel Dekker. New York.

19. SINGH, B., E. FRAGA & M. A. BARTON. 1978. Characterization and genetic control of the immune responses to synthetic polypeptide antigens of defined geometry. J. Immunol. **121:** 784–789.

20. ALTER, B. J. & F. H. BACH. 1979. Speculations on alternative pathways of T-lymphocyte response. Scand. J. Immunol. **10:** 87–93.

21. LAKE, P. & N. A. MITCHISON. 1976. Regulatory mechanisms in the immune response to cell surface antigens. *In* Cold Spring Harbor Symposia on Quantitative Biology. **31:** 589–595. Cold Spring Harbor Press. Cold Spring Harbor, NY.

22. MOSMANN, T. R., H. CHERWINSKI, M. W. BOND, M. A. GIEDLIN & R. L. COFFMAN.

1986. Two types of murine helper T cell clone. I. Definition according to profiles of lymphokine activities and secreted proteins. J. Immunol. **136:** 2348–2357.

23. FOTEDAR, A., W. SMART, J. WIDTMAN, E. FRAGA & B. SINGH. 1985. Fine specificity of antigen recognition by T cell hybridoma clones specific for poly 18. A synthetic polypeptide antigen of defined sequence and conformation. J. Immunol. **135:** 3028–3033.

24. SHIOZAWA, C., S. SAWADA, M. INAZAWA & E. DIENER. 1984. Triggering of affinity-enriched B cells. J. Immunol. **132:** 1892–1899.

25. SHIOZAWA, C., S. SONIK, B. SINGH & E. DIENER. 1980. Antigen specific T-cell derived helper factor. *In* Biochemical Characterization of Lymphokines. (A. L. DeWeck, F. Kristensen & M. Landy, Eds: 557–561. Academic Press. New York.

26. ROEHM, N., L. HERRON, J. CAMBIER, D. DIGUISTO, K. HASKINS, J. KAPPLER & P. MARRACK. 1984. The major histocompatibility complex-restricted antigen receptor on T cells: Distribution on thymus and peripheral T cells. Cell **38:** 577–583.

27. STAERZ, U. D., H.-G. RAMMANSEE, J. D. BENEDETTO & M. J. BEVAN. 1985. Characterization of a murine monoclonal antibody specific for an allotypic determinant on T cell receptor. J. Immunol. **134:** 3994–4000.

28. BRETSCHER, P. A. 1972. The control of humoral and associative antibody synthesis. Transplant. Rev. **11:** 217–267.

29. WATSON, J. D. & J. MARBROOK, Eds. 1985. Recognition and regulation in cell-mediated immunity. Marcel Dekker Inc. New York.

Cytokines Involved in the Generation of Cytolytic Effector T Lymphocytes[a]

JANET M. D. PLATE, TERESA L. LUKASZEWSKA,
G. BUSTAMANTE, AND ROBERTA L. HAYES

Departments of Internal Medicine and
Immunology/Microbiology
Section of Medical Oncology
Rush-Presbyterian-St. Luke's Medical Center
Chicago, Illinois 60612

CYTOKINES FUNCTION IN EFFECTOR T-CELL DEVELOPMENT

Cytokines are required as signals for the development of cytolytic effector T cells (CTL). The cytokines that are derived from antigen-presenting cells are termed monokines, whereas those derived from T lymphocytes are termed lymphokines.[1] Two apparently distinct monokines are required for the activation of the T-cell subsets involved in CTL differentiation. Interleukin-1 (IL-1) is required for the activation of helper T cells. The presentation of antigen and IL-1 to the helper T cells results in events that lead to their ability to synthesize lymphokines, including interleukin-2 (IL-2), and lymphokine receptors, especially IL-2 receptors. IL-1 may not be required as a direct signal to trigger the CTL precursor.[2] A second monokine called IL-2 receptor–inducing factor (RIF) has been described, which is required for the acquisition of IL-2 receptors on L3T4-depleted, Lyt-2$^+$ T cells. Data presented in this volume suggest that RIF is biochemically distinct from IL-1 or interleukin-4 (IL-4).[3] The two monokines may induce the expression of distinct chains of the IL-2 receptor and may also activate distinct T-cell subsets. We demonstrate here that the major effect of IL-1, in helper T-cell induction, is on the MHC class II–restricted T-cell subset, and that IL-1 has little effect on the MHC class I–restricted T-cell subsets. It will be of interest, then, for us to understand the biological relevance of the distinctions between monokines and the nature of the differential monokine receptor expression under normal physiological conditions.

A number of distinct lymphokines have also been demonstrated to function during the development of CTL. The precise steps at which these lymphokines function are not clear, with the exception of IL-2, which serves as a growth-promoting signal. We have begun to characterize the roles of some of the known recombinant lymphokines and our own hybridoma-derived lymphokines with respect to the T-cell subset affected by each. Our data demonstrate that a differential receptivity to signals transmitted by cytokines is evidenced by the two distinct helper T-cell subsets that have been demonstrated to respond to antigens of the major histocompatibility complex (MHC).[4] Helper T-cell subsets are distinguished by their associative recognition of MHC class I or class II antigens; hence, they are MHC-restricted in their responses. The helper T cells of the MHC class II-restricted subsets are responsive to signals presented in the presence of antigen-presenting cells by IL-1, IL-3, and interferon-gamma (IFN-gamma), as

[a] This work was supported in part by NIH Grant CA 25612.

149

well as by IL-2. The helper T cells and CTL precursors that are MHC class I–
restricted readily respond to IL-2 but are substantially less responsive to signals
presented by IL-1, IL-3, and IFN-gamma.

RESULTS

Effect of Monoclonal Antibodies to CD4 on CTL Generation

MHC Class II–Dependent Responses

The monoclonal antibody (mAb) GK1.5 recognizes the murine equivalent of
the L3T4 cell-surface antigens (CD4) on T cells.[5] CD4+ T cells recognize antigen
in association with MHC class II antigens. Antibodies bound to CD4 molecules
block the ability of these T cells to recognize antigen. The mAb GK1.5, therefore,
readily blocks MHC class II–restricted T-cell responses.[5] We took advantage of
the effects mediated by mAb GK1.5 in order to evaluate the ability of cytokines to
support MHC class II–dependent responses. We initially examined the effect of
the mAb GK1.5 on CTL responses, which had been shown to be entirely depen-

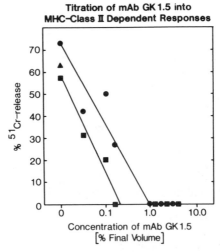

FIGURE 1. Effect of the anti-CD4 monoclonal antibody, GK1.5, on the generation of
cytolytic T cells directed against TNP-altered self-MHC antigens. Lymph node cells from
B10.D2 mice were cultured for five days against TNP-haptenated B10.D2 nucleated splenic
cells. The spleen cells were hapten-labeled with 10 mM 2,4,6-trinitrobenzene sulfonic acid
(Eastman Kodak Co., Rochester, NY) in Hanks' balanced salt solution for 10 min at 37°C in
the dark. The washed cells were irradiated with 1000 rads (^{137}Cs gamma source) and cultured
with responder lymph node cells (LNC), each at 5×10^6 cells/ml in RPMI-1640 medium
containing 10% human serum, 2 mM L-glutamine, and antibiotics. The mAb, GK1.5, was
added at the initiation of the culture period as dilutions of the Hb101 hybridoma spent
medium. Following culture, the recovered viable lymphocytes were harvested, titrated, and
assayed in a standard 4 hour ^{51}Cr release assay against TNP-haptenated ^{51}Cr-labeled MHC-
identical P815-X2 tumor cells. ●—●, ■—■, represent two separate experiments. ▲, cultures with 4% final concentration of Hb101 diluent.

TABLE 1. CD4-Depleted Responder Cells Generate Allogeneic CTL[a]

CTL Generation	Recovered Lymphocyte-To-Target Ratio				
	20 : 1	10 : 1	5 : 1	2.5 : 1	1.25 : 1
MHC Class I and II Differences			Percent ^{51}Cr-Release		
C57BL/10 + B10.D2, gamma-irradiated					
Hybridoma medium + rabbit complement	75.5	68.4	49.8	27.7	
mAb GK1.5 + RC	59.7	46.6	26.5	15.1	7.8
mAb GK1.5 + + RC, plus HFS	73.5	68.0	42.9	23.5	13.3
MHC Class II Difference					
C57BL/10 + B10.A(18R), gamma-irradiated					
Hybridoma medium	88.9	81.8	75.6	55.0	
mAb GK1.5 + RC	76.2	63.7	43.8	25.0	

[a] C57BL/10 (H-2[b]) lymph node cells at 4×10^7 were treated with hybridoma medium or mAb GK1.5 (1 : 20), and washed and incubated with rabbit complement twice before culture with irradiated (2000 rads) splenic cells from B10.D2 (H-2[d]) or B10.A(18R) (H-2[i18]) mice. We have confirmed by immunofluorescence with FITC-labeled goat anti-rat immunoglobulin antibodies and with mAb GK1.5 that all detectable L3T4a[+] cells are removed by this treatment. CD8[+] cells remained and stained positively with mAb to Lyt-2, HO-2.2. Helper factor supernates (HFS) were prepared in a two-step manner from mixed lymphocyte cultures as previously described.[14] These HFS preparations do not support the growth of IL-2–dependent CTLL-20 cells.

dent on MHC class II–associated antigen presentation, that is, CTL responses to trinitrophenylated (TNP)-self MHC antigens.[6] CTL responses were generated in a mixed lymphocyte culture reaction (MLR) with lymph node cells from B10.D2 mice stimulated by TNP-coupled and irradiated B10.D2 spleen cells. Monoclonal antibody GK1.5 was titrated in dilutions ranging from 1 : 20 to 1 : 2000 into these MLR cultures at their initiation. All detectable CTL generation was blocked by mAb GK1.5 at a 1 : 100 dilution or less (FIG. 1). Generally, dilutions around 1 : 500 served as an end point for total inhibition by mAb GK1.5. The recombinant forms of IL-1, IL-3, and IFN-gamma could not restore generation of TNP-altered self CTL to these anti-CD4-blocked cultures either when added individually over a broad range of concentrations (data not included), or when added in combination with each other (TABLE 1). Recombinant IL-2 (rIL-2) added at concentrations greater than that generally obtained from TNP–self-stimulated cultures (2 U/ml), also, would not overcome anti-CD4-blocked TNP responses. High concentrations of rIL-2 alone, or supernates from rat spleen cells stimulated for 24 hours with concanavalin A (RCAS), or rIL-2 plus a novel factor produced by our T-cell hybridoma D6T-5C12,[10] could support TNP-altered–self CTL generation (TABLE 1). These data, plus other studies not included here, have led us to suggest that our D6T-5C12–derived lymphokine represents a novel lymphokine that functions in a synergistic manner with rIL-2 to support MHC class I–CTL generation. RCAS serve as a rich source of cytokines that also support MHC class I–restricted CTL generation. High quantities of rIL-2, sufficient to act through low-affinity receptors, also can support the generation of TNP-altered self CTL under anti-CD4-blocked MLR culture conditions.

MHC Class I Differences Alone and in Combination with Class II Differences

CD4[+] T cells were depleted from C57BL/10 responder lymph node cell suspensions by treatment with mAb GK1.5 and rabbit complement. CTL generation

TABLE 2. Effect of Recombinant Cytokines and Hybridoma D6T-5C12 Supernate on Anti-CD4-Blocked CTL Generation to TNP-Haptenated Self Spleen Cells[a]

Additions mAb	Cytokine U/ml	Percent specific TNP CTL killing effector : target ratios		
		20 : 1[b]	10 : 1	5 : 1
A. —	—	40.2	33.2	23.0
GK1.5 1 : 200	—	—	2.0	0.3
GK1.5 1 : 200	rIFN-gamma, rIL-1, rIL-3[c]	3.4	1.8	0.0
GK1.5 1 : 200	RCAS[d], 7%	35.4	27.9	13.3
B. —	—	78	65	42
GK1.5 1 : 300	—	8	3	1
GK1.5 1 : 300	rIL-2, 2U	—	1	1
GK1.5 1 : 300	D6T.5C12[e], 25%	3	2	1
GK1.5 1 : 300	D6T.5C12, 25% + rIL-2, 2U	40	14	6

[a] B10.D2 LNC were stimulated with TNP-haptenated B10.D2 spleen cells for five days in culture with medium, mAb GK1.5, or GK1.5 plus cytokines.

[b] Effector to target ratio in experiment A was 20 : 1, and in B was 40 : 1.

[c] COS-1 supernates as described in legend to FIGURE 2.

[d] Crude cytokine-rich supernate from 24 hour culture of rat spleen cells with concanavalin A.

[e] The T-cell hybridoma, D6T.5C12, was isolated in our laboratory from a fusion between BW5147 thymoma cells and B10.D2 lymph node cells, which had previously been activated by syngeneic TNP-modified self splenic B10.D2 cells.[10]

was somewhat depressed after removal of CD4[+] cells but certainly not inhibited (TABLE 2). A number of previous studies have demonstrated that helper T cells are definitely required for CTL generation. The CTL generated under these CD4-depleted circumstances must have received their helper signals then from a second population of helper T cells, which are not MHC class II–restricted but which recognize MHC class I alloantigens in association with self MHC class I determinants.[4,7] The cells of this second helper T-cell subset, like most CTL, are MHC class I–restricted. The addition of our crude helper factor supernates (HFS), which do not contain IL-2, revealed that cytokines could enhance CTL generation of MHC class I–dependent responses (TABLE 2). We sought, then, to determine the responsiveness of these MHC class I–restricted cells to recombinant- and hybridoma-derived cytokines. Inasmuch as allogeneic CTL were not totally dependent upon CD4[+] cells for help, however, the mAb GK1.5 alone could not be used to eliminate endogenous help. Instead, a helper-deficient system was devised whereby antigen-presenting cells were removed by passage over Sephadex G10.[8]

Effect of Monoclonal Anti-CD4 on Cytokine Function

The passage of stimulator strain B10.D2 splenic cells over Sephadex G10 followed by culture in endotoxin-free conditions with C57BL/10 lymph node cells results in the loss of their ability to trigger differentiation of both helper T cells and cytotoxic precursor cells (FIG. 2, part C, line 1). Unfractionated stimulator cells readily triggered CTL differentiation (FIG. 2, part A). The addition of the mAb GK1.5 at the initiation of these cultures results in a slight depression of CTL generation similar to that observed upon removal of CD4$^+$ cells with antibody and complement (FIG. 2, part B). The continuous presence of the mAb GK1.5 did not lead to a greater depression of responsiveness than did the removal of CD4$^+$ cells as observed in TABLE 2. The Sephadex G10 fractionated stimulator cells thus served as the best model system in which helper T cells were not endogenously activated. The addition of the recombinant lymphokines, IL-3, IFN-gamma, and IL-2, as well as a distinct hybridoma-derived lymphokine, 4G7.C1, were able to support CTL differentiation in this model system (FIG. 2, part C). The addition of the mAb Gk1.5 into the cultures, however, readily suppressed the help for CTL generation provided by rIL-3 and the 4G7.C1 hybridoma. Only a slight depressive

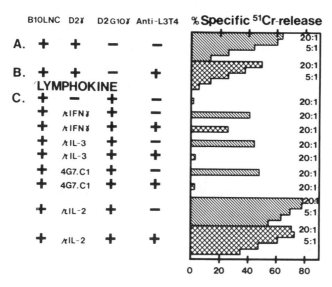

FIGURE 2. Recombinant lymphokines, IFN-gamma and IL-3, provide help for class II–dependent helpers, whereas rIL-2 provides help for both MHC class II–dependent and –independent responses. CTL generation in allogeneic cultures between mouse strain combinations that expressed both MHC class I and class II H-2 differences was examined with C57BL/10 lymph node cell donors and irradiated stimulator spleen cells from B10.D2 (D2-gamma). An exogenous helper factor-dependent assay system was devised by the passage of B10.D2 spleen cells over an 8 mm column length of Sephadex G10 before irradiation (D2G10-gamma). ▨▨▨, the anti-L3T4 mAb, GK1.5, was added at a final concentration of 1 : 300; ▨▨, no mAb added. The viable cells recovered on day 5 were titrated against ^{51}Cr-labeled target cells at ratios of 20 : 1, 10 : 1, 5 : 1, 2.5 : 1, and 1.25 : 1. Only the 20 : 1 ratios are presented in part C where cell recoveries were lower except in cultures provided with the growth factor, IL-2. Final concentrations of the lymphokines added on day 1 were as follows: COS IFN-gamma, 50 U/ml; COS IL-3, 2.4 U/ml; COS IL-2, 15 U/ml; and T hybridoma 4G7.Cl^b supernate at 20%. Each of the COS-derived lymphokines provided little or no help at a 10^{-1} dilution of these concentrations. WEHI-3 supernate added to these assays at concentrations up to 94 U/ml were totally blocked from providing help by the anti-L3T4 mAb, GK1.5. Higher concentrations of COS-IFN-gamma (or of purified IFN-gamma) were inhibitory to CTL generation.

^{b} The 4G7.C1 cell line was isolated following the fusion of B10 LNC from skin graft–primed mice and EL-4 cells. The 4G7.C1 supernates do not contain detectable levels of IL-2, IFN-gamma, IL-3, or IL-1.

effect was noted on IL-2–supported responses, particularly at the lower CTL-to-target ratios (FIG. 2, part C). Higher concentrations of mAb GK1.5 largely suppressed CTL generation supported by rIFN-gamma and rIL-1 (FIG. 3). A greater suppression of responses supported by rIL-2 was not effected with the higher concentrations of mAb GK1.5 (FIG. 3). It is apparent, thus, that rIL-1, rIFN-gamma, and rIL-3 readily support events that lead to the differentiation of T cells; however, those responses are also readily suppressible with anti-CD4. The majority of these CD4$^+$ cells are helper T cells that are MHC class II–restricted. The

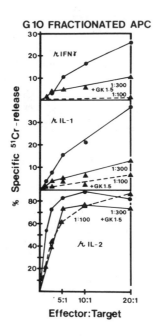

FIGURE 3. The effect of anti-CD4 mAb on the helper-induction effects mediated by recombinant murine IL-2, IFN-gamma, and IL-1. ●—●, no mAb; ▲—▲, mAb GK1.5 at 1:300; ▲---▲, mAb GK1.5 at a 1:100 final concentration. C57BL/10 LNC were stimulated for 5 days in culture with G10-passaged and irradiated B10.A(18R) spleen cells. The B10.A(18R) mice are congenic recombinants derived from C57BL/10 and B10.A. The B10.A(18R) cells differ from those of the C57BL/10 at only the MHC class I region, H-2D^d. The COS-1–derived rIFN-gamma and rIL-2 were added as outlined in FIG. 2. The rIL-1 was added at a final concentration of 2.5 U/ml.

recombinant cytokines, rIL-1, rIL-3, and rIFN-gamma do not appear to directly initiate MHC class I T-cell differentiation of either the helper T-cell subset or the CTL precursor.

DISCUSSION

Cytokines play distinct roles in the maturation of T-cell responses to cell-bound antigens. IL-1 appears to directly trigger helper T cells, in the presence of antigens, to synthesize IL-2 and the TAC$^+$ lighter molecular weight chain of the

IL-2 receptor. We had demonstrated previously that IL-1 was not required as a direct signal for MHC class I–restricted cytotoxic precursor T-cell maturation.[2] In addition, our data, presented here, suggest that IL-1 signals are received mainly by T cells that are MHC class II–restricted. MHC class I–restricted helper T cells were not activated by IL-1, hence could not provide sufficient help for CTL generation.

The role of IFN-gamma in CTL maturation has been a matter of controversy for some time. Our data demonstrate that in the CTL differentiation pathway, signals presented by IFN-gamma result largely in the triggering of MHC class II–restricted helper T cells. The manner in which these signals are executed is unclear, but it is possible that their effects on helper T cells may largely be indirect. The expression of Ia or DR antigens on macrophage cell surfaces is significantly upregulated by IFN-gamma.[9] The enhanced expression of Ia/DR on antigen-presenting cells results in a more efficient presentation of antigen. The T cells activated, then, would be those restricted to the recognition of antigen in association with MHC class II antigens, largely helper T cells. The activation of MHC class II–restricted helper T cells would result in a greater concentration of lymphokines being produced and made available for the support of precursor CTL differentiation. One would expect, under these circumstances, that a mAb such as GK1.5, which blocks MHC class II–associative recognition, would depress CTL differentiation by virtue of the fact that lymphokine production by CD4+ helper T cells was prevented. The effects of IFN-gamma were indeed suppressible by anti-CD4, although higher concentrations of mAb GK1.5 were required to fully block IFN-gamma from supporting CTL differentiation.

The nature of the effects of IL-3 on helper T cells is not well-understood; however, IL-3 does appear to support short-term survival or growth of T cells. Our data demonstrate that the IL-3 effect on CTL generation is directed largely to CD4+ MHC class II–restricted T cells.

The hybridoma-derived supernate, 4G7.C1, also provides signals for the MHC-restricted class II cells, as its effects are blocked by mAb Gk1.5. The D6T.5C12-derived hybridoma supernate, however, is not blocked by mAb Gk1.5. The D6T.5C12 lymphokine, thus, appears to function in the MHC class I–restricted CTL differentiation pathway. The D6T.5C12 lymphokine functions in a synergistic and dependent manner with rIL-2. The characterization of this lymphokine has not been completed, but we have presented evidence that is distinct from IL-1, IL-2, IL-3, IL-4, and IFN-gamma.[10]

IL-2 provides growth signals to T cells in an MHC-unrestricted manner. Anti-CD4 had little depressive effect on clonal growth and the differentiative support provided by rIL-2. These data were of interest especially because mAb GK1.5 depressed the effects supported by IL-1. One would normally expect endogenously produced IL-1 to provide signals for the expression of the alpha-chain or TAC molecule of the IL-2 receptor; however, as we have shown here, IL-1 activation was blocked in the presence of mAb GK1.5. Even though these data might suggest that IL-2 could serve as a single ultimate differentiative signal, we tend to favor the possibility, however, that IL-2 alone is not sufficient[11] for the triggering of antigen-specific CTL differentiation. A second molecule then would be required to trigger IL-2–receptor acquisition and helper-cell activation under our culture conditions. The activation of MHC class I–restricted helper T cells by other cytokines, such as RIF, IL-5, or IL-6, may trigger signals that would lead to their production of lymphokines that serve as differentiative signals such as the D6T.5C12 factor described above. These lymphokines would then synergize with IL-2 to support CTL expansion and differentiation. The nature of all of the various lymphokines involved in CTL differentiation is not entirely known at this time. The effects of IL-4 and IL-5, for example, have not yet been fully examined.[12,13] Furthermore, the cDNA cloning of additional lymphokines that activate a particular subset of T cells and not another, or lymphokines that are produced after recognition of antigen in association with MHC class I versus class II antigens, has not yet been accomplished. Despite these limitations, we have already gained a substantial knowledge of the role of cytokines in the differentiative pathways of CTL maturation (FIG. 4). There remains, however, a great deal of information yet to be learned. The facts that some of the cytokines function mainly on a particular MHC-restricted subset of T cells and that there are two distinct MHC-restricted helper T-cell subsets, lead us toward a greater understanding of CTL differentiation (FIG. 4).

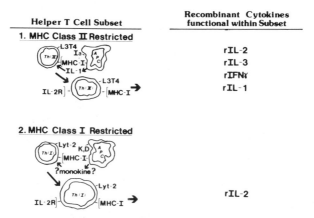

FIGURE 4. Schematic model of MHC class I– and class II–restricted helper T-cell subsets and recombinant cytokines known to interact with each subset. The helper T-cell subsets depicted here each have antigen-specific T-cell receptors for MHC class I alloantigens. The MHC associative structure or restricting elements, L3T4 (CD4) and Lyt-2 (CD8), on the two helper T-cell subsets, differ; hence number 1 recognizes alloantigen in association with Ia or MHC class II–self determinants, whereas number 2 recognizes alloantigens in association with H-2K or H-2D self-MHC class I determinants.

SUMMARY

The differentiation of precursor, antigen-competent, T cells into effective helper and/or cytolytic cells involves a number of different steps that are signaled by soluble molecules termed cytokines. We demonstrate here that subsets of T cells, distinguished on the basis of their expression of cell-surface markers, CD4 and CD8, receive distinct signals for differentiation. The precursor T cells of a T-cell subset that is MHC class II–restricted are readily activated by signals provided by rIL-1, rIL-2, rIL-3, or IFN-gamma. The precursor T cells of the MHC class I–restricted T-cell subset, on the other hand, are not readily activated by signals provided by rIL-1, rIL-3, or IFN-gamma. Recombinant IL-2 apparently functions in a nonrestricted manner, in that it can provide growth signals to both MHC class I– and class II–restricted T cells.

ACKNOWLEDGMENT

We thank Ms. Donna Dickerson for excellent secretarial assistance and the typing of this manuscript.

REFERENCES

1. MIZEL, S. B. & J. J. FARRAR. 1979. Cell. Immunol. **48:** 433–436.
2. MCMANNIS, J. D. & J. M. D. PLATE. 1985. Proc. Natl. Acad. Sci. USA **82:** 1513.
3. HARDT, C., T. DIAMANSTEIN & H. WAGNER. 1985. Eur. J. Immunol. **15:** 472–478.
4. PLATE, J. M. D., T. L. LUKASZEWSKA, G. BUSTAMANTE & R. L. HAYES. 1987. Submitted for Publication.
5. DIALYNAS, D. P., D. B. WILDE, P. MARRACK, A. PIERRES, K. A. WALL, W. HOWRAN, G. OTTEN, M. R. LOKEN, M. PIERRES, J. KAPPLER & F. W. FITCH. 1983. Immunol. Rev. **74:** 29.
6. PETTINELLI, C. B., A. M. SCHMITT-VERHULST & G. SHEARER. 1979. J. Immunol. **122:** 847.
7. MIZOUCHI, T., H. GOLDING, A. S. ROSENBERG, L. H. GLIMCHER, T. R. MALEK & A. SINGER. 1985. J. Exp. Med. **162:** 427.
8. LY, I. A. & R. I. MISHELL. 1974. J. Immunol. Methods **5:** 239.
9. ARENZANA-SEISDEDOS, F., J. L. VIRELIZIER & W. FIERS. 1985. J. Immunol. **134:** 2444.
10. HAYES, R. L. & J. M. D. PLATE. 1985. Fed. Proc. **44:** 951.
11. HAYES, R. L. & J. M. D. PLATE. 1984. Lymphokine Res. **3:** 248.
12. YOSHIHIKO, N., P. SIDERAS, N. TAKAYUKI, S. BERGSTEDT-LINDQUIST *et al.* 1986. Nature **319:** 640.
13. TAKATSU, K., Y. KIKUCHI, T. TAKAHASHI, T. HONJO, M. MATSUMOTO, N. HARADA, N. YAMAGUCHI & A. TOMINAGA. 1987. Proc. Natl. Acad. Sci. USA **84:** 4234.
14. PLATE, J. M. D. 1977. Cell. Immunol. **32:** 183.

Cooperation between Helper T Cells and Cytotoxic T Lymphocyte Precursors

L. A. HUSMANN[a] AND M. J. BEVAN

Department of Immunology
Research Institute of Scripps Clinic
10666 North Torrey Pines Road
La Jolla, California 92037

INTRODUCTION

The L3T4 (CD4) molecule, defined in the mouse by the monoclonal antibody (mAb) GK1.5,[1] is expressed on a distinct subpopulation of mature peripheral T cells. Cells positive for L3T4 are often termed helper T cells because they are able to promote both humoral and cellular immunity.[1-3] This subset of T cells responds predominantly to antigen in association with class II major histocompatibility complex antigens (class II MHC) on antigen-presenting cells.[1,3-5] *In vitro*, mAb to L3T4 inhibits class II MHC–restricted T-cell responses by either blocking essential interactions between helper T cells and accessory cells or by the delivery of a negative signal.[3-5] *In vivo*, administration of mAb to L3T4 depletes L3T4–positive cells from the blood, spleen, and lymph nodes.[6] Treatment of mice with anti-L3T4 mAb has been shown to block humoral responses,[6-8] induce tolerance to specific antigens,[9,10] delay allograft rejection,[11,12] and retard the onset of autoimmune diseases.[13-17]

To investigate the role of helper T cells in cytotoxic responses, we attempted to antigen-prime cytotoxic T lymphocyte (CTL) precursors after depletion of specific T-cell subsets. Our studies consisted of depleting the L3T4-positive subset of peripheral T cells by injecting GK1.5 mAb *in vivo* or fractionating lymphoid cells by antibody- and complement (c')-killing *in vitro*, and injecting the subpopulations into syngeneic, irradiated, bone marrow (BM)–reconstituted mice. After treatment, mice were primed with either the male-specific histocompatibility antigen, H-Y, or autosomal minor histocompatibility (minor H) antigens. Spleens were subsequently removed, and the level of priming of CTL was tested in cytotoxicity assays following *in vitro* stimulation in mixed lymphocyte culture (MLC).

In these systems, the absence of L3T4-positive helper T cells reduced the level of CTL priming. As L3T4-positive helper T cells regenerated, the level of CTL priming increased. In some cases, very large doses of antigen partly overcame the dependence of CTL on L3T4-positive cells. From these observations, we conclude that the presence of L3T4-positive helper T cells can enhance the CTL response *in vivo*.

[a] L. A. Husmann is a graduate student in the Department of Biology, University of California, San Diego.

MATERIAL AND METHODS

Mice

BALB.B, BALB/cbyJ, C57BL/6J (B6), C57BL/10 (B10), B10.D2/nSn, and B10.BR/SgSn mice were produced in the animal colony at Scripps Clinic and Research Foundation, La Jolla, CA. Female mice 6–10 weeks of age were used as hosts. Mice up to 9 months of age were used as donors of cells for *in vivo* priming and as stimulators in MLC.

Reagents

The hybridomas 3.168 (rat IgM, anti-Lyt-2),[18] GK1.5 (rat IgG_{2b}, anti-L3T4),[1] RL172.4 (rat IgM, anti-L3T4),[19] 13.4 (mouse IgM, anti-Thy-1.2),[20] and T24 (rat IgG_{2a}, anti-Thy-1)[21] were grown as ascites. Fluorescein isothiocyanate (FITC)-conjugated goat anti-rat Ig was purchased from Cappel Laboratories, Cooper Biomedical Inc., Malvern, PA and absorbed on mouse IgG coupled to Sepharose beads to make it rat Ig–specific.

Complement Lysis

Cell suspensions, prepared in Hanks' balanced salt solution (HBSS) containing 5% (v/v) fetal calf serum ((FCS), Flow Laboratories, McLean, VA), were washed and resuspended at $1-2 \times 10^7$/ml in mAb diluted in HBSS/5% FCS. After incubation of 30–45 minutes on ice, cells were pelleted by centrifugation and were resuspended in guinea pig serum or rabbit serum as a source of complement. After additional incubation at 37° for 30–45 minutes, cell suspensions were filtered through nylon mesh to remove aggregated debris, and washed twice. Viable cell yields were determined by Trypan blue exclusion.

Fluorescent Staining and Analysis

Aliquots of $0.5-1.0 \times 10^6$ cells were stained for analysis on the fluorescence-activated cell sorter (FACS). Optimum concentrations of staining reagents were determined in preliminary experiments. All incubations were in 0.1 ml HBSS/5% FCS with diluted antibody for 30–45 minutes on ice. Cells were then washed and resuspended in 0.1 ml FITC-conjugated antibody diluted in HBSS/5% FCS. The second incubation was 45 minutes on ice in the dark. Cells were again washed, then resuspended in 1% formalin in phosphate-buffered saline. Controls involved omission of the primary antibody. Cells were analyzed for fluorescence using a FACS IV (Becton Dickinson, Mountain View, CA) with a single laser and logarithmic intensity scales. Dead cells were excluded from analysis by selective gating. Stained samples, 10^4 cells each, were analyzed as single color histograms.

In Vivo *Priming*

Mice were primed by intraperitoneal (i.p.) injection of $1-100 \times 10^6$ viable, T cell–depleted spleen cells suspended in HBSS. Animals were immunized against either minor (non-H-2) histocompatibility differences or the male-specific antigen H-Y.

In Vivo *Depletion of L3T4-Positive Cells*

GK1.5 (anti-L3T4) ascites was injected i.p. in quantities determined to deplete L3T4$^+$ peripheral cells for 2–3 weeks after one injection. Mice received either one injection of GK1.5 or a series of injections, one every 3–4 days.

Immunization in Adoptive Transfer

Host mice for the adoptive transfers were exposed to whole-body irradiation (850 rd from a ^{137}Cs source) and then injected i.v. with 2–3 × 10^6 syngeneic bone marrow cells that had been treated with anti-Thy-1 mAb and complement. Two days later these irradiated, bone marrow–reconstituted hosts were injected i.v. with fractionated responder lymphocytes and irradiated antigenic cells. Normal spleen and lymph node cells were treated with anti-L3T4 (RL172.4) or anti-Lyt-2 antibody plus c′ or with c′ alone. Minor H–different priming cells were spleen cells treated with anti-Thy-1 plus c′ and 1000 rd. Four × 10^7 responder cells (c′-treated, anti-L3T4–treated, anti-Lyt-2–treated, or mixtures) were injected i.v. into the adoptive hosts along with 1 × 10^7 antigenic cells. Host mice were sacrificed 4–9 days later and spleen cell suspensions boosted in MLC with stimulator cells from the minor H–different strain. Cytotoxicity assays were performed 4 days later.

Mixed Lymphocyte Culture and Cytotoxicity Assay

Mixed lymphocyte cultures (MLC) were set up in 24-well Costar plates with 6 × 10^6 responder spleen cells per well, boosted with appropriate anti-Thy-1–treated irradiated spleen cells and assayed 4–8 days later for cytotoxic activity directed against ^{51}Cr-labeled targets. Target cells were P815 (DBA/2, H-2^d), CBA.D1 (CBA, H-2^k), and EL4 (C57BL/6, H-2^b) tumor cell lines or 2–3 day Con A–stimulated spleen cell blasts made from appropriate mouse strains. Serial threefold dilutions of responder cells were added to 1 × 10^4 labeled targets, and the percent specific lysis after 3–5 hours of incubation at 37° was calculated in the following manner:

$$100 \times \frac{\text{cpm released in presence of responders} - \text{cpm spontaneously released}}{\text{cpm released by detergent} - \text{cpm spontaneously released}}$$

RESULTS

Titration of GK1.5 in Vivo

To determine a protocol for the effective *in vivo* depletion of peripheral L3T4-positive cells, BALB/c mice were injected i.p. with varying concentrations of GK1.5 ascites fluid. Subsequent analysis of lymph nodes over a period of time indicated a depletion of L3T4-positive cells in animals injected with GK1.5, compared to control mice injected with HBSS (TABLE 1). Animals treated with as little as 25 μl GK1.5 ascites showed a highly significant depletion of L3T4-positive cells at an early time point. These mice started to recover L3T4-positive lymphocytes

TABLE 1. Percent L3T4-Positive Cells in Lymph Nodes of Mice Treated with a Single i.p. Injection of GK1.5 (Anti-L3T4)[a]

	Day after Injection				
Dose	5	9	13	21	37
0.4 ml HBSS	49.5	51.7	42.1	49.8	53.2
0.025 ml GK1.5	4.3	nd[b]	9.6	20.2	nd
0.1 ml GK1.5	0	0	0	9.7	30.2
0.4 ml GK1.5	2.2	nd	0	2.9	nd

[a] Mice were injected i.p. with varying doses of GK1.5 ascites (anti-L3T4). Lymph node cell suspensions were assayed by flow cytometry on subsequent days. Numbers indicate percent positive over background staining controls.

[b] nd = not done.

soon after injection, whereas those treated with higher doses remained depleted for a longer time. In future experiments, we chose to treat mice with either a single dose or multiple doses of 0.1 ml GK1.5 ascites once every 3–4 days.

Representative FACS analysis of lymph node cells from mice injected with anti-L3T4 is shown in FIGURE 1. Animals injected with GK1.5 ascites showed a clear depletion of L3T4-positive cells when compared to HBSS-injected controls (panels b and e). Conversely, they showed a significant increase in the percentage

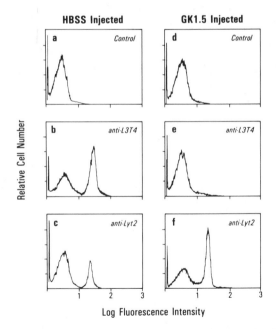

FIGURE 1. Mice were given a single i.p. injection of 0.1 ml GK1.5 ascites fluid (anti-L3T4), (panels d, e, f) or HBSS (panels a, b, c). Lymph node cell suspensions were analyzed on the FACS IV nine days after injection following staining with a control second antibody (FITC-conjugated goat anti-rat Ig, panels a, d), GK1.5 (anti-L3T4, panels b, e), or 3.168 (anti-Lyt-2, panels c, f).

of Lyt-2–positive cells (panels c and f). These results indicate that the L3T4-positive cells have not merely internalized bound antibody but that the cells are actually depleted.

In Vivo *Depletion and Subsequent Priming*

BALB.B female mice were depleted of L3T4-positive T cells by injections of GK1.5 ascites every 3–4 days and primed on day 10 after initial injection with 1 × 10^7 T-depleted cells as described. Spleen cells from either BALB.B males (H-Y antigen) or B10 females (minor H antigens) were the source of antigen for *in vivo* priming and for boosting in MLC. The *in vitro* boosts were performed either with or without rat spleen Con A supernatant (CAS) as a source of interleukin-2 (IL-2). After 5 days in MLC, surviving cells were assayed for cytotoxic activity on ^{51}Cr-labeled BALB.B female and male, and B10 female, targets. The results in FIGURE

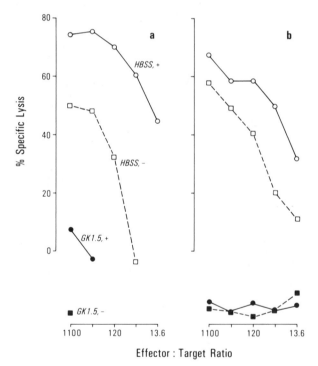

FIGURE 2. BALB.B female mice were i.p. injected with 0.1 ml GK1.5 (anti-L3T4) ascites fluid (closed symbols) or HBSS (open symbols) every 3–4 days and primed with 1 × 10^7 B10 spleen cells (minor H antigens) (panel a) or BALB.B male spleen cells (H-Y) (panel b) on day 10 after initial injection. Mice were sacrificed 10 days after antigen priming, and spleen cells were boosted in MLC with (○,●) or without (□,■) rat spleen Con A supernatant. On day 5 of MLC, cells were assayed for specific lysis of ^{51}Cr-labeled B10 female (panel a), BALB.B male (panel b), and BALB.B female (not shown) three-day Con A blast target cells. Lysis of BALB.B female target cells was <0% in all cases.

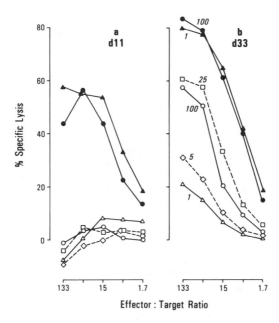

FIGURE 3. BALB.B female mice were injected days 0, 3, and 6 with 0.1 ml GK1.5 ascites fluid (open symbols) or HBSS (closed symbols) and primed with varying doses of T-depleted B6 spleen cells as indicated (number × 10⁶) on day 3. Mice were sacrificed on day 11 (panel a) or day 33 (panel b) after initial injection; spleen cells were boosted in MLC in the presence of Con A supernatant and assayed for specific lysis of ^{51}Cr-labeled CBA.D1 (H-2^k, control) and EL-4 (H-2^b) tumor cell lines. Shown is specific killing of EL-4 targets.

2 show that the antigen-primed animals depleted of L3T4-positive cells (those injected with GK1.5) did not show a response to appropriate targets after stimulation in MLC, whereas HBSS-injected, antigen-primed animals showed significant lysis. Furthermore, the degree of killing was not affected significantly by the addition of CAS to the MLC.

Kinetics of Recovery of CTL Response and the Effect of Antigen Dose

To determine whether the regeneration of L3T4-positive cells or the antigen dose affected antigen priming of CTL, BALB.B female mice were injected on days 0, 3, and 6 with GK1.5 ascites or HBSS and primed on day 3 with varying numbers of T-depleted B6 spleen cells (minor H antigens). Mice were sacrificed on day 11 or day 33 after initial injection, and spleen cells were boosted in MLC with irradiated B6 spleen cells in the presence of CAS. On day 5 of MLC, cells were assayed for specific lysis of ^{51}Cr-labeled CBA.D1(H-2^k control) and EL4(H-2^b) targets (FIG. 3). Spleen cells from L3T4-depleted mice did not show a response at any priming dose during the time that L3T4-positive cells remained depleted. When L3T4-positive cells had regenerated, however, specific killing response increased in a dose-dependent manner. Spleen cells from HBSS injected–control mice killed H-2–matched targets on all days tested.

Adoptive Transfers and Subsequent Priming

Hosts for adoptive transfers were irradiated and reconstituted with syngeneic BM as described in MATERIALS AND METHODS, then injected i.v. with fractionated syngeneic spleen and lymph node cells as responders, and primed with T-depleted–irradiated spleen cells across a minor H difference.

Responder cells were fractionated *in vitro* by using either anti-L3T4 or anti-Lyt-2 plus c'. Controls included cells treated with c' alone and a mixture of the two antibody-treated subpopulations. Nine days later, spleen cells from the adoptive hosts (B10 mice) were stimulated in MLC with irradiated BALB.B cells either with or without CAS and assayed for specific lysis four days later. When responder cells were c' treated or were a mixture of L3T4-depleted plus Lyt-2–depleted populations, high specific killing of targets was observed (TABLE 2). Responders depleted of either L3T4-positive or Lyt-2–positive cells showed little or no specific lysis of BALB.B target cells. These results indicate that both subsets of peripheral T cells are necessary at the same time for efficient priming of CTL *in vivo*.

Kinetics of CTL Response after Adoptive Transfer

Irradiated and BM reconstituted BALB.B mice were primed with T depleted–spleen cells of B6 mice (minor H antigens) and adoptively transferred with syngeneic spleen and lymph node cells that had been treated with either anti-L3T4 and complement or complement alone. MLC were set up in the presence of CAS on days 4, 6, and 8 after adoptive transfer using irradiated spleen cells from B6 mice as stimulators. FIGURE 4 shows that the spleen cells from animals adoptively transferred with cells treated with c' alone have high specific killing ability on all days tested. Spleen cells from animals that had been adoptively transferred with

TABLE 2. Synergy between L3T4$^+$ and Lyt-2$^+$ Cells in the CTL Response to Minor H Antigens[a]

Adoptive host no.	Responder cells treated with	Percent Specific Lysis of Targets[b]			
		Without CAS		With CAS	
		BALB.B	B10	BALB.B	B10
1	c' alone	73/39	−4/−3	80/57	−2/−3
2	c' alone	77/38	−1/−2	76/57	−3/−3
3	α Lyt-2 plus c'	25/−3	−6/−3	2/−1	−9/−3
4	α Lyt-2 plus c'	3/−3	−10/−2	9/1	−7/−5
5	α L3T4 plus c'	0/0	−7/−3	1/−3	−6/−4
6	α L3T4 plus c'	3/0	−7/−4	10/2	−6/−3
7	Mixture	72/36	−2/−2	82/59	−3/−2
8	Mixture	67/34	−3/−4	74/47	−5/−4

[a] C57BL/10 (H-2^b) adoptive host mice (850 rd plus T depleted–syngeneic BM) were i.v. injected with 4×10^7 fractionated responder cells plus 1×10^7 1000 rd, anti-Thy-1, plus c'-treated BALB.B (H-2^b) spleen cells. Nine days later, spleen cells from the adoptive hosts were stimulated in MLC with irradiated BALB.B cells either with or without exogenous rat spleen Con A supernatant and assayed for specific lysis four days later.

[b] Target cells were spleen cells from BALB.B or B10 mice cultured with Con A for two days. Values given are for lysis at effector:target ratios of 100:1 and 10:1.

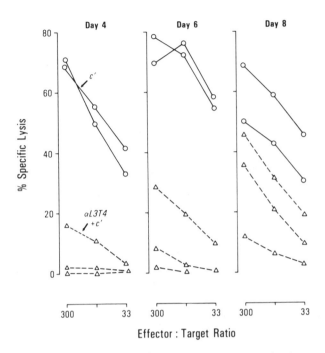

FIGURE 4. Spleen and lymph node cells from normal BALB.B (H-2^h) mice were pretreated with complement alone (O---O) or with RL.172.4 anti-L3T4 mAb plus complement (△---△) and immunized in syngeneic adoptive hosts against C57BL/6 (H-2^h) cells. Adoptive hosts were sacrificed on the indicated day post-transfer; spleen cells boosted in MLC and assayed for lysis of ^{51}Cr-EL4 target cells. Lysis of a control target cell, P815, was <10% in all cases. For each time point, two hosts of c'-treated cells and three hosts of L3T4-depleted cells are shown.

L3T4-depleted cells show a low specific killing response on day 4, which increases gradually with time.

DISCUSSION

GK1.5 is a monoclonal antibody that recognizes T-helper cells in the mouse. When administered *in vitro*, GK1.5 inhibits MHC class II–restricted responses.[3–5] *In vivo*, GK1.5 has been shown to deplete the peripheral T-cell population of helper cells.[6,7,10,11,13,14,16] The effect of T helper cell depletion on humoral responses to antigen and on tolerance induction has been studied.[6–10] Here we have examined the effect of T helper cell depletion on the *in vivo* priming of Lyt-2–positive CTL precursors.

Treatment of young adult mice with a single injection of GK1.5 mAb has a marked effect on the peripheral T-cell population. Goronzy *et al.*[22] have shown that mice treated with a total dose of 600 µg of anti-L3T4 had a long-term inversion of the L3T4/Lyt-2 ratio and that the elimination of L3T4-positive cells in the lymph nodes is dependent on the antibody dose. Our findings are consistent with those results. Mice treated with a low dose (25 μl) start to recover more quickly after antibody injection than those treated with a high dose.

The mechanism of action of GK1.5 mAb *in vivo* is not known. Analysis of the FACS profiles of lymph nodes of L3T4-depleted animals, however, indicates that whereas there is a decrease in L3T4-positive cells compared to controls, there is a concurrent increase in the fraction of Lyt-2–positive cells. If the antibody had been bound and internalized, we would expect to see a similar profile for control and L3T4-depleted–lymph node cells stained with anti-Lyt-2. Instead we see an increase in the percentage of Lyt-2–positive cells from approximately 20% to more than 50 percent. This indicated that, in fact, the L3T4-positive cells have been removed from the lymph nodes.

Using GK1.5 injection as a method of selectively depleting the helper subpopulation of peripheral T cells, we explored the function of the CTL subpopulation *in vivo* in the absence of the helper subset. Mice were selectively depleted of L3T4-positive cells, then primed to either male specific–H-Y or autosomal minor H antigens. Responder spleen cells from helper-depleted mice were unable to cause specific ^{51}Cr release after 5 days in MLC with irradiated stimulator cells, whereas the control mice showed a significant response. The necessity to culture responder spleen cells with stimulators in order to detect cytotoxic response has been previously shown.[29,30]

To determine whether the response could be restored with exogenous IL-2, MLC were set up in the presence or absence of rat spleen Con A supernatant. If the response were restored, it could be argued that the L3T4-positive cells were important at the secondary MLC level rather than at the priming level. Exogenous IL-2, however, did not restore the cytotoxic response, implying that the lack of L3T4-positive–helper T cells is important at the level of CTL priming. Therefore, in the absence of L3T4-positive cells, CTL precursors cannot be primed to significant levels.

When the L3T4-positive subpopulation began to regenerate at about two weeks after GK1.5 injection, CTL response to priming increased. That is, specific responses to antigen could be seen. In addition, spleen cells of those mice primed with large numbers of cells had a higher specific killing with regeneration of L3T4-positive cells than those mice primed with low numbers of cells. These results indicate that the regenerating helper cells can function in the priming of CTL when the priming antigen is already present and that this function is dose-dependent.

Goronzy *et al.*[22] have not found a direct correlation between the reappearance of L3T4-positive cells and the restoration of the humoral immune responsiveness with some antigens. This may be due to the immunogenicities of the antigens and the doses given. Our results indicated that with a higher antigen dose, specific cytotoxic responses recover faster.

It has been previously shown[27,28] that purified Lyt-2–positive cells can respond *in vitro* to class I MHC differences without the participation of L3T4-positive cells. In addition, Cobbold *et al.*[12] have shown that both L3T4-positive and Lyt-2–positive subsets can reject skin grafts relatively independently. This would at first seem to contradict our findings that Lyt-2–positive cells cannot be antigen-primed in the absence of L3T4-positive cells. Lack of detectable L3T4-positive cells, however, may mean that a small population below the threshold of detectability still exists and, as shown in our studies, high amounts of antigen can elicit a strong cytotoxic response as L3T4-positive cells are regenerating, that is, even when they are at a low level.

Goronzy *et al.*[22] have also indicated that GK1.5 treatment does not completely eliminate L3T4-positive cells from the lymph nodes of treated animals. We are unable to find significant numbers of L3T4-positive cells after GK1.5 treatment, but this may be due to lack of detectability on FACS analysis. In addition, it has been shown in both the rat[23,24] and the human[25,26] that the L3T4 equivalent molecule in these species is present on some macrophages. To avoid the objections raised by these points, we turned to adoptive transfer of *in vitro* fractionated subpopulations of peripheral T cells and asked whether either of these subpopulations could be primed in the absence of the other. In our hands, irradiated, syngeneic BM-reconstituted mice that were adoptively transferred with L3T4-depleted or Lyt-2–depleted spleen and lymph node cells alone were unable to respond or responded poorly in cytotoxicity assays after 5 day MLC with appropriate stimulators. Mice that had received either c'-treated or a mixture of L3T4-depleted and Lyt-2–depleted spleen and lymph node cells, however, responded well to minor H challenge, indicating that both subsets are necessary for efficient priming of CTL. In this system we can be more confident that there was complete killing of fractionated responder cells and that we are not depleting additional subpopulations such as macrophages.

Our results suggest that the efficiency of priming CTL precursors to minor H antigens *in vivo* is enhanced by the presence of the T cells that express L3T4. It may be that the requirement for L3T4-positive–helper cells is not absolute and can be overridden by high doses of antigenic cells, or that the kinetics of response may be only delayed. Some CTL may be relatively independent of exogenous help. Alternatively, CTL are totally dependent on helper cells, but the techniques we use for depletion allow for the survival of some helper cells. L3T4-negative– or anti-L3T4–resistant helper cells, for example, would escape the treatment.

SUMMARY

We have investigated the requirement for the presence of L3T4-positive T cells in the *in vivo* priming of Lyt-2–positive cytotoxic T-lymphocyte precursors. The antigens used were the male-specific antigen H-Y and autosomal minor histocompatibility antigens. In some experiments, responder mice were depleted of L3T4-positive cells by repeated intraperitoneal injections of the anti-L3T4 antibody, GK1.5. In other experiments, lymphoid cells from normal mice were fractionated *in vitro* by antibody-plus-complement treatment and the populations primed in irradiated adoptive hosts. In these antigen systems, depletion of L3T4-positive helper cells decreases the level of priming of cytotoxic T lymphocytes. With regeneration of the L3T4-positive subpopulation, the CTL response to antigen increases. To some extent, the reliance on L3T4-positive cells can be overcome by increasing the antigen dose. We conclude that in most physiological responses, L3T4-positive T cells enhance the cytotoxic T-cell response.

REFERENCES

1. DIALYNAS, D. P., D. B. WILDE, P. MARRACK, A. PIERRES, K. A. WALL, W. HAVRAN, G. OTTEN, M. R. LOKEN, M. PIERRES, J. KAPPLER & F. W. FITCH. 1983. Characterization of the murine antigenic determinant, designated L3T4a, recognized by monoclonal antibody GK1.5: Expression of L3T4a by functional T cell clones appears to correlate primarily with class II MHC antigen reactivity. Immunol. Rev. **74:** 29–55.

2. DIALYNAS, D. P., Z. S. QUAN, K. A. WALL, A. PIERRES, J. QUINTANS, M. R. LOKEN, M. PIERRES & F. W. FITCH. 1983. Characterization of the murine T cell surface molecule, designated L3T4, identified by monoclonal antibody GK1.5: Similarity of L3T4 to human Leu-3/T4 molecule. J. Immunol. **131:** 2445–2451.

3. WILDE, D. B., P. MARRACK, J. KAPPLER, D. P. DIALYNAS & F. W. FITCH. 1983. Evidence implicating L3T4 in class II MHC antigen reactivity: Monoclonal antibody GK1.5 (anti-L3T4a) blocks class II MHC antigen-specific proliferation, release of lymphokines, and binding by cloned murine helper T lymphocyte lines. J. Immunol. **131:** 2178–2183.

4. SWAIN, S. L. 1983. T cell subsets and the recognition of MHC class. Immunol. Rev. **74:** 129–142.

5. SWAIN, S. L., D. P. DIALYNAS, F. W. FITCH & M. ENGLISH. 1984. Monoclonal antibody to L3T4 blocks the function of T cells specific for class II major histocompatibility complex antigens. J. Immunol. **132:** 1118–1123.

6. WOFSY, D., D. C. MAYES, J. WOODCOCK & W. E. SEAMAN. 1985. Inhibition of humoral immunity *in vivo* by monoclonal antibody to L3T4: Studies with soluble antigens in intact mice. J. Immunol. **135:** 1698–1701.

7. COBBOLD, S. P., A. JAYASURIYA, A. NASH, T. D. PROSPERO & H. WALDMANN. 1984. Therapy with monoclonal antibodies by elimination of T cell subsets *in vivo*. Nature **312:** 548–551.

8. COULIE, P. G., J.-P. COUTELIER, C. UYHENHOVE, P. LAMBOTE & J. V. SNICK. 1985. *In vivo* suppression of T-dependent antibody responses by treatment with a monoclonal anti-L3T4 antibody. Eur. J. Immunol. **15:** 638–640.

9. BENJAMIN, R. J. & H. WALDMANN. 1986. Induction of tolerance by monoclonal antibody therapy. Nature **320:** 449–451.

10. GUTSTEIN, N. L., W. E. SEAMAN, J. H. SCOTT & D. WOFSY. 1986. Induction of immune tolerance by administration of monoclonal antibody to L3T4. J. Immunol. **137:** 1127–1132.

11. WOODCOCK, J., D. WOFSY, E. ERIKSSON, J. H. SCOTT & W. E. SEAMAN. 1986. Rejection of skin grafts and generation of cytotoxic T cells by mice depleted of L3T4+ cells. Transplantation **42:** 636–642.

12. COBBOLD, S. P., G. MARTIN, S. QIN & H. WALDMANN. 1986. Monoclonal antibodies to promote marrow engraftment and tissue graft tolerance. Nature **323:** 164–166.

13. WALDOR, M. K., S. SRIRAM, R. HARDY, L. A. HERZENBERG, L. LANIER, M. LIM & L. STEINMAN. 1985. Reversal of experimental allergic encephalomyelitis with monoclonal antibody to a T cell subset marker. Science **227:** 415–417.

14. WOFSY, D. & W. E. SEAMAN. 1985. Successful treatment of autoimmunity in NZB/NZW F$_1$ mice with monoclonal antibody to L3T4. J. Exp. Med. **161:** 378–391.

15. RANGES, G. E., S. SRIRAM & S. M. COOPER. 1985. Prevention of type II collagen-induced arthritis by *in vivo* treatment with anti-L3T4. J. Exp. Med. **162:** 1105–1110.

16. WOFSY, D. 1986. Administration of monoclonal anti-T cell antibodies retards lupus in BXSB mice. J. Immunol. **136:** 4554–4560.

17. CHRISTADOSS, R. & M. J. DAUPHINEE. 1986. Immunotherapy for myasthenia gravis: A murine model. J. Immunol. **136:** 2437–2440.

18. SARMIENTO, M., A. L. GLASEBROOK & F. W. FITCH. 1980. IgG or IgM monoclonal antibodies reactive with the different determinants on the molecular complex bearing Lyt-2 antigen block T cell mediated cytolysis in the absence of complement. J. Immunol. **125:** 2665–2672.

19. CEREDIG, R., J. W. LOWENTHAL, M. NABHOLZ & H. R. MACDONALD. 1985. Expression of interleukin-2 receptors as a differentiation marker on intrathymic stem cells. Nature **314:** 98–100.

20. DENNERT, F., R. HYMAN, J. LESLEY & I. S. TROWBRIDGE. 1980. Effects of cytotoxic monoclonal antibody specific for T200 glycoprotein on functional lymphoid cell populations. Cell. Immunol. **53:** 350–364.

21. MARSHAK-ROTHSTEIN, A., P. FINK, T. GRIDLEY, D. H. RAULET, M. J. BEVAN & M. L. GEFTER. 1979. Properties and applications of monoclonal antibodies directed against determinants of the Thy-1 locus. J. Immunol. **122:** 2491–2497.

22. GORONZY, J., C. M. WEYLAND & C. G. FATHMAN. 1986. Long-term humoral unresponsiveness *in vivo*, induced by treatment with monoclonal antibody against L3T4. J. Exp. Med. **164:** 911–923.
23. BARCLAY, A. N. 1981. The localization of populations of lymphocytes defined by monoclonal antibodies in rat lymphoid tissues. Immunology **42:** 593–600.
24. JEFFRIES, W. A., J. R. GREEN & A. F. WILLIAMS. 1985. Authentic T helper CD4 (W3/25) antigen on rat peritoneal macrophages. J. Exp. Med. **162:** 117–127.
25. WOOD, G. S., N. L. WARNER & R. A. WARNKE. 1983. Anti-Leu-3/T4 antibodies react with cells of monocyte-macrophage and Langerhans lineage. J. Immunol. **131:** 212–216.
26. MOSCICKI, R. A., E. P. AMENTO, S. M. KRANE, J. T. KURNICK & R. B. COLVIN. 1983. Modulation of surface antigens of a human monocyte cell line, U937, during incubation with T lymphocyte-conditioned medium: Detection of T4 antigen and its presence on normal blood monocytes. J. Immunol. **131:** 743–748.
27. MIZOUCHI, T., H. GOLDING, A. S. ROSENBERG, L. H. GLIMCHER, T. R. MALEK & A. SINGER. 1985. Both L3T4+ and Lyt 2+ helper T cells initiate cytotoxic T lymphocyte responses against allogeneic major histocompatibility antigens but not against trinitrophenyl-modified self. J. Exp. Med. **162:** 427–443.
28. SPRENT, J. & M. SCHAEFER. 1985. Properties of purified T cell subsets. I. *In vitro* responses to class I versus class II H-2 antigens. J. Exp. Med. **162:** 2068–2088.
29. WAGNER, H., A. STARZINSKI-POWITZ, K. PFIZENMAIER & M. ROLLINGHOFF. 1976. T-T cell collaboration during *in vivo* responses to antigens coded by the peripheral and central region of the MHC. Nature **263:** 235–237.
30. BAUM, L. L. & L. M. PILARSKI. 1981. The *in vivo* cytotoxic T cell response to alloantigen requires a Lyt 1+ helper T lymphocyte. Transplantation **32:** 409–413.

The Veto Phenomenon in T-Cell Regulation[a]

RICHARD G. MILLER, SHIZUKO MURAOKA,[b]
MOGENS H. CLAESSON,[c] JORG REIMANN,[d]
AND PATRICIA BENVENISTE

Ontario Cancer Institute
and
Department of Immunology
University of Toronto
Toronto, Ontario, Canada M4X 1K9

T cells see antigen in association with self-major histocompatibility complex (MHC). The processes underlying the development of a specificity repertoire exhibiting this property, referred to as MHC-restricted recognition, remain to be fully explained. It is widely accepted that the environment in which the T cells develop plays an important role. A very high frequency of T cells capable of reacting against allogeneic MHC products are also produced, presumably because a particular allogeneic MHC product resembles self-MHC plus some antigen. It is highly likely that T cells capable of directly recognizing self-MHC products are also produced. Thus there must be a mechanism(s) to prevent such self-reactive cells from becoming destructive. The veto phenomenon represents one such mechanism. A veto cell is defined as being a cell that, when recognized by a T cell, can produce the inactivation of the T cell recognizing it.[1] Thus, T cells reactive to surface determinants, H determinants, or any foreign antigens it might carry, can potentially be inactivated. This process could clearly produce tolerance to self-MHC. As will be reviewed below, many tissues contain cells with veto activity (see TABLE 1). Cells possessing this activity seem to be at different stages of the T-cell development pathway, varying in surface phenotype from Thy-1$^+$, Ly-1$^-$, Ly-2$^-$ noncytolytic lymphoid cells, which can be grown from bone marrow,[2] to mature Thy-1$^+$, L3T4$^-$, Ly-2$^+$ functional cytolytic T lymphocytes (CTL).[9–11]

An alternative model for establishing self-tolerance is the anti-idiotype model in which there are suppressor cells with receptors that can recognize receptors on T cells specific for self-products. It is difficult to envisage mechanisms that would enable the development of a repertoire of anti-idiotypic receptors capable of controlling all cells carrying receptors directed against self without simultaneously generating reactivity to nonself receptors. This problem is totally avoided by the veto mechanism: the veto cell need only carry the self-MHC determinant or self-MHC determinant plus antigen against which responses are to be inactivated. Nevertheless, there is very strong evidence that responses to allogeneic

[a] This work was supported by the Medical Research Council of Canada (MT-3017) and the National Cancer Institute of Canada.
[b] Present address: Trudeau Institute, Inc., P.O. Box 59, Saranac Lake, NY 12983.
[c] Present address: Institute of Medical Anatomy, Dept. A, University of Copenhagen, The Panum Institute, Blegdamsvej 3, DK-2200 Copenhagen, N. Denmark.
[d] Present address: Abteilung Medizinische Mikrobiologie und Immunologie, Universitat Ulm, Postfach 4066, D-7900 Ulm, West Germany.

MHC products can be regulated by anti-idiotypic suppressor cells.[12,13] These suppressor cells are induced (or at least greatly expanded in number) after the animal has been exposed to allogeneic cells. Veto and anti-idiotypic models can be most easily distinguished by the initial direction of recognition: the T cell to be suppressed recognizes (veto model) or is recognized by (anti-idiotypic model) the suppressor cell.

DETECTION OF VETO ACTIVITY

Veto activity associated with class I MHC products was first demonstrated in studies of an A anti-B mixed lymphocyte reaction (MLR).[2-4] Lymphoid cells from one source (responder cells from, *e.g.,* mouse strain A) were cultured with x-irradiated lymphoid cells from a second source (stimulator cells from MHC-incompatibile mouse strain B). CTL develop from precursor cells in the A responder cells. These CTL can recognize and kill cells from B and from any other source carrying the same class I MHC determinants; the CTL directly recognize differences in the class I MHC products of B as compared to A. They only infrequently kill cells from a third, MHC-unrelated source, C. To search for a veto cell, one looks for a cell subpopulation from strain B that, when added to the MLR, suppresses the development of A anti-B CTL, but does not suppress CTL development in a B anti-A or A anti-C MLR. The added cell is suppressing the development of a response against its own cell-surface determinants. From the point of view of the added cell, an anti-self response is being suppressed.

The suppression is most easily explained by assuming the added cell is triggered to suppress when its cell-surface determinants are recognized. The most direct evidence for this has been obtained in an assay involving chemically modified self (*i.e.,* A reacting with trinitrophenyl (TNP)-modified A). When A veto cells were added to this MLR, they produced no suppression of the development of cytotoxic activity unless they were first TNP-modified, thus allowing them to be recognized by the CTL precursors.[4]

Using this MLR assay, cells with veto activity have been identified in bone marrow, thymus, and fetal liver of normal mice; and spleen and bone marrow of athymic nude mice (see TABLE 1). Active cells have also been found in lymphoid colonies grown in semisolid methylcellulose (MeC) medium from immature precursors in bone marrow and fetal liver (see TABLE 1). TABLE 2 presents experimental evidence showing directly that the veto activity in lymphoid colonies grown from bone marrow maps to class I MHC. Considering this table in detail, one can make the following conclusions: (1) Suppression requires identity of MHC between veto and stimulator; identity of background genes is not sufficient (compare lines 1 and 2). (2) Suppression requires identity at class I MHC (K and/ or D); identity at class II MHC is not sufficient (compare lines 1 and 3). (3) Identity at a single class I locus (K or D) is sufficient for suppression (compare lines 4 to 7). Note that in other experiments (data not shown), it was found that most of the B10 anti-A.SW response is directed to the K^s rather than D^s determinant.

Veto activity is not found on direct *in vitro* testing of such tissues as spleen or lymph node.[3-5] Normally, these tissues contain predominantly mature, resting small lymphocytes. Mature T cells in spleen can acquire veto activity after a brief *in vitro* incubation, however.[5] During this time, many of the T cells become activated, and it appears that at least some simultaneously acquire veto activity.

TABLE 1. Tissue Distribution of Veto Activity[a]

Tissue		Relative Potency	Reference
Bone marrow	—normal	+	2
	—athymic nude	+	unpublished
	—MeC lymphoid colonies	+ +	2
Spleen	—normal	+/−	3,4,5
	—athymic nude	+	3,4
	—cultured normal	+	5
	—MeC lymphoid colonies	−	unpublished
Thymus	—normal	+/−	6,7
	—thymocyte depleted	+ to + + +	6, unpublished
Fetal liver	—normal	+	8
	—MeC lymphoid colonies	+ +	8
CTL lines		+ + +	9,10,11

[a] Tested in MLR cultures as described in the text by adding cells syngeneic to the stimulator cells from the tissue under test to cultures containing 3×10^4 responder cells and 3×10^5 stimulator cells. Potency (+) corresponds to 10^4–10^5 cells required for significant suppression; + +, 3×10^2 to 3×10^3; and + + +, 30 to 300.

Mature CTL have veto activity against CTL precursors capable of recognizing them.[9-11] Thus, cells from an established CTL line originating from strain A will, when added to an MLR, suppress the development of CTL against A or any strain sharing MHC with A, independent of the specificity of the added CTL and independent of the strain of origin of the responder cells. The mechanism does not appear to involve the antigen-specific receptor on the CTL nor to depend directly on the cytotoxic machinery of the CTL.[9,11]

Several conclusions have been reached about the details of how the veto mechanism operates. (1) Veto occurs through the inactivation of CTL precursors. This can be shown by using limiting dilution analysis to measure the frequency of CTL precursors in the presence and absence of veto cells. One finds that the CTL-precursor frequency is greatly reduced.[2,4] Further, one finds that the number of

TABLE 2. Veto Maps to Class I MHC[a]

Responder	Stimulator	Veto	Target	MHC Antigens Shared by Stimulator and Veto[b]	Response (Percent control)
1 B10	B10.BR	B10.BR	B10.BR	K,IA,IE,D	42 ± 10*
2 B10	B10.BR	B10.D2	B10.BR	None	97 ± 8
3 B10	B10.BR	A.TL	B10.BR	IA,IE	126 ± 27
4 B10	A.SW	A.SW	A.SW	K,IA,IE,D	28 ± 7*
5 B10	A.SW	A.TH	A.SW	K,IA,IE	19 ± 5*
6 B10	A.SW	A.TL	A.SW	K	29 ± 5*
7 B10	B10.A	B10.D2	B10.D2	D	31 ± 9*

[a] Responder lymph node cells (3×10^4) were cultured in 8-fold replicates with 3×10^5 irradiated (1500 rads) stimulator spleen cells with (experimental) or without (control) 10^3–2×10^3 cells from pooled lymphoid colony cells grown from bone marrow as described previously.[2] Cultures were assayed for cytotoxic activity against ^{51}C-labeled Con A blasts after 5 days of cultures. The experimental results are expressed as percent of control. Groups showing significant suppression are indicated.*

[b] K and D, mouse class I MHC antigens; IA and IE, mouse class II MHC antigens.

CTL produced by those CTL precursors escaping inactivation is normal or slightly enhanced,[2,4] suggesting that veto has little effect on CTL proliferation. (2) CTL precursors become sensitive to veto action some time following activation and before differentiation into mature CTL. This can be shown by delayed addition and/or early removal of veto cells from an MLR culture.[9,14] The conclusion is that resting CTL precursors are not subject to veto but achieve maximum sensitivity to its effects 24–48 hr after culture initiation. (3) Attempts to isolate a suppressive factor responsible for the veto phenomenon have not been successful.

It may be that there is not a factor. There are several reports that T-helper clones or hybridomas stop proliferating when exposed to antigen under certain conditions. Human T-helper clones cultured in large antigen excess became growth arrested, apparently permanently.[15]

As human T-helper cells express Ia antigens, it is possible they present antigen to each other in association with Ia. It has been observed that murine IL-2–secreting T hybridomas presented with their appropriate antigen-MHC combination at concentrations sufficiently high to trigger IL-2 release are blocked from proliferating, a block that appears to be irreversible after 24 hr of exposure.[16] It has also been shown that antigen-reactive T hybridomas can be rendered incapable of growth by certain modes of antigen presentation.[17] It is possible that in all these instances, the block in growth has the same underlying basis as the block in CTL production produced by the veto mechanism. There are strong similarities between the cytostatic mechanism proposed here for the action of the veto phenomenon and the mechanism for tolerization of immature B lymphocytes by specific antigen or anti-μ antibody leading to clonal abortion.[18] The tolerized cells do not appear to be killed but are incapable of growth.

Veto activity against class I MHC and against class I MHC–restricted responses can be seen following *in vivo* injection of appropriate allogeneic lymphoid cells.[19-24] Thus, if A mice are injected with appropriate F_1 (A × B) lymphoid cells, then, on subsequent *in vitro* testing, one finds that CTL precursors directed towards B class I antigens have been specifically inactivated.[19,24] Similarly, responses against minor H antigens can be suppressed by injection of class I compatible but minor H incompatible lymphoid cells.[20-23] This may at least partly explain the partial or complete tolerance to tissue grafts reported by many investigators (*e.g.,* references 25–27) that is induced when peripheral blood or bone marrow syngeneic to the graft is also injected.

A veto-like recognition event has recently been implicated as the final step in the series of T-T interactions leading to the down-regulation of T-helper cells (T_h).[28,29] Interaction between the T suppressor effector (T_{se}) and T_h is both antigen-specific and class II MHC–restricted. Restriction is to the class II MHC of the T_{se},[28,29] and this cell does, in fact, carry class II MHC determinants.[29] Thus suppression is most easily explained by assuming that the T_h recognizes the antigen in association with class II MHC on the surface of the T_{se}, which is then triggered to suppress (veto) the T_h. The recognition step would thus be analogous to the recently proposed T_h–B-cell–interaction model in which it is proposed that the T_h recognizes antigen in association with class II MHC on the B-cell surface.[30]

BIOLOGICAL ROLE OF VETO ACTIVITY

What is the role of class I-restricted veto cell activity? A model in which the T-cell repertoire is postulated to develop from precursors initially reactive against self-MHC[31,32] provides an attractive basis for explaining the role of the environment in T-cell development, the high frequency of alloreactive T cells, and MHC restriction. According to the model, stimulation of self-reactive cells by self-MHC determinants in the environment induces them (by mechanisms unknown) to diversify their receptor specificity. A potential problem is that one might expect some of these cells to differentiate into self-reactive cells instead of diversifying. The veto phenomenon would prevent this, but at the same time would not delete all self-reactive precursors: T cells only become susceptible to veto action beyond some critical step in their activation pathway.[9,14] Thus, only those self-reactive T cells that become committed to the activation pathway before being diversified away from self-reactivity would be subject to veto. The veto mechanism would also maintain tolerance to minor H determinants. Because these determinants would be seen on the veto-cell surface in association with self-MHC, the model predicts that tolerance to minor H determinants should be MHC-restricted. This, in fact, appears to be the case.[33–36]

Cytotoxic cells bearing T-cell markers and with specificity for self-class I MHC products, apparently produced from prethymic precursors of bone marrow origin, can be demonstrated both in vitro[37,38] and in vivo.[39] Cells with veto activity can be found in all those tissues in which early stages of T-cell development can occur, that is, in bone marrow,[2] fetal liver,[8] and thymus.[6,7] Cells with veto activity do not all have the same cell-surface markers, but results are consistent with the conclusion that all cells with veto activity are T cells at various stages along the T cell–development pathway.

It is clear why it is useful for mature T cells such as T_{se} to possess veto activity. But why should mature class I-reactive T cells such as CTL possess veto activity? One possibility is that the T-cell repertoire continues to develop during an ongoing immune response and does so through diversification of cells initially reactive against self-MHC. The veto phenomenon would then maintain self-tolerance in the same manner as proposed above for T-cell ontogeny. Production of self-reactive cytotoxic T cells preceding the appearance of virus-specific cytotoxic T cells has been observed both in vivo[40] and in vitro.[41] Extremely rapid diversification in specificity within single clones of developing CTL has also been observed.[42] These results are consistent with the conclusion that the T-cell repertoire is under continuous expansion through specificity changes driven positively by stimulation with self or other antigens and selected negatively for self-tolerance by regulatory cells such as veto cells. It should be noted that extremely rapid antigen-driven diversification of the B-cell repertoire is now a well-documented phenomenon.[43–47]

Recent observations with alloreactive CTL lines appear to be producing evidence for a direct link between anti-self responses and veto activity. When cultured under appropriate conditions (i.e., with an IL-2–containing supernatant and stimulator cells), the CTL maintain their allospecificity, exhibit veto activity, and are not autoreactive.[9] When cultured without appropriate stimulator cells, but instead with syngeneic or third-party stimulator cells, however, some lines (so far 6/16 tested) became autoreactive with specificity for self-MHC (reference 48 and unpublished data). These cells will still also kill their appropriate allo-target but will not kill third party or natural killer targets. Preliminary results indicate that the appearance of autoreactivity is due to the expression of a second receptor and that when a CTL line becomes autoreactive, it can no longer veto. We would like to interpret these results as being due to re-expression of an antiself receptor used early in ontogeny and somehow involved in selection of the adult repertoire whose re-expression is normally prevented by the veto mechanism.

REFERENCES

1. MILLER, R. G. 1980. *In* Strategies of Immune Regulation. E. E. Sercarz & A. J. Cunningham, Eds.: 507–512. Academic Press. New York.
2. MURAOKA, S. & R. G. MILLER. 1980. J. Exp. Med. **152:** 54–71.
3. MILLER, R. G. & H. DERRY. 1979. J. Immunol. **122:** 1502–1509.
4. MILLER, R. G. 1980. Nature **287:** 544–546.
5. RAMMENSEE, H.-G., Z. A. NAGY & J. KLEIN. 1982. Eur. J. Immunol. **12:** 930–934.
6. MILLER, R. G. 1981. Ciba Found. Symp. **84:** 236–240.
7. CLAESSON, M. H. & C. ROPKE. 1986. Curr. Top. Microbiol. Immunol. **126:** 381–409.
8. MURAOKA, S. & R. G. MILLER. 1983. J. Immunol. **131:** 45–49.
9. CLAESSON, M. H. & R. G. MILLER. 1984. J. Exp. Med. **160:** 1702–1716.
10. FINK, P. J., H.-G. RAMMENSEE, J. D. BENEDETTO, U. D. STAERZ, L. LEFRANCOIS & M. J. BEVAN. 1984. J. Immunol. **133:** 1769–1774.
11. FINK, P. J., H.-G. RAMMENSEE & M. J. BEVAN. 1984. J. Immunol. **133:** 1775–1781.
12. KIMURA, H. & D. B. WILSON. 1984. Nature **308:** 463–464.
13. LANCASTER, F., Y. L. CHUI & J. R. BATCHELOR. 1985. Nature **315:** 336–337.
14. MURAOKA, S., D. L. EHMAN & R. G. MILLER. 1984. Eur. J. Immunol. **14:** 1010–1016.
15. LAMB, J. R. & M. FELDMANN. 1984. Nature **308:** 72–74.
16. ASHWELL, J. D., R. E. CUNNINGHAM, P. D. NOGUCHI & D. HERNANDEZ. 1987. J. Exp. Med. **165:** 173–194.
17. JENKINS, M. K. & R. H. SCHWARTZ. 1987. J. Exp. Med. **165:** 302–319.
18. NOSSAL, G. J. V. & B. L. PIKE. 1981. Proc. Natl. Acad. Sci. USA **78:** 3844–3849.
19. RAMMENSEE, H.-G., P. J. FINK & M. J. BEVAN. 1984. J. Immunol. **133:** 2390–2396.
20. RAMMENSEE, H.-G., P. J. FINK & M. J. BEVAN. 1985. Transplant. Proc. **17:** 689–692.
21. FINK, P. J., I. L. WEISSMAN & M. J. BEVAN. 1983. J. Exp. Med. **157:** 141–154.
22. RAMMENSEE, H.-G., A. JURETIC, Z. A. NAGY & J. KLEIN. 1984. J. Immunol. **132:** 668–672.
23. ISHIKAWA, H., H. SUZUKI, T. HINO, E. KUBOTA & K. SAITO. 1985. J. Immunol. **135:** 3681–3685.
24. MILLER, R. G. & R. A. PHILLIPS. 1976. J. Immunol. **117:** 1913–1921.
25. MAKI, T., R. GOTTSCHALK, M. L. WOOD & A. P. MONACO. 1981. J. Immunol. **127:** 1433–1438.
26. LAU, H., K. REEMTSMA & M. A. HARDY. 1983. Science **221:** 754–756.
27. MARTINELLI, G. P., D. RACELIS, G. GIANNONE, C. M. MILLER, E. GRETZ & H. SCHANZER. 1983. Transplant. Proc. **15:** 988–993.
28. BAXEVANIS, C. N., N. ISHII, Z. A. NAGY & J. KLEIN. 1982. J. Exp. Med. **156:** 822–833.
29. ARANEO, B. A. & R. L. YOWELL. 1985. J. Immunol. **135:** 73–79.
30. LANZAVECCHIA, A. 1985. Nature **314:** 537–539.
31. JERNE, N. K. 1971. Eur. J. Immunol. **1:** 1–9.
32. VON BOEHMER, H., W. HAAS & N. K. JERNE. 1978. Proc. Natl. Acad. Sci. USA **75:** 2439–2442.
33. DOS REIS, G. A. & E. M. SHEVACH. 1983. J. Exp. Med. **157:** 1287–1299.
34. GROVES, E. S. & A. SINGER. 1983. J. Exp. Med. **158:** 1483–1497.
35. RAMMENSEE, H.-G. & M. J. BEVAN. 1984. Nature **308:** 741–744.
36. MATZINGER, P., R. ZAMOYSKA & H. WALDMANN. 1984. Nature **308:** 738–741.
37. REIMANN, J. & R. G. MILLER. 1983. J. Exp. Med. **158:** 1672–1692.
38. BENVENISTE, P. & R. G. MILLER. 1986. J. Immunol. **136:** 4399–4406.
39. HURME, M. & M. SIHVOLA. 1985. J. Immunol. **135:** 1108–1112.
40. PFIZENMAIER, K., H. TROSTMANN, M. ROLLINGHOFF & H. WAGNER. 1975. Nature **258:** 238–240.
41. KOMATSU, Y., Y. NAWA, A. R. BELLAMY & J. MARBROOK. 1978. Nature **274:** 802–804.
42. REIMANN, J. & R. G. MILLER. 1985. Cell **40:** 571–581.
43. CUNNINGHAM, A. J. & S. A. FORDHAM. 1974. Nature **250:** 669–671.

44. PILARSKI, L. M. & A. J. CUNNINGHAM. 1974. Eur. J. Immunol. **4:** 762–767.
45. PILARSKI, L. M. & A. J. CUNNINGHAM. 1975. Eur. J. Immunol. **5:** 10–16.
46. MCKEAN, D., K. HUPPI, M. BELL, L. STANDT, W. GERHARD & M. WEIGERT. 1984.
     Proc. Natl. Acad. Sci. USA **81:** 3180–3184.
47. GRIFFITHS, G. M., C. BEREK, M. KAARTINEN & C. MILSTEIN. 1984. Nature **312:** 271–
     275.
48. CLAESSON, M. H. & R. G. MILLER. 1985. J. Immunol. **134:** 684–690.

Down-regulation of Cytotoxic T Lymphocyte Generation by Two Distinct Suppressor-Cell Systems[a]

J. R. BATTISTO, S. C. GAUTAM, AND K. N. CHOW

Department of Immunology and Cancer
The Research Institute
Cleveland Clinic Foundation
Cleveland, Ohio 44106

INTRODUCTION

That cytotoxic T lymphocytes (CTL) are concerned with elimination of cells from the body that have been infected with viruses or cells that have undergone neoplastic transformation is now well-established. Viral infection or neoplastic transformation may result in the appearance of cell-surface determinants formed as a result of modification of self-antigens or that are recognized by the immune system in conjunction with self-antigens. Workers in many laboratories, for instance, have reported generation of specific CTL against virally infected cells[1] and syngeneic tumors.[2] Indeed, the CTL limb of cell-mediated immunity is commonly thought to have evolved primarily for these purposes.

An excellent model for the study of altered self-antigens is the use of hapten-modified cell-surface determinants. Shearer[3] demonstrated that trinitrophenyl-ated spleen cells could stimulate syngeneic spleen cells to differentiate into trinitrophenyl (TNP)-specific CTL provided the immunization occurred *in vitro*. Generally the CTL response is directed to altered class I major histocompatibility antigens,[4] and the effector cells could readily distinguish between trinitrophenyl- and dinitrophenyl-conjugated syngeneic cells.[5] When TNP-specific CTL were sought by immunizations *in vivo*, however, none were found. Ultimately the inability to immunize host animals to hapten-altered self-antigens was found to be attributable to the presence of a naturally occurring suppressor T cell[6,7] that controls serum levels of an inhibitor of interleukin-2 (IL-2).[8] Two methods have thus far been developed to overcome the inability to immunize for CTL directed to hapten-altered self-antigens. One is by pretreating animals with cyclophosphamide prior to immunization. The natural suppressor T cell is apparently sensitive to such treatment, whereas the development of CTL is not.[6,8] The other is to stimulate additional helper T cells by providing minor locus allogenicity simultaneously with syngeneic hapten-altered cells used for immunization.[9]

The latter system for generating CTL has allowed an examination of down-regulation of CTL *in vivo* where events are well-known to occur that are not always detected *in vitro*. Because the system uses haptenated self-antigens (TNP-H-2^k) as well as a minor histocompatibility locus (Mls) antigenic disparity to achieve CTL, tolerance regimens directed to both the hapten as well as to the Mls antigen can be examined for their effects upon CTL generation.

[a] This work was supported by Grants AI 18305 and AI 17657 from the National Institutes of Health.

We have already reported that the method by which immunotolerance is induced toward a hapten determines whether hapten-specific killer T cells will be generated *in vivo*. Thus, hapten-specific CTL generation was readily prevented when nascent hapten was administered intravenously[10] or orally[11,12] but was not diminished by intravenously injected hapten-coupled syngeneic spleen cells.[10]

Tolerance to Mls was originally described for mixed lymphocyte reactions (MLR)[13,14] where it was found that lymphoid cells from animals made tolerant of Mls exhibited suppressed proliferative responses. Additionally, tolerance to Mls has been shown to control *in vivo* development of CTL directed to syngeneic antigens altered by hapten[9,15,16] as well as to allogeneic antigens.[17,18] In point of fact, the tolerance that is achievable by injecting Mls^d into Mls^c-containing mice, controls CTL generation by way of an induced suppressor T cell.[16]

In this presentation we report upon the identification of the Mls^d-induced suppressor T cell (T_s) as well as the manner in which it achieves suppression of CTL development by operating in conjunction with macrophages. In addition, we compare and contrast this suppressor system with a suppressor system that consists of three T cells. The three T_s are induced by tolerance techniques directed to the TNP hapten and are known to function sequentially in cascade fashion to suppress cell-mediated responses of both types, that is, delayed-type hypersensitivity (DTH)[19,20] and CTL.[21,22]

A major point of interest to be shown is that the two dissimilar systems operate to control CTL development at the early inductive phase.

MATERIAL AND METHODS

Mice

Eight-week-old female C3H/HeN ($H-2^k$, Mls^c) mice were purchased from Charles River Breeding Laboratories, Wilmington, Massachusetts. CBA/J ($H-2^k$, Mls^d) and C57BL/6 ($H-2^b$) female mice were obtained from The Jackson Laboratory, Bar Harbor, Maine.

Preparation of Hapten-Modified Cells

Normal spleen cells (free of red cells), intended to be used for inducing tolerance, were adjusted to 2×10^7 cells/ml in Earle's balanced salt solution (EBSS) and mixed with an equal volume of 10 mM trinitro-benzene sulfonic acid (TNBS) dissolved in EBSS, pH 7.4, for 30 minutes at room temperature.

Cells to be used as stimulators for immunizing mice to make CTL were haptenated by incubating 6×10^7 spleen cells in 1 ml of 10 mM TNBS dissolved in EBSS for 10 minutes at 37°C. After haptenation, cells were washed twice with EBSS and were adjusted to the desired concentration.

Induction of DTH

Delayed cutaneous contact sensitivity to the hapten 2, 4, 6-trinitrochlorobenzene (TNCB) was induced in C3H/HeN mice by painting each mouse with 0.1 ml of 7% solution of picryl chloride (TNCB) in absolute alcohol on the clipped abdomen.[11] Thereafter, the mice were rested for five days before further use.

Sensitization with 4-ethoxymethylene-2-phenyloxazol-5-one (oxazolone, OX) was done by painting each mouse with 0.1 ml of 3% solution of OX in absolute alcohol. When animals were assayed for TNP-specific DTH, each side of one ear was painted with 10 μl of a 1% solution of TNCB in olive oil. Before and 24 hours after hapten application, the thickness of the ear was measured with a Mitutoya engineer's micrometer (Schlesinger Tools, Dobbs Ferry, NY). The difference in ear thickness was recorded in units of 10^{-4} inches.

Induction of TNP-Specific CTL in Vivo

Mice were sensitized for *in vivo* development of CTL as reported previously.[9,10] In brief: 2×10^7 TNP-modified C3H syngeneic spleen cells were injected in each hind paw of C3H/HeN mice with or without 2×10^7 CBA/J spleen cells. After an interval of five days, draining popliteal lymph nodes were removed and dispersed into a single-cell suspension in cold EBSS. Cells were washed twice with EBSS, their viability was checked by the dye exclusion method, and they were adjusted to a concentration of 12.5×10^6 cells/ml.

Introduction of Tolerance to Hapten

Two different methods were used to induce hapten-specific unresponsiveness. The first, described by Battisto and Bloom[23] and used in a modified form here, involves the injection, by way of the retro-orbital sinus, of hapten-coupled lymphoid cells (50×10^6/mouse). For hapten modification, spleen cells were first treated with 0.83% NH_4Cl to lyse the red blood cells. After this treatment, the cells were washed once with Hanks' balanced salt solution (HBSS). Thereafter, the cells were resuspended at 20×10^6/ml HBSS, and 5 ml of this suspension was added to an equal volume of 10 mM TNBS and incubated for 30 minutes at room temperature. The cells were then pelleted and washed twice before use in the tolerogenic injections. Spleen cells treated with 0.83% NH_4Cl, but not hapten-modified, were used as controls.

The second method for tolerance-induction is adopted from Asherson and Ptak.[24] Each mouse to be rendered tolerant to the hapten, TNP, was injected i.v. with 5 mg of TNBS (dissolved in a total volume of 0.2 ml of phosphate-buffered saline with pH adjusted to 7.4 with 7.5% $NaHCO_3$). As control upon the specificity of the tolerance, other groups of animals were injected i.v. with 5 mg of dinitrobenzene sulfonic acid (DNBS) in 0.2 ml of phosphate-buffered saline.

After tolerization by either method, animals were rested for seven days before use in experimental systems.

Cytotoxicity Assay

Hapten-specific cytolytic activity of effector cells generated *in vivo* and *in vitro* was determined in a ^{51}Cr assay as described by Simpson *et al.*[25] with some modifications. Except where noted, C3H/HeN thymoma cells (MT-1820), that had been maintained in culture, were used as targets. Thymoma cells (1 ml, 3×10^7 cells) were incubated with 100–150 μCi $Na_2{}^{51}CrO_4$ (specific activity: 478 mCi/mg, New England Nuclear Corp., Boston, MA) for 75 to 90 minutes at 37°C. After incubation, cells were washed twice with EBSS, and the portion of cells to be TNP- or dinitrophenyl (DNP)-modified was adjusted to 4×10^7 cells/ml in EBSS. Two milliliters of 10 mM trinitrobenzene sulfonate or dinitrobenzene sulfonate solution in EBSS, pH 7.4, was added to each milliliter of cell suspension. Cells were incubated for ten minutes at 37°C and then washed two times with RPMI-1640. Graded numbers of effector cells were added to 2.5×10^4 target cells in each well of a 96-well round-bottom microtiter plate (Microbiological Associates, Bethesda, MD) to obtain effector to target (E : T) ratios of 100 : 1, 50 : 1, and 25 : 1. Plates were centrifuged at 45 g for five minutes and incubated at 37°C, 5% CO_2, for three hours. Maximum release of ^{51}Cr was determined by adding 1% sodium dodecyl sulfate to appropriate numbers of target cells alone, and spontaneous release was measured by incubating the target cells in medium alone. After incubation, the plates were centrifuged for ten minutes at 100 g, and 100 μl of supernatant was removed and counted for radioactivity in a Beckman 310 gamma counter. Results have been expressed as percentage specific lysis, calculated as

$$\% \text{ specific lysis} = \frac{\text{experimental release} - \text{spontaneous release}}{\text{maximum release} - \text{spontaneous release}} \times 100.$$

Spontaneous release was never more than 15% of maximum release.

Tolerization of C3H/HeN Mice with Cells Possessing Mls^d

Tolerization was accomplished by a retro-orbital injection of 50×10^6 CBA/J or (CBA $\times$ C3H/HeN)F1 spleen cells in a total volume of 0.5 ml into normal C3H/ HeN mice.[13,14] When tolerizing for the eventual transfer of various spleen cell (SC) populations, CBA-SC were inactivated by irradiation (2000 R, Mark Irradiator) before injection to eliminate the induction of tolerance *de novo* with surviving Mls^d-positive cells. A period of five to seven days was allowed to elapse after the i.v. injection, and randomly selected animals were tested for tolerance by mixed lymphocyte reaction (MLR) with mitomycin-C–treated CBA/J SC. A 60–70% reduction in MLR was commonly observed in tolerant mice.

Production of Mixed Lymphocyte Culture (MLC) Supernatants

Nylon wool nonadherent responder SC (20×10^6) from either normal or Mls^d-tolerized C3H/HeN mice were mixed with 20×10^6 CBA/J mitomycin-treated stimulator SC. They were incubated in a total volume of 6 ml RPMI-1640 medium with 10% fetal calf serum (FCS) in an upright tissue culture flask (25 cm^2, Falcon, Oxnard, CA) for 48 hours at 37°C and 5% CO_2. Supernatants were removed and spun at $200 \times g$ for ten minutes and then filtered through a 0.45 μm Milex filter unit (Millipore Corp., Bedford, MA). Supernatants were used immediately or stored at 4°C.

In Vitro Generation of CTL

The procedure for generating *in vitro* CTL specific for modified self-antigens was conducted as described by Finke *et al.*,[26] with some modifications. C3H/HeN TNP-modified thymic cells (10^7) that had been inactivated by heat treatment at 45°C for one hour were cocultured with 10^7 syngeneic C3H nylon wool nonadherent

SC. Cells were cultured for five days at 37°C in 3.0 ml of RPMI-1640 culture medium (of which 40–80% was supernatant from 48 hours MLC). At the end of the incubation period, cells were washed twice in media, and their viability was determined and adjusted to a final concentration of 5×10^6 cells/ml.

Selective Deletion of Cell Populations by Using Antibodies and Complement

Single cell suspensions of pooled spleens from mice tolerized seven days earlier were split equally into three 17×100 mm sterile tubes. One tube was left on ice as an untreated control, and the other two were spun at $200 \times g$ for ten minutes to sediment the cells. In one tube, the anti-Thy-1.2 antibodies (0.5 ml/100 $\times 10^6$ cells) were added; and to the other, goat α-mouse IgG (0.5 ml/100 $\times 10^6$ cells) was added. These tubes were placed on ice for 45 minutes with frequent shakings. Cells were again sedimented, resuspended in rabbit complement (1/6 dilution) at 0.5 ml/100 $\times 10^6$ cells, and incubated at 37°C, 5% CO_2 for 30 minutes. Cells were washed twice with EBSS, and viable cells were counted by the dye exclusion method. To ascertain that T cells had been effectively removed from the purified B cells and vice versa, batches of cells were tested for the ability to respond blastogenically to 1 μg of the mitogens lipopolysaccharide (LPS from *Escherichia coli* 055 : B5; Difco Laboratories, Detroit, MI) and concanavalin A (Con A; Miles Laboratories, Kankakee, IL) per 10^6 cells. Optimally, B-cell preparations showed 4000 cpm for background, 9000 cpm to Con A, and 58,000 cpm to LPS. By contrast, T-cell preparations gave 200 cpm for background, 900 cpm to LPS, and 23,000 cpm to Con A. Thus, only slight contamination of each type of cell was evident. No effort was made to exclude macrophages.

Cyclophosphamide (CY) Treatment

Mice were injected with a 150 mg/kg dose of CY (Cytoxan: Mead Johnson & Co., Evansville, IN) as sodium salt in a volume of 0.3 ml intraperitoneally.

Statistics

All comparisons between groups were made by analysis of variance followed by the Newman-Keuls multiple range test.

RESULTS

Achieving CTL to Haptenated Self in Vivo

For some time we have been using an *in vivo* method for generating CTL to hapten-conjugated self-antigens that relies primarily upon stimulating extra helper factors.[9,10] That is, the system overcomes a natural suppressor T cell that apparently controls plasma levels of an IL-2 inhibitor and thereby prevents development of CTL to haptenated self-antigens *in vivo*.[6–8] As outlined in TABLE 1, host mice (in our system, those of the C3H/HeN strain) are injected with a Mls disparate splenic cell that otherwise is compatible with the host at the major histocompatibility locus along with hapten-altered syngeneic splenic cells. The Mls^d stimu-

TABLE 1. Generating *in Vivo* Cytotoxic T Lymphocyte Response to TNP Self-Antigens[a]

Immunization Phase (Afferent Limb, 5 days) C3H/HeN Mice Given Hind Paw Injection of Spleen Cells		Effector Phase (Efferent Limb, 3 hours)	
		Effectors vs	Targets
TNP-C3H/HeN + CBA/J	$H-2^k$, Mls^c $H-2^k$, Mls^d	C3H/HeN popliteal lymph node cells	TNP-C3H/ HeN splenic T cell blasts

[a] To generate CTL specific for TNP self-antigens *in vivo*, C3H/HeN mice were injected into hind paws with syngeneic SC as well as those from CBA/J mice (2×10^7 of each together in 0.05 ml/paw). Only the syngeneic spleen cells were haptenated. Five days later, popliteal lymph node cells were used as effectors, and syngeneic T-cell blasts were chromium-labeled as well as haptenated so that they might be used as targets. Following this three hour *in vitro* effector phase, supernatants were assayed for released ^{51}chromium as an indication of cytotoxic activity.

lus is known to stimulate additional host helper T cells (T_h) to provide the helper factors required by CTL precursors.[27] Five days are allowed to elapse following the injection, and if the site for the latter is the hind paws, then draining popliteal lymph node cells are examined for cytotoxicity toward appropriate targets in a three-hour effector phase. The latter is the standard chromium release assay in which an array of targets that are primarily in a dividing state and labeled with ^{51}Cr are coincubated with the effector cells in various ratios.

As may be seen from TABLE 2, when mice were immunized with trinitrophenylated syngeneic spleen cells alone, no appreciable lysis of the haptenated targets occurred at either 25:1 or 100:1 effector to target ratios. By contrast, when the nonhaptenated Mls disparate cell was incorporated with the TNP-C3H spleen cells, lysis of such targets occurred. The level of cytolysis that is readily achieved by this immunization is 15–25% for ratios of 25:1 and 25–50% for ratios of 100:1. Although this represents a wide range, the lytic values were generally consistent over a much narrower range within individual experiments. When syngeneic nonhaptenated splenic cells were substituted for the Mls disparate splenic cells, no

TABLE 2. Generation of CTL to Hapten-Altered Self-Antigens *in Vivo*[a]

Identity of Spleen Cells Injected into C3H/HeN Hind Footpads	Percentage Lysis of TNP-C3H/HeN Splenic T-cell Blasts	
	25:1	100:1
TNP-C3H	3.9	3.5
TNP-C3H + CBA/J	18.1	33.8
TNP-C3H + C3H	4.3	8.5
TNP-CBA/J	39.5	51.2

[a] Spleen cells that were either haptenated or not were injected into the hind paws of C3H/ HeN mice (2×10^7 of each). After five days, popliteal lymph nodes draining the injection sites were removed and used as effector cells against TNP-C3H/HeN splenic T-cell blasts at E:T ratios of 25:1 and 100:1.

CTL were generated. In addition, if Mls disparate cells that were hapten-conjugated were injected alone, CTL were developed. Thus, exposing lymph node cells to syngeneic TNP-spleen cells will generate CTL *in vivo* when an extra stimulus for helper T cells is concomitantly provided.

The CTL Developed in Vivo Are Antigen-Specific and Genetically Restricted

A number of experiments to determine the characteristics of the CTL were conducted.[9,10] They have been identified as T cells, and their specificity is shown in TABLE 3. The effector cells generated *in vivo* are able to lyse targets that are haptenated, syngeneic antigens but are unable to attack syngeneic blast cells devoid of hapten, syngeneic blast cells coupled with a related but different hapten (DNP), or allogeneic blast cells conjugated with homologous hapten. Thus, CTL developed by our immunization method are restricted genetically and are antigen-specific.

TABLE 3. The CTL Generated *in Vivo* with an Auxiliary Stimulus Are Antigen-Specific and Genetically Restricted[a]

Spleen Cells Injected into C3H Host Foot Pads	Percent Specific Lysis at 100:1 Targets			
	TNP-C3H	C3H	DNP-C3H	TNP-C57
TNP-C3H	5.7(1.1)	3.6(1.7)	1.8(0.9)	8.4(2.2)
TNP-C3H and CBA/J	44.2(1.6)	4.2(3.6)	2.7(0.4)	1.6(0.1)

[a] Mice were immunized in the hind paws with haptenated syngeneic spleen cells with and without the CBA/J auxilliary spleen cells. After five days, the popliteal lymph node cells were used as effectors against the target cells shown. The effector to target ratio was 100:1. The target cells were haptenated as described in MATERIAL AND METHODS. The C57BL/6 targets were obtained from splenic cells incubated with Con A for two days (1 μg Con A/10^6 cells) *in vitro*.

Is the Suppressor T-Cell System That Is Operative in DTH Effective in CML?

We have investigated whether a method for initiating suppression of DTH to TNP self-antigens is applicable to preventing development of hapten-specific CTL *in vivo*. Mice that were painted epidermally with an ethanolic solution of TNCB developed DTH to the hapten that was detectable within six days as an ear thickening response upon re-exposure to the hapten (TABLE 4). The DTH was easily suppressed by injecting either nascent hapten or hapten-coupled syngeneic spleen cells intravenously a week before attempting sensitization of the mice (TABLE 4). By contrast, treating hosts with DNBS prior to sensitization with TNCB was unable to suppress development of TNP-specific DTH. Thus, for suppression of DTH to be achieved, the hapten used in pretreatment must be identical to that used for sensitization.

We sought to determine whether these methods of tolerization towards the hapten would be effective upon the *in vivo* cell-mediated lympholysis (CML) system. We found that injecting trinitrobenzene sulfonic acid (TNBS) intravenously a week prior to immunizing for CTL suppressed development of hapten-

TABLE 4. Suppression of DTH by Pretreating Hosts with Hapten[a]

I.V. Injection of Host C3H Mice Day (−7)	Epidermally Sensitized with TNCB Day (0)	TNP-Specific DTH Change in Ear Thickness (10^{-4} in.) Day (6)
None	+	32.7(2.8)
None	0	8.9(3.6)
TNBS	+	7.1(1.6)
DNBS	+	$\overline{29.8}$(1.0)
TNP-C3H spleen	+	12.6(2.2)

[a] Mice were injected i.v. with the tolerogens, or not, rested one week, and epidermally painted with an ethanolic solution of trinitrochlorobenzene, or not, in an attempt to induce DTH (see MATERIAL AND METHODS). Five days after painting, all animals were assayed for DTH by applying 1% TNCB in olive oil to one ear. The differences in ear thickness before and 24 hours after painting are noted.

specific CTL (TABLE 5, line 3). Injecting haptenated spleen cells in the same manner and time frame, however, was not able to down-regulate CTL development (TABLE 5, line 5). As this dichotomy posed a notable question, we sought its answer.

Description of the Suppressor T-Cell Cascade That Regulates DTH[20]

Close examination of the T_s cascade that is known to affect DTH (FIG. 1), reveals that two sets of T_s are developed at different times. That is, the cellular participants in the suppressor system for DTH are not all derived by injecting membrane-coupled hapten intravenously. Only the initial T_s (i.e., efferently acting, T_s eff-1) has been shown to make its appearance in the spleen within seven days of intravenously injecting tolerogen. Attempting sensitization by applying TNCB to epidermis causes two other suppressor cell participants to appear along with the effector cells for DTH. An intermediary cell, termed an acceptor cell (T_s acc), is capable of receiving factor elaborated by T_s eff-1. Upon experiencing

TABLE 5. Suppression of CTL Generation by Pretreating Hosts with Nascent Hapten[a]

Day (−7) I.V. Injection of Host C3H Mice	Day (0) Immunized with TNP-C3H Spleen Plus	Day (5) Percent Specific Lysis of TNP-C3H Targets	
		25 : 1	100 : 1
None	CBA/J spleen	25.6(2.0)	46.9(4.5)
None	0	0.9(1.2)	7.2(1.6)
TNBS	CBA/J spleen	9.8(0.6)	15.4(2.2)
DNBS	CBA/J spleen	$2\overline{2.1}$(2.4)	$\overline{46.8}$(1.6)
TNP-C3H spl	CBA/J spleen	24.7(1.3)	44.2(3.6)

[a] Mice were injected intravenously with the tolerogens, or not, as in TABLE 4. After one week, the mice were immunized in hind paws with TNP-C3H SC with and without CBA/J auxillary SC as indicated. Five days later, the popliteal lymph node cells were used as effector cells with TNP-C3H target cells at the indicated ratios.

haptenated antigen plus I-J of the homologous haplotype, the "armed" T_s acc cell elaborates a nonspecific soluble factor that is taken up by the final effector suppressor cell (T_s eff-2). This cell, when triggered by antigen alone, elaborates a nonspecific factor that is I-A$^+$, and this factor is able to suppress T cells that mediate DTH of any specificity.

Does the Entire T_s Cascade Work to Suppress CTL Development?

We reasoned that the T_s cascade operative on DTH was not completely present in mice intravenously injected with membrane-coupled hapten and immunized in hind paws seven days later for CTL. As T_s acc and T_s eff-2 that arise

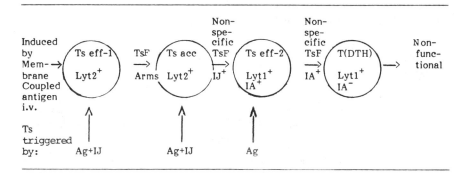

FIGURE 1. Schematic representation of the suppressor T cell cascade that has been described as down-regulating the efferent limb of DTH. The initial T_s is induced by membrane-conjugated hapten injected intravenously into syngeneic mice. T_s eff-1 appears in the spleen within seven days, and when triggered by homologous membrane-conjugated hapten, it elaborates a soluble factor that arms an acceptor T cell. Coincubation of the armed T_s acc with homologous membrane-conjugated hapten induces production of a nonspecific T_s factor that is I-J$^+$. The latter is taken up by a final T_s effector cell that differs in phenotype from the other two. When exposed to antigen, the T_s eff-2 makes a nonspecific factor that is I-A$^+$ and capable of suppressing the function of fully mature T_{DTH} cells. The cells T_s acc, T_s eff-2, and T_{DTH} are readily recoverable four to five days after mice have been painted epidermally with hapten capable of conjugating to skin antigens.

when hapten is epidermally painted most likely were absent, we sought to determine whether these would function either separately or with T_s eff-1 to suppress CTL generation. Accordingly, mice were given TNP-SC intravenously seven days before they were simultaneously painted with TNCB and immunized for CTL. Such mice showed marked suppression of the CTL response (TABLE 6, line 4). On the other hand, mice tolerized only with TNP-SC, as well as those receiving splenic cells from tolerized donors prior to immunization for CTL, showed little or no suppression of the CTL response (TABLE 6, lines 1 and 2, respectively). In like fashion, animals that had been painted epidermally with hapten and immunized for CTL on the same day (line 3) developed CTL only slightly below the level of positive control mice that had been immunized only (see footnote of TABLE 6). Furthermore, dermally painted recipients of splenic cells from TNP-

TABLE 6. Demonstration of Cooperation between Suppressor Cells That Down-regulate CTL Generation[a]

Given TNP-SC i.v. Day(−7)	Adoptive Transfer of SC from TNP-SC− Injected Mice Day(0)	Sensitized Epidermally with Hapten Day(0)	Immunized for TNP- Self CTL Day(0)	Percent Suppression
+	−	−	+	12
−	+	−	+	0
−	−	TNCB	+	22
+	−	TNCB	+	88
−	+	TNCB	+	$\overline{70}$
−	−	OX	+	$\overline{12}$
+	−	OX	+	$\overline{60}$

[a] To determine whether the suppressor T cell cascade that affects DTH would also regulate CTL production, C3H/HeN mice were injected intravenously with TNP-coupled syngeneic SC (to induce T_s eff-1), and seven days later they were (line 1) immunized in the hind paws for TNP self-specific CTL, (lines 2 and 5) used as donors of SC (5×10^7) to naive recipients, (line 4) painted epidermally with TNCB and immunized for CTL, or painted epidermally with OX and immunized for CTL. Other control groups of mice were simply painted with TNCB or OX just prior to being immunized for CTL (lines 3, 6). The epidermal painting was done to induce T_s acc and T_s eff-2 as well as to trigger T_s eff-1 cells. Thus, mice shown in lines 4, 5, and 7 possessed both sets of suppressor T cells, and mice in lines 4 as well as 5 had T_s with identical specificities, whereas those in line 7 had dissimilar specificities. Five days after immunization for CTL, cytolytic response of popliteal lymph node cells at an E : T ratio of 100 : 1 was determined. Positive control animals showed 24% specific lysis, and negative controls displayed 95% smaller responses. Values in lines 4, 5, and 7 are significantly different from positive controls ($p < 0.01$).

SC—injected mice also demonstrated reduced capacity to develop CTL (TABLE 6, line 5). These data establish that at least two sets of cells are required to work in conjunction with each other to depress CTL development.

One Set of Suppressor Cells in the Cascade Need Not be Generated by Homologous Hapten

One fact concerning the T_s cascade that is operative on DTH, that is well-known, is that the T_s acc and T_s eff-2 need not possess the same hapten specificity as T_s eff-1.[20] That is, T_s acc and T_s eff-2 can be generated by exposing mice to hapten unrelated to that which induced T_s eff-1. The factor from T_s eff-1 arms the T_s acc and confers upon it the specificity and genetic restriction originally acquired by T_s eff-1. Thereafter, if T_s acc is exposed to the original haptenated tolerogen, it will make a nonspecific factor that interacts with T_s eff-2 (cf FIG. 1).

We sought to determine whether a haptenic mismatch in the induction of T_s eff-1 and the other two T_s would still cause suppression of CTL development.[21] To accomplish this, mice that were normal and mice that were tolerized with TNP-SC were painted epidermally with OX on the same day that they were immunized in hind paws for TNP self-specific CTL. Whereas mice that had been only painted with OX and immunized to TNP-coupled self-antigens showed almost fully positive CTL responses, those that had been tolerized with TNP-SC as well as painted with OX shortly before immunization showed suppressed TNP self-specific CTL responses (TABLE 6, lines 6 and 7, respectively). Thus, the two sets of suppressor cells with the capacity to down-regulate CTL development need not be generated by exposure to the same hapten.

Identification of Two Sets of Suppressor Cells in the Cascade

To further establish the necessity for more than one suppressor cell in this system, we undertook adoptive transfer experiments in the other direction.[22] That is, the existence of T_s eff-1 had been established by transferring it to mice possessing the remainder of the cells in the cascade (cf TABLE 6). Now transfers of suppressor cells from epidermally sensitized mice into animals already possessing T_s eff-1 were deemed essential. Such adoptive transfers would also facilitate identification of the cells involved.

As may be seen in TABLE 7, mice possessing T_s eff-1 (line 1) and mice with T_s acc plus T_s eff-2 (line 2) demonstrated CTL responses only slightly below those of positive control mice. Furthermore, adoptive transfer of T_s acc and T_s eff-2 cells from hapten-painted donors to naive recipients that were immediately immunized for CTL (line 3) did not cause meaningful reduction of CTL. When aliquots of the same cells were transferred to animals possessing T_s eff-1 just prior to immunization (line 5), however, reduction in the CTL response was seen. The diminution achieved was roughly equivalent to that seen in mice possessing T_s eff-1 that were painted with hapten (line 4).

Because induction of T_s acc has been described as being sensitive to CY,[28] some mice that were to serve as donors of such cells were given small doses of CY a day prior to being painted with hapten. Four days later, their lymphoid cells

TABLE 7. Two Sets of Suppressor Cells Interact to Prevent Generation of CTL[a]

Given TNP-SC i.v. Day (−7)	Sensitized Epidermally with TNCB Day (0)	Adoptive Transfer of Lymphoid Cells from Epidermally Sensitized Mice Day (0)	Immunized for TNP-Self CTL Day (0)	Percent Suppression
+	−	−	+	24
−	+	−	+	22
−	−	+	+	5
+	+	−	+	61
+	−	+	+	82
+	−	+(cy)	+	39

[a] A second type of experiment was done to determine whether the T_s cascade that affects DTH would affect CTL production. In this instance the T_s from mice epidermally painted with TNCB (T_s acc plus T_s eff-2) were transferred into mice possessing (line 5) and lacking (line 3) T_s eff-1. In addition, T_s from cyclophosphamide-pretreated and TNCB-painted mice were given to mice having T_s eff-1. CY pretreatment is known to prevent the induction of the T_s acc normally induced following epidermal painting with hapten.[28] Negative-control mice possessing only T_s eff-1 (line 1) and those having only T_s acc plus T_s eff-2 (line 2) were included. In addition, control mice possessing both sets of cells (line 4) were immunized for CTL at the same time. Five days later, cytolytic activity of popliteal lymph node cells at an E:T of 100:1 revealed 25% (±3.0) specific lysis for positive controls, and negative controls were 97% less.

TABLE 8. Identification of the Cells Mediating Hapten-Specific Suppression of CTL Generation[a]

Method for Generating the Suppressor Cells	Characteristics of the Suppressors				
	Thy-1.2	CY-Sensitive	Lyt-1[+]	Lyt-2.1[+]	Soluble Factor
TNP-SC i.v.	+	0	0	+	Hapten-specific genetically restricted
Epidermal TNCB	+	+	+	+	Nonspecific

[a] Certain characteristics of the suppressor cells generated by the two methods were determined by adoptive transfer experiments (data not shown). Just prior to adoptive transfer of suppressor T cells induced by either method, the SC were treated with antibodies directed to different surface antigens and complement. The cells remaining after serological deletion were transferred to new animals and examined for function. In addition, prior to inducing the suppressor T cells of both types, the animals were pretreated with CY. In these manners the characteristics of the suppressor cells shown in the table were established.[21,22]

were transferred to mice possessing T_s eff-1, and the latter were immunized for CTL. That such recipients (TABLE 7, line 6) did not demonstrate a comparable degree of suppression of the CTL response reveals the CY-sensitivity of the suppressor cells developed in epidermally painted mice.

Other experiments were conducted to establish the phenotypes of the two sets of suppressor cells, and these data, summarized in TABLE 8, have been published elsewhere.[22] Essentially the splenic suppressor cell induced by intravenously administered membrane-coupled hapten is an Lyt-2.1[+] T cell that is insensitive to CY. Upon proper stimulation with hapten, the cell elaborates a hapten-specific and genetically restricted suppressor factor that is active at the efferent limb of DTH.

The set of suppressor cells within epidermal painted mice are also T cells; one is Lyt-2.1[+], and the other is Lyt-1[+]. The T_s acc is not generated in CY-treated mice that are painted with hapten, primarily because a subset of macrophages prominent in their induction is sensitive to CY.[28] This set of T_s cells, after incubation with factor from T_s eff-1 and proper triggering with membrane-coupled hapten, elaborates a nonspecific suppressor factor that acts directly upon DTH effector T cells (T_{DTH}) (TABLE 8).[20,29]

Each of the suppressor factors are currently under investigation in our laboratory. We wish to learn precisely how the suppression of the CTL is ultimately mediated by them.

Suppression of CTL by the Cascade Is Directed to the Inductive Phase of the Response

The suppression mediated by the described set of cells down-regulates DTH by acting upon effector T_{DTH} cells of any specificity. Thus, for DTH the cascade is efferently directed.[20]

To learn whether this was equally true for the CTL response, adoptive transfer experiments were performed in which mice with one set of T_s were given the other set of T_s cells at various times relative to initiation of immunization for CTL. Having the complete suppressor cascade present both early and late in immunization would thereby provide an indication of which limb of the response was being affected. As may be seen from TABLE 9, significant suppression of the CTL response was manifest only when the T_s from hapten-painted mice were transferred on day 0 into mice possessing T_s eff-1. Although still evident on days one and two following immunization, the suppression was not as pronounced as that seen when the cells were introduced on the day of immunization, for example, on day 0.

With adoptive transfers in the opposite direction, suppression of CTL development was also best seen when T_s eff-1 were given to hapten-painted mice early in immunization, that is, days 0 through 2 (TABLE 9). Thus, both sorts of transfers indicate that the inductive phase or afferent limb of the CTL response is affected by the suppressor T cell cascade.

A Different Suppressor System That Down-regulates CTL

As has been indicated, our system for generating CTL to hapten-altered self-antigens *in vivo* necessitates stimulating T_h with an antigen other than haptenated self-antigens. We have used the Mls antigen for this purpose. In addition to stimulating helper factors from T_h,[30] Mls antigens are well-known for inducing T_s cells.[13–16] Down-regulation of CTL development has, therefore, been studied using Mls-induced suppression.[9,15,16]

We have reported that *in vivo* CTL response to TNP-H-2^k can be prevented by intravenously injecting Mls-disparate cells seven days before mice were to be immunized for CTL. Thus, C3H/HeN mice that possess Mls^c antigen were injected with (CBA/J × C3H/HeN)F$_1$ SC possessing $Mls^{d,c}$ antigens (TABLE 10, experiment A) or with CBA/J SC possessing only Mls^d antigen (TABLE 10, experiment B). When immunized seven days later for CTL, such mice produced little if any response. By contrast, mice given syngeneic splenic cells intravenously and immunized in parallel showed no significant reduction of the CTL reaction. Thus, intravenously exposing Mls^c mice to Mls^d antigen either on F$_1$ splenic cells or on H-2–compatible splenic cells is able to induce a nonresponsive state *in vivo* for a

TABLE 9. The Afferent Phase of CTL Development Is Affected by the Two Sets of T_s Cells^a

Cells Transferred from	Recipients Have	Day of Transfer Relative to Immunization	Percent Suppression
Hapten-painted	T_s eff-1	Day 0	60.0
(T_s acc		1,2	42.5
T_s eff-2)		3,4	18.5
Tolerant mice	T_s acc	Day 0,1,2	80.1
(T_s eff-1)	T_s eff-2	4	30.0

^{a} To determine which phase of the CTL response was affected by the suppressor T cell cascade, mice tolerized so as to induce T_s eff-1 were immunized for CTL in foot pads and given SC from epidermally painted mice at various times thereafter as shown. In the second type of experiment (lower half of TABLE) mice were painted with hapten on the same day that immunization for CTL was initiated. They then were injected with T_s eff-1 on various days thereafter. Five days after starting immunization, the draining popliteal lymph nodes were assayed for TNP self-antigen–specific CTL.

TABLE 10. Induction of Tolerance toward Mls^d Antigen Prevents Generation of CTL to Haptenated Self^a

Experiment	Injection of C3H/HeN Mice i.v. with Spleen Cells Day (−7)	Immunization Day (0)	Percent Specific Lysis of TNP-H-2^k 100:1	Percent Suppression
A	None	+	32.3(1.3)	
	(CBA/J × C3H/HeN)F$_1$	+	12.2(2.4)	62
	C3H/HeN	+	26.9(0.7)	15
B	None	+	33.0(3.0)	
	CBA/J	+	4.0(0.6)	88

^{a} To determine whether inducing tolerance toward minor histocompatibility antigen would affect the generation of CTL to haptenated self, C3H/HeN mice were intravenously injected with splenic cells (5 × 10^7) possessing Mls^d antigen ([CBA/J × C3H/HeN]F$_1$ or CBA/J spleen cells, experiments A and B, respectively) or Mls^c antigen (C3H/HeN spleen cells, experiment A only). Thereafter, they, along with uninjected control mice, were immunized for CTL (TNP-C3H/HeN SC and nonhaptenated CBA/J SC in hind paws). Five days later, the draining popliteal lymph node cells were examined for haptenated self-specific CTL at an E:T ratio of 100:1.

reaction that is dependent upon the very same Mls antigenic disparity to stimulate help and thereby initiate the response.

Identification of the Suppressor Cell Induced by Mls^d

We have sought to characterize the suppressor cell induced by Mls^d antigen by using serological deletion techniques coupled with adoptive transfer of the residual cells to the sites of immunization for CTL.[16,31]

TABLE 11. Mls^d-Induced Splenic Suppressor Cell Is Thy-1.2$^+$ and Lyt-1^{+a}

Experiment	Treatment of Tolerant Spleen Cells	Transfer by Way of Footpad before CTL Immunization	Percent Specific Lysis of TNP-H-2^k 100:1	Percent Suppression
A	—	None transferred	20(1.0)	
	C^b	+	10(0.6)	50
	α Thy-1.2 + C	+	19(5.1)	5
B	—	None transferred	31(1.2)	
	C	+	15(0.0)	52
	α Lyt-1.1 + C	+	30(3.2)	3
	α Lyt-2.1 + C	+	13(2.0)	58

^{a} To determine what mediated the suppression that was induced by Mls^d antigen, SC from tolerized mice were transferred to naive mice. Some of the SC were treated serologically with complement alone, others with anti-Thy-1.2 antibodies plus complement, anti-Lyt-1.1 antibodies plus complement, and anti-Lyt-2.1 antibodies plus complement. Following serological treatment, the remaining washed cells were put into the immunization sites (2 to 4 × 10^7) of separate groups of mice, and the latter were immunized for CTL. Five days later the popliteal lymph node cells were assayed for TNP-H-2^k–specific CTL at an E:T ratio of 100:1.

^{b} C = complement.

Splenic cells from tolerized mice, when treated with complement, were still able to confer nonresponsivity to mice (TABLE 11, lines 2 of experiments A and B). Treatment of such splenic cells with anti-Thy-1.2 antibodies plus complement virtually eliminated the suppressive activity of the remainder of the cells (experiment A, line 3). Furthermore, treatment of tolerant spleen cells with anti-Lyt-1.1 antibodies and complement also eliminated the suppressor subpopulation of cells, whereas, treatment with anti-Lyt-2.1 antibodies and complement did not. Thus, the Mls^d-induced suppressor cell is a T cell with an Lyt-1$^+$ phenotype.

Involvement of Macrophages in the T_s-Induced Suppression

To learn whether suppressor cells could be found elsewhere in the body, we examined lymphoid cells from the peritonea of mice that had been tolerized

TABLE 12. Peritoneal T Cells and Macrophages from Mls^d-Tolerized Mice May Each Be Involved in Suppression[a]

Transfer of Tolerized PEC	Treatment of Tolerized PEC before Transfer	Sensitization for CTL	Percent TNP-H-2^k– Specific Lysis	Percent Suppression
0	0	+	32(4.0)	0
+	0	+	4(5.3)	88
+	α Thy-1.2 + C	+	30(2.3)	6
+	α Mac-1 + C	+	18(1.9)	44

[a] In addition to finding T$_s$ in spleens of Mls^d-tolerized mice, the peritoneal exudate cells of mice were examined for suppression. PEC from tolerized mice were transferred to naive mice (4 × 10^7/paw) both before and after serological treatments to eliminate cells bearing Thy-1.2 and Mac-1 surface markers. In this way the contributions to suppression of T cells and macrophages could be ascertained. Recipients were immunized for CTL 2 hours after cell transfer, and a five-day immunization interval preceded assay for specific lysis at an E : T ratio of 100 : 1.

intravenously with CBA/J spleen cells. To induce exudates, such tolerized as well as normal mice were given the same inactivated CBA/J spleen cells intraperitoneally one day prior to harvesting peritoneal exudate cells (PEC).

Transfer of whole populations of PEC to footpads two hours before immunization was successful in suppressing CTL generation only when the PEC were derived from Mls^d-tolerized mice (TABLE 12, line 2). PEC derived from normal mice were not active in this regard (data not given). When PEC from tolerized mice were treated serologically to remove T cells, the remaining cells appeared incapable of mediating suppression (TABLE 12, line 3). When tolerant PEC were treated serologically to remove macrophages, however, a partial restoration of normal reactivity was also apparent (TABLE 12, line 4). As this suggested the macrophage might also be involved in suppression, we sought to examine this aspect in greater detail. To accomplish this, an *in vitro* method for generating CTL was used where tight control of each participant in the response could be exercised.

TABLE 13. *In Vitro* System for Generating CTL[a]

C3H/HeN Responders	C3H/HeN Stimulators	IL-2 + DF	Specific CTL
Splenic T	TNP-Thymus	0	0
Splenic T	TNP-Thymus	+	+

[a] The manner in which CTL are generated to hapten-altered self-antigens *in vitro* is shown. The naturally existing suppressor T cell is nonoperative *in vitro*, thus there is no need to provide an auxilary SC to trigger helper T cells. When C3H/HeN splenic T cells are cocultured with TNP-coupled thymus cells that are heat-treated at 45°C for 30 to 60 minutes, the latter stimulator cells do not stimulate T_h, and no CTL develop unless exogenously produced helper factors are put into culture. Such factors can be derived from mouse allogeneic mixed lymphocyte reaction supernatants or from supernatants of mouse or rat splenic cells that have been stimulated with Con A. Normally, between 10 to 15 units of IL-2 and an undetermined amount of differentiation factors suffice to yield readily detectable TNP self-specific CTL.

Description of in Vitro System for Generating TNP Self-Specific CTL

The responding cells in our *in vitro* system for generating CTL specific for haptenated self-antigen were normal splenic T cells acquired by nonadherence to nylon wool columns. The stimulators cocultured with such cells were syngeneic thymic cells that had been coupled with hapten as well as treated with heat at 45°C for one hour. No CTL were developed in such cultures primarily because the haptenated thymic cells are incapable of stimulating lymphokines such as IL-2 and differentiation factor from contained helper T cells (TABLE 13, line 1). When, however, lymphokines were provided in culture, CTL were developed that are specific for hapten-conjugated self-antigens (TABLE 13, line 2). The exogenously produced lymphokines may be derived from mouse allogeneic mixed-lymphocyte–reaction supernatants or T-cell mitogen-stimulated mouse or rat supernatants.

Suppression Mediated by Lyt-1⁺ T_s–Macrophage Interaction

Using the described *in vitro* system for generating CTL, splenic Lyt-1⁺ T cells from normal as well as Mls^d-tolerized mice were incorporated into cultures with and without peritoneal macrophages from normal as well as tolerized mice (TABLE 14). No suppression was observed when normal or tolerized splenic T cells or normal macrophages were put separately into culture (TABLE 14, lines 2, 3, and 4, respectively). Macrophages from tolerized mice, however, were somewhat suppressive (39%, line 5). Furthermore, normal Lyt-1⁺ T cells in combination with normal macrophages caused little suppression (line 6), and normal Lyt-1⁺ T cells in combination with macrophages from tolerized mice showed no more suppression than macrophages from tolerized mice alone (36%, line 7). In addition, Lyt-1⁺ T cells from tolerized mice in combination with normal macrophages caused suppression of CTL generation (line 8). This contrasts markedly with the fact that the tolerized T cells accomplish nothing when incorporated alone (compare lines 3 and 8). Finally, T cells and macrophages from Mls^d-tolerized mice suppressed the CTL response when in combination with each other (line 9). Thus, Lyt-1⁺-tolerant T cells are able to achieve suppression only in the presence of macrophages, no matter whether the latter are from tolerized or normal mice. Presumably, those macrophages from tolerized mice that are able to suppress in the absence of T_s do so because they have had prior input from T_s.

For Suppression to Be Manifest, Macrophages Interact with a T_s Product

Although the data shown in TABLE 14 suggested strongly that macrophages may be the final mediator of suppression caused by the T_s-macrophage interaction, we sought to test this possibility in another manner. Supernatants were prepared from splenic and peritoneal T cells taken from Mls^d tolerized mice. The splenic T cells were further subdivided into those enriched for Lyt-2$^+$ and Lyt-1$^+$ by plating and/or negative-selection techniques. Such T cells were incubated for 48 hours after which the supernatants were filtered and added to *in vitro* cultures containing and lacking normal macrophages (TABLE 15). We observed that none of the supernatants were suppressive of CTL development in the absence of macrophages. This suggested, as does the data of TABLE 14, that the T_s and its factor are inoperative alone. Furthermore, supernatants from PEC T cells as well as splenic Lyt-1$^+$ cells from tolerized animals were highly effective at achieving suppression when in the presence of normal macrophages (TABLE 15). By contrast, supernatant from Lyt-2$^+$ T cells from tolerized mice was ineffective in the presence of normal macrophages. Thus, in the suppressor cascade involving Lyt-1$^+$ T_s and macrophages, the latter appear to be the final mediator of suppression. In addition, because the *in vitro* culturing system is so structured as to make the T_h a nonparticipating member, the mechanism of suppression is undoubtedly directed to some participant other than the T_h. This may be the precursor CTL and its utilization of helper as well as differentiation factors (FIG. 2).

TABLE 14. Lyt-1$^+$ Suppressor Cell Interacts with Macrophages to Prevent CTL Development *in Vitro*[a]

Splenic Lyt-1$^+$ T cells		Peritoneal Macrophages		Percent Specific Lysis 40:1	Percent Suppression of CTL to TNP-H-2^k
Norm	Tol	Norm	Tol		
0	0	0	0	58.0(3.2)	—
+	0	0	0	63.8	0.0
0	+	0	0	59.6	0.0
0	0	+	0	55.0	5.0
0	0	0	+	35.0	39.0
+	0	+	0	56.3	3.0
+	0	0	+	37.1	36.0
0	+	+	0	33.7	42.5
0	+	0	+	20.3	65.0

[a] *In vitro* cultures were set up to determine whether Lyt-1$^+$ cells from tolerized (tol) and normal (norm) mice would affect the generation of hapten-specific CTL in the presence of macrophages from normal and Mls^d-tolerized mice. The cultures consisted of normal splenic T cells as responders (5 × 10^6/well), TNP-thymic cells as stimulators (5 × 10^6/well), excess helper factors, and Lyt-1$^+$ T cells (5 × 10^6) from normal and tolerized mice mixed with macrophages (1 × 10^6) from normal and tolerized mice. The number of each sort of cell added was determined by preliminary experiments. After five days of culture, the cells were washed, counted, and assayed for CTL at an E:T ratio of 40:1.

TABLE 15. Supernatant from Lyt-1⁺ Suppressor Cell Prevents CTL Generation when Macrophages (MØ) Are Present in Culture[a]

Supernatants from Tolerant Spleen Cells	PEC	Percent Suppression in Cultures That Were	
		Without Normal MØ	With Normal MØ
0	T	-7	57
Lyt-2⁺	0	-23	19
Lyt-1⁺	0	0	52

[a] We wished to determine whether a soluble factor made from tolerized mouse splenic or peritoneal exudative T cells was suppressive of CTL generation *in vitro*. The factors made, as described in MATERIAL AND METHODS, were added at 60% by volume to *in vitro* cultures of splenic T cells as responders, plus TNP-thymus cells as stimulators and excess helper factors. In addition, normal macrophages (10^6) were added to some cultures but not others. After five days of culture, the cells were assayed for CTL at an E : T ratio of 40 : 1. The positive-control specific lysis for cultures containing macrophages was $30 \pm (2.5)$, and for those without macrophages, it was $21 \pm (1.3)$.

DISCUSSION

In the *in vivo* system we have used for generating hapten-altered self-specific CTL, two dissimilar stimuli are required. Syngeneic, TNP-coupled splenic cells as well as H-2–compatible, Mlsᵈ-bearing SC are injected together into the hind footpaws of mice that have the genetic makeup of H-2ᵏ and Mlsᶜ. Five days thereafter, draining popliteal lymph nodes possess CTL specific for TNP-H-2ᵏ antigens, attesting to the fact that precursor CTL received the TNP-H-2ᵏ antigenic input in addition to the proper helper lymphokines stimulated by the Mls disparity.

Because two separate antigenic stimuli must be provided in the immunizations, we have had the opportunity to examine CTL development using tolerance-inducing techniques to each antigen. Although several modalities exist for producing hapten-oriented tolerance, we have focused here upon that system that

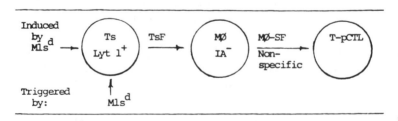

FIGURE 2. A schematic representation of the suppression of CTL development as indicated by the T_s-macrophage interaction is shown. The Lyt-1⁺ T_s is induced by Mlsᵈ antigen; it is re-exposed to the cells bearing the antigen to cause release of a soluble factor (T_sF). This, in turn, causes I-A⁻ macrophages to become suppressive by expressing a factor without the necessity for exposure to the antigen. The macrophage-derived suppressor factor is thought to affect precursor CTL because it is suppressive in cultures that bypass helper T cells.

uses hapten-conjugated syngeneic cells to induce suppressor T cells. We had shown earlier that pretreating host animals intravenously with this tolerogen would readily prevent hapten-specific DTH reactions but that it had no effect upon hapten-specific CTL generation.[15] In reality, the suppressor T cell engendered by this tolerogen (T_s eff-1) or its soluble product will not alone cause diminished DTH responses either. T_s eff-1 will only operate through another set of two cells that arise concomitantly with the DTH effector cell. The three T cells have been shown to appear in mice following epidermal sensitization with nascent hapten.[20] One T_s of the set is an acceptor cell that receives soluble factor from T_s eff-1. It derives its specificity and genetic restriction from that factor so that it can only be triggered by TNP-conjugated cells of the same haplotype used to induce T_s eff-1. The factor produced by the acceptor T cell is then taken up by the final effector T_s which in turn produces a nonspecific factor capable of acting on DTH effector cells of any specificity.[32,33]

By a series of adoptive transfer experiments in which mice possessing T_s eff-1 have been populated with cells from mice having the other two T_s and vice versa, we have observed that hapten-specific CTL generation is inhibited when both sets of cells are present but not when either is present alone.

In addition, a set of timing experiments have shown that both sets of cells must be present early in the immunization for CTL. This strongly suggests an effect upon the inductive stage of CTL development.

Curiously, when both sets of T_s were transferred to naive mice, the latter were able to develop CTL without hindrance (data not shown). This observation suggests contrasuppression may be operative in this special situation or that some parameter essential to suppression is absented in the dual transfers. We are currently addressing this problem by a variety of approaches.

We are also in the process of examining the function of these cells and their products in our *in vitro* system for generating hapten-specific CTL. Notable is the fact that Malkovsky *et al.*, have reported that the nonspecific inhibitor produced by the final effector T_s, while it is able to suppress passive transfer of contact sensitivity, does not affect either primary or secondary CTL responses generated *in vitro*.[32,33]

As has been reported from this laboratory in the past, inducing tolerance for Mls^d antigen prevents hapten-specific CTL from being generated *in vivo* by our system. The tolerogen was shown to induce a suppressor T cell that acted at the helper level to prevent CTL induction.[9,10,15,16] Now the T_s has been identified as Lyt-1$^+$, and we have shown it functions in conjunction with macrophages. Futhermore, the T_s provides a soluble factor that of itself is not suppressive in *in vitro* cultures unless macrophages are present. The macrophages are shown to elaborate a factor that alone appears to inhibit the utilization of IL-2 by T cells addicted to this lymphokine for replication (data not given here). For this reason, the site at which suppression of this sort might be active is thought to be replication of precursor CTL.

Others have reported on the induction of T_s using Mls antigens.[13,14] In their hands they have shown that T_s inhibit the mixed lymphocyte reaction. Because this reponse is also one of replication, the two sets of data complement one another.

Factors from other suppressor cell systems have also been reported to affect IL-2. For instance Maki *et al.*[34] have shown a factor termed contra–IL-2 interferes with T-cell replication despite provision of IL-2.

Still others have reported upon a T_s-macrophage interaction for the suppression of antibody synthesis.[35] The suppressor factor ultimately derived from the macrophage has been reported to affect the cell's inner structure to achieve suppression.[36] We have not had the opportunity to determine whether this occurs in precursor CTL in our system.

Finally, the T_s-macrophage system has been shown to be operative at the inductive phase of CTL development. Thus, the two quite dissimilar suppressor systems affect the CTL system apparently at the inductive level, although the hapten specific T_s cascade has not yet been studied for its effect upon the helper cells involved with CTL development.

Following completion of this manuscript, new information relative to the Mls antigenic system appeared.[37] The authors report that Mls^a-like and Mls^c-like determinants are present on CBA/J (Mls^d) cells. Furthermore, Mls^a and Mls^c are encoded by nonallelic, unlinked genes. Thus, Mls^d is not an independent genotype, but instead represents coexpression of Mls^a and Mls^c. In the light of these new findings, our system of generating CTL and of inducing T_s by exposing Mls^c mice to Mls^d cells amounts to exposing them to $Mls^{a,c}$. Therefore, it is the Mls^a antigen that is the actual stimulus in Mls^c mice.

SUMMARY

Two distinct suppressor systems have been described that are capable of down-regulating *in vivo* generation of cytotoxic T cells directed toward hapten-altered self-antigens. One system, induced by hapten, involves three T cells that others have shown to function sequentially to suppress DTH. The initiator of this cascade is a T cell that is readily induced in spleens of mice injected intravenously with syngenic membrane-coupled hapten. This T_s, when triggered by the same syngeneic membrane-coupled hapten that induced it, elaborates a factor. The other two T_s arise in lymph nodes and spleens of mice painted epidermally with hapten. One of the two T_s in this set is readily armed by the factor of the first T_s. The factor confers its specificity and genetic restriction upon the accepting T_s. The latter, when properly triggered, makes a factor that is taken up by its companion T_s, which actually suppresses by way of a nonspecific factor. Whereas this T_s cascade is operative at the efferent limb of DTH, it mediates suppression only at the afferent phase of the CTL response.

A distinctly different suppressor system is induced by minor locus (Mls) antigen. When Mls^d lymphoid cells are injected intravenously into Mls^c-possessing mice, an $Lyt-1^+$ T-suppressor cell is generated that can be found in the spleen as well as among peritoneal exudate cells. This T_s interacts with macrophages to accomplish nonspecific suppression of the CTL response that is detectable both *in vivo* as well as *in vitro*. A T_s soluble product has been found to be effective to suppress CTL generation *in vitro* only when macrophages are present in culture. The macrophage that accomplishes suppression is $I-A^-$.

Although the afferent limb of the CTL response is down-regulated by this suppressor system, our *in vitro* culturing system is so structured as to make the helper T cell inactive. Thus, the mechanism of suppression must be oriented to the other early participants in the response, namely, precursor CTL, helper and differentiation factors, and/or the antigen-presenting cell.

ACKNOWLEDGMENT

The authors thank Ms. Robbie Martin for typing the manuscript.

REFERENCES

1. ZINKERNAGEL, R. M. & P. C. DOHERTY. 1974. Immunological surveillance against altered self components by sensitized T lymphocytes in lymphocytic choriomeningitis. Nature **251:** 547.
2. HASKELL, J. S., P. HAYRY & L. A. RADOR. 1978. Systemic and local immunity in allograft and cancer rejection. *In* Contemp. Top. Immunobiol. O. Stutman, Ed.: **8:** 107. Plenum Press. New York.
3. SHEARER, G. M. 1974. Cell-mediated cytotoxicity to trinitrophenyl-modified lymphocytes. Eur. J. Immunol. **4:** 527.
4. SHEARER, G. M., T. G. REHN & C. A. GARBARINO. 1975. Cell mediated lympholysis of trinitrophenyl-modified autologous lymphocytes. Effector cell specificity to modified cell surface components controlled by the H-2K and H-2D serological regions of the major histocompatibility complex. J. Exp. Med. **141:** 1348.
5. FORMAN, J. 1977. Cytotoxic T cells distinguish between trinitrophenyl- and dinitrophenylenyl-modified syngeneic cells. J. Exp. Med. **146:** 600.
6. ROLLINGHOFF, M., A. STARZINSKI-POWITZ, K. PFIZENMAIER & R. H. WAGNER. 1977. Cyclophosphamide-sensitive T lymphocytes suppress the *in vivo* generation of antigen specific cytotoxic T lymphocytes. J. Exp. Med. **145:** 455.
7. TAGART, V. B., W. R. THOMAS & G. L. ASHERSON. 1978. Suppressor T cells which block the induction of cytotoxic T cells *in vivo*. Immunology **34:** 1109.
8. HARDT, C., M. ROLLINGHOFF, K. PFIZENMAIER, H. MOSMANN & H. WAGNER. 1981. Lyt2,3+ cyclophosphamide-sensitive T cells regulate the activity of an interleukin 2 inhibitor *in vivo*. J. Exp. Med. **154:** 262.
9. BUTLER, L. D. & J R. BATTISTO. 1979. *In vivo* generation of hapten-specific killer T cells without elimination of suppressor cells. J. Immunol. **122:** 1578.
10. BUTLER, L. D., H. L. WONG & J. R. BATTISTO. 1980. Use of immunotolerance to dissect the mechanisms regulating appearance of hapten-specific killer T cells *in vivo*. J. Immunol. **124:** 1245.
11. GAUTAM, S. C. & J. R. BATTISTO. 1983. Suppression of contact sensitivity and cell mediated lympholysis by oral administration of hapten is caused by different mechanisms. Cell. Immunol. **78:** 295.
12. GAUTAM, S. C. & J. R. BATTISTO. 1988. Suppression of hapten-specific cell-mediated lympholysis by oral administration of hapten is reversed *in vitro* by normal helper T cells or helper factors. Ann. N.Y. Acad. Sci. This volume.
13. MATOSSIAN-ROGERS, A. & H. FESTENSTEIN. 1977. Generation of suppressor cells in mice with M-locus-incompatible lymphocytes. Transplantation **23:** 316.
14. LILLIEHOOK, B., H. BLOMGREN, H. JACOBSON & B. ANDERSON. 1977. Induction of tolerance against Mls antigen in mice. Cell. Immunol. **29:** 223.
15. BATTISTO, J. R., L. D. BUTLER & H. L. WONG. 1980. Use of hapten-altered self moieties to probe the cell mediated lympholytic response and immunotolerance interface. Immunol. Rev. **50:** 47.
16. VARGO, P. M. & J. R. BATTISTO. 1984. Tolerance to Mls-disparate cells induces suppressor T cells that act at the helper level to prevent *in vivo* generation of cytolytic lymphocytes to hapten-altered self. J. Immunol. **132:** 2796.
17. HAYES, R. & H. CLAMAN. 1982. The induction of alloreactive cytotoxic responses *in vivo* are inhibited by pretreatment with Mls-disparate cells. J. Immunol. **129:** 232.
18. HAYES, R. & H. CLAMAN. 1983. Pretreatment with minor histocompatibility antigens prevents the development of functional CTL helper cell activity. J. Immunol. **130:** 56.
19. CLAMAN, H. N., S. D. MILLER, P. J. CONLON & J. W. MOORHEAD. 1980. Control of experimental contact sensitivity. Adv. Immunol. **30:** 121.
20. ZEMBALA, M., G. C. ROMANO, V. COLIZZI, J. A. LITTLE & G. L. ASHERSON. 1986. Non-specific T suppressor factor (nsTsf) cascade in contact sensitivity: nsTsF-1 causes an Ly-1+2− I-A+ immune T cell to produce a second, genetically restricted, nsTsF-2. J. Immunol. **137:** 1138.
21. GAUTAM, S. C., K. D. BECKMAN, H. L. WONG & J. R. BATTISTO. 1983. Two distinct

suppressor T cells acting in concert cause suppression of cytolytic T lymphocyte (CTL) response to hapten-altered self *in vivo*. J. Immunol. **130:** 2557.

22. GAUTAM, S. C., K. D. BECKMAN, H. L. WONG & J. R. BATTISTO. 1984. Characterization of two suppressor cells that together prevent *in vivo* development of cytolytic T cells to hapten-altered self. Cell. Immunol. **87:** 23.
23. BATTISTO, J. R. & B. R. BLOOM. 1966. Mechanisms of immunologic unresponsiveness: A new approach. Fed. Proc. **25:** 152.
24. ASHERSON, G. L. & W. PTAK. 1970. Contact and delayed hypersensitivity in the mouse. III. Depression of contact sensitivity by pretreatment with antigen and the restoration of immune competence in tolerant mice by normal lymphoid and bone marrow cells. Immunology **18:** 99.
25. SIMPSON, E., R. GORDON, M. TAYLOR, J. MERTIN & P. CHANDLER. 1975. Micromethods for induction and assay of mouse mixed lymphocyte reaction and cytotoxicity. Eur. J. Immunol. **5:** 451.
26. FINKE, J. H., C. G. OROSZ & J. R. BATTISTO. 1977. Splenic T killer cells can be generated by allogeneic thymic cells in conjunction with assisting factor. Nature **267:** 353.
27. GAUTAM, S. C., M. L. HILFIKER & J. R. BATTISTO. 1983. *In vivo* development of cytolytic T lymphocytes (CTL) to hapten-altered self: Mls-disparate cells facilitate the response by neutralizing IL2 inhibitor. J. Immunol. **130:** 533.
28. LOWY, A., A. TOMINAGA, J. A. DREBIN, M. TAKAOKI, B. BENACERRAF & M. GREENE. 1983. Identification of an I-J⁺ antigen-presenting cell required for third order suppressor cell activation. J. Exp. Med. **157:** 353.
29. WONG, H. L. & J. R. BATTISTO. 1981. *In vivo* development and regulation of cytolytic T cells specific for altered self antigen. *In* Proceedings of the International Workshop on Lymphokines and Thymic Factors. A. L. Goldstein and M. A. Chirigos, Eds.: 227–237. Raven Press. New York.
30. SCOTT, J. W., N. W. PONZIO, C. G. OROSZ & J. H. FINKE. 1980. H-2K/H-2D and Mls and I region-associated antigens stimulate helper factor(s) involved in the generation of cytotoxic T lymphocytes. J. Immunol. **124:** 2378.
31. CHOW, K. N. & J. R. BATTISTO. 1988. Prevention of CTL generation by an induced suppressor T cell that cooperates with IA⁻ macrophages. Ann. N.Y. Acad. Sci. This volume.
32. ASHERSON, G. L., V. COLIZZI & M. ZEMBALA. 1986. An overview of T suppressor cell circuits. Annu. Rev. Immunol. **4:** 37.
33. MALKOVSKY, M., G. L. ASHERSON, P. CHANDLER, V. COLIZZI, M. C. WATKINS & M. A. ZEMBALA. 1983. Non-specific inhibitor of DNA synthesis elaborated by T acceptor cells. 1. Specific hapten and I-J driven liberation of an inhibitor of cell proliferation by Lyt1⁻2⁺ cyclophosphamide-sensitive T acceptor cells armed with a product of Lyt1⁺2⁺ specific suppressor cells. J. Immunol. **130:** 785.
34. MAKI, T., S. SATOMI, M. GOTOH & A. P. MONACO. 1986. Contra-IL2: A suppressor lymphokine that inhibits IL2 activity. J. Immunol. **136:** 3298.
35. AUNE, T. M. & C. W. PIERCE. 1981. Identification and initial characterization of a nonspecific suppressor factor (macrophage-SF) produced by soluble immune response suppressor (SIRS)-treated macrophages. J. Immunol. **127:** 1828.
36. IRONS, R. D., R. W. PFEIFER, T. M. AUNE & C. W. PIERCE. 1984. Soluble immune response suppressor (SIRS) inhibits microtubule function *in vivo* and microtubule assembly *in vitro*. J. Immunol. **133:** 2032.
37. ABE, R., J. J. RYAN & R. J. HODES. 1987. Clonal analysis of the Mls system: A reappraisal of polymorphism and allelism among Mlsᵃ, Mlsᶜ, and Mlsᵈ. J. Exp. Med. **165:** 1113.

Functional Analysis of CD2, CD4, and CD8 in T-Cell Activation[a]

BARBARA E. BIERER,[b,c,e] JULIA L. GREENSTEIN,[c,f]
BARRY SLECKMAN,[c] SHELDON RATNOFSKY,[c]
ANDY PETERSON,[d,g] BRIAN SEED,[d,g] AND
STEVEN J. BURAKOFF[c,h]

*[b]Department of Medicine
Brigham and Women's Hospital
Boston, Massachusetts*

*[c]Department of Pediatric Oncology
Dana-Farber Cancer Institute
Boston, Massachusetts*

*[d]Massachusetts General Hospital
Boston, Massachusetts*

*Departments of [e]Medicine, [f]Pathology, [g]Genetics, and
[h]Pediatrics
Harvard Medical School
Boston, Massachusetts*

INTRODUCTION

T cells may be activated by the antigen-specific T-cell receptor (TCR)–CD3 complex upon interaction with allogeneic major histocompatibility complex (MHC) antigens or foreign antigens in association with syngeneic MHC molecules. In addition to the TCR, several other cell-surface molecules are important for T-cell adhesion and activation. These molecules include lymphocyte-function associated antigen (LFA)-1, CD2 (Tll, Leu 5, LFA-2), CD4 (T4, Leu 3 in the human, L3T4 in the mouse), and CD8 (T8, Leu 2 in the human, Lyt-2 in the mouse) on the T cell, and LFA-3 on the target or stimulator cell (TABLE 1). LFA-1 is a heterodimer involved in antigen-independent conjugate formation between the T cell and target or stimulator cell, and may play a wider role in cell adhesion of lymphoid cells.[1,2] CD2 is a receptor on T cells whose natural ligand on the stimulator cell is LFA-3, a broadly distributed glycoprotein.[1-4] Although the CD2/LFA-3 interaction clearly functions in cell–cell adhesion, recent data suggest that it may play a role in T-cell activation. Functional studies and monoclonal antibody (mAb)–inhibition data indicate that the CD4 and CD8 glycoproteins appear to interact with nonpolymorphic regions of MHC class II and class I molecules, respectively, and may serve to enhance antigen-specific recognition.[5]

Much of our understanding about the cell-surface antigens CD2, CD4, and CD8 has been derived from the analysis of the functional effect of mAb directed against these molecules. In the last several years, it has become clear that the

[a] This work was supported in part by NIH Grants AI-17258 and CA-34129 (S. J. Burakoff), CA-39264 (J. L. Greenstein), and a Grant from Hoechst AG (A. Peterson and B. Seed). J. L. Greenstein is the recipient of a Leukemia Society Special Fellowship. B. E. Bierer is a recipient of a Clinician-Scientist Award from the American Heart Association.

TABLE 1. Functional T Cell–Surface Molecules

Molecule (Murine Homologue)	mAb	MW + Structure	Tissue Distribution	Putative Ligand
T Cell				
TCR		80–90 kDa polymorphic	thymocytes, peripheral T cells	MHC alloantigens or foreign antigen plus self-MHC
CD3	OKT3, Leu 4	γ: 25–28 kDa, δ: 20 kDa, ε: 20 kDa, ? others	thymocytes, peripheral T cells	
CD2	TII 9.6, Leu 5 9-1, LFA-2	50–55 kDa	thymocytes, T cells, natural killer cells	LFA-3
CD4 (L3T4)	T4, Leu 3	55 kDa	thymocytes, subpopulation of T cells, monocytes	MHC class II proteins
CD8 (Lyt-2)	T8, Leu 2	30–34 kDa homodimer (human) heterodimer (murine)	thymocytes, subpopulation of T cells	MHC class I proteins
CD11a/CD18 LFA-1		177,95 kDa heterodimer	thymocytes, T cells, B cells, granulocytes, proportion of bone marrow cells	ICAM-1[a], others not identified
Target or Stimulator Cell				
MHC antigens				
Class I		44 kDa complexed to 12 kDa β_2 microglobulin	all nucleated cells	
Class II		35,29 kDa heterodimer	B cells, monocytes, endothelium, activated T cells (human)	
LFA-3	TS2/9	55–70 kDa	all human cells except thymocytes, some resting T cells	CD2

[a] ICAM-1 = Intracellular adhesion molecule-1.

functional effect of mAb is critically dependent on the epitope of the surface structure to which the mAb binds. The ability of mAb binding to a molecule to inhibit T-cell function may result from steric inhibition, preventing a receptor from interacting with its ligand. For instance, anti-CD4 mAb may inhibit antigen-specific T-cell function by preventing CD4 on the T cell from interacting with nonpolymorphic determinants of MHC class II molecules on the stimulator cell. Recently, it has been demonstrated that, in addition to steric inhibition, mAb may act as receptor agonists and transduce either a negative or a positive signal directly to the cell. In the absence of any antigen-presenting cells, T cells may be stimulated directly with mAb directed against the TCR or CD3. Anti-CD3 mAb stimulation of T-cell proliferation has been examined in the presence or absence of anti-CD4 mAb.[6] OKT4C mAb, directed against a given epitope of the molecule, inhibited anti-CD3 mAb stimulation of proliferation in the absence of MHC class II antigens, suggesting that this antibody was capable of delivering a negative signal to the T cell. Other anti-CD4 mAb did not inhibit T-cell proliferation, demonstrating that the epitope to which a mAb binds may influence the effect upon the cell.

Recently, the cDNAs for the cell-surface glycoproteins CD2, CD4, and CD8 have been cloned and sequenced.[7-9] In order to directly analyze the role of these molecules in T-cell activation, we have infected the cDNAs encoding these molecules into an antigen-specific murine xenogeneic hybridoma, specific for human MHC class II antigens. C57BL/6 mice were primed *in vivo* with the human Epstein-Barr virus (EBV)-transformed cell line JY (HLA-A2,2; B7,7; DR4,6; DQ1,3; DP2,4); spleen cells were restimulated *in vitro* with JY and fused with the murine thymoma BW5147. Hybridomas were selected for antigen-specific stimulation of interleukin-2 (IL-2) production in response to JY. The murine hybridoma 155.16, isolated from this fusion, produces IL-2 upon stimulation with the MHC class II HLA-DR antigens of JY, and this stimulation is inhibited by incubation with mAb directed against a monomorphic determinant of HLA-DR. Furthermore, the hybridoma produces IL-2 in response to liposomes containing HLA-DR molecules purified from JY, confirming that the TCR recognizes human MHC class II determinants. This hybridoma has been infected with the cDNAs encoding CD2, CD4, and CD8 using retroviral vectors. An analysis of the antigen-specific response of these hybridomas allows one to dissect the role of CD2, CD4, and CD8 in T-cell activation.

CD2 AND T-CELL ACTIVATION

Expressed early in thymic ontogeny and on all T cells, the sheep red blood cell receptor or CD2 molecule is a M_r 50,000 nonpolymorphic molecule. Binding to the T cell, certain anti-CD2 mAb inhibit conjugate formation between the T cell and target or stimulator cell, and thus may inhibit a number of T-cell functions such as alloantigen- or mitogen-specific T-cell proliferation and cytolytic T lymphocyte–mediated cytolysis.[10] Appropriate pairs of anti-CD2 mAb, however, will also stimulate T-cell proliferation and effector function, suggesting that the molecule plays a role in T-cell activation.[11,12] Recent evidence suggests that LFA-3, a widely distributed protein of M_r 55,000–70,000, may be the natural ligand on the stimulator cell for CD2 on the T cell. Anti-LFA-3 mAb inhibits antigen-independent conjugate formation by binding to the stimulator cell, not to the T cell.[1,2] Purified LFA-3 reconstituted into planar membranes[3] or lipid vesi-

TABLE 2. IL-2 Production by CD2$^+$ Hybridomas Stimulated by Pairs of Anti-CD2 mAb and by JY Cells^a

	IL-2 Production	
Addition to Culture	16.Neo	16.CD2
0	−	−
9.6 mAb	−	−
9-1 mAb	−	−
9.6 + 9-1 mAb	−	+ +
JY cells	+ +	+ + + +
+αCD2 mAb	+ +	+ +
+αLFA-3 mAb	+ +	+ +
+αTCR mAb	−	−
+αHLA-DR mAb	−	−

^{a} 5 × 10^4 hybridoma cells were cultured with either 1 μg ml^{-1} mAb or 10^5 irradiated JY cells in a final volume of 1 ml RPMI-1640 containing 10% heat-inactivated fetal bovine serum, 100 U ml^{-1} penicillin, 100 μg ml^{-1} streptomycin, and 50 μM 2-mercaptoethanol. After 24 hours, supernatants from cultured cells were assayed for IL-2 content by their ability to support the growth of an IL-2–dependent murine cell line, CTLL20.[15] IL-2 production is compared to a standard rat concanavalin A supernatant.

cles[4] will bind to CD2$^+$ T cells. We have investigated the role of the interaction of the CD2 receptor with its ligand LFA-3 in T-cell activation.

The cDNA encoding CD2[7] has been inserted into a retroviral vector. The vector has retroviral transcription and integration sequences in the long terminal repeats (LTR) derived from Moloney murine leukemia virus. A gene encoding neomycin resistance confers resistance to the neomycin analogue geneticin (G418) in eucaryotic cells. The CD2 cDNA is expressed from sequences initiated by the cytomegalovirus (CMV) early promoter. The retroviral constructs have been packaged into viral particles by amphotrophic helper cell lines. The hybridoma 155.16 was cocultured with the virus-producing cell line; infected cells were selected by resistance to G418 and screened for CD2 expression by indirect immunofluorescence. A number of cell lines have been isolated, here termed 16.CD2, which express the CD2 molecule by indirect immunofluorescent staining. The parent and CD2$^+$ cell lines continue to express the antigen-specific TCR as defined by an allotypic anti-TCR mAb (F23.1).[13] The response of the CD2$^+$ hybridomas has been compared to a cell line infected with a retroviral vector containing the gene encoding neomycin resistance alone, 16.Neo. Pairs of anti-CD2 mAb that stimulate human peripheral T-cell proliferation[12] induce 16.CD2, but not 16.Neo, to produce IL-2 (TABLE 2), demonstrating that CD2 expressed in a murine T-cell hybridoma is functional.

The CD2$^+$ hybridomas retain the ability to respond to JY by producing IL-2 (TABLE 2). The antigen-specific stimulation of both 16.CD2 and 16.Neo can be blocked by anti-TCR mAb, expressed on the hybridoma, and by anti-HLA-DR mAb, expressed on the stimulator cell. The infectant 16.CD2, however, but not 16.Neo, is inhibited by anti-CD2 mAb and by anti-LFA-3 mAb. These data suggest that CD2 on the infected hybridomas interacts with LFA-3 on the stimulator cell. In the absence of CD2 expression, LFA-3 on the stimulator cell does not participate in T-cell activation. The CD2$^+$ hybridomas respond to four- to tenfold fewer stimulator cells than the Neo$^+$ CD2$^-$ hybridomas, suggesting that CD2 expression increases the efficiency of stimulation.

CD4 AND CD8 RECEPTORS

CD4 and CD8 are coexpressed on immature thymocytes; however, on mature T cells, the CD4 and CD8 glycoproteins are expressed on mutually exclusive subpopulations of T cells.[14] Initially, it was thought that the expression of CD4 or CD8 correlated with the function of the T cell, that CD4$^+$ T cells functioned as helper cells and the CD8$^+$ T cells functioned as cytotoxic or suppressor cells. It was later demonstrated that the expression of CD4 or CD8 was more closely correlated with the MHC specificity of the T cell rather than its function.[5] In general, CD4$^+$ T cells are specific for, or restricted by, class II MHC antigens, whereas CD8$^+$ T cells are specific for, or restricted by, class I MHC antigens. It has been proposed that the CD4 and CD8 molecules are receptors that may enhance the avidity with which the T cell binds to the stimulator or target cell by interacting with nonpolymorphic regions of MHC class II and class I molecules, respectively. Both CD4 and CD8 are members of the TCR/immunoglobulin supergene family, consistent with the proposal that they may be recognition structures involved in cellular interactions.

The hybridoma 155.16 has been infected with retroviral vectors similar to those used for CD2, capable of imparting CD4[8] or CD8[9] expression and neomycin resistance to the host cell. A number of hybridomas have been selected by resistance to G418 and screened by indirect immunofluorescence for either CD4 or CD8 expression. Both the CD4$^+$ and CD8$^+$ hybridomas, here called 16.CD4 and 16.CD8, respectively, retain the capacity to respond to JY stimulation by producing IL-2.

The antigen-specific response of the CD8$^+$ hybridoma was compared to 16.Neo (TABLE 3). 16.CD8 responds to tenfold fewer stimulator cells than 16.Neo, despite the fact that the surface density of the TCR is approximately equivalent. Furthermore, in response to a given number of JY stimulator cells, 16.CD8 produces approximately tenfold more IL-2 than 16.Neo. The antigen-specific stimulation of both 16.CD8 and 16.Neo is inhibited by anti-TCR and anti-HLA-DR mAb; however, only the CD8$^+$ hybridoma is inhibited by anti-CD8 mAb. Anti-class I MHC mAb did not inhibit the stimulation of 16.Neo with JY.

TABLE 3. IL-2 Production by CD8$^+$ Hybridomas to JY and Daudi Stimulator Cells[a]

| | IL-2 Production Stimulation with: | | | |
| | JY (MHC Class I$^+$ II$^+$) | | Daudi (MHC Class I$^+$ II$^-$) | |
Addition to Culture	16.Neo	16.CD8	16.Neo	16.CD8
0	−	−	−	−
10^5 stimulators	+ +	+ + + +	+	+
+αLeu 2 mAb	+ +	+ +	+	+
+OKT8c mAb	+ +	+	+	−
+OKT4 mAb	+ +	+ + + +	+	+
+αHLA-A2,B7 mAb	+ +	+ +	+	+
+αHLA-DR mAb	−	−	−	−

[a] Hybridoma cells were cultured in the presence of JY or Daudi stimulator cells, in the presence or absence of mAb, as indicated. Culture conditions and assay for IL-2 production was performed as described in the legend to TABLE 2.

Incubation of the CD8$^+$ hybridoma with JY cells in the presence of anti-class I MHC mAb, however, decreased the response to that of 16.Neo, suggesting that the enhanced stimulation of 16.CD8 is mediated by the interaction of CD8 on the T cell with MHC class I molecules on the stimulator cells. This conclusion is further supported by the observation that the level of response of 16.Neo and 16.CD8 is equivalent when the hybridomas are stimulated by Daudi, a human cell line that expresses class II MHC molecules but fails to express class I MHC molecules. Only when the stimulator cell expresses class I MHC antigens does CD8 increase T-cell activation.

It appears that some anti-CD8 mAb may affect the response of 16.CD8 by disrupting the putative receptor-ligand interaction between CD8 and class I MHC antigens. By contrast, other anti-CD8 mAb may affect T-cell activation in the absence of a putative ligand. Both anti-CD8 mAb anti-Leu 2 and OKT8c inhibit the enhanced response of 16.CD8 to JY stimulator cells. When 16.CD8 is, however, stimulated by Daudi cells that lack class I MHC antigens, OKT8c, but not anti-Leu 2 mAb, inhibits the response, suggesting that binding the mAb OKT8c

TABLE 4. IL-2 Production by CD4$^+$ Hybridomas to Daudi Stimulator Cells[a]

	IL-2 Production		
Stimulator Cells	16.Neo	16.CD4	16.CD4Δ
0	−	−	−
Daudi cells	+	+ + + +	+ + + +
+αLeu mAb	+	+	+
+OKT4 mAb	+	+ +	+ + + +
+OKT8 mAb	+	+ + + +	+ + + +
+αHLA-DR mAb	−	−	−

[a] Hybridoma cells were cultured in the presence of Daudi stimulator cells, in the presence or absence of mAb, and assayed for IL-2 production as described in the legend to TABLE 2.

delivers a negative signal to the cell in the absence of a ligand. This negative signal appears to depend on the epitope to which the mAb is directed.

The responsiveness to Daudi stimulation of the hybridomas expressing CD4 differs significantly from that observed with 16.CD8 (TABLE 4). Stimulation of 16.CD4 with Daudi cells markedly enhances the amount of IL-2 produced in comparison to 16.Neo or 16.CD8. The hybridomas expressing CD4 respond to tenfold fewer Daudi cells. The stimulation of both 16.Neo and 16.CD4 may be blocked by anti-TCR and anti-HLA-DR mAb, but only 16.CD4, and not 16.Neo, is inhibited by the addition of anti-CD4 mAb, confirming that the enhanced responsiveness is dependent on the expression of CD4. Both anti-Leu 3 and OKT4 inhibit IL-2 production; however, anti-Leu 3 mAb inhibits the antigen-specific response more effectively than OKT4 mAb. Furthermore, the response of 16.CD4 to liposomes containing HLA-DR is markedly enhanced in comparison to 16.Neo, supporting the hypothesis that the CD4 molecule interacts with class II MHC antigens expressed on the stimulator cells. We are presently pursuing direct binding studies to determine whether there is a physical interaction between CD4 and class II MHC molecules.

We have generated a mutant of CD4, termed here CD4Δ, in which the majority of the intracytoplasmic tail, including all possible substrates of phosphorylation, has been deleted. 155.16 was infected with the CD4Δ cDNA (TABLE 4). The infected hybridomas, termed 16.CD4Δ, respond to stimulation with Daudi cells with a similar dose-response curve as 16.CD4, infected with the full-length cDNA. Thus the extracellular and transmembrane portions of the CD4 molecule are sufficient to mediate enhancement of T-cell responsiveness, suggesting that phosphorylation of CD4 is not a necessary event for this function.

CONCLUSIONS

The ability to use retroviral expression vectors to generate murine T-cell hybridomas expressing CD2, CD4, and CD8 provides a powerful system to examine the functional domains of the molecules, the physiological mechanism by which they function, and their natural ligands. The hybridomas selected not only retain antigen-specificity but in all cases respond to tenfold fewer stimulator cells, suggesting an increased efficiency of activation. The natural ligands for CD2, CD4, and CD8 have been examined. LFA-3 appears to interact with CD2 on the hybridoma, and nonpolymorphic determinants of MHC class II and class I molecules appear to interact with CD4 and CD8, respectively. Monoclonal antibody–inhibition studies confirm that CD2, CD4, and CD8 when expressed in the murine hybridoma are functional and that a number of effects of mAb may be observed. Monoclonal antibodies may interrupt the interaction of the receptors with their natural ligands. There is evidence that certain anti-CD8 and anti-CD4 mAb may deliver a negative signal to the cell. Finally, pairs of anti-CD2 mAb may activate the CD2$^+$ hybridoma. The transmembrane signal(s) delivered by the receptors interacting with mAb or with their natural ligands can now be examined. Furthermore, by constructing mutants of CD2, CD4, and CD8, we can begin to define the structural domains of the molecules that are required for binding and for signaling. This approach should allow us to examine the biological mechanism by which the cell-surface molecules CD2, CD4, and CD8 regulate T-cell activation.

REFERENCES

1. KRENSKY, A. M., E. ROBBINS, T. A. SPRINGER & S. J. BURAKOFF. 1984. J. Immunol. **132:** 2180.
2. SHAW, S., G. E. G. LUCE, R. QUINONES, R. E. GRESS, T. A. SPRINGER & M. E. SANDERS. 1986. Nature (London) **323:** 262.
3. DUSTIN, M. L., M. E. SANDERS, S. SHAW & T. A. SPRINGER. 1987. J. Exp. Med. **165:** 677.
4. TAKAI, Y., M. REED, S. J. BURAKOFF & S. HERRMANN. 1987. Proc. Natl. Acad. Sci. USA **84:** 6864.
5. SWAIN, S. L. 1981. Proc. Natl. Acad. Sci. USA **78:** 7101.
6. BANK, I. & L. CHESS. 1985. J. Exp. Med. **162:** 1294.
7. SEED, B. & A. ARUFFO. 1987. Proc. Natl. Acad. Sci. USA **84:** 3365.
8. MADDON, P. J., D. R. LITTMAN, M. GODFREY, D. E. MADDON, L. CHESS & R. AXEL. 1985. Cell **42:** 93.
9. LITTMANN, D. R., Y. THOMAS, P. J. MADDON, L. CHESS & R. AXEL. 1985. Cell **40:** 237.
10. KRENSKY, A. M., F. SANCHEZ-MADRID, E. ROBBINS, J. NAGY, T. A. SPRINGER & S. J. BURAKOFF. 1983. J. Immunol. **131:** 611.

11. MEUER, S. C., R. E. HUSSEY, M. FABBI, D. FOX, O. ACUTO, A. FITZGERALD, J. C. HODGDON, J. P. PROTENTIS, S. F. SCHLOSSMAN & E. L. REINHERZ. 1984. Cell **36:** 897.
12. YANG, S. Y., S. CHOUAIB & B. DUPONT. 1986. J. Immunol. **137:** 1097.
13. STAERZ, V. D., H.-G. RAMMENSEE, J. D. BENEDETTO & M. J. BEVAN. 1985. J. Immunol. **134:** 3994.
14. REINHERZ, E. L. & S. F. SCHLOSSMAN. 1980. Cell **19:** 821.
15. ELY, J. M., M. B. PRYSTOWSKY, L. EISENBERG, J. QUINTANS, E. GOLDWASSER, A. L. GLASEBROOK & F. W. FITCH. 1981. J. Immunol. **127:** 2345.

Suppression of Human Cytotoxic T Lymphocyte Responses by Adherent Peripheral Blood Leukocytes

DENISE C. BERNSTEIN AND GENE M. SHEARER

Immunology Branch
National Cancer Institute
National Institutes of Health
Bethesda, Maryland 20892

INTRODUCTION

The cytotoxic T lymphocyte (CTL) responses of human peripheral blood leukocytes (PBL) to influenza A virus (FLU) has been found to be strong in most healthy donors,[1,2] whereas the CTL response to HLA alloantigens (ALLO) is surprisingly weak in most of the same donors.[2] Based on the general impression that T-cell responses (including CTL) to major histocompatibility complex alloantigens are at least as potent than those to soluble antigens, viruses, and haptens, we have investigated whether the unexpected weak CTL response to ALLO reflected the absolute response potential or some type of down-regulation of the response. We report here that the CTL response to ALLO is regulated by a population of plastic-adherent cells, and that depletion of adherent cells results in elevation of ALLO CTL activity.

METHODS

Peripheral blood leukocytes were separated from heparinized blood of healthy volunteers by centrifugation through lymphocyte separation medium (Organon Teknika Corp., Durham, NC). The PBL were sensitized *in vitro* to FLU and ALLO as described previously.[1,2] The effector cells generated were assayed seven days later for CTL activity against uninfected self, influenza-infected self, and alloantigens in a six-hour ^{51}Cr-release assay as described elsewhere.[1,2] Four different effector : target ratios were tested, although the CTL data presented are shown only for the highest effector : target ratio of 40 : 1.

Adherent cells were removed from the PBL by a two-step procedure. First, $10–15 \times 10^6$ PBL in 5 ml of RPMI-1640 medium were incubated at 37°C, 7% CO_2, in 100 ml plastic petri dishes for one hour. Second, the nonadherent cells were gently removed by pipette and incubated on a column of Sephadex G10 as described previously[3] to remove additional adherent PBL. The two-step procedure resulted in the removal of all Leu M3[+] cells (macrophages), with no change in the proportion of CD3[+], CD4[+], or CD8[+] cells, as detected by flow microfluorometry. Responding PBL depleted of adherent cells in this way will be referred to as PBL$_{N/G}$, and their CTL responses will be compared with those of unseparated PBL.

EXPERIMENTAL

An experiment representative of CTL responses by unseparated PBL to FLU and ALLO is shown in FIGURE 1, as well as by PBL from the same donor that were adhered to plastic and passed over G10 (PBL$_{N/G}$) prior to *in vitro* sensitization. The results illustrate that a strong FLU, but a negative (or often weak) ALLO CTL, response was generated by unseparated PBL. By contrast, PBL depleted of adherent cells generated no FLU CTL but strong ALLO CTL activity. Thus, depletion of Leu M3$^+$ cells by adherence to plastic and G10 abrogated the FLU response, but enhanced the ALLO response.

The elevation in the ALLO response could have been due to the removal of an irrelevant cell with a concomitant enrichment of a cell necessary for ALLO CTL activity, or it could have been due to removal of a cell type that has suppressive function. To distinguish between these two possibilities, the ALLO-CTL responses were compared among PBL, PBL$_{N/G}$, and PBL$_{N/G}$ to which either adher-

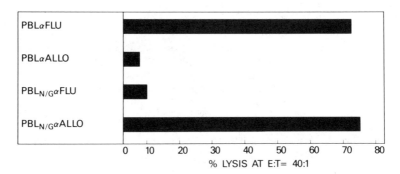

FIGURE 1. Illustration of the weak CTL response to HLA alloantigens (ALLO) compared to the CTL response to influenza virus (FLU), and the changes that occur as a result of adherent-cell depletion. PBL α FLU and PBL α ALLO groups indicate responder PBL stimulated with influenza virus and HLA alloantigens, respectively. PBL$_{N/G}$ groups indicate that responder PBL were adhered to plastic and passed over Sephadex G10 columns.

ent PBL or unseparated PBL had been added to the sensitization cultures. Both of the cell populations added to the PBL$_{N/G}$ were irradiated with 2000 rd prior to addition to the cultures. The results (FIG. 2) verify that the ALLO CTL response of PBL was weak, whereas the response of PBL$_{N/G}$ was strong. The results also show that addition of PBL, either unseparated or of those that were adherent to plastics, suppressed the CTL response to ALLO. Thus, these data indicate that the weak *in vitro* CTL response to ALLO can be attributed to suppression that is mediated by or induced by adherent PBL.

It is interesting that the ALLO but not the FLU-CTL response appears to be affected by this type of suppression. This difference in suppression of these two CTL responses could be due to one of a few possibilities: the ALLO-CTL response can be suppressed but the FLU-CTL response cannot be suppressed; ALLO stimulation activates suppression, but stimulation with FLU does not; or addition of influenza virus to the cultures inactivates suppression. To distinguish among these possibilities, two types of experiments were performed. First, if

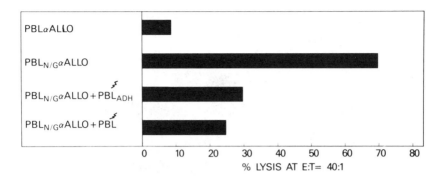

FIGURE 2. Elevation of the ALLO-CTL response by removal of adherent cells (ADH), and suppression of the elevated ALLO-CTL response by addition of adherent or unfractionated PBL. PBL added to cultures were irradiated with 2000 rd.

influenza virus inactivates suppression, then costimulation of PBL with ALLO + FLU might result in elevation of the specific CTL response to ALLO. Representative data of such an experiment are summarized in FIGURE 3. Costimulation with ALLO + FLU resulted in an elevation of the ALLO CTL response that was comparable to that obtained when the ALLO response was generated by $PBL_{N/G}$.

The second approach involved a two-stage experiment in which the suppressor activity was generated by a five-day culture of PBL stimulated with ALLO only or by ALLO + FLU. These cells were harvested, irradiated with 2000 rd, and added to a fresh culture of autologous $PBL_{N/G}$ stimulated with ALLO or of autologous PBL stimulated with FLU. The results, summarized in FIGURE 4, demonstrate that suppression for ALLO can be generated in a two-stage experiment (second line). Suppressor activity for ALLO is abrogated by coculture of PBL in the first stage with ALLO + FLU (third line); partial suppression of the FLU-CTL response can be demonstrated by the two-stage approach (fifth line); and suppression of the FLU-CTL response is also abrogated by coculture of PBL in the first stage by ALLO + FLU (sixth line). Thus, the data of FIGURES 3 and 4 demonstrate that this suppression can be abolished by the presence of influenza virus in the cultures.

We have observed one clinical situation in which weak ALLO-CTL activity is not as prevalent as that described above. This situation exists in PBL from human

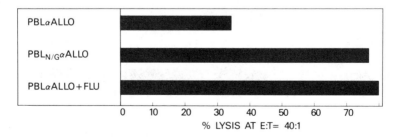

FIGURE 3. Illustration that addition of influenza virus to ALLO-stimulated cultures elevates ALLO-CTL activity as efficiently as removal of adherent cells.

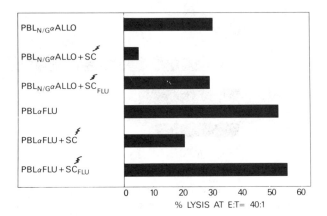

FIGURE 4. Demonstration that FLU and ALLO-CTL responses can be generated by precultured PBL and that the generation of precultured suppression can be inhibited by influenza virus. SC indicates suppressor cells generated by ALLO stimulation 5 days before addition to primary anti-ALLO and anti-FLU-CTL responses. SC_{FLU} indicates suppressor cells generated for 5 days with ALLO plus influenza virus stimulation. SC were irradiated with 2000 rd.

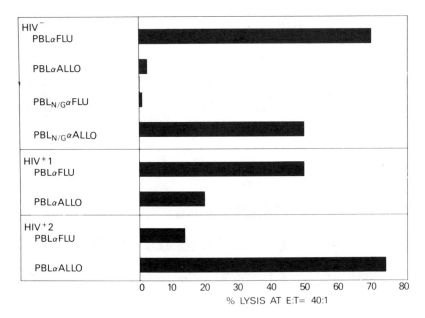

FIGURE 5. Comparison of FLU- and ALLO-CTL responses using PBL from HIV⁻ donor with and without removal of adherent Leu M3⁺ cells, and with CTL responses of PBL from two HIV⁺ donors.

immunodeficiency virus (HIV) seropositive donors without AIDS, from AIDS patients,[2] and from HIV seronegative homosexual men.[4] In all three groups, PBL from 50–60% of the donors exhibited elevated ALLO-CTL responses,[2,4] compared with approximately 15% of age-matched, seronegative, heterosexual men.[4] The data of FIGURE 5 illustrate the FLU- and ALLO-CTL responses of PBL from a control donor before and after removal of adherent cells, as well the responses of two HIV seropositive donors. Donor HIV$^+$1 exhibited FLU- and ALLO-CTL response patterns similar to that of PBL from the control donor. The CD4 cell number in the PBL of donor HIV$^+$2 exceeded 1000/mm,[3] and this donor was without any symptoms. By contrast, PBL from donor HIV$^+$2 exhibited FLU- and ALLO-CTL response patterns similar to that of PBL$_{N/G}$ from the control donor, that is, PBL in which adherent cells had been depleted. The CD4 cell number in the PBL of donor HIV$^+$2 was less than 300/mm,[3] and the donor had previously had lymphadenopathy. Thus, there was a similarity in the FLU- and ALLO-CTL responses between unseparated PBL from a control donor and PBL from the asymptomatic HIV seropositive donor. There was also a striking similarity in the change in the FLU- and ALLO-CTL patterns between PBL from the control donor after depletion of adherent cells and PBL from the HIV seropositive with a low number of CD4 cells and symptoms. Thus, depletion of Leu M3$^+$ cells from the PBL of HIV seronegative individuals resulted in loss of the FLU-CTL response similar to the absence of a FLU CTL response in many HIV-seropositive individuals and in all AIDS patients,[2] and elevation of ALLO-CTL activity similar to the elevated ALLO CTL activity of many seropositive donors and AIDS patients.[2] Because HIV has been shown to infect monocytes,[5,6] this set of parallel data raises the possibility that HIV infection can reduce antigen-presenting cell function for MHC self-restricted T-cell responses by macrophages, and also inactivate the normal suppression of allogeneic T-cell responses by monocytes.

DISCUSSION

This report briefly summarizes some unexpected observations that we have recently made concerning CTL responses to HLA alloantigens. First, the *in vitro*–generated ALLO-CTL response is weak (and often undetectable) in PBL from approximately 80% of randomly selected healthy donors and is much weaker than the CTL response to FLU using the same conditions of tissue culture. This weak CTL activity contrasts with the ALLO-proliferative response that is much stronger (data not shown). The weak ALLO-CTL response was attributed to suppression by *in vitro* mixing experiments. Suppression was removed by depletion of adherent cells from the responder cell population. Suppressor activity was "inactivated" by the presence of FLU in the cultures in which suppression was generated.

If these *in vitro* observations can be extended to an *in vivo* situation, then they could be relevant for transplantation immunology. For example, if a tissue allograft was tolerated by the host and if the type of suppression described here contributed to acceptance of the graft, then infection with a virus that inactivates the suppression could lead to enhanced graft rejection.

The results described here also have some practical value, in that elevated ALLO-CTL responses could provide an efficient means for expanding CTL lines and establishing CTL clones.

A clinical situation in which this suppression appeared not to be effective *in vivo* was observed in some but not all HIV seropositive individuals, in some AIDS patients, and in some seronegative homosexual men. Although we do not yet know whether this observation is relevant for susceptibility to HIV infection or for progression to AIDS in seropositive donors, a few possibilities can be considered. First, it is possible that the elevated ALLO-CTL responses in HIV-seropositive donors is due to HIV infection and that HIV inactivates the suppression of ALLO-CTL activity *in vivo* in the same way as that observed for FLU inactivation *in vitro*. Not all HIV-seropositive donors, however, exhibit a loss of suppressor activity, and thus HIV infection of the individual is not necessarily associated with loss of suppression. It is possible that those seropositive individuals in which loss of suppression is observed will have a high proportion of monocytes that are HIV-infected, whereas seropositive individuals in which suppression is not reduced will exhibit more extensive HIV infection in T cells than in monocytes. The observation that more than 50% of HIV-seronegative homosexual men also exhibit elevated ALLO-CTL activity could indicate that these individuals (as well as HIV-seropositive donors) have been infected with other viruses, which inactivated suppression. Inasmuch as cultures of activated leukocytes are more easily infected with HIV than unstimulated cultures,[7] it is possible that *in vivo* inactivation of this suppressor cell would make an individual more susceptible to HIV infection, because the T-cell responses to both viruses and alloantigens are downregulated by this suppression. It is also possible that HIV-seropositive individuals without symptoms could progress to symptomatic AIDS if this suppression is lost and other antigenic stimuli activate T cells. Studies are in progress to test these possibilities.

SUMMARY

Cytotoxic T lymphocyte (CTL) responses to HLA alloantigens are unexpectedly weak compared to the CTL response to influenza virus. Allogeneic CTL activity was increased dramatically by removal of a Leu M3$^+$ cell with adherence properties. The Leu M3$^+$–enriched population was capable of suppressing the allogeneic-CTL response. Precultured cells suppressed both allogeneic and influenza-specific CTL responses. Inactivation of suppression was achieved by addition of influenza virus to the cultures in which suppressor activity was generated. A high proportion of asymptomatic HIV-seropositive and AIDS patients, as well as one high-risk group appear to have lost suppressor-cell activity. These findings are discussed with respect to the possible role of this suppressor system in transplantation immunology and the T cell–immune abnormalities observed in development of AIDS.

REFERENCES

1. BIDDISON, W. E., S. SHAW & D. L. NELSON. 1979. Virus specificity of human influenza virus increase cytotoxic T cells. J. Immunol. **122:** 660–666.
2. SHEARER, G. M., D. C. BERNSTEIN, K. S. K. TUN, C. S. VIA, R. REDFIELD, S. Z. SALAHUDDIN & R. C. GALLO. 1986. A model for selective loss of major histocompatibility complex self-restricted T cell immune responses during the development of acquired immune deficiency syndrome (AIDS). J. Immunol. **137:** 2514–2521.
3. SINGER, A., A. M. KRUISBEEK & P. M. ANDRYSIAK. 1984. T cell-accessory cell interactions that initiate allospecific cytotoxic T lymphocyte responses: Existence of both Ia-restricted and Ia-unrestricted cellular interaction pathways. J. Immunol. **132:** 2199–2207.

4. TUNG, K. S. K., F. KOSTER, D. C. BERNSTEIN, P. W. KRIEBEL, S. M. PANE & G. M. SHEARER. 1985. Elevated allogeneic cytotoxic T lymphocyte activity in peripheral blood leukocytes of homosexual men. J. Immunol. **135:** 3163–3171.
5. HO, D. D., T. R. ROTA & M. S. HIRSCH. 1986. Infection of monocyte/macrophages by human T lymphotropic virus type III. J. Clin. Invest. **77:** 1712–1715.
6. GARTNER, S., P. MARKOVITZ, D. M. MARKOVITZ, M. H. KAPLAN, R. C. GALLO & M. POPOVIC. 1986. The role of mononuclear phagocytes in HTLV-III/LAV infection. Science **233:** 215–217.
7. MARGOLICK, J. B., D. J. VOLKMAN, T. M. FOLKS & A. S. FAUCI. 1987. Amplification of HTLV-III/LAV infection by antigen-induced activation of T cells and direct suppression by virus of lymphocyte blastogenic responses. J. Immunol. **138:** 1719–1723.

Analysis of HLA-A3 Determinants Recognized by MHC-Restricted and Alloreactive Cytotoxic T Lymphocytes Using Site-Directed Mutagenesis[a]

MARY LOU JELACHICH,[b] ELLIOT P. COWAN,[b]
JOHN E. COLIGAN,[c] AND WILLIAM E. BIDDISON[b]

[b] The Neuroimmunology Branch
National Institute of Neurological and Communicative
Disorders and Stroke

[c] Laboratory of Immunogenetics
National Institute of Allergy and Infectious Diseases
National Institutes of Health
Bethesda, Maryland 20892

INTRODUCTION

The class I–major histocompatibility complex (MHC) molecules function as restriction elements for antigen-specific T cells and as targets for alloreactive T cells.[1-3] Even though the precise structural features of the class I molecules that are important for T-cell recognition are not clearly understood, one region in the alpha-2 domain between residues 146–160 has been implicated as an area on the molecule that affects both mouse and human cytotoxic T lymphocyte (CTL) recognition.[4-8] Each of the CTL-defined variants of the HLA-A2,[4,5] HLA-A3,[6,7] and two of the four HLA-B27 variants[8] have amino acid substitutions within the 146–160 region of these class I molecules. In the mouse, the H-2K^b murine mutant, bml, differs from the parent class I molecule at positions 152, 155, and 156 and is the only mutant in the bm series that cannot be recognized by each of seven different virus-specific CTL populations that are restricted by the parent K^b molecule.[3]

The human HLA-A3 molecule has one known variant (A3.2) with changes at positions 152 and 156.[6,7] These differences produce the following significant changes in T-cell recognition: Virus-infected A3.2-bearing cells are not recognized as targets by virus-specific A3.1-restricted CTL,[9] and A3.2-bearing cells induce a strong allogeneic response by A3.1-bearing responder cells in a mixed-lymphocyte response (MLR).[10] Thus, these two amino acid differences affect self-restriction elements as well as alloantigenic determinants. It is unclear, however, whether both amino acid differences contribute equally to the formation of these antigenic determinants, or whether a single residue difference can affect the formation of either type of epitope. To address these issues, we have employed the technique of site-directed mutagenesis to create HLA-A3 molecules that differ from one another at position 152 or 156 only, and have analyzed their ability to be

[a] This work was supported by Grant FG-703-A-1 from the National Multiple Sclerosis Society.

recognized by virus-immune and alloimmune CTL. The results indicate that the difference of glutamic acid (A3.1) and valine (3.2) at position 152 is of primary importance in forming determinants recognized by both self-restricted and allo-specific T cells.

MATERIAL AND METHODS

Site-Directed Mutagenesis and Transfection

The two oligonucleotides used to prime site-directed mutagenesis, 5'-CGGCCCATGAGGCGGAGC-3' (to generate the $152^{A3.1}$-$156^{A3.2}$ mutant) and 5'-CGGAGCAGCTGAGAGCCT-3' (to generate the $152^{A3.2}$-$156^{A3.1}$ mutant), and the HLA-A3 exon 3 sequencing primer 5'-GACTGGGCTGACCGC-3' (used to confirm the presence of mutations and the integrity of sequences) were obtained in acrylamide gel-purified form from OCS Labs (Denton, TX). The mutagenic oligonucleotides were 5' phosphorylated using T4 polynucleotide kinase (Bethesda Research Laboratories, Gaithersburg, MD). Site-directed mutagenesis of the 212 bp *Kpn* fragment was performed as previously described.[11] Plasmid clones containing the mutant A3.2 genes were introduced into P815-HTR cells along with pSV2gpt as described previously.[11] Selection took place in selective medium described previously.[11]

Transformed cells expressed the A3 gene products to comparable levels; however, the $152^{3.2}$-$156^{3.1}$ mutant molecule was expressed approximately five- to tenfold higher than the other transformed cells.[11] Transformed cells were periodically tested to insure the stability of expression of the transfected gene.

Generation and Assay of CTL

A/JAP influenza-specific CTL restricted to A3.1 were generated by a protocol described in detail elsewhere.[11] Q36 (HLA-A3,28, -B35,44, -DR1,5) anti-B/Ann Arbor was generated by multiple *in vitro* stimulations using B/Ann Arbor–infected irradiated A3.1⁺ peripheral blood lymphocytes (PBL) stimulators. The specificity of the 1D3 and Q36 lines was established by assaying the lines on a panel of influenza A/Jap or B/AA-infected and uninfected HLA-typed targets. The A3.2 allospecific CTL line M3 anti-E1 was generated as previously described.[10] The cell lines 2D4, 3C6, and 7C4 were generated from cultures that were plated at 10 cells/well from the parent bulk M3 anti-E1 culture. CTL activity was assayed in a 4–5 hour ^{51}Cr-release cytotoxicity assay as previously described.[9] Target cells were either phytohemagglutinin (PHA)-stimulated PBL,[9] P815 cells, or influenza virus-infected cells prepared as described.[9] Results are expressed as the mean percent specific lysis of triplicate determinations.[9]

RESULTS

MHC-Restricted Recognition of P815-HTR Cells
Transformed with HLA-A3 Genes

Plasmids containing the A3.1, A3.2, $152^{A3.1}$-$156^{A3.2}$, and $152^{A3.2}$-$156^{A3.1}$ genes (Fig. 1) were introduced into P815-HTR cells, and following selection, were

		152					156	
		(GLU)					(LEU)	
A3.1 (NORMAL)	CAT	GAG	GCG	GAG	CAG		TTG	AGA
A3.2 (VARIANT)	---	-T- (VAL)	---	---	---		CA- (GLN)	---
		(GLU)					(GLN)	
152 (A3.1) - 156 (A3.2)	---	---	---	---	---		CA-	---
152 (A3.2) - 156 (A3.1)	---	-T- (VAL)	---	---	---		C-- (LEU)	---

FIGURE 1. Sequence comparison of the "normal" HLA-A3.1, the "variant" A3.2, and the site-directed mutants 152^A3.1-156^A3.2 and 152^A3.2-156^A3.1.

49610.1D3 ANTI−A/JAP

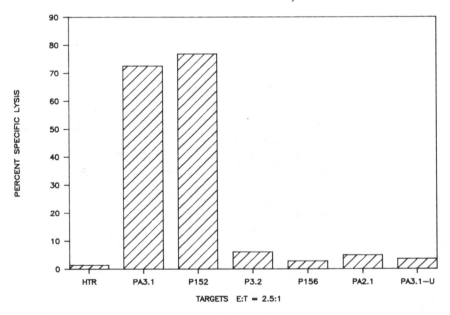

FIGURE 2. The recognition of HLA-A3–transfected P815-HTR cells by an A/Jap influenza-specific HLA-A3.1–restricted human CTL line. The 1D3 cell line lyses A/Jap-infected P815-HTR cells transfected with the A3.1 gene (PA3.1) and the mutant 152^A3.1-156^A3.1 gene (P152), but not infected cells transfected with the A3.2 (P3.2) or 152^A3.2-156^A3.1 (P156) genes. Infected, untransfected P815-HTR cells and uninfected, transfected cells are not lysed; neither are cells transfected with the HLA-A2 gene (PA2.1). The effector : target ratio (E : T) is 2.5 : 1. Results are expressed as mean percent specific lysis of triplicate determinations.

assayed by indirect immunofluorescence for cell-surface expression of human class I molecules as previously described.[11]

Influenza virus-specific CTL restricted to the A3.1 molecule fail to recognize virus-infected targets that express the A3.2 molecule.[9] This recognition pattern is also seen with the transfectants expressing the A3.1 and A3.2 molecules (FIGURES 2 and 3), with CTL specific for either A/JAP (FIG. 2) or B/Ann Arbor (FIG. 3). When virus-infected transfectants expressing the mutated genes were used as targets, only those cells expressing the $152^{A3.1}$-$156^{A3.2}$ molecules were able to be lysed (FIGURES 2 and 3). This same reactivity pattern was seen with three inde-

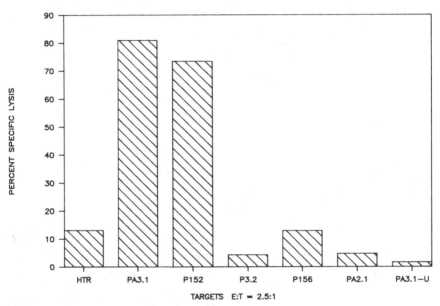

Q36 ANTI—B/ANN ARBOR

FIGURE 3. The recognition of HLA-A3–transfected P815-HTR cells by a B/Ann Arbor influenza-specific HLA-A3.1–restricted human CTL line. The Q36 line lyses the B/Ann Arbor–infected PA3.1 cells as well as the P152 cells, but does not lyse the PA3.2 or the P156 cells (see FIG. 2). Infected, untransfected P815-HTR cells are not lysed, neither are cells that are transfected, but uninfected. Infected PA2.1 cells are also not lysed. E : T = 2.5 : 1. Results are expressed as mean percent specific lysis of triplicate determinations.

pendently derived influenza-specific CTL lines obtained from A3.1[+] donors (data not shown). These observations are apparently unrelated to class I–molecule density on the target cells, because infected $P152^{A3.2}$-$156^{A3.1}$ transformants were not lysed, despite the five- to tenfold higher expression of this molecule. These results indicate that not only do virus-specific A3.1-restricted CTL discriminate between A3.1 and A3.2 as restriction elements on the virus-infected transformants, but also that the single substitution of the A3.2-encoded valine for glutamic acid at position 152 in the A3.1 molecule completely destroys the A3.1 restriction elements. By contrast, retention of the glutamic acid at position 152 and substitution of glutamine for leucine at position 156 did not have a detectable effect on the A3.1-restricted recognition. Thus retention of the A3.1 residue at position 152 alone is sufficient to maintain determinants recognized by virus-specific A3.1-restricted CTL.

Allorecognition of P815 Cells Transformed with HLA-A3 Genes

The two amino acid differences between A3.1 and A3.2 can be recognized by A3.1-positive donors in an allogeneic response.[10] In previous studies, these cells (M3 anti-E1) were shown to be able to recognize the A3.2 gene product after transfection into murine L cells.[10] The current studies show that the A3.2 gene product can also be recognized on the P815-HTR transformants by the M3 anti-E1 cells, whereas the A3.1 gene product is not recognized, as expected (FIG. 4). The P152$^{A3.2}$-156$^{A3.1}$ transformant was lysed as well as the PA3.2 transformant, whereas P152$^{A3.1}$-156$^{A3.2}$ and the untransfected P815-HTR were not lysed at all (FIG. 4). Three cell lines derived from M3 anti-E1 all showed the same reactivity pattern (FIG. 5). An A2-specific alloreactive cell line, A5, did not lyse any of the transformants (data no shown). These results indicate that the presence of the A3.2 valine at position 152 is sufficient to maintain the determinants recognized by

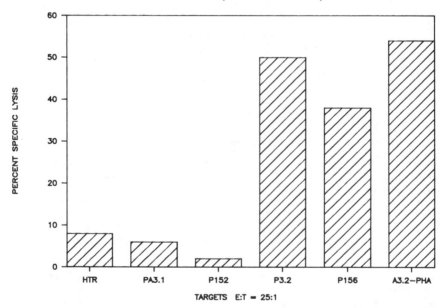

FIGURE 4. Allospecific recognition of HLA-A3–transfected P815-HTR cells by human CTL. A human CTL line specific for A3.2 lyses A3.2-bearing PHA blasts and P815-HTR cells transfected with A3.2 and 152$^{A3.2\text{-}156A3.1}$ (P156), but not cells containing the A3.1 or the 152$^{A3.1}$-156$^{A3.2}$ (P156) genes. Untransfected P815-HTR cells are not lysed. E : T = 25 : 1. Results are expressed as mean percent specific lysis of triplicate determinations.

A3.1 ANTI—A3.2 (M3 ANTI—E1) CELL LINES

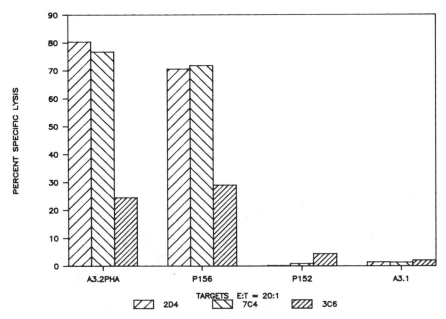

FIGURE 5. Allorecognition of HLA-A3–transfected P815-HTR cells by human CTL cell lines generated at 10 cells/well. These CTL cell lines lyse A3.2-bearing PHA blasts and P156 cells, but do not lyse PA3.1 and P152. E : T = 20 : 1. Results are expressed as mean percent specific lysis of triplicate determinations.

alloreactive CTL specific for A3.2, and that the substitution of a glutamic acid at that position destroys those determinants. By contrast, changing the amino acid at position 156 from leucine to glutamine had no detectable effect on the recognition of A3.2 by A3.2-specific alloreactive CTL.

DISCUSSION

The fact that the difference between the two subtypes of the HLA-A3 molecule can be distinguished by both alloreactive- and HLA-restricted–CTL lines means that the two amino acids at position 152 and 156 play a role in the determination of epitopes required for that recognition. The experiments presented here examine the fine specificity of that recognition. From these studies, it is apparent that the amino acid at position 152 is important in the determination of epitopes required not only for the recognition of two types of influenza virus, A and B (which are non-cross-reactive), but also for the recognition of allogeneic determinants. Because uncloned CTL populations can readily discriminate between the two subtypes of HLA-A3, the CTL lines studied in these series of experiments are felt to represent a substantial proportion of the T-cell clones responding to the two amino acid changes between the subtypes, A3.1 and A3.2. These studies, however, cannot determine whether the difference in amino acids at position 152 alters epitopes recognized by the T-cell receptor or whether it alters the ability of the class I molecule to interact with viral peptides or class I peptides.

Inasmuch as the target cells used in these studies express only one human gene, the HLA-A3 gene, the differences in the recognition of this gene product by human CTL cannot be attributed to effects of other human cell-surface molecules. These murine P815-HTR cells have been used by other investigators[12] to demonstrate HLA-A2–restricted influenza-specific–CTL recognition, indicating that these murine cells can serve as targets for other human CTL responses. Despite this fact, it has been difficult to achieve the reciprocal of the experiments presented here. Human alloreactive CTL specific for the A3.1 molecule show poor reactivity on the P815-A3.1 transformant. Also, A3.2 is apparently a low responder allele for influenza A/Jap–specific T-cell responses.

Although the data presented here suggest that the amino acid at position 152 is crucial for the formation of HLA-A3 epitopes recognized by CTL, it is important to consider the particular amino acid changes that have occurred. Previously, Monos et al.[13] have postulated that the most significant type of change recognized by CTL is that of an amino acid substitution resulting in a charge difference. Our data are consistent with this hypothesis. Whereas the change from the hydrophobic leucine to the uncharged hydrophilic glutamine at position 156 is not recognized by CTL, the change from the negatively charged glutamic acid to the hydrophobic valine at position 152 is readily detected. Therefore, it is possible that introducing a charge difference at position 156 could also alter the HLA-A3–CTL determinants. This possibility is being currently investigated by constructing another sit-directed mutant molecule containing the gene coding glutamic acid at position 156.

REFERENCES

1. KIMBALL, E. S. & J. E. COLIGAN. 1983. Contemp. Top. Mol. Immunol. **9:** 1–63.
2. LOPEZ DE CASTRO, J. A., J. A. BARBOSA, M. S. KRANGEL, P. A. BIRO & J. L. STROMINGER. 1985. Immunol. Rev. **85:** 149–168.
3. NATHENSON, S. G., J. GELIEBTER, G. M. PFAFFENBACH & R. A. ZEFF. 1986. Annu. Rev. Immunol. **4:** 471–502.
4. KRANGEL, M. S., S. TAKETANI, W. E. BIDDISON, D. M. STRONG & J. L. STROMINGER. 1982. Biochemistry **21:** 6313–6321.
5. KRANGEL, M. S., W. E. BIDDISON & J. L. STROMINGER. 1983. J. Immunol. **130:** 1856–1862.
6. VAN SCHRAVENDIJK, M. R., W. E. BIDDISON, A. E. BERGER & J. E. COLIGAN. 1985. J. Immunol. **134:** 410–416.
7. COWAN, E. P., B. R. JORDAN & J. E. COLIGAN. 1985. J. Immunol. **135:** 2835–2841.
8. VEGA, M. A., L. WALLACE, S. ROJO, R. BRAGADO, P. APARICIO & J. A. LOPEZ DE CASTRO. 1985. J. Immunol. **135:** 3323–3332.
9. BIDDISON, W. E., G. M. SHEARER & S. SHAW. 1981. J. Immunol. **127:** 2231–2235.
10. COWAN, E. P., J. E. COLIGAN & W. E. BIDDISON. 1985. Proc. Natl. Acad. Sci. USA **82:** 4490–4494.
11. COWAN, E. P., M. L. JELACHICH, J. E. COLIGAN & W. E. BIDDISON. 1987. Proc. Natl. Acad. Sci. USA. **84:** 5014.
12. GOMARD, E., B. BEGUE, S. SODOYER, J. L. MARYANSKI, B. R. JORDAN & J. P. LEVY. 1986. Nature **319:** 153–154.
13. MONOS, D. S., W. A. TEKOLF, S. SHAW & H. L. COOPER. 1984. J. Immunol. **132:** 1379–1385.

Cytotoxic T Cells in Autoimmune Disease of the Central Nervous System[a]

D. SUN, R. MEYERMANN, AND H. WEKERLE

Max Planck Society
Clinical Research Unit for Multiple Sclerosis
Würzburg, Federal Republic of Germany

INTRODUCTION

Cytotoxic T lymphocytes (CTL) have well-established roles in infectious diseases. In the central nervous system (CNS), CTL seem to have a physiological role in clearing away persistent viruses without demonstrable tissue damage.[1] In other situations, these cells are less beneficial. Virus-specific CTL can be detrimental by destroying essential cellular structures of CNS that express viral determinants.[2,3]

CTL have also been suspected to be the pathogens in CNS-restricted autoimmune diseases, like experimental autoimmune encephalomyelitis (EAE). EAE is induced in susceptible animals by immunization with the major myelin protein, myelin basic protein (MBP). The fact that EAE can be transferred to naive hosts by immune cells, rather than by humoral antibodies, was interpreted as evidence for CTL mechanism involvement in the effector phase of this disease.[4] Indeed, $CD8^+$ T cells can be regularly seen in EAE lesions,[5] although in the development of a lesion, they appear later than $CD4^+$ T cells and seem to be localized in areas of lower activity.[6]

Two observations were, however, difficult to reconcile with classical CTL effects in EAE. First, the target autoantigen, MBP, is localized on the cytoplasmic side, but not on the surface of myelin-forming cell membranes,[7] and thus should be inaccessible to autoimmune CTL. Second, EAE is transferable only by $CD4^+$ T cells, as documented by experiments using MBP monospecific T lines[8,9] and primed T-cell populations.[10]

Recent work in our laboratory indicates that, nevertheless, CTL have vital roles in the pathogenesis of EAE. First, and most surprisingly, it became clear that the encephalitogenic, MBP-specific T lines, have indeed cytolytic potential. They are Ia-restricted, $CD4^+$ CTL.[11] So far, without any exception, the encephalitogenic potential of an MBP-specific rat T-cell line is associated with cytotoxic capacity and recognition of a strictly defined encephalitogenic epitope on the MBP autoantigen.

More recently, a second CTL population with completely different functional characteristics was isolated from the spleens of rats that had recovered from T line–mediated EAE. These cells are $CD8^+$, and respond *in vitro* by proliferation to MBP-specific T-line cells, but do not recognize MBP presented on antigen-presenting cells (APC). More important, these cells strongly lyse MBP-specific T-line cells, and in transfer experiments they effectively protect host rats from lethal

---

[a] The Clinical Research Unit is supported by funds from the Hermann and Lilly Schilling Foundation.

doses of encephalitogenic line cells. These T cells behave like self-protective suppressor T cells, which could be involved in the termination of cellular autoimmune diseases and, perhaps, in the maintenance of immunological self-tolerance.

ENCEPHALITOGENIC T-LYMPHOCYTE LINES

MBP-specific T lymphocytes are isolated from MBP-immunized or unprimed Lewis rats, applying a sequence of positive-selection procedures. First, lymph node cells from Lewis rats, which have been immunized 9–11 days earlier with MBP/complete Freund's adjuvant (CFA) are dissociated and cocultured *in vitro* with the putative autoantigen MBP.

In these cultures MBP-specific T cells are selectively activated to proliferate and to change into large activated T lymphoblasts. These specifically activated lymphoblasts are further enriched by subsequent incubation in interleukin-2–containing medium for 10–14 days. Preactivated, but not resting, T cells express high concentrations of interleukin-2 receptors on their surface, and thus are preferentially supported by interleukin-2. Periodic restimulation using antigen and APC is required to establish and to maintain antigen-specific T lines.

A panel of permanent MBP-specific T lines was obtained and characterized in our laboratory. All lines recognize antigen exclusively in the context of Ia products of the rat major histocompatibility complex (MHC), and they all, irrespective of their antigen specificities, belong to the $CD4^+$ subset of the T-cell compartment. These cells bind the monoclonal rat subset marker W3/25, but not OX8.

MBP-specific T cells are not only exclusively autoreactive against MBP as autoantigen, but are violently autoaggressive. When injected in graded doses into syngeneic normal adult recipient rats, activated T-line cells transfer definite though transient EAE starting from doses as low as 2×10^4 cells per recipient. Single intravenous injection of $1–2 \times 10^6$ cells leads to death in about 50% of the injected animals within 3–7 days. The surviving rats recover from clinical symptoms in another 3–4 days and gain body weight gradually. Furthermore, animals recovered from passively induced EAE were resistant to subsequent active induction of EAE.

THE LESION OF T LINE–CELL-MEDIATED EAE

The histological lesion arising during T line–mediated EAE is practically identical with the one seen in acute EAE induced by active immunization. The key morphological features are a dominantly mononuclear infiltration concentrated around perivascular areas of the central nervous system. Immunohistochemical staining reveals that most, if not all, of the early infiltrating lymphocytes express the CD4 ace marker (W3/25), whereas T cells with the CD8 surface marker can only be detected in the later recovery stages of the disease.

Studies using transfers of isotope prelabeled encephalitogenic T-line cells demonstrated that the overwhelming majority of the infiltrating cells are contributed by the host immune system. This has further been confirmed in transfers of encephalitogenic T-line cells into lethally irradiated hosts, which developed clinical disease, like unirradiated control rats, but, as revealed by histological examination, completely lack the dense perivascular infiltrations (Fig. 1). Thus, a few

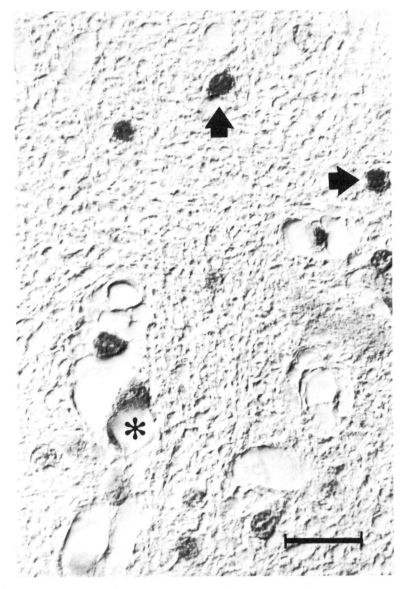

FIGURE 1. T line–transferred EAE in irradiated recipient rat. Disseminated infiltration of CNS parenchyma by activated T cells expressing the receptor for IL-2 (arrows). Note absence of perivascular mononuclear infiltrates (star); bar = 20 μm.

TABLE 1. Cytolytic Activity of Antigen-Specific T-Line Cells: Technical Procedures

T-Line Code	Target Antigen	Antigen (10 μg/ml)	Blocking mAb (dilution 1 : 4000)	^{51}Cr Release (%) Exp. 1 (18 hr)	Exp. 2 (9 hr)
Z1a	(MBP, 68-88)	MBP	0	80.5 ± 4.6	78.4 ± 6.6
		Ovalbumin	0	13.8 ± 0.1	4.4 ± 0.1
		MBP	OX3 (class II)	19.4 ± 3.2	15.7 ± 1.8
		MBP	OX18 (class I)	85.3 ± 2.5	64.5 ± 1.9
L.BP644	(MBP, 68-88)	0	0	15.0 ± 2.2	
		MBP	0	73.4 ± 1.6	
bs84	(MBP, conformation?)	MBP	0	33.6 ± 9.1	15.0 ± 1.0
L.C2	(MBP, 48-67)	MBP	0	39.1 ± 8.6	29.8 ± 2.8
L.0A	(Ovalbumin)	MBP	0	22.4 ± 8.6	5.2 ± 0.5
		Ovalbumin	0	21.6 ± 2.0	9.1 ± 0.3
None (spontaneous release)		0	0	13.2 ± 1.1	7.4 ± 0.2

activated T lymphoblasts invading the CNS are associated with full clinical EAE, indicating that the transferred encephalitogenic line cells are sufficient to induce autoimmune disease and do not require the help by host immunocytes.

MBP-SPECIFIC CD4+ T-LINE CELLS ARE IA-RESTRICTED T-KILLER CELLS

Morphological observations provided the first evidence for the cytolytic capacity of MBP-specific T-line cells. Activated encephalitogenic T cells will completely destroy monolayers of astrocytes in the presence, but not in the absence, of MBP. Pretreatment of the astrocytes with interferon-γ (IFN-γ), which induces Ia on the astrocyte membranes, strongly enhances the lysis effect. T cell–dependent lysis of astrocytes can be readily quantified using a conventional isotope release assay. Dependent on the effector/target ratios and on the antigen doses, ^{51}Cr-labeled astrocytes may specifically release up to 70% of their incorporated ^{51}Cr within 12 hours. In cytolysis, antigen recognition is restricted by the same MHC restriction determinants that act in T-cell proliferation. Monoclonal antibodies against products of the I-A region of the rat MHC (OX3 or OX6) are able to almost completely block antigen-dependent cytolysis, whereas monoclonal antibodies binding the I-E region (OX17) or class I–MHC products (OX18) are completely without effect (TABLE 1).

Cytolysis of MBP-specific T cells is by no means limited to astrocytes as targets, but applies to any cell type capable of immunologically presenting antigen to T cells. Thus, Ia-induced peritoneal macrophages are lysed as efficiently as astrocytes. By contrast, fibroblasts of skin origin that are negative for Ia antigen on their membrane surface, and fail to immunologically present antigen, completely resist T cell–mediated cytotoxicity.

MODULATION OF APC FUNCTION BY MBP-SPECIFIC T LINES

It was of interest to learn whether *in vitro* cytolysis by encephalitogenic T cells is associated with suppression of antigen-presenting capacity of astrocytes or macrophages. Cytotoxic and noncytotoxic (*vide infra*) rat T-line cells were coincubated with syngeneic Ia-induced astrocytes or macrophages, in the presence or absence of T cell–specific antigens for 48 hours. Thereafter, the T cells were cautiously washed off, the cultures were irradiated, and the antigen-presenting activities of astrocytes and macrophages were evaluated in a second round. As shown in FIGURE 2, pretreatment of astrocytes and macrophages with encephalitogenic, MBP-specific T cells abolished antigen-presenting capacity. This effect critically depended on the presence of the relevant antigen (MBP). Unexpectedly, in cultures where astrocytes interacted with encephalitogenic T cells in the absence of MBP, the antigen-presenting capacity was increased. This was also seen in cultures with T cells specific for nonmyelin antigens (PPD or ovalbumin). Enhancement of antigen presentation was accompanied by strong induction of MHC–class II antigen on the APC during the first round of T-cell/APC interaction (FIG. 2).

CYTOTOXIC CAPACITY OF T-LINE CELLS IS ASSOCIATED WITH THE EPITOPE AND THE ENCEPHALITOGENIC POTENTIALS

So far, in our studies, the cytotoxicity capacity of a given T line is strictly associated with its encephalitogenic capacity. In the Lewis rat, only T-line cells recognizing MBP, and among them only those specific for its amino acid sequence 68-88, are capable of lysing their presenter cells upon antigen recognition, and these lines are the only ones able to mediate EAE. On the other hand, T-line cells specific for irrelevant foreign antigens, for example, PPD or OVA, are never able to kill their APC. Even more intriguing, T-line cells recognizing an MBP epitope distinct from sequence 68-88, for example, peptide 45-67, neither kill APC nor mediate EAE (TABLE 1).

ISOLATION OF COUNTER-REGULATORY T CELLS ANTAGONISTIC TO MBP-SPECIFIC ENCEPHALITOGENIC T CELLS FROM THE EAE-RECOVERED LEWIS RAT

Lewis rats having recovered from EAE reliably develop resistance against later attempts to actively induce the disease. Down-regulatory suppressor cells

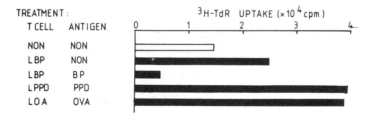

FIGURE 2. Modulation of the antigen-presenting capacity of astrocytes by interaction with T-line cells. Astrocytes were pretreated with recombinant IFN-γ for 48 hr and were coincubated in a first round with rat T-line cells of different specificities, in the presence or absence of specific antigens as indicated. Twenty-four hours later, the cultures were rinsed free of lymphocytes and heavily irradiated; the antigen-presenting capacities in the cultures were reevaluated in a second round by coculture with a new panel of T lines and antigen.

were claimed to be responsible for post-EAE resistance, but, so far, these suppressor cells have not been isolated.

Recently, we succeeded in enriching a T-cell population with CD8$^+$ phenotype from the spleens of Lewis rats that had recovered from EAE caused by transfers of an MBP-specific T line. *In vitro* coincubation of nylon-wool–enriched splenic T cells with irradiated encephalitogenic, MBP-specific T cells led to selective proliferation of an OX8$^+$, OX6$^+$, W3/25$^-$ cell population. The T cells, thus obtained, strongly suppress antigen- and Con A–mediated activation of the "primary" T line. Furthermore, when injected *in vivo*, these cells abolished the encephalitogenic activity of the autoaggressive T cells. Employing a conventional ^{51}Cr release assay, we found that these OX8$^+$ cells could specifically kill the MBP-specific encephalitogenic T line cells, which had been used for the induction of EAE in the donor rat. T cells of irrelevant antigen specificities (*e.g.* OVA-specific, PPD-specific) and even some distinct T lines specific for MBP were not lysed (FIG. 3).

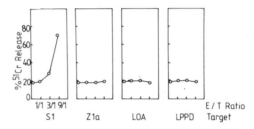

FIGURE 3. Cytolytic effect of CD8$^+$ anti-T-line T lymphocytes on target T-line cells. Target T-line cells were labeled with ^{51}Cr. Graded doses of anti-S$_1$ cells were cocultured with 2×10^4 ^{51}Cr-labeled T-line cells. Cell-free supernatant cocultures were collected after 20 hr to calculate ^{51}Cr release (%).

DISCUSSION

The fact that classical CTL (CD8$^+$ T cells recognizing autoantigen in the context of class I–MHC determinants) have not yet been demonstrated in EAE does by no means rule out cytotoxicity phenomena in the course of this disease. Indeed, we demonstrate here two autoreactive T-lymphocyte populations with unusual properties, which seem to function at distinct stages of EAE. First, Ia-restricted, CD4$^+$ T cells that recognize the encephalitogenic epitope of MBP and transfer EAE to naive syngeneic recipients are shown to lyse strongly and specifically any Ia$^+$ cell-presenting MBP in an immunogenic way.[11] These cells may be involved in initiating the autoimmune inflammatory reaction in T line–mediated EAE. Second, we describe a CD8$^+$ T-lymphocyte population that is extractable from the peripheral immune system of rats after having recovered from T line–mediated EAE. These cells specifically recognize and lyse the relevant encephalitogenic MBP-specific T line but fail to respond to MBP. Anti-T-line cells neutralize the encephalitogenic capacity of MBP-specific T-line cells *in vivo* and thus may have a role in termination of monophasic clinical EAE.

CTL have been traditionally thought to express the CD8 phenotype and to be restricted by class I–MHC products in antigen recognition. During the past few years, it became clear, however, that, especially in certain viral infections, a considerable proportion of all CTL are CD4$^+$ and recognize their target epitopes in the context of Ia antigens.[12-14] Functionally, these cells are indistinguishable from classical CD8$^+$ CTL. CTL of either phenotype lyse their target cells with high efficiency and specificity,[15] and recent analysis has established that at least some CD4 cells contain functional markers typical for CTL.[16] We screened a panel of T lines specific for MBP or for other protein antigens. Quite remarkably, target lysis was restricted to T lines recognizing MBP and, among all MBP-specific lines, to those with receptors for the encephalitogenic epitope representing amino acid sequence 68-88.[11] Functionally, a CTL potential of an individual line strictly correlates with its encephalitogenic capacity *in vivo*. This observation, in context with the finding that irradiated recipient rats develop EAE in the absence of host-derived mononuclear infiltrates (FIG. 1 and reference 17), suggests that the transferred activated T-line lymphocytes are autonomous in causing the encephalitic CNS lesions and that cytotoxic mechanisms may be involved in this process. We have suggested that Ia-inducible astrocytes incorporating, processing, and presenting myelin components may be the primary target of an encephalitogenic CTL attack.[18]

All the rat T lines established in our laboratory were indistinguishable by all morphological and functional criteria. They all were CD4 cells, but they all were cytotoxic in lectin-dependent CTL assays. The fact that only peptide 68-88–specific, encephalitogenic T cells lysed APC supports the view that the quality of target epitope rather than a functional program peculiar to the effector cell determines the character of the T cell–target interaction initiated by antigen recognition. The structure of the nominal peptide *per se*, or the peptide Ia complex, could favor cytolytic effects. It remains, furthermore, to be seen how far our observations are related to a concept of Goodman and Sercarz,[19] who distinguish protein epitopes determining helper T cell responses from others triggering suppressor T cells.

A second CTL population involved in EAE was isolated from the spleen of rats that had recovered from T line–mediated EAE. These cells express the CD8 phenotype, bind OX8 monoclonal antibodies, but exclude the rat CD4 marker, W3/25. These cells specifically recognize and lyse the T line that originally induced EAE in the donor rat. Other T lines, irrespective of their antigen specificity, are ignored, and there is neither class I– nor class II–MHC restriction demonstrable. *In vivo*, these cells again selectively suppress the encephalitogenic capacity of "their" target T line. CTL with suppressor-cell properties have been reported repeatedly. In the mouse, CD8$^+$ cytolytic suppressor T lines were isolated from tolerant donors. These cells, however, had receptors for the protein antigen rather than for antigen-reactive T lymphocytes.[20] On the other hand, Lamb and Feldman recruited a CD8$^+$ T-cell population from human peripheral blood that specifically interacted with virus-antigen–specific CD4$^+$ cells.[21] Idiotypic interactions were proposed to underly these interactions. We have not yet established whether similar interactions between autoantigen-specific CD4$^+$ cells and counter-regulatory CD8$^+$ cells are involved in our EAE systems. Still, it is tempting to speculate that the intercellular interactions observed *in vivo* and *in vitro* might represent some regulatory processes involved in termination of monophasic autoimmune disease. It will be of even greater interest to determine whether analogous mechanisms are involved in maintenance of tissue-specific immunological self-tolerance.[22]

ACKNOWLEDGMENT

We thank Ms. C. Hammerich for typing the manuscript.

REFERENCES

1. OLDSTONE, M. B. A., P. BLOUNT, P. J. SOUTHERN & P. W. LAMPERT. 1986. Cytoimmunotherapy for persistent virus infection reveals a unique clearance pattern from the central nervous system. Nature **321:** 239–243.
2. SCHWENDEMANN, G., J. LOHLER & F. LEHMANN-GRUBE. 1983. Evidence for cytotoxic T-lymphocyte-target cell interaction in brains of mice infected intracerebrally with lymphocytic choriomeningitis virus. Acta Neuropathol. **61:** 183–195.
3. BAENZIGER, J., H. HENGARTNER, R. M. ZINKERNAGEL & G. A. COLE. 1986. Induction or prevention of immunopathological disease by cloned cytotoxic T cell lines specific for lymphocytic choriomeningitis virus. Eur. J. Immunol. **16:** 387–392.
4. PATERSON, P. Y. 1976. Experimental allergic encephalomyelitis: Role of fibrin deposition in immunopathogenesis of inflammation in rats. Fed. Proc. **35:** 2428–2434.
5. HICKEY, W. F. & N. K. GONATAS. 1984. Suppressor T lymphocytes in the spinal cord of Lewis rats recovered from acute experimental allergic encephalomyelitis. Cell. Immunol. **85:** 284–288.
6. TRAUGOTT, U., D. E. MCFARLIN & C. S. RAINE. 1986. Immunopathology of the lesion in chronic relapsing experimental encephalomyelitis in the mouse. Cell. Immunol. **99:** 395–410.
7. OMLIN, F. X., H. DE F. WEBSTER, C. G. PALKOVITS & S. R. COHEN. 1982. Immunocytochemical localization of basic protein in major dense line regions of central and peripheral myelin. J. Cell. Biol. **95:** 242–248.
8. BEN-NUN, A. & I. R. COHEN. 1982. Experimental autoimmune encephalomyelitis (EAE) mediated by T cell lines: Progress of selection of lines and characterization of the cells. J. Immunol. **129:** 303–308.
9. SCHLUESENER, H. J. & H. WEKERLE. 1985. Autoaggressive T lymphocyte lines recognizing the encephalitogenic region of myelin basic protein: *In vitro* selection from unprimed rat T lymphocyte populations. J. Immunol. **135:** 3128–3133.
10. SWANBORG, R. H. 1983. Autoimmune effector cells. V. A monoclonal antibody specific for rat T helper cells inhibits adoptive transfer of autoimmune encephalomyelitis. J. Immunol. **130:** 1503–1505.
11. SUN, D. & H. WEKERLE. 1986. Ia-restricted encephalitogenic T lymphocytes mediating EAE lyse autoantigen-presenting astrocytes. Nature **320:** 70–72.
12. JACOBSON, S., J. R. RICHERT, W. E. BIDDISON, A. SATINSKY, R. J. HARTZMAN & H. F. MCFARLAND. 1984. Measles virus-specific T4$^+$ human cytotoxic T cell clones are restricted by class II HLA antigens. J. Immunol. **133:** 754–757.
13. YASUKAWA, M. & J. M. ZARLING. 1984. Human cytotoxic T cell clones directed against herpes simplex virus-infected cells. I. Lysis restricted by HLA class II MB and DR antigens. J. Immunol. **133:** 422–427.
14. KAPLAN, D. R., R. GRIFFITH, V. L. BRACIALE & T. J. BRACIALE. 1984. Influenza virus-specific human cytotoxic T cell clones: Heterogeneity in antigenic specificity and restriction by class II MHC products. Cell. Immunol. **88:** 193–204.
15. LUKACHER, A. E., L. A. MORRISON, V. L. BRACIALE, B. MALISSEN & T. J. BRACIALE. 1985. Expression of specific cytolytic activity by H-2I restricted influenza-specific T lymphocyte clones. J. Exp. Med. **162:** 171–187.
16. SIMON, M. M., U. FRUTH, H. G. SIMON & M. D. CRAMER. 1986. A specific serine proteinase is inducible in Lyt2$^+$, L3T4$^-$ and Lyt2$^-$, L3T4$^+$ T cells *in vitro* but is mainly associated with Lyt2$^+$, L3T4$^-$ effector cells *in vivo*. Eur. J. Immunol. **16:** 1559–1568.
17. SEDGWICK, J., S. BROSTOFF & D. MASON. 1987. Experimental allergic encephalomyelitis in the absence of classical delayed hypersensitivity reaction. Severe paralytic

disease correlates with the presence of interleukin-2 receptor positive cells infiltrating the central nervous system. J. Exp. Med. **165:** 1058–1075.

18. WEKERLE, H., C. LININGTON, H. LASSMANN & R. MEYERMANN. 1986. Cellular immune reactivity within the central nervous system: Surveillance of the blind spot. TINS **9:** 271–277.

19. GOODMAN, J. W. & E. E. SERCARZ. 1983. The complexity of structures involved in T-cell activation. Ann. Rev. Immunol. **1:** 465–498.

20. DEGWERT, J., R. BETTMANN, J. HEUER & E. KOLSCH. 1987. Isolation of a bovine serum albumin-specific T-suppressor cell clone and evaluation of its *in vitro* functions. Immunology **60:** 345–352.

21. LAMB, J. R. & M. FELDMAN. 1982. A human supressor T cell clone which recognizes an autologous helper T cell clone. Nature **300:** 456–458.

22. TAGUCHI, O. & Y. NISHIZUKA. 1987. Self tolerance and localized autoimmunity. Mouse models of autoimmune disease that suggest tissue-specific suppressor T cells are involved in self tolerance. J. Exp. Med. **165:** 146–156.

Cytotoxic T Cells in Influenza Infection

BRIGITTE A. ASKONAS, PATRICIA M. TAYLOR, AND
FERNANDO ESQUIVEL[a]

Division of Immunology
National Institute for Medical Research
Mill Hill, London NW7 1AA

INTRODUCTION

Our studies have concerned several aspects of cytotoxic T cell (T_c) responses and recognition patterns in a mouse model of influenza infection. T cells are an important arm of the immune defence once an influenza infection has occurred and are of particular interest, because a major proportion of T_c (and some T-helper cells (T_h)) do not discriminate among serologically distinct influenza viruses within a type, both in the human and the mouse. T_c recognition of influenza-infected cells contrasts with the viral recognition pattern of B cells and neutralizing antibodies that are directed mainly to the variable regions of the surface glycoprotein coat of the virus. In this paper we shall discuss the repertoire for the influenza components of class I–major histocompatibility complex (MHC)–restricted T_c, the genetics of T_c responsiveness, and the *in vivo* function of T_c (using T-cell clones) in murine infection in comparison to the function of T_h.

CLASS I-MHC–RESTRICTED T_c: REPERTOIRE FOR INFLUENZA PROTEINS

We find that following influenza infection most of the memory T_c are class I-MHC–restricted and inhibited in the presence of antibody to Lyt-2$^+$. Hence our specificity studies have focused on Lyt-2$^+$ cells, and of particular interest are those that see all type A influenza viruses (these will be referred to as A virus cross-reactive), but that do not recognize targets infected with type B virus.[1] It is now clear that A virus cross-reactive T_c can recognize the internal proteins of the virus, nucleoprotein (NP),[2] the polymerases, and NS1.[3,4] In mice matrix (M), protein is not seen by most mouse strains tested,[4] but some human donors have M protein–specific T_c.[5] Whereas about two-thirds of T_c are A virus cross-reactive (M. Stringfellow, unpublished), more than 80% of T_c see internal proteins after intranasal (i.n.) infection.[6] Hemagglutinin (HA) is a minor component of the T_c memory population following intranasal infection with H1N1 virus; that is, by limiting dilution experiments, we find less than 5% of T_c able to lyse target cells transfected with DNA coding for HA (H1) (P. M. Taylor, unpublished). HA-specific T_c, however, can be selected by priming with HA.VAC[7,2] or *in vitro* selection.[8,9] These do not recognize all type A viruses and are subtype A-virus–specific. Poor T_c recognition of HA after infection remains a puzzle, although HA is a major immunogen for B cells and also the target antigen for 50% of T_h following infection (F. Esquivel, manuscript in preparation). It has also become clear that T_c and B cells differ in their epitope specificities, because so far no

---

[a] F. Esquivel is sponsored by CONACYT, Mexico.

antibodies to influenza proteins have inhibited T cell–mediated cytotoxicity with different specificity. Again this contrasts T_h recognition, inasmuch as Thomas and associates[10] find that HA-specific T_h recognize three of the antigenic sites previously mapped for B-cell recognition. The negative results with T_c are generally not published, but our laboratory and Townsend and associates have tested many polyclonal and monoclonal antibodies to NP, for example. None of the antibodies have inhibited target lysis by NP-specific T_c clones or lines. The definition of T_c specificity for NP, therefore, required molecular biology techniques and transfection of cells with viral genes;[2,9] vaccinia vectors containing individual influenza genes provided a powerful tool for immunization and also for target-cell infection (*e.g.*, reference 11).

GENETICS OF NP-SPECIFIC T_c RESPONSES

Because NP is an important target antigen for influenza-virus–cross-reactive T_c in the mouse and human,[2,11,12] we examined the genetics of NP-specific–T_c responses in three strains of mice (H-2^b, H-2^k, H-2^d) and congenic recombinant strains. Target cells were infected with NP.VAC (vaccinia virus containing the influenza NP gene was kindly donated by B. Moss and G. L. Smith). We found four nonresponder class I–MHC alleles and no NP-specific T_c were induced that were restricted to D^{d}L^d, D^k, or K^b.[13] Nonresponsiveness was not overcome following vaccination with NP.VAC (R. Pemberton, unpublished). Thus in these mouse strains, NP-specific T_c are restricted only by D^b, K^d, or K^k. With the exception of K^b, as a relatively low-responder class I–locus, influenza-infected mice are able to mount strong A virus cross-reactive T_c responses restricted to NP nonresponder alleles and specific for other internal influenza proteins. These responses show additional genetic differences.[4]

Genetic differences in T_c responses are even greater when we define the fine specificity of NP-specific T_c for NP epitopes. Townsend *et al.*[14,15] defined NP peptides 365-379 for D^b and 50-63 for K^k-restricted–polyclonal and cloned-NP–specific T_c. We defined the NP peptide 147-161, and more recently 147-158, seen in conjunction with K^d,[16] and NP sequence 335-349 is recognized by human T_c restricted by HLA B37.[12]

TABLE 1 shows that of the four epitopes defined so far, each class I–MHC molecule restricts a unique NP sequence. Once more, when we primed congenic mice expressing K^d or H-2$^{d/b}$ F1 mice, we observed that K^d-restricted NP-specific T_c always recognize NP peptide 147-158 regardless of the other C57Bl or C3H background genes of the congenic mice.[16] This leads us to conclude that it is the class I–MHC molecule (in our case K^d) that dictates the NP epitope 147-158 to be recognized by T_c. BALB/b (K^{b}D^b) mice only recognize NP sequence 365-379, although they possess non-MHC BALB/c background genes. Similarly in H-2$^{d/b}$ F1 mice, peptide 365-380 is seen only in conjunction with D^b. These genetic differences have obvious implications for attempts to develop simpler vaccines, particularly those involving the use of peptides. The results, however, do not exclude the possibility that some viral proteins may possess a particularly strong immunodominant region that provides epitopes for B cells, T_h and T_c in different haplotypes. In influenza, we have not found this to be so. So far in mice, for example, none of the NP peptides defined for T_c recognition are seen by T_h primed by influenza infection (F. Esquivel, unpublished).

We carried out experiments to examine whether NP peptides 365-380 or 147-158 could prime T_c responses in responder or nonresponder mice when administered with Freund's adjuvant (IFA or CFA) or other adjuvants such as Alum by different routes. Two injections with the most potent Freund's adjuvant, however, induced only very low levels of memory T_c in responder strains. After *in vitro* antigen stimulation, we generally observed 5–15% virus or peptide-specific target lysis at high K/T ratios of 20–40. TABLE 2 illustrates two representative experiments. Although we found no evidence for priming of T_h by the peptide, significant levels of antibodies to the peptide were detected in the serum. Thus, relevant peptides are poorly immunogenic for T_c in responder mouse strains, and we could not prime T_h cells or induce T_c responses in nonresponder strains.

ROLE AND EFFECTOR FUNCTION OF T_c IN INFLUENZA INFECTION: COMPARISON WITH T_h

Earlier studies have shown that primed T cells could clear a persistent influenza infection in nu/nu athymic mice[17] and that following transfer of semiallo-

TABLE 1. Genetics of Influenza NP-Specific T_c Responses[a]

Mice Primed by Intranasal (i.n.) Infection	NP Class I-MHC– Responder Allele	T_c Recognition Target Cells	NP Peptides	Ref.
C57BL/10	D^b	L/D^b	365-379	14
		EL-4	365-379	
CBA	K^k	L cells	50-63	15
BALB/c	K^d	P815	147-158	16
(C57BL/10 × DBA$_2$)F1	⌈D^b	L/D^b	365-380	16
		EL-4	365-380	
(C57BL/10 × DBA$_2$)F1	⌊K^d	P815	147-158	
B10.HTG(K^dD^k)	K^d	P815	147-158	16
C3H.H-2^{02}	K^dD^b	P815	147-158	16
BALB/b	D^b	EL4	365-380	16
HLA B37[b]	D^b	B37+	335-349	12

[a] Mice were infected i.n. with A/X31 or A/NT/68 influenza virus and 3–10 weeks later stimulated *in vitro* for 5 days with influenza-infected stimulator cells. Target cells for cytotoxicity assays are as indicated and are treated with 0.5–1 μM peptide and ^{51}Cr for 1 hr at 37° and then washed 3 times.[14]

[b] Human PBL restimulated *in vitro* with influenza virus.

genic primed T cells into congenic mice, protective effects were noted only when host and donor shared class I-MHC antigens, rather than class II-MHC molecules.[18] The protective capacity of T_c was established by the transfer of cloned Lyt-2$^+$ T_c, which were either cross-reactive for type A virus or subtype-specific.[19,20] Intravenous (i.v.) transfer of T_c clones into influenza-infected hosts protects against lethal influenza challenge and limits virus replication in the lung and trachea *in vivo*.[21] NP-specific T_c protect against different A virus subtypes and thus recognize cells that express antigens and replicate virus, although they can also recognize antigen in the form of peptide epitopes *in vitro*.[16,21] The mechanism of this capacity of T_c to limit lung virus replication is not clear. Is the lysis of infected cells *in vivo* an important facet, or does the immune interferon (IFNγ) released by T_c on contact with infected target cells prevent further spread of

TABLE 2. Antibody and T_c Responses after Priming with Influenza NP Epitopes in Responder Mice[a]

Priming	In Vitro Stimulation	K/T	Percent A/X31 Specific Target Lysis		Antibody ELISA Units[b]
			P815	EL4	
A/X31 i.n.	A/X31	20	+ 58		12.6
		10	+ 64		
P141-161 20 μg subcutaneous (s.c.) alum	A/X31	20	+ 18		2.8
Boost: P141-161 50 μg alum intraperitoneal (i.p.)		10	+ 8		
A/X31 i.n.	A/X31	20	66	+	5
		10	66	+	
P365-380 50 μg i.p. IFA[c]	A/X31	20	4	+	3.5
Boost: 365-380 20 μg s.c. IFA		10	5	+	

[a] (C57BL × DBA$_2$)F1 mice were primed and boosted 3–4 weeks later as indicated.

[b] Antibody ELISA units: serum ELISA assay three weeks post-boost using purified influenza NP as antigen and peroxidase-labeled rabbit anti-mouse immunoglobulin. Units are calculated as follows:

$$\frac{O.D._{492} \text{ of experimental serum sample } (1/200)}{O.D._{492} \text{ of } 1/200 \text{ normal mouse serum}}$$

Target cells were P815 cells for H-2^d T_c and EL-4 cells for H-2^b T_c.

[c] IFA = incomplete Freund's adjuvant.

virus? It is clear that if IFNγ is important, its antiviral effect is entirely local in relation to contact with infected cells *in vivo*.[20] Or are the effects of IFNγ related to their activation of macrophages or effect on B- and T-cell maturation? Experiments are under way to investigate the effect of monoclonal antibodies (mAb), that neutralize mouse IFNγ, on viral clearance following T_c transfer. In preliminary experiments, such antibodies do not inhibit the protective capacity of the T_c clones. In one of two typical experiments (TABLE 3), the R46A2 mAb[22] had no effect on lung virus clearance by cloned T_c (experiment A), but in some experiments, viral clearance by T_c clones is enhanced in the presence of antibody to

TABLE 3. Transfer of T_c Clone T9/13 into A/X31 Influenza Virus–Infected Mice[a]

Group	T_c Clone 9/13	Lung Virus Titers (Log_{10} EID$_{50}$)	
		Experiment A (Day 5)	Experiment B (Day 6)
A/X31	−	4.8	4.2
A/X31 + R46A2	−	5.2	5.5
A/X31	+	2.5	2.8
A/X31 + R46A2	+	3.2	0.8

[a] BALB/c mice were infected i.n. with 4 hemagglutination units (HAU) A/X31 virus, and 2 hr later 10^7 cloned NP-specific T_c were transferred intravenously (i.v.). 24 and 72 hr later, the mice were treated i.v. and i.p. with 0.1 ml ascitic fluid (mAb R46A2) donated by E. A. Havell,[22] neutralizing 32,000 U of mouse IFNγ. Lung virus was titered 5 (experiment A) or 6 days (experiment B) postinfection, as described previously.[21]

IFNγ (experiment B). At present, although we cannot rule out nonspecific antiviral effects due to the presence of large amounts of foreign protein (*e.g.* macrophage activation), we conclude that the antiviral action of IFNγ is not essential for the protective effect of cloned T_c; it is possible that other effects of IFNγ on lymphoid cells play a role.

Influenza specific T_h also release IFNγ in the presence of influenza-infected cells, and we examined whether cloned influenza-specific T_h transferred into infected host mice were equally effective as T_c in limiting virus replication *in vivo*.

Gerhard and associates have already shown that transfer of T_h clones into mice enhances antibody formation, which in the longer term results in viral clearance.[23,24] We were particularly interested in any possible rapid-effector function of T_h similar to T_c within the first days of host infection. We have tested a number of T_h clones (donated by K. Mills and D. B. Thomas[10]) specific for HA or M protein, but we had no NP-specific–T_h clones available as yet. We find that effector function *in vivo* of T_h clones is much more variable than that of cloned T_c. TABLE 4 shows the lung virus titers of influenza-infected hosts following the i.v.

TABLE 4. Cloned T_h are Less Efficient at Rapid Viral Clearance than T_c[a]

T_h Clone	Influenza Specificity	No. of T_h Transferred	Days Postinfection	Lung Influenza Titer (Log$_{10}$ EID^{50})
BAE 5	HA	—	4	6.2
		10^7		5.8
		5×10^6		5.5
BA 6.1	HA	—	6	4.2
		5×10^6		4.9
3.14	M	—	6	5.5
		8×10^6		3.8
5.5	M	—	7	3.5
		5×10^6		2.8

[a] Cloned T_h donated by D. B. Thomas and K. Mills[10] were transferred i.v. into mice within 2 hours of i.n. infection with 4 HAU A/X31 (H3N2) virus. The M-specific T_h clones were A virus–cross-reactive, and the HA-specific T_h clones were selected with H3 of X31 virus. Lung virus titers were determined as previously described.[21]

transfer of four different T_h clones and illustrates four typical experiments. Of five HA-specific–T_h clones tested, four had no protective effect, and one slightly enhanced virus replication in the lung. Our M protein–specific clones either had no effect or gave some protection. Cloned T_h on a cell number basis release somewhat more IFNγ on contact with infected cells than cloned T_c, induce far stronger local delayed-type hypersensitivity (DTH) reactions, and also release additional B- and T-cell growth factors and interleukins. Strong DTH-type reactions in the lung may account for the lower efficiency of T_h compared to T_c in viral clearance *in vivo*. Further studies are required to resolve these questions.

CONCLUSIONS

Our particular interest has been influenza A virus–cross-reactive cytotoxic T cells, their fine specificity for internal viral proteins in conjunction with class I-MHC molecules, the genetics of NP-specific–T_c responsiveness, and the effector function of cloned T_c *in vivo* in a mouse influenza infection. Because NP is an important target antigen for A virus–cross-reactive T_c (but by no means the only one) both in the mouse and human,[2,4,11,12] our recent studies have focused on NP-specific T_c.

We have defined NP peptide 147-158 as the NP epitope seen in conjunction with K^d in BALB/c mice.[16] K^d is the only H-2^d class I-MHC–responder locus for NP, and our experiments with H-2$^{d/b}$ F1 mice and congenic mice show that it is the expression of the K^d gene that determines recognition of the NP epitope 147-158 rather than other B10 or C3H background genes of congenic mice. In (C57BL × DBA$_2$)F1 mice, NP sequence 147-158 is recognized by T_c only on H-2^d target cells, and not on H-2^b targets, whereas peptide 365-380 is seen only presented by H-2^b and not H-2^d target cells. Once more, BALB/b mice recognize only NP epitope 365-380, and not P147-158 seen by BALB/c mice.[16] Townsend and associates have defined NP sequence 365-380 (D^b-restricted), 50-63 (K^k-restricted),[15] and 335-349 (HLAB37-restricted).[14] Thus, of epitopes defined so far, each class I-MHC molecule restricts a unique NP sequence.

The genetic differences have important implications for the development of peptide vaccines. In addition, we find that peptides, though administered with potent adjuvants, for example Freund's adjuvant, are very poor in priming virus and peptide-specific T_c memory cells, even in responder strains. We have no evidence that NP-specific class II-MHC–restricted T_h recognize any of the NP peptide epitopes restricted by class I-MHC. The T_c peptides given in Freund's adjuvant, however, do induce significant antibody responses.

Transfers of cloned cytotoxic T cells are effective in preventing lethal influenza infection in a mouse model, in reducing virus replication in the lungs and trachea, and in speeding recovery. This includes NP-specific–T_c clones that can recognize an NP peptide epitope and clearly recognize also cells replicating influenza virus.[21] Cloned T_c are more effective in clearing virus than cloned T_h. Priming with purified NP, inducing NP-specific T_c and T_h, does not prevent infection but protects against lethal infection with any of the type A viruses.[25] Priming with NP needs to be tested in humans as a possible useful addition to the present-day influenza vaccines. The protective capacity of T_c in influenza cannot be generalized to other viruses. Recent unpublished experiments by M. Cannon and P. Openshaw in our laboratory show that T_c lines and clones specific for respiratory syncytial virus exacerbate disease and induce lung pathology in a mouse model infection with this virus. It was known previously that T_c can be responsible for immunopathology in certain virus infections, such as intracerebral infection with lymphocytic choriomeningitis virus.[26] It clearly becomes important to define protective T-cell responses, as well as those that induce immunopathology, for the design of improved vaccines.

REFERENCES

1. ZWEERINK, H. J., S. A. COURTNEIDGE, J. J. SKEHEL, M. CRUMPTON & B. A. ASKONAS. 1977. Cytotoxic T cells kill influenza infected cells but do not distinguish between type A viruses. Nature **267:** 354–356.
2. TOWNSEND, A. R. M., A. J. MCMICHAEL, N. P. CARTER, J. A. HUDDLESTON & G. G. BROWNLEE. 1984. Cytotoxic T cell recognition of the influenza nucleoprotein and haemagglutinin expressed in transfected mouse L cells. Cell **39:** 13–25.
3. BENNINK, J. R., J. W. YEWDELL & W. GERHARD. 1982. A viral polymerase involved in recognition of influenza virus-infected cells by a cytotoxic T cell clone. Nature **296:** 75–76.

4. BENNINK, J. R., J. W. YEWDELL, G. L. SMITH & B. MOSS. 1987. Anti-influenza virus cytotoxic T-lymphocytes recognise the three viral polymerases and a nonstructural protein. J. Virol. **61:** 1098–1102.
5. GOTCH, F., A. J. MCMICHAEL, G. L. SMITH & B. MOSS. 1987. Identification of viral molecules recognised by influenza specific human cytotoxic T lymphocytes. J. Exp. Med. **165:** 408–416.
6. KEES, U. & P. H. KRAMMER. 1984. Most influenza A virus specific memory cytotoxic T lymphocytes react with antigenic epitopes associated with internal virus determinants. J. Exp. Med. **159:** 365–377.
7. BENNINK, J. R., J. W. YEWDELL, G. L. SMITH & B. MOSS. 1986. Recognition of cloned influenza virus hemagglutinin gene products by cytotoxic T lymphocytes. J. Virol. **57:** 786–791.
8. BRACIALE, T. J. 1979. Specificity of cytotoxic T-cells directed to influenza virus haemagglutinin. J. Exp. Med. **149:** 856–869.
9. BRACIALE, T. J., V. L. BRACIALE, T. J. HENKEL, J. SAMBROOK & M. J. GETHING. 1984. Cytotoxic T lymphocyte recognition of the influenza haemagglutinin gene product expressed by DNA-mediated gene transfer. J. Exp. Med. **159:** 341–354.
10. THOMAS, D. B., J. J. SKEHEL, K. H. G. MILLS & C. M. GRAHAM. 1987. A single amino acid substitution in influenza haemagglutinin abrogates recognition by monoclonal antibodies and a spectrum of subtype-specific L3T4+ T-cell clones. Eur. J. Immunol. **17:** 133–136.
11. YEWDELL, J. W., J. R. BENNINK, G. L. SMITH & B. MOSS. 1985. Influenza A virus nucleoprotein is a major target antigen for cross-reactive anti-influenza A virus cytotoxic T lymphocytes. Proc. Natl. Acad. Sci. USA **82:** 1785–1789.
12. MCMICHAEL, A. J., F. M. GOTCH & J. ROTHBARD. 1986. HLA B37 determines an influenza A virus nucleoprotein epitope recognised by cytotoxic T-lymphocytes. J. Exp. Med. **164:** 1397–1406.
13. PALA, P. & B. A. ASKONAS. 1986. Low responder MHC alleles for Tc recognition of influenza nucleoprotein. Immunogenetics **23:** 379–384.
14. TOWNSEND, A. R. M., J. ROTHBARD, F. M. GOTCH, G. BAHADUR, D. C. WRAITH & A. J. MCMICHAEL. 1986. The epitopes of influenza nucleoprotein recognised by cytotoxic T lymphocytes can be defined with short synthetic peptides. Cell **44:** 959–968.
15. BASTIN, J., J. ROTHBARD, J. DAVEY, I. JONES & A. R. M. TOWNSEND. 1987. Use of synthetic peptides of influenza nucleoprotein to define epitopes recognized by class I restricted cytotoxic T-lymphocytes. J. Exp. Med. **165:** 1508–1523.
16. TAYLOR, P. M., J. DAVEY, K. HOWLAND, J. B. ROTHBARD & B. A. ASKONAS. 1987. Class I MHC molecules rather than other mouse genes dictate influenza epitope recognition by cytotoxic T-cells. Immunogenetics. **26:** 267–272.
17. WELLS, M. A., S. DANIEL, J. Y. DJEU, S. C. KILEY & F. A. ENNIS. 1983. Recovery from a viral respiratory tract infection. IV. Specificity of protection by cytotoxic T lymphocytes. J. Immunol. **130:** 2908–2914.
18. ADA, G. L., K.-N. LEUNG & H. ERTL. 1981. An analysis of effector T cell generation and function in mice exposed to influenza A or Sendai viruses. Immunol. Rev. **58:** 5–24.
19. LIN, Y. L. & B. A. ASKONAS. 1981. Biological properties of an influenza virus-specific killer T cell clone. J. Exp. Med. **154:** 225–234.
20. LUKACHER, E., V. L. BRACIALE & T. J. BRACIALE. 1984. *In vivo* effector function of influenza virus specific cytotoxic T lymphocyte clones is highly specific. J. Exp. Med. **160:** 814–826.
21. TAYLOR, P. M. & B. A. ASKONAS. 1986. Influenza nucleoprotein-specific cytotoxic T-cell clones are protective *in vivo*. Immunology **58:** 417–420.
22. SPITALNY, G. L. & E. A. HAVELL. 1984. Monoclonal antibody to murine gamma interferon inhibits lymphokine-induced antiviral and macrophage tumoricidal activities. J. Exp. Med. **159:** 1560–1565.
23. GERHARD, W., C. HACKETT & F. MELCHERS. 1983. The recognition specificity of a murine helper T cell for haemagglutinin of influenza virus A/PR/8/34. J. Immunol. **130:** 2379–2385.

24. SCHERLE, P. A. & W. GERHARD. 1986. Functional analysis of influenza specific helper T-cells *in vivo*. J. Exp. Med. **164:** 1114–1128.
25. WRAITH, D. C., A. E. VESSEY & B. A. ASKONAS. 1987. Purified influenza virus nucleoprotein protects mice from lethal infection. J. Gen. Virol. **68:** 433–440.
26. LEIST, T. P., S. P. COBBOLD, H. WALDMANN, M. AGUET & R. M. ZINKERNAGEL. 1987. Functional analysis of T lymphocyte subsets in antiviral host defence. J. Immunol. **138:** 2278–2281.

Recovery from Acute Virus Infection

Role of Cytotoxic T Lymphocytes in the Elimination of Lymphocytic Choriomeningitis Virus from Spleens of Mice[a]

FRITZ LEHMANN-GRUBE, DEMETRIUS MOSKOPHIDIS,
AND JÜRGEN LÖHLER

*Heinrich-Pette-Institut für Experimentelle Virologie
und Immunologie
an der Universität Hamburg
2000 Hamburg 20, Federal Republic of Germany*

INTRODUCTION

One, and presumably the, most important, task of the immune system is to protect against infectious agents, and in the termination of primary virus infections, T lymphocytes are centrally involved. Although these statements rest on solid evidence, information as to how T cells function is less certain. The currently prevailing opinion is that specifically activated cytotoxic T lymphocytes (CTL) lyse infected cells, thereby preventing further replication of the agent; already-formed virus is assumed to be removed by mononuclear phagocytes (MNP) and neutralizing antibody.[1] Whereas this hypothesis is simple and attractive, it does not account for all that is known. For instance, the mouse, experimentally infected with herpes simplex virus (HSV), does not appear to have difficulties getting rid of the agent, although T lymphocytes with the ability to lyse *in vitro* HSV-infected target cells cannot be detected.[2,3] Such cells do appear and, being restricted by molecules encoded by class I loci of the major histocompatibility gene complex (MHC)[2] and expressing the Lyt-2 surface antigen,[4] have all the properties of HSV-specific CTL. In order to demonstrate them, however, "tricks" have to be applied.[2,3,5] Elimination of HSV from the mouse appears to be mediated by Lyt-1⁺2⁻ cells that are restricted by K(D) and I-A and not known to be lytically active *in vitro*.[6–8]

The influenza A virus–infected mouse is another example. Intravenous (i.v.) inoculation of cells of the class I-restricted virus-specific cytotoxic clone, L4, reduced virus in the lungs of intranasally infected mice, but another cytolytic clone, T5/5, did not act in like manner *in vivo*, although more cells of the latter had migrated to the lungs. Inasmuch as L4 cells released much more interferon-γ on contact with appropriate target cells *in vitro* than T5/5 cells, the ability of L4 to curtail virus replication *in vivo* was related to release of soluble factors.[9,10] A similar conclusion was derived by Schiltknecht and Ada who failed to adoptively immunize influenza virus–infected mice if these were under treatment with cyclosporin A.[11]

[a] Work done in the authors' laboratory was aided by research Grants from Deutsche Forschungsgemeinschaft and Wilhelm Sander-Stiftung. The Heinrich-Pette-Institut is financially supported by Freie und Hansestadt Hamburg and Bundesministerium für Jugend, Familie, Frauen und Gesundheit.

As a third example, we mention the mouse infected with murine cytomegalovirus (MCMV). As few as 10^4 i.v. inoculated day eight–immune lymph node cells sufficed to reduce significantly virus replication in lungs, livers, and spleens of infected and irradiated BALB/c recipients. In experiments performed with a similar protocol, Lyt-2$^+$, L3T4$^-$ cells were found to be antivirally active, and the frequency of MCMV-specific CTL and CTL precursors (CTLP) among *in vivo*–activated lymph node cells had been known from limiting dilution (LD) assays. With these data, it was calculated that approximately 10 specifically sensitized CTL and CTLP had diminished virus replication in several organs of the adoptively immunized mice,[12] which is a surprisingly low number even if one concedes that these cells had probably expanded during the 14 days between their inoculation and virus titration.

These observations are not easily reconciled with the notion that CTL restrain virus replication *in vivo* by lysing infected tissue cells. We asked whether in the well-established model for studying the function of virus-specific CTL, the adult mouse acutely infected with lymphocytic choriomeningitis (LCM) virus, cytolysis would be required to control the infection.

THE MODEL

After i.v. inoculation of 10^3 mouse infectious units (IU), the strain WE LCM virus multiplies in all major organs of the mouse, attaining maximal titers 4 to 6 days later; subsequently, the infectivity drops rapidly, and around the tenth day infectivity can usually not be detected. The animals remain outwardly healthy, and histologic inspection reveals only minor changes in most tissues, although hepatitis may be marked in mice of certain strains.[13] We have confined this investigation to the effector phase of virus elimination and have concentrated our efforts on the spleen, because in this organ the virus reaches concentrations as high as 10^9 IU per g of tissue, the effects of adoptive immunization are pronounced, and histologic alterations are essentially absent during the time virus is eliminated.[13] We also analyze other organs and have, so far, not found principal differences.

Elimination of the Virus Is Mediated by Cytotoxic T Lymphocytes

Thy-1$^+$ cells include two subpopulations. The cytotoxic/suppressive T lymphocytes carry Lyt-2, and their activity is restricted by molecules encoded by class I loci (K, D, L) of the MHC, whereas the helper/inducer T lymphocytes express L3T4 and are restricted by class II molecules (Ia antigens).[14–16]

During infection of mice with LCM virus, T lymphocytes appear in the spleens that lyse *in vitro* LCM virus–infected target cells.[1] They are of Lyt-2, L3T4$^+$ phenotype[17] and restricted by class I molecules of the MHC;[1] hence, they have the properties of CTL. The kinetics of appearance and disappearance of CTL in the murine spleen correlate well with clearance of virus from the mouse.[18,13] Furthermore, the accelerated removal of LCM virus from the spleens of acutely infected mice following transfusion of lymphoid cells from mice that are just recuperating from the infection is restricted by products of the K and/or D loci of the MHC,[19] and the effector cells are positive for Lyt-2 and negative for L3T4.[17] Also, transfer of cloned H-2D^b–restricted Lyt-2$^+$ CTL into acutely infected

TABLE 1. Effect of Treatment with Anti-Thy-1 Monoclonal Antibody on the Ability of CBA/J Mice to Eliminate LCM Virus from Spleens

Day After Infection	No Antibody	Day Antibody[a]		
		5	6	7
5	$5.5 \pm 1.0 \times 10^{8b}$	—	—	—
6	$2.7 \pm 1.0 \times 10^7$	$5.3 \pm 0.8 \times 10^8$	—	—
7	$1.8 \pm 0.5 \times 10^6$	$2.1 \pm 1.0 \times 10^9$	$2.2 \pm 0.6 \times 10^8$	—
8	$2.5 \pm 1.3 \times 10^5$	$6.8 \pm 1.1 \times 10^8$	$2.0 \pm 0.2 \times 10^8$	$1.5 \pm 0.5 \times 10^6$
9	$\sim 4 \times 10^4$	$4.4 \pm 0.6 \times 10^8$	$6.9 \pm 0.5 \times 10^8$	$4.1 \pm 1.3 \times 10^7$
10	$<2 \times 10^4$	$1.5 \pm 0.4 \times 10^9$	$6.3 \pm 0.6 \times 10^8$	$1.8 \pm 1.0 \times 10^8$

[a] CBA/J mice were infected intravenously with 10^3 mouse infectious units of WE strain LCM virus and inoculated once intravenously 5, 6, or 7 days later per g mouse with 20 µl of mouse anti-Thy-1.2 monoclonal antibody.[23] At intervals thereafter, spleen virus concentrations were determined.

[b] Mean ± standard error infectious units per g of spleen in five mice.

C57BL/6J (B6) mice diminished virus in the spleens of the recipients,[20] and LCM-immune memory cells with the same properties have been shown to mediate virus reduction in LCM virus–carrier mice.[21]

Although the conclusion seems to be cogent that virus clearance is mediated by CTL, most of these findings were obtained with the method of adoptive immunization, which is rather drastic. As an alternative protocol, we have introduced one that we call serologic surgery.[22] After infection, mice were treated once with monoclonal antibody (mAb) directed at T lymphocytes or their subsets, and the effects this had on virus clearance as well as antiviral immune responses were determined. Inoculation of anti-Thy-1 or anti-Lyt-2 mAb blocked elimination of the virus (TABLES 1 and 2) and profoundly diminished the activity of spleen CTL, but reduced partially (anti-Thy-1) or even increased (anti-Lyt-2) the numbers of spleen cells forming antiviral antibodies (AFC) of both major immunoglobulin subclasses. By contrast, treatment with an antibody directed against L3T4 had essentially no effect on either virus clearance (TABLE 3) or CTL response but depleted IgM and IgG AFC. These findings demonstrate that Lyt-2$^+$ T lympho-

TABLE 2. Effect of Treatment with Anti-Lyt-2 Monoclonal Antibody on the Ability of CBA/J Mice to Eliminate LCM Virus from Spleens

Day After Infection	No Antibody	Day Antibody[a]		
		5	6	7
5	$1.8 \pm 0.4 \times 10^{8b}$	—	—	—
6	$1.3 \pm 0.7 \times 10^8$	$1.2 \pm 0.5 \times 10^9$	—	—
7	$2.2 \pm 1.4 \times 10^7$	$6.0 \pm 0.8 \times 10^8$	$9.7 \pm 2.5 \times 10^8$	—
8	$3.8 \pm 0.7 \times 10^5$	$5.1 \pm 0.4 \times 10^8$	$4.2 \pm 1.1 \times 10^8$	$1.6 \pm 0.7 \times 10^7$
9	$1.6 \pm 0.7 \times 10^5$	$2.3 \pm 0.8 \times 10^8$	nd	$7.8 \pm 5.9 \times 10^6$
10	$<6 \times 10^4$	$3.2 \pm 1.1 \times 10^8$	$2.0 \pm 0.5 \times 10^8$	$4.0 \pm 3.6 \times 10^7$

[a] CBA/J mice were infected intravenously with 10^3 mouse infectious units of WE strain LCM virus and inoculated once intravenously 5, 6, or 7 days later per g mouse with 40 µg specific rat anti-Lyt-2 monoclonal antibody.[24] At intervals thereafter, spleen virus concentrations were determined.

[b] Mean ± standard error infectious units per g of spleen in five mice.

cytes (presumably CTL) are needed for controlling the infection, thereby corroborating the already-mentioned results. They, furthermore, show that for clearance of the LCM virus from the organs of the acutely infected mouse, antiviral antibodies are not required, although these are produced in considerable quantities during the effector phase of virus elimination;[25] this, again, confirms previous observations.[18,26,27] Interestingly, there appears to be some functional relationship between antibody production and Lyt-2$^+$ T lymphocytes, in that the latter downregulate AFC.[22]

MNP, especially if activated, are often assumed to protect against viruses.[28–30] During the time the LCM virus is cleared from the murine spleen, this organ's MNP are activated,[31] suggesting that these cells play some part in the termination of the infection. We have examined this possibility experimentally with the following results.[32,33] (1) MNP were not demonstrably activated during the time virus was removed due to adoptive immunization with small or large numbers of immune T lymphocytes. (2) In mice, γ-irradiated with doses between 400 and 950

TABLE 3. Effect of Treatment with Anti-L3T4 Monoclonal Antibody on the Ability of CBA/J Mice to Eliminate LCM Virus from Spleens

Day After Infection	No Antibody	Day Antibody[a]		
		5	6	7
5	$1.8 \pm 0.4 \times 10^{8b}$	—	—	—
6	$1.3 \pm 0.7 \times 10^8$	$3.5 \pm 1.6 \times 10^8$	—	—
7	$2.2 \pm 1.4 \times 10^7$	$8.5 \pm 4.8 \times 10^7$	$9.3 \pm 6.0 \times 10^7$	—
8	$3.8 \pm 0.7 \times 10^5$	$1.4 \pm 0.7 \times 10^5$	$3.0 \pm 1.6 \times 10^6$	$1.1 \pm 0.6 \times 10^6$
9	$1.6 \pm 0.7 \times 10^5$	$3.1 \pm 1.8 \times 10^5$	nd	$1.6 \pm 0.7 \times 10^5$
10	$<6 \times 10^4$	$\sim2 \times 10^5$	$\sim7 \times 10^4$	$\sim8 \times 10^4$

[a] CBA/J mice were infected intravenously with 10^3 mouse infectious units of WE strain LCM virus and inoculated once intravenously 5, 6, or 7 days later per g mouse with 40 µg specific rat anti-L3T4 monoclonal antibody.[24] At intervals thereafter, spleen virus concentrations were determined.

[b] Mean ± standard error infectious units per g of spleen in five mice.

rad or inoculated with 200 mg per kg of cyclophosphamide before infection, adoptive immunization reduced the spleen virus titers just as effectively as in untreated controls. (3) In conventionally raised athymic nude mice, the MNP are permanently activated,[34,35] and in the spleens of such animals, the virus replicated slightly but reproducibly less than in their furred counterparts. In the spleens of mice, however, whose MNP had been activated before infection by the inoculation of inactivated *Corynebacterium parvum*, the LCM virus attained considerably higher concentrations than in untreated controls, whereas the rates of elimination were not affected. Dextran sulfate with a molecular weight of 500,000 (DS500) severely damages macrophages and related elements in the mouse.[36] We, too, found that inoculation of DS500 functionally incapacitated MNP, but when mice thus treated were infected, the spleen virus titers were just as elevated as in mice, the MNP of which had been activated with *C. parvum*.

The lack of a correlation between replication and subsequent removal of LCM virus from the murine spleen on one hand and the functional state of the MNP system on the other does not support any hypothesis in which MNP are assigned a role in the control of the infection. *Mutatis mutandis*, the same is true for natural killer (NK) cells that, although markedly activated in the infected mouse,[37] do not appear to contribute to elimination of the LCM virus.[38] Having come to essentially the same conclusion with regard to antiviral antibodies (see above), we may state that of the components assumed to be major parts of the mechanism with which higher organisms defend themselves against viruses, in the LCM virus-infected mouse, only CTL were found to be relevant. Indeed, all our observations are compatible with the assumption that CTL alone clear the virus.

Low Numbers of CTL Block Virus Replication

The activities of LCM virus-specific CTL vary between mouse strains.[39] Here, we employed low-responder CBA/J (CBA) mice, high-responder B6 mice, and DBA/1 mice, the LCM virus–specific CTL activity of which is higher than that of all other strains tested by us. Inasmuch as in one study the conclusion was drawn that cells mediating delayed-type hypersensitivity (DTH) rather than CTL are important for controlling the acute infection of the mouse with LCM virus,[40] the split-responder AKR mouse was included. The activity of CTL is not always correlated with the degree of DTH measured as primary foot pad swelling after local inoculation of the virus.[41] In AKR mice, the former is low, whereas DTH is high.[39,42] AKR and CBA mice are of the same haplotype (H-2^k), and the difference between them with regard to DTH contradicts the widely held opinion that immune responses are always determined by genes located in the MHC. One alternative explanation could be dissimilar antigen concentrations. We found that slightly more virus was generated in the feet of AKR than in the feet of CBA mice (FIG. 1). In further experiments (not shown), however, in which 20 times more virus was inoculated into CBA than into AKR mice, similar quantities of infectious virus were produced in the feet of both strains, but the swellings deviated just as markedly. We conclude that the AKR mouse is, indeed, a high responder for LCM virus–specific DTH.

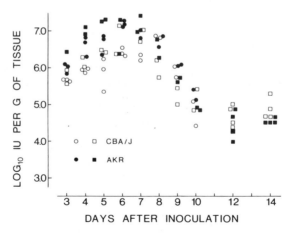

FIGURE 1. Replication of LCM virus in hind feet of CBA/J and AKR mice. At intervals after subcutaneous inoculation of 10^3 infectious units into the right hind feet, these were homogenized, and infectivity was titrated. Each data point denotes the virus concentration in the foot of one mouse, circles and squares signifying different experiments.

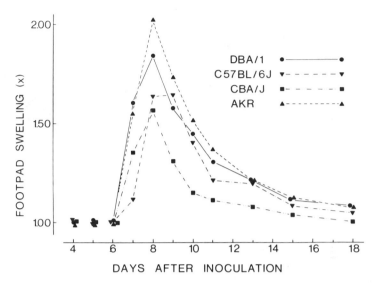

FIGURE 2. Foot pad swelling in mice of four strains after local infection with LCM virus. At intervals after subcutaneous inoculation of 10^3 infectious units into the right hind feet, these were measured. Swelling is expressed as the factor with which the thicknesses of the inoculated hind feet exceeded the thicknesses of the uninoculated contralateral feet. Data points signify mean values of 22 mice in two experiments. (Lehmann-Grube *et al.*[13] With permission from the American Association of Immunologists.)

Our expectation that the dissimilar T-cell activities of mice of the four strains (FIGURES 2 and 3) would be reflected in their ability to cope with the virus was not experimentally confirmed (FIG. 4); the rates of elimination from spleens were essentially identical in high, low, and split responders. The only correlation is between appearance of CTL and beginning of virus elimination, which is well underway on day 5 in DBA/1 mice and on day 6 in mice of the other strains. In none of the mice was the foot pad swelling detectable before day 7, at a time when most of the infectious virus had left the spleen. We conclude that a correlation exists between virus elimination and activity of CTL but that the latter is not rate-limiting, meaning that CTL are generated in excess.

For estimating the numbers that are actually needed, experiments were performed using the methods of adoptive immunization and LD. Donor mice were immunized by infection, and variable numbers of their spleen cells were inoculated into previously infected mice. Subsequently, the infectious titers in the recipients' spleens were determined and compared with the titers in control mice that had not received cells. The results (FIG. 5) show that in the spleens of B6 and DBA/1 mice, infectious virus was reduced to less than 50% by transfer of approximately 10^4 immune T lymphocytes, whereas in CBA and AKR mice, the same effect was accomplished with about 10^5 cells.

To determine the extent to which the spleen was reached by the infused cells, these were radioactively labeled. In repeated experiments always around 20% of the marker was found in this organ,[13] which allows the calculation that in the case of the high responder B6 and DBA/1 mice, as few as 2×10^3 T cell–enriched day

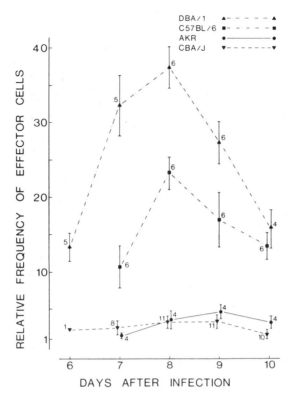

FIGURE 3. LCM virus–specific cytotoxic T lymphocyte responses of mice of four strains determined with the ^{51}Cr-release assay of Miller and Dunkley,[43] adapted to enumerate virus-specific cytotoxic T lymphocytes by Moskophidis and Lehmann-Grube.[39] Graded numbers of spleen cells, taken at intervals after intravenous infection with 10^3 infectious units, and constant numbers of LCM virus–infected and ^{51}Cr-labeled syngeneic fibroblastic target cells were incubated for 2.5 hours at 37°C and subsequently for 1 hour at 45°C, the shift of temperature promoting the release of label from previously damaged target cells, yet preventing new cytolytic encounters. The specific fractional lysis (p) was then calculated for each spleen cell-target cell combination, and the estimates of p for different numbers of sensitized spleen cells (N) were plotted against N on a log-log scale. For each value falling on a straight line with slope 1, the relative frequency of effector cells (α) was calculated according to the formula $\alpha = \ln(1 - p)/Nt$, where t is the time of incubation in hours at 37°C. From the α values thus determined, the means were calculated, and these were the data from which means (data points) and standard errors (vertical bars) were derived. The figures along the curves denote the numbers of independent determinations on which calculations of both these values were based. To simplify plotting, all α values were multiplied by 10^8. (Lehmann-Grube *et al.*[13] With permission from the American Association of Immunologists.)

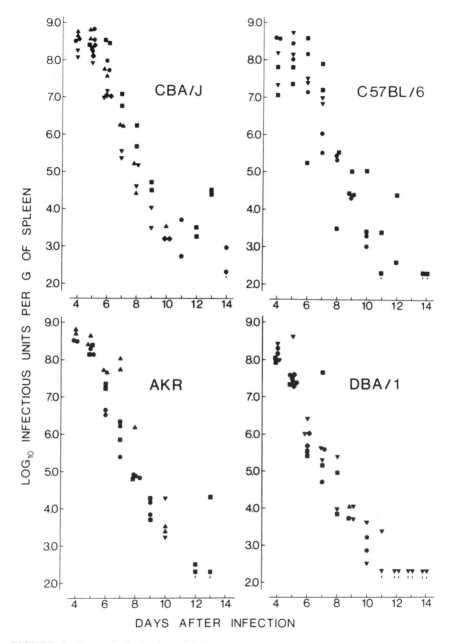

FIGURE 4. Rates of elimination of LCM virus from spleens of mice. At intervals after intravenous infection with 10³ infectious units, spleens were homogenized and infectious titers determined. Each symbol stands for the virus concentration of one organ, different shapes signifying different experiments. (Lehmann-Grube *et al.*[13] With permission from the American Association of Immunologists.)

seven–immune spleen cells reduced virus replication in the recipients' spleens by more than 50 percent.

CTL in mice have been enumerated for several viruses under a variety of conditions, usually by employing the method of LD. The reported frequencies varied but were usually below one CTL or CTLP in 2×10^3 lymphoid cells.

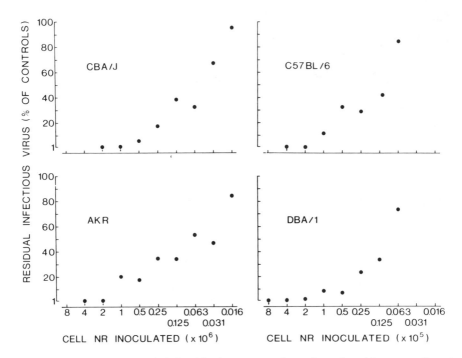

FIGURE 5. Dose-response relationships between numbers of transferred immune cells and reduction of virus replication in the spleens of infected recipient mice. Seven days (C57BL/6J and DBA/1 mice) and 8 days (CBA/J and AKR mice) after intravenous inoculation of 10^3 infectious units, spleen cells of donor mice were enriched for T lymphocytes by passage through nylon wool columns[44] and counted as viable on the basis of Trypan blue exclusion. Recipient mice were intravenously infected with 10^3 infectious units, and 16 hours later groups of five mice were inoculated with graded numbers of immune cells; seven infected mice received no cells (controls). Forty hours after cell transfer (56 hours after infection), spleen virus concentrations were determined individually, and the means were calculated for each group. In the FIGURE, the means of virus concentrations in cell recipients are expressed as percentages of the means of virus concentrations in control mice. Note that the abscissa values differ by the factor 10. (Lehmann-Grube *et al.*[13] With permission from the American Association of Immunologists.)

Because it appeared unlikely that one LCM virus-specific CTL or activated CTLP in the spleen would measurably reduce virus replication, we determined the numbers of LCM virus–specific spleen CTL(P) in infected B6 and CBA mice by use of the LD method.[45] The results of one experiment with B6 mice are given in TABLE 4, and the data for days 7 and 8 after infection are depicted in FIGURE 6. CTLP

TABLE 4. Frequencies of LCM Virus–Specific CTL and their Precursors in Spleens of Acutely Infected C57BL/6J Mice Determined by LD Analysis[45]

Day After Infection[a]	Frequencies[b]	
	Per Number of Cells	Per Spleen ($\times 10^3$)
0	$<1/10^5$	—
3	$<1/10^5$	—
5	1/7590	21.4
6	1/80	1340.0
7	1/48	2933.4
8	1/10	16000.0
9	$>1/25^c$	>7680.0
10	1/62	5987.2
14	1/50	3488.0

[a] At intervals after intravenous infection with 10^3 mouse infectious units, defined numbers of cells were cultivated with virus-infected syngeneic stimulator cells and T-cell growth factor in multiple wells of microculture plates. After 7 days, individual cell cultures were tested for their ability to cause release of ^{51}Cr from infected and uninfected syngeneic target cells.

[b] Calculated according to Taswell.[46]

[c] At 78 cells per cup, all cultures were positive.

were never detected in uninfected mice. In infected B6 mice, first, positive microcultures developed from cells obtained on day 5 after infection. Their numbers increased, reaching maxima of approximately 1/10 on day 8, and fell again to values between 1/50 and 1/100 on day 14. In low-responder CBA mice, the corresponding values were 10 to 20 times lower. Most cytolytic clones thus determined

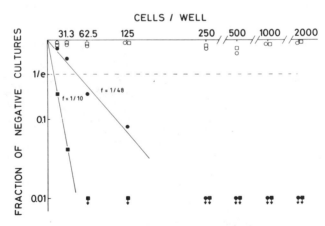

FIGURE 6. Determination by limiting dilution analysis of the frequency of LCM virus–specific cytotoxic T lymphocytes and their activated precursors in the spleen of the LCM virus–infected C57BL/6J mouse. Seven (squares) and 8 (circles) days after intravenous infection with 10^3 infectious units, defined numbers of cells were cultivated with virus-infected syngeneic stimulator cells and T cell–growth factor in multiple wells of microculture plates. After 7 days, individual cell cultures were tested for ability to cause release of ^{51}Cr from infected (closed symbols) and uninfected (open symbols) syngeneic target cells. Frequencies were calculated according to Taswell.[46]

were virus-specific. A low proportion of microcultures also lysed uninfected syngeneic target cells, but regular dose-response relationships between seeded cells
and positive cultures were not apparent, and much fewer counts were released
from uninfected than from infected targets. Negative and positive selection of
responder cells disclosed that they were predominantly Lyt-2$^+$, L3T4$^-$ T lymphocytes. A proportion of the lytic cultures also expressed NK cell–like activity,
probably as a result of the prolonged cultivation of CTL. We conclude that most
spleen cells, which during acute infection with LCM virus developed the ability to
expand *in vitro* into cytolytic clones, were true LCM virus–specific CTL and/or
activated CTLP.

We had already estimated that in the case of the adoptively immunized B6
mouse, 2×10^3 day seven–immune T lymphocytes settling in the spleen reduced
virus replication by more than 50 percent. With the added information that approximately 10% of the injected cells are virus-specific CTL or activated CTLP,
we now calculate that under these experimental conditions, as few as 200 LCM
virus–specific CTL(P) are capable of promoting virus clearance from the spleen.

TABLE 5. Spleen Virus Titer in LCM Virus–Infected C57BL/6J Mice 6 Hours
after Adoptive Immunization with Immune Spleen T Lymphocytes[13]

Hours After[a]		Number of Cells Transferred[b]			
Infection	Cell Transfer	0 (Control)	10^5	10^6	10^7
16	0[c]	$2.7 \pm 0.7 \times 10^3$ (7)[d]	—	—	—
22	6	$4.7 \pm 1.6 \times 10^4$ (7)	$4.3 \pm 1.2 \times 10^4$ (7)	$\sim 4 \times 10^3$ (7)	Trace (7)
46	30	$6.6 \pm 1.5 \times 10^6$ (3)	$2.0 \pm 0.5 \times 10^6$ (3)	nd	nd

[a] Sixteen hours after intravenous infection with 10^3 infectious units, mice were adoptively
immunized with day eight–immune T cell–enriched spleen cells, and 6 hours (30 hours for
control purposes) later, viral concentrations in spleens were determined.

[b] Donor mice were intravenously infected with 10^3 infectious units. Eight days later their
spleen cells were enriched for T lymphocytes[44] and counted as "living," on the basis of
Trypan blue exclusion.

[c] No cells transferred.

[d] Mean infectious units per g of spleen $\pm$ standard error; number of mice in parentheses.

The CTL-Mediated Block of Virus Replication in Vivo Is Rapid

In the adoptive immunization experiments of the previous section, the time
periods between cell transfers and virus titrations were 40 hours (56 hours after
infection), which is long if one wishes to ascertain whether and to what extent
isolated elements of the immune system contribute to the outcome. In further
trials, the intervals allowed for immune lymphocytes to exert their antiviral effects in the recipients were shortened. Decreased virus concentrations in spleens
were evident as early as 8 hours after transfer (24 hours after infection) even with
low numbers of immune spleen cells, namely 1×10^5 from B6 and 5×10^5 from
CBA mice.[13] With the same inocula, a further decrease of the interval led to
erratic results, but with 10^6 or 10^7 cells, protection was manifest as early as 6
hours after transfusion (TABLE 5). Reduction of virus due to adoptive immunization is measured relative to continuing virus replication in the organs of control
mice. Thus, a minimal time span has to elapse before differences become apparent, which will be relatively long if the immune cells merely halt the virus replication in the cell recipients. The speed with which the numbers of IU were measur-

ably reduced in these experiments suggested that the infectivity was actually inactivated or the virus removed from the organ. Data in TABLE 5 support this assumption; they show that in the spleens of mice adoptively immunized with 10^7 immune T lymphocytes, the virus titers were higher at the time of transfer than they were 6 hours later.

The demonstration of Zinkernagel and Welsh that adoptive immunization of mice acutely infected with LCM virus required compatibility at the K and/or D regions of the MHC had been obtained with a protocol in which the interval between transfer of 10^7 or 10^8 immune spleen cells and titration of spleen virus was 24 to 48 hours.[19] Our own experiments (not shown) disclosed that 8 hours after the injection of up to 10^8 immune spleen cells the virus concentrations in the spleens of allogeneic recipients were not lower than in the spleens of the control mice, indicating that under these conditions the rules of H-2 restriction applied. Because the whereabouts of the infused cells had not been determined, it was still possible that they did not home to the allogeneic target organ, but more probably they did not function.

Ability of the Effector Cells to Mediate Virus Clearance in Vivo *Is Not Dependent on Lysis* in Vitro

In the BALB/c mouse the activity of CTL has been shown to be restricted solely by the gene product of the L locus of the MHC. L cells ($H-2^k$), transfected with DNA clones containing sequences coding for K^d, D^d, or L^d, were lysed by BALB/c CTL only when expressing L^d.[47,48] The BALB/c-derived C-H-2^{dm2} mouse, which represents a loss mutant in L,[49,50] was unable to generate CTL lysing *in vitro* any of the transformed L target cells.[47,48] The conclusion that the mutant mouse is a nonresponder with respect to LCM virus is fully convincing as far as the findings *in vitro* go.

Through the kind help of Dr. Jan Klein (Tübingen), who supplied us with the animals, we were able to perform experiments that established that adult infected C-H-2^{dm2} mice are fully capable of eliminating the LCM virus and do not become persistently infected, which should have been the case if target cell lysis were required for virus elimination. Having shown that very few CTL are needed to cope with the virus (see above), it appeared possible that a low lytic potential in these mice might be just sufficient to deal with the infectious agent. We, therefore, determined the ability of C-H-2^{dm2} mice to generate LCM virus–specific CTL for C-H-2^{dm2} and BALB/c targets and of BALB/c mice to generate CTL for BALB/c and C-H-2^{dm2} targets. In confirmation of findings of Allan and Doherty,[51] some lysis was usually observed, but when effector and target cells were of C-H-2^{dm2} and BALB/c origin, respectively, the ^{51}Cr release approached zero levels (FIG. 7). Adoptive immunization revealed that the C-H-2^{dm2} immune cells were quite capable of promoting virus elimination from the spleens of BALB/c recipients (TABLE 6), and we conclude that the ability to lyse *in vitro* is not a precondition for T lymphocytes to protect *in vivo*.

Cell Damage in the Spleen Does Not Correlate with Virus Elimination Occurring Spontaneously or Following Adoptive Immunization

One corollary of the assumption that virus replication *in vivo* is terminated by lysis of infected cells is that every successfully controlled virus infection is accompanied by pathology. It may generally be difficult to differentiate histologi-

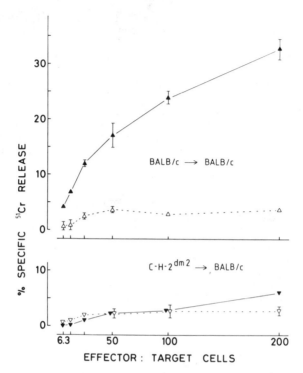

FIGURE 7. LCM virus–specific cytotoxic T cell responses of BALB/c and C-H-2^{dm2} mice assayed with BALB/c target cells. Mice were infected intravenously with 10^3 infectious units. Eight days later, spleen cells from two mice were pooled and counted as "living" on the basis of Trypan blue exclusion, and graded numbers were allowed to interact for 4 hours at 37°C with constant numbers of ^{51}Cr-labeled LCM virus–infected (closed symbols) and uninfected (open symbols) primary fibroblastic cells. Percent specific release is the mean from four samples, each calculated with the formula 100 × (a − b)/(c − b); a is the ^{51}Cr release in the presence of effector cells, b is the spontaneous release, and c is the maximum release (target cells dissolved by the addition of detergent). Data points and vertical bars signify means and standard errors from two independent experiments.

TABLE 6. Adoptive Immunization of BALB/c Mice with Immune Spleen T Lymphocytes from C-H-2^{dm2} Mice

Number of Cells Transferred[a]	Virus Concentration[b]	Percent Residual Infectious Virus
8 × 10^6	9.5 ± 4.7 × 10^{4c}	<1
2 × 10^6	5.6 ± 0.3 × 10^6	9
5 × 10^5	1.3 ± 0.4 × 10^7	20
0	6.5 ± 1.9 × 10^7	100

[a] Donor mice were intravenously infected with 10^3 infectious units. Eight days later their spleen cells were enriched for T lymphocytes[44] and counted as "living" on the basis of Trypan blue exclusion. Sixteen hours after intravenous infection with 10^3 infectious units, mice were adoptively immunized by intravenous inoculation of day eight–immune T cell–enriched spleen cells.

[b] Mean ± standard error infectious units per g of spleen in five mice.

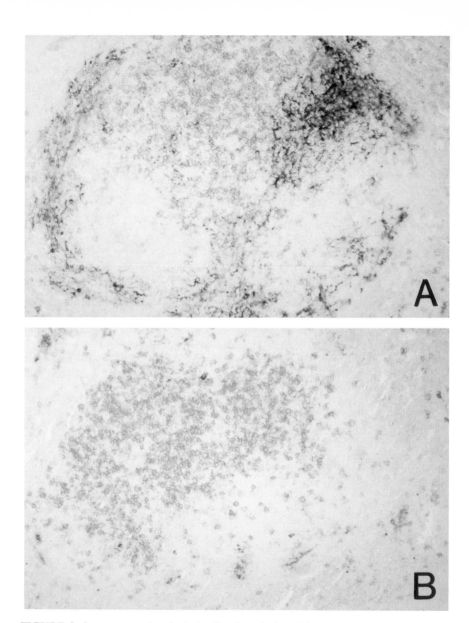

FIGURE 8. Immunocytochemical visualization of virus (blue color) in the spleen of an LCM virus–infected B6.PL-Ly-2^a Ly-3^a/Cy mouse adoptively immunized with spleen cells from C57BL/6J mice. **(A)** Control mouse 48 hours after intravenous infection with 10^5 infectious units. Viral antigen is seen in macrophages, histiocytes, and fibroblastic reticulum cells predominantly in the marginal zone and to a lesser extent in the inner parts of the white pulp. T cells (brown) are mainly localized around the central artery. **(B)** Mouse 48 hours after intravenous infection with 10^5 infectious units and 24 hours after intravenous inoculation of 10^7 spleen cells from donor mice that had been infected intravenously 8 days previously with 10^3 infectious units. Most of the viral antigen (blue) has disappeared. T cells (brown) are similar as in the control mouse. Frozen sections were doubly stained by the indirect immunoenzymatic method with rabbit anti-LCM virus antiserum[53] plus alkaline phosphatase-conjugated IgG F(ab')$_2$ fragments of sheep anti-rabbit IgG (Sigma, St. Louis, Missouri) and rat anti-Thy-1 monoclonal antibody 30-H12[54] plus peroxidase-conjugated IgG F(ab')$_2$ fragments of sheep anti-rat Ig (Amersham Laboratories, Amersham, U.K.); × 100.

cally between immunologically mediated cell damage and virus-induced cytopathology, but in the case of the LCM virus–infected mouse, in which direct cytopathic effects are assumed to be absent,[52] lysis of target cells by CTL *in situ* should become demonstrable. In particular, this should be possible in the spleen, in which virus is cleared within 5 days from a height of almost 10^9 IU per g to approximately 10^3 IU per g, that is, at a rate higher than 90% per 24 hours. During this time, some fibrinoid necrosis could be detected, although the extent did not correspond to either appearance or disappearance of virus. Furthermore, despite essentially identical kinetics of virus clearance (FIG. 4), the alterations among the four mouse strains varied markedly from virtually absent in AKR to intermediate in B6 mice. After adoptive immunization, no tissue damage at all indicative of cell lysis could be recognized despite efficient viral removal.[13] One explanation for these contrasting findings could be quantitative differences in the numbers of CTL that are active in the spleen, high during spontaneous recovery but relatively low after adoptive immunization (see above).

These observations were extended by analyzing immunocytochemically the events following adoptive immunization. In order to allow visualization of virus soon after infection, the inoculum was increased to 10^5 IU and the time between virus infection and injection of immune cells extended to 24 hours. For the localization of potential effector cells, donor and recipient mice were congenic for Lyt-2. FIGURE 8 demonstrates the viral antigen present 48 hours after infection and its virtual absence in mice that had been adoptively immunized 24 hours previously, a finding mirrored in the infectious titers, which were $1.5 \pm 0.2 \times 10^9$ and $3.1 \pm 1.2 \times 10^8$ (mean $\pm$ standard error in three mice) IU per g of tissue in control mice (corresponding to FIG. 8A and 10A) and adoptively immunized mice (corresponding to FIG. 8B, 9, and 10B), respectively. In evaluating FIGURE 9, it should be kept in mind that the stained cells represent all Lyt-2.2$^+$ donor cells that have homed to this area of the spleen. Knowing that only approximately 10% of the injected cells are LCM virus–specific CTL(P) (see above), it is obvious that the marked reduction of virus was accomplished by very few cells. FIGURE 10, finally, demonstrates that despite rapid elimination of virus, the tissue remained essentially devoid of cytolytic changes.

CONCLUDING REMARKS

For the elimination of LCM virus from the acutely infected mouse, virus-specific CTL are essential, but very few are actually needed. For the B6 mouse, for instance, we calculate that 200 LCM virus–specific CTL and/or CTLP reduce replication of the virus in the spleen by more than 50 percent. This effect was seen 40 hours after transfer of immune cells, in which time they might have gone through two to three rounds of replication. Not many more immune cells, however, were needed to make diminished virus replication evident 8 hours after cell transfer, and when 10^7 cells were infused, the virus was actually inactivated (or, less likely, removed from the organ), which, according to our calculation, must have been accomplished by 2×10^5 CTL and was apparent 6 hours after transfer. Notwithstanding the low number and the short time, some cell-to-cell contact *in vivo* is needed for antiviral effects. In adoptive immunization, in which the time between cell transfer and determination of virus in the recipient mouse was 8 hours, the rules of MHC restriction remained applicable (see above).

The spleen consists of around 10^8 cells, of which a minority is infected at the time of transfer; how do the CTL find so efficiently all of their targets? Unless we assume that signals are exchanged across distances, in our opinion the most probable answer is that CTL, upon contact with target cells, release a factor (or factors) or induce other cells to do so, which blocks viral replication in surrounding cells. Antiviral activity of a factor (rather than CTL-mediated lysis) would also account for the lack of cytolytic alterations during the time virus is cleared either spontaneously or due to adoptive immunization. The findings with the C-H-2^{dm2} mouse, which is obviously capable of eliminating the virus despite its diminished ability to generate cells that are lytically active *in vitro,* might indicate that lysis and production (or induction) of a factor are restricted by different class I MHC products. Perhaps the former requires compatibility at L, whereas factor production is regulated through K and/or D. We are currently exploring this possibility.

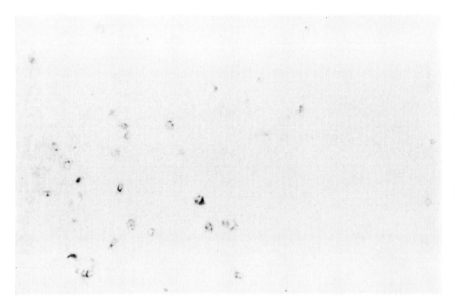

FIGURE 9. Immunocytochemical localization of donor spleen cells in the spleen of a virus-infected adoptively immunized mouse. A B6.PL-Ly-2^a Ly-3^a/Cy (Lyt-2.1) mouse was infected and adoptively immunized with day eight–immune spleen cells from C57BL/6J (Lyt-2.2) mice as described for FIGURE 8B. Frozen section was stained by indirect immunoenzymatic method with rat anti-Lyt-2.2 monoclonal antibody 3.239[55] followed by rabbit anti-rat IgG (Zymed, San Francisco, California) and alkaline phosphatase-conjugated IgG F(ab')$_2$ fragments of sheep anti-rabbit IgG (Sigma); × 250.

We do not postulate that CTL-mediated cell destruction never occurs *in vivo.* On the contrary, it may well account for immunopathologic phenomena often accompanying viral infections and especially infection of the mouse with the LCM virus.[56–59] But rather than assuming that these are the cause for viral elimination, we prefer to think that the infection is terminated despite immunopathology. We admit that the evidence is predominantly of a negative nature. Furthermore, we know of no lymphokine that is capable of blocking viral replication in an already infected cell, although interferon-γ might not have been adequately inves-

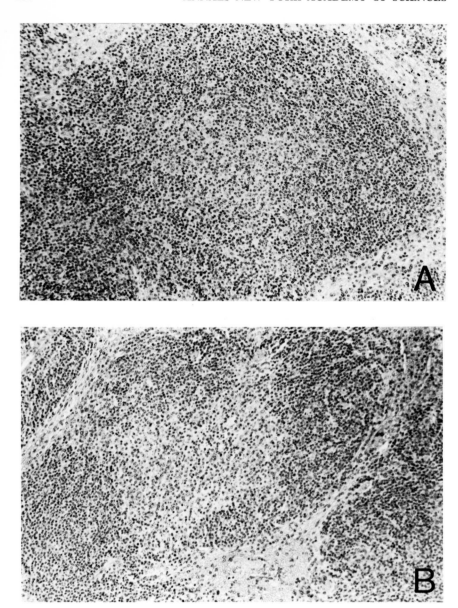

FIGURE 10. Spleen of an LCM virus–infected B6.PL-Ly-2ᵃ Ly-3ᵃ/Cy mouse adoptively immunized with spleen cells from C57BL/6J mice. **(A)** Control mouse 48 hours after intravenous infection with 10^5 infectious units. There is blast-cell proliferation of the T-cell area, but no tissue damage. **(B)** Mouse 48 hours after intravenous infection with 10^5 infectious units and 24 hours after intravenous inoculation of 10^7 day eight–immune spleen cells. The proliferative response in the thymus-dependent zone is more pronounced than in the spleen of the virus control mouse (FIG. 10A), but, again, cytolytic tissue damage is conspicuously absent. Paraffin sections, hematoxylin and eosin; × 150.

tigated in this respect. There is also the observation of McIntyre and his colleagues,[60] who showed that in mice infected with LCM virus alone or the related
Pichinde virus alone, or both together, adoptive immunization diminished only
the virus that had been employed to immunize the donor mice. Similar findings
were reported by Lukacher *et al.*,[61] whose model was the lung of the influenza
virus–infected mouse. These observations argue in favor of direct cytotoxicity or
an extremely localized effect of diffusible factors.

Thus, there are uncertainties, and all we can say at the moment is that we
prefer a mechanism in which lymphokines are decisive, if only because this would
be a more elegant way to control a viral infection than the alternative, which
centers around immunopathologic destruction of infected cells.

REFERENCES

1. ZINKERNAGEL, R. M. & P. C. DOHERTY. 1979. Adv. Immunol. **27:** 51–177.
2. PFIZENMAIER, K., H. JUNG, A. STARZINSKI-POWITZ, M. ROLLINGHOFF & H. WAGNER. 1977. J. Immunol. **119:** 939–944.
3. NASH, A. A., R. QUARTEY-PAPAFIO & P. WILDY. 1980. J. Gen. Virol. **49:** 309–317.
4. ROUSE, B. T., H. S. LARSEN & H. WAGNER. 1983. Infect. Immun. **39:** 785–792.
5. SETHI, K. K. 1983. J. Gen. Virol. **64:** 2033–2037.
6. NASH, A. A., J. PHELAN & P. WILDY. 1981. J. Immunol. **126:** 1260–1262.
7. NASH, A. A. & P. G. H. GELL. 1983. Cell. Immunol. **75:** 348–355.
8. LARSEN, H. S., M.-F. FENG, D. W. HOROHOV, R. N. MOORE & B. T. ROUSE. 1984. J. Virol. **50:** 56–59.
9. LIN, Y.-L. & B. A. ASKONAS. 1981. J. Exp. Med. **154:** 225–234.
10. TAYLOR, P. M. & B. A. ASKONAS. 1983. Eur. J. Immunol. **13:** 707–711.
11. SCHILTKNECHT, E. & G. L. ADA. 1985. Scand. J. Immunol. **22:** 99–103.
12. REDDEHASE, M. J., F. WEILAND, K. MÜNCH, S. JONJIC, A. LÜSKE & U. H. KOSZINOWSKI. 1985. J. Virol. **55:** 264–273.
13. LEHMANN-GRUBE, F., U. ASSMANN, C. LOLIGER, D. MOSKOPHIDIS & J. LOHLER. 1985. J. Immunol. **134:** 608–615.
14. CANTOR, H. & E. A. BOYSE. 1977. Immunol. Rev. **33:** 105–124.
15. SWAIN, S. L., D. P. DIALYNAS, F. W. FITCH & M. ENGLISH. 1984. J. Immunol. **132:** 1118–1123.
16. WILLIAMS, A. F. & A. N. BARCLAY. 1986. *In* Handbook of Experimental Immunology, 4th edit. Vol. 1, Immunochemistry. D. M. Weir, Ed.: 22.1–22.24. Blackwell. Oxford.
17. ASSMANN-WISCHER, U., M. M. SIMON & F. LEHMANN-GRUBE. 1985. Med. Microbiol. Immunol. **174:** 249–256.
18. MARKER, O. & M. VOLKERT. 1973. J. Exp. Med. **137:** 1511–1525.
19. ZINKERNAGEL, R. M. & R. M. WELSH. 1976. J. Immunol. **117:** 1495–1502.
20. BYRNE, J. A. & M. B. A. OLDSTONE. 1984. J. Virol. **51:** 682–686.
21. OLDSTONE, M. B. A., P. BLOUNT, P. J. SOUTHERN & P. W. LAMPERT. 1986. Nature **321:** 239–243.
22. MOSKOPHIDIS, D., S. P. COBBOLD, H. WALDMANN & F. LEHMANN-GRUBE. 1987. J. Virol. **138:** 2282–2289.
23. OPITZ, H. G., U. OPITZ, G. HEWLETT & H. D. SCHLUMBERGER. 1982. Immunobiology **160:** 438–453.
24. COBBOLD, S. P., A. JAYASURIYA, A. NASH, T. D. PROSPERO & H. WALDMANN. 1984. Nature **312:** 548–551.
25. MOSKOPHIDIS, D. & F. LEHMANN-GRUBE. 1984. J. Immunol. **133:** 3366–3370.
26. LEHMANN-GRUBE, F. 1971. Lymphocytic Choriomeningitis Virus. Virology Monographs Vol. 10. Springer-Verlag. Wien and New York.
27. AHMED, R., A. SALMI, L. D. BUTLER, J. M. CHILLER & M. B. A. OLDSTONE. 1984. J. Exp. Med. **160:** 521–540.

28. MIMS, C. A. 1964. Bacteriol. Rev. **28:** 30–71.
29. BLANDEN, R. V., A. J. HAPEL, P. C. DOHERTY & R. M. ZINKERNAGEL. 1976. *In* Immunobiology of the Macrophage. D. S. Nelson, Ed.: 367–400. Academic Press. New York.
30. MORAHAN, P. S., J. R. CONNOR & K. R. LEARY. 1985. Br. Med. Bull. **41:** 15–21.
31. BLANDEN, R. V. & C. A. MIMS. 1973. Aust. J. Exp. Biol. Med. Sci. **51:** 393–398.
32. LEHMANN-GRUBE, F., U. ASSMANN-WISCHER, R. SCHWACHENWALD, I. KRENZ, T. KRAHNERT & D. MOSKOPHIDIS. 1986. Med. Microbiol. Immunol. **175:** 145–148.
33. LEHMANN-GRUBE, F., I. KRENZ, T. KRAHNERT, R. SCHWACHENWALD, D. MOSKOPHIDIS, J. LÖHLER & C. J. VILLEDA POSADA. 1987. J. Immunol. **61:** 1867–1874.
34. CHEERS, C. & R. WALLER. 1975. J. Immunol. **115:** 844–847.
35. MOGENSEN, S. C. & H. K. ANDERSEN. 1978. Infect. Immun. **19:** 792–798.
36. HAHN, H. & M. BIERTHER. 1974. Infect. Immun. **10:** 1110–1119.
37. WELSH, R. M. 1978. J. Exp. Med. **148:** 163–181.
38. BUKOWSKI, J. F., J. F. WARNER, G. DENNERT & R. M. WELSH. 1985. J. Exp. Med. **161:** 40–52.
39. MOSKOPHIDIS, D. & F. LEHMANN-GRUBE. 1983. Cell. Immunol. **77:** 279–289.
40. THOMSEN, A. R., M. VOLKERT & K. BRO-JØRGENSEN. 1983. Scand. J. Immunol. **17:** 489–495.
41. HOTCHIN, J. 1962. Virology **17:** 214–216.
42. LEHMANN-GRUBE, F. & J. LOHLER. 1981. Lab. Invest. **44:** 205–213.
43. MILLER, R. G. & M. DUNKLEY. 1974. Cell. Immunol. **14:** 284–302.
44. JULIUS, M. H., E. SIMPSON & L. A. HERZENBERG. 1973. Eur. J. Immunol. **3:** 645–649.
45. ASSMANN-WISCHER, U., D. MOSKOPHIDIS, M. M. SIMON & F. LEHMANN-GRUBE. 1986. Med. Microbiol. Immunol. **175:** 141–143.
46. TASWELL, C. 1981. J. Immunol. **126:** 1614–1619.
47. ÖRN, A., R. S. GOODENOW, L. HOOD, P. R. BRAYTON, J. G. WOODWARD, R. C. HARMON & J. A. FRELINGER. 1982. Nature **297:** 415–417.
48. FRELINGER, J. A., A. ORN, P. R. BRAYTON & L. HOOD. 1983. Transplant. Proc. **15:** 2024–2026.
49. MCKENZIE, I. F. C., G. M. MORGAN, R. W. MELVOLD & H. I. KOHN. 1977. Immunogenetics **4:** 333–347.
50. HANSEN, T. H., S. B. CULLEN, R. MELVOLD, H. KOHN, L. FLAHERTY & D. H. SACHS. 1977. J. Exp. Med. **145:** 1550–1558.
51. ALLAN, J. E. & P. C. DOHERTY. 1985. Immunogenetics **21:** 581–589.
52. LEHMANN-GRUBE, F., L. MARTÍNEZ PERALTA, M. BRUNS & J. LOHLER. 1983. Comp. Virol. **18:** 43–103.
53. GSCHWENDER, H. H., G. RUTTER & F. LEHMANN-GRUBE. 1976. Med. Microbiol. Immunol. **162:** 119–131.
54. LEDBETTER, J. A. & L. A. HERZENBERG. 1979. Immunol. Rev. **47:** 63–90.
55. SARMIENTO, M., A. L. GLASEBROOK & F. W. FITCH. 1980. J. Immunol. **125:** 2665–2672.
56. HOTCHIN, J. 1962. Cold Spring Harbor Symp. Quant. Biol. **27:** 479–499.
57. COLE, G. A., D. H. GILDEN, A. A. MONJAN & N. NATHANSON. 1971. Fed. Proc. **30:** 1831–1841.
58. LOHLER, J. & F. LEHMANN-GRUBE. 1981. Lab. Invest. **44:** 193–204.
59. ZINKERNAGEL, R. M., E. HAENSELER, T. LEIST, A. CERNY, H. HENGARTNER & A. ALTHAGE. 1986. J. Exp. Med. **164:** 1075–1092.
60. MCINTYRE, K. W., J. F. BUKOWSKI & R. M. WELSH. 1985. Antiviral Res. **5:** 299–305.
61. LUKACHER, A. E., V. L. BRACIALE & T. J. BRACIALE. 1984. J. Exp. Med. **160:** 814–826.

Cytotoxic T Lymphocytes

Their Relevance in Herpesvirus Infections[a]

STEPHEN MARTIN, ED CANTIN,[b] AND
BARRY T. ROUSE[c]

Department of Microbiology
College of Veterinary Medicine
University of Tennessee
Knoxville, Tennessee 37996-0845

[b] *City of Hope National Medical Center*
Duarte, California 91010-0269

INTRODUCTION

Counteracting virus infections by destroying infected cells could be the major function that cytotoxic T lymphocytes (CTL) subserve in the body. Their property of recognizing viral antigens only in the context of major histocompatibility complex (MHC) antigens focuses their activity on infected cells, and it appears that the killing of such cells is a principal means by which animals recover from viral infections.[1] Other aspects of T-cell and humoral immunity also serve to effect recovery, and these may be adequate in situations where the challenge infection is slight.[2] As has been shown when working in mice with herpesviruses, however, a functional CTL system may be essential for immunity when the load of infection is high (reviewed in reference 3). This was shown initially by adoptive cell transfer experiments where optimal immunity to a lethal challenge required that class I- as well as class II-MHC–restricted cells (probably CTL) be included in the cell transfers.[4] The idea received support in later experiments using animals depleted *in vivo* of either Lyt-2+ or L3T4+ cells. Whereas at low-dose herpes simplex virus (HSV) challenge the function of L3T4+ cells sufficed for protection, when the challenge was high, intact Lyt-2+ lymphocyte function (presumably CTL) was necessary for immunity.[2,5] Further evidence for an essential role of class I-MHC–restricted Lyt-2+ cells with a CTL function to clear a high-dose challenge of virus is presented in this communication.

Because CTL appear necessary for complete immunity to herpetic infections, an acceptable vaccine can only be one that adequately stimulates this aspect of immunity. As we have shown previously,[6] inactivated forms of antigen seem inappropriate immunogens to stimulate MHC-class I–restricted CTL responses against HSV, possibly because only antigen endogenously synthesized in cells constitute CTL-recognizable entities.[7] Consequently, only vaccine formats that permit endogenous protein synthesis may adequately stimulate the CTL arm of the immune response. The recombinant vaccinia virus vector system promises to be an acceptable one, inasmuch as it permits such endogenous protein synthesis. A CTL response to influenza A gene products has been shown to occur following immunization with the appropriate vaccinia recombinant.[8] To obtain an accept-

[a] This work was supported by Public Health Service grant AI 14981 from the National Institute of Allergy and Infectious Diseases.
[c] To whom correspondence should be addressed.

able CTL response to HSV, however, we have yet to establish which viral HSV genes to include in the vector construct. Earlier studies on HSV-1 had implicated glycoproteins, abundantly present in the envelope of the virion and at the surface of infected cells, as likely candidates as targets for CTL.[9-11]

In this report, we have used two recombinant vaccinia virus vectors to investigate the role of glycoproteins B and D as targets for CTL and as *in vivo* activators of HSV-specific–CTL responses. Surprisingly, whereas certain aspects of T- and B-cell immunity were stimulated, no CTL response was detected. Although all glycoproteins of HSV have not been studied, it may be, as is becoming evident from studies with certain other viruses,[11a] that proteins other than glycoproteins, and which are not abundantly present at the cell surface, may act as major CTL targets. We show a likely role for the immediate early gene products as CTL targets and discuss the value of recognizing such early gene products to curtail infection.

MATERIAL AND METHODS

Mice

C3H/HeJ mice (H-2^k) and BALB/c byj (H-2^d) mice were obtained from the University of Tennessee Memorial Research Center Hospital, Knoxville.

Viruses

HSV-1 strain KOS was grown and titered as described previously.[12] The vaccinia recombinants containing the cloned genes for HSV-1 glycoprotein D (gD) and the influenza virus (A/JAP/305/57) hemagglutinin (HA) molecule were the kind gift of Dr. B. Moss (NIH, Bethesda, MD) and were prepared as described previously.[13] The construction and characteristics of the vaccinia recombinant containing the cloned gene for HSV-1 glycoprotein B (gB) have been described recently.[14]

In Vitro *and* in Vivo *Assays*

HSV-1 alpha gene-expressing cells were prepared by treating L(H-2^k) or A31(H-2^d) cells with cycloheximide (75 μg/ml) one hour prior to infection with HSV-1 KOS (MOI 1). After 6–8 hr incubation at 37°C actinomycin (Act) D was added to the cultures to a final concentration of 5 μg/ml, and after a further 1 hr incubation, cycloheximide was removed by washing the cells five times in medium containing Act D (5 μg/ml). The cells were then labeled with sodium 51 chromate (200 μCi) for 2 hr in the presence of Act D (5 μg/ml) before being washed and used as target cells in a 4 hr chromium release assay. The CTL assay was also performed in medium containing Act D (5 μg/ml).

All other procedures referred to in this text are standard techniques described in detail previously.[15,16]

RESULTS

Glycoproteins and CTL

To assess the CTL-inducing activity of two major glycoproteins of HSV-1, gB and gD, the response of mice to immunization with recombinant vaccinia viruses containing the gB (Vac-gB) and gD (Vac-gD) genes was measured and compared to the response to HSV-1 virus. Neither recombinant vaccinia virus elicited an HSV-specific–CTL response detectable 5 days after acute immunization and a further *in vitro* culture period of 3 days (TABLE 1). This is the original Pfizenmaier procedure,[17] an effective way of inducing an HSV-1–specific response after immunization with infectious virus. A modification of this procedure that includes a 5 day *in vitro* culture with antigen[6] and induces a potent HSV-specific–CTL response also produced no CTL response in Vac-vector immunized mice (TABLE 2). Even more telling, lymph node cells or splenocytes, from mice immunized *in vivo* with HSV and then their memory populations restimulated *in vitro* with recombinant vaccinia viruses, failed to elicit HSV-specific CTL. As shown previously,[9] however, HSV-stimulated memory populations generated potent CTL activity (TABLE 3). It was also evident that memory cells from mice immunized with recombinant vaccinia viruses, but stimulated *in vitro* with HSV, also failed to elicit HSV-specific CTL (TABLE 3). Moreover, lymphoid populations with potent HSV-specific–CTL activity were incapable of lysing target cells infected with either Vac-gB or Vac-gD (TABLE 4). In all instances, however, the Vac vector–infected targets could be lysed by vaccinia-specific CTL. The failure to detect HSV-specific–CTL activity was not because recombinant virus–infected cells did not express glycoproteins, for infected targets could be lysed by appropriate antibody and complement (reference 15 and data not shown), and the glycoproteins could be detected by direct binding assays (TABLE 5).

Whereas our efforts to demonstrate CTL induction or activity with either Vac-gB or Vac-gD containing recombinant vaccinia virus vectors ended in failure, other aspects of T-cell immunity as well as antibody production (a thymus-dependent response[18]) were detectable (TABLE 6). For example, lymphoid cells, from mice immunized with either Vac-vector, proliferated upon stimulation with HSV-1 (TABLE 6), which at least in the case of Vac-gD was a response that involved both Lyt-2$^+$ and L3T4$^+$ T cells.[15] The finding of proliferating Lyt-2$^+$ cells made our failure to detect CTL even more surprising. We know from previous studies with the gD-containing vector, however, that a potent suppressor-cell response is induced.[15] Consequently, one possibility is that many of the proliferating Lyt-2$^+$ cells function as suppressors.

Although class I–restricted CTL could not be demonstrated, by using class II expressing virus-infected targets (IA$^+$ L cells), we detected some gD-specific T-cell cytotoxicity, an effect we attribute to class II–restricted CTL (FIG. 1). Such cells were detected in HSV-primed and HSV-restimulated populations tested against Vac-gD–infected IA$^+$ L-cell targets.

Immunization with either Vac-vector led to potent HSV-specific delayed-type hypersensitivity (DTH) responses (TABLE 6), which by adoptive transfer was shown for Vac-gD lymphocytes to be mediated by L3T4$^+$ cells.[16] In addition, either Vac-vector could elicit a DTH reaction when injected intradermally into HSV-immune mice (data not shown).

Our results, therefore, indicate that both recombinant vaccinia virus vectors stimulate numerous aspects of immunity but not a CTL response. This selective failure to induce CTL provided an opportunity to assess the consequence of this

TABLE 1. CTL Activity in DLN Cells Five Days after *in Vivo* Immunization and Three Days *in Vitro* Culture[a]

	Percent Specific Lysis		
Immunogen	L	HSV-L	HSV-A31
HSV	3.2 ± 2.6	*19.10* + 1.0	2.97 ± 0.7
Vac-gD	4.6 ± 3.3	4.24 ± 2.8	6.53 ± 6.6
Vac-gB	5.9 ± 2.3	2.33 ± 0.7	3.30 ± 2.4

[a] Five days after ear-flap immunization with 10^6 $TCID_{50}$ of virus, the draining retropharyngeal lymph nodes from C3H/HeJ mice were excised, single cell suspensions prepared and cultured *in vitro* for 3 days in the absence of antigen. Cells were then washed and used as CTL effectors in a 4 hr chromium release assay against various target cells at an E/T ratio of 40:1. Results are shown as the mean percent specific lysis of four replicate cultures plus or minus one standard deviation. Target cells were autologous L cells ($H-2^k$) or allogeneic A31 cells ($H-2^d$), which were either mock or HSV-1 infected. Italicized results are significantly greater than the levels detected against mock infected target cells.

TABLE 2. CTL Activity in DLN Cells Seven Days after *in Vivo* Immunization and Five Days *in Vitro* Stimulation with HSV[a]

	Target Cell Population			
Immunogen	L	L-HSV-1	L-PRV	A31-HSV
HSV	1.7 ± 2.1	*33.6* ± 3.5	6.9 ± 2.3	4.1 ± 0.7
Vac-gD	6.0 ± 2.3	6.0 ± 4.7	3.3 ± 0.7	2.7 ± 4.3
Vac-gB	4.1 ± 1.2	4.5 ± 0.7	4.5 ± 2.0	5.1 ± 6.1
Vac-Ha	2.3 ± 2.0	1.1 ± 2.3	2.9 ± 1.7	2.4 ± 1.8

[a] Seven days after immunization of the pinnae with 10^6 $TCID_{50}$ of the respective viruses, the draining retropharyngeal lymph nodes were excised, and single cell suspensions were prepared. After *in vitro* culture for 5 days with UV-inactivated–HSV-1 KOS (multiplicity of infection (MOI-2) before inactivation), cells were washed and used as CTL effectors in a 4 hr chromium release assay at an E/T ratio of 40:1. Results are shown as the mean percent specific lysis plus or minus one standard deviation. Italicized results are significantly greater than the levels detected against mock infected target cells.

TABLE 3. CTL Induction in Mice Immunized with HSV-1 and Vaccinia Virus Recombinants Containing gD and gB Genes[a]

In Vivo Immunogen	*In Vitro* Stimulation	Percent Specific Lysis			
		L	L-HSV-1	A31-HSV	L-vaccinia
HSV	HSV	3.5 ± 1.5	45.7 ± 2.0	8.1 ± 0.9	7.6 ± 0.8
HSV	Vac-gD	1.1 ± 0.7	1.3 ± 1.30	0.5 ± 0.4	12.1 ± 0.9
HSV	Vac-gB	3.3 ± 3.7	1.1 ± 1.50	2.9 ± 1.7	10.5 ± 1.2
Vac-gD	HSV	0.5 ± 0.5	2.9 ± 1.7	0.0 ± 4.3	nd
Vac-gD	—	5.8 ± 2.0	7.50 ± 1.9	2.9 ± 4.2	46.6 ± 6.8
Vac-gB	HSV	8.6 ± 5.3	4.6 ± 0.7	0.0	nd
Vac-gB	—	12 ± 1.9	14 ± 1.1	13 ± 1.0	40 ± 7.9

[a] Mice were immunized 4 wk previously with 5×10^6 $TCID_{50}$ of the appropriate virus. Four wk postinfection, immune splenocytes were harvested or restimulated for 5 days *in vitro* with the appropriate UV-inactivated virus (MOI of 2 before inactivation). Cells were then washed and used in a 4 hr chromium release assay at an effector to target ratio of 25:1. Mice were immunized 6 days before their splenocytes were obtained and used directly in a 5 hr chromium release assay at an E/T ratio of 25:1. Results are expressed as the mean of four replicates plus or minus one standard deviation.

TABLE 4. HSV-Specific CTL Fail to Lyse gD or gB Expressing Target Cells[a]

	E/T Ratio		
Target Cell	100 : 1	50 : 1	25 : 1
L cell	20.9[c] ± 0.9	23.4 ± 5.4	15.0 ± 2.9
L-HSV-1	*53.7* ± 5.0	*42.8* ± 2.4	*32.5* ± 2.0
L-Vac-gB[b]	21.6 ± 2.5	19.3 ± 3.1	9.9 ± 2.4
L-Vac-gD[b]	23.9 ± 3.2	17.3 ± 1.8	10.1 ± 1.6
gDL	15.0 ± 2.9	12.8 ± 0.9	4.7 ± 2.4
gDL-HSV	*59.5* ± 2.7	*50.3* ± 2.1	*38.5* ± 1.1
gDL-Vac-gB[b]	22.1 ± 1.8	19.5 ± 1.1	13.8 ± 1.2
A-31	23.6 ± 6.2	17.1 ± 1.6	7.4 ± 2.6
A-HSV	19.4 ± 2.2	12.6 ± 3.0	5.3 ± 1.8
A-Vac-gB	20.9 ± 1.6	20.5 ± 2.2	10.6 ± 0.8
A-Vac-gD	25.8 ± 2.7	17.3 ± 2.3	8.7 ± 2.4

[a] Cytotoxicity assays (4 hr) were performed by using C3H/HeJ splenocytes and ^{51}Cr-labeled MHC-matched L cells (H-2^k) and gDL cells (transfected L cell that expresses HSV-1 gD), or mismatched A31 cells (H-2^d). Italicized results are significantly greater than the levels detected against mock infected target cells.

failure in terms of the level of protective immunity induced by the vectors. To measure the extent of immunity, we used a mouse system in which the clearance of a local epidermal infection of the pinna by different immune populations could be assessed. Using the adoptive transfer of immune draining lymph node (DLN) populations to naive mice, which were subsequently challenged with 10^4 tissue culture infectious dose 50 (TCID$_{50}$) of HSV-1 in the pinna, we demonstrated a role for L3T4$^+$ cells in the protective response afforded by HSV, Vac-gB, or Vac-gD immune lymphocytes (FIG. 2). It can also be seen that the removal of Lyt-2$^+$ cells from these populations had no apparent deleterious effect on their ability to clear a 10^4 TCID$_{50}$ HSV epithelial challenge (FIG. 2).

According to the work of others, a role for Lyt-2$^+$ cells becomes apparent when the HSV challenge dose is raised to much higher levels.[2] To analyze the compromise, if any, of Vac-vector immunized animals to control high-dose HSV challenge, mice immunized 10 days previously were challenged with low (10^4), intermediate (10^5), or high (10^6) doses of HSV, and their ear clearance assessed four days later. The data in FIGURE 3 reveal that whereas HSV-immune animals (which demonstrate CTL memory) cleared low- and high-dose challenges, the Vac-gB and Vac-gD immune animals (which fail to express CTL priming) could

TABLE 5. Expression of gD and gB on Infected L Cells[a]

	^{125}I and gB	^{125}I and gD
L cell	1,357 ± 62	1,883 ± 66
L-Vac-HA	1,820 ± 52	1,876 ± 45
L-Vac-gB	12,290 ± 103	2,153 ± 94
L-Vac-gD	2,301 ± 70	5,690 ± 92
L-HSV-1	6,611 ± 29	4,813 ± 130

[a] Murine L929 cells were infected with the respective viruses shown (MOI-2-5) for 12 hours. The cells were then mixed with an excess of ^{125}I-labeled monoclonal anti-gD or anti-gB for 1 hr on ice. After five washes, samples were measured for bound antibody and the results expressed as the mean bound counts per minute of four replicates plus or minus 1 standard error.

TABLE 6. Other Aspects of Anti-HSV Immunity Induced by Recombinant Vaccinia Vectors

Measure of Immunity	Aspects of Anti-HSV T-Cell Immunity Induced by Various Vaccinia Recombinant Immunizing Virus[a]			
	HSV KOS[a]	Vac-HA[a]	Vac-gD[a]	Vac-gB[a]
[b] HSV-specific lymphoproliferation	44,202 ± 2,278	3,684 ± 334	25,248 ± 5,305	20,749 ± 2,904
[c] HSV-specific delayed-type hypersensitivity	25.7 ± 1.3	2.75 ± 2.1	19.75 ± 4.8	16.75 ± 3.7
[d] HSV-specific antibody response	2867	28	1792	896
[e] Protection against a local HSV challenge (4 logs)	<0.47, <0.47 <0.47, 1.04 (0.6125 ± 0.25)	3.5, 2.3 1.7, 2.5, 4.6 (2.92 ± 1.02)	0.5, 1.1, 1.04 <0.47, <0.47 (0.528 ± 0.47)	1.6, 1.2, <0.47 <0.47, <0.47 (0.56 ± 0.7)

[a] Groups of C3H/HeJ (H-2^k) mice were immunized in each ear flap with 10^6 TCID$_{50}$.

[b] Thirty days after immunization, draining retropharyngeal lymph nodes were excised, and single cell suspensions were obtained and cultured for 5 days with 5×10^5 x-irradiated C3H/TEN splenocytes infected with UV-inactivated HSV-1 KOS. During the last 24 hr of culture, samples were labeled by the addition of 0.5 μCi of tritiated thymidine/microtiter well. Incorporation of tritium into cellular DNA was used as a measure of lymphoproliferation, with the results expressed as mean cpm ± 1 standard error (n = 12).

[c] Seven days after immunization, groups of 4 or 5 mice received 5×10^6 TCID$_{50}$ of UV-inactivated HSV-1 in the left rear footpad and an equal volume (20 μl) of Vero-cell extract in the right foot. An increase in left footpad swelling over right footpad swelling was measured with spring gauge calipers 24 hr later. Results are expressed in units of 10^{-3} cm ± 1 standard deviation.

[d] Seven days after immunization, mice were bled from the retro-orbital sinus and the HSV-specific antibody titer determined in an indirect ELISA assay. Antibody titers are represented as the reciprocal of the highest dilution of serum that gave an OD$_{490}$ nm value of 0.1 above a negative control normal mouse serum.

[e] Seven days after immunization, groups of 4 or 5 mice were challenged with 10^4 TCID$_{50}$ of HSV-1 KOS in the left ear flap. Three days later, the ear flap was removed and homogenized, and the infectious virus titer was determined. Results are expressed as log virus titer/individual ear. Results in parentheses are the mean group values ± 1 standard deviation.

only efficiently clear low-dose HSV challenge. This could mean that it is the lack of Lyt-2$^+$ CTL activity that compromises the vaccinia vector immunized animal's ability to clear the intermediate and high-challenge doses of HSV. This interpretation is further substantiated by the ability of L3T4$^-$, B cell$^-$ (J11d.2^{-19}), Lyt-2$^+$ HSV-CTL populations to mediate clearance of intermediate and high-challenge doses of HSV-1 when adoptively transferred to naive animals (FIG. 4).

Our failure to demonstrate CTL reactive against two major surface glycoproteins of HSV does not mean that other glycoproteins do not act as CTL targets. Indeed, indirect evidence has implied that gC acts as a target,[11] a result recently directly confirmed using target L cells transfected with the gC gene.[20] In this latter study, the workers also failed to detect HSV-specific CTL reactive with gD, gB, or gE using similar approaches that provided positive results with gC. Lacking as yet a recombinant vaccinia virus with the gC gene, we are unable to evaluate the CTL-inducing activity of this glycoprotein in our systems.

Early Antigens as CTL Targets

Initially it was assumed that because of their prominent virion and cell-surface expression, viral glycoproteins would act as the principal, or perhaps the only, targets for viral-specific CTL. This appears to be true in some systems,[21] but in others it is becoming clear that numerous nonglycosylated structural and non-structural proteins may act as targets,[22–24] many of which are not usually considered to be expressed at the cell surface. In fact, it might be argued teleologically that early viral gene products represent logical CTL targets, because infected cells could be recognized early after infection and killed by viral-specific CTL before infectious virus had replicated and spread to other cells. In this situation, infection would be readily curtailed and recovery would be expected to occur. Such early viral gene products appear to act as targets in the cytomegalovirus system[25] and in addition, as shown below, appear to act as such in the case of HSV. To demonstrate this, we took advantage of the coordinated regulation of herpesvirus gene expression that involves a cascade-like reaction.[26] In the case of HSV, it has been shown that the immediate early or alpha-gene expression is necessary for expression of the early or beta genes. In turn, one or several of the beta gene products shut off the expression of the alpha genes, and whereas others induce the expression of gamma genes, some shut off the expression of the beta genes.

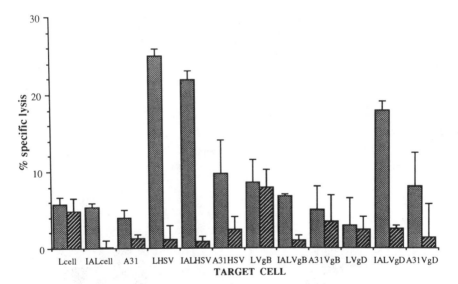

FIGURE 1. Recognition of vaccinia gD–infected L cells by cytotoxic T cells in the context of IA antigen. Cytotoxicity assays were performed with ^{51}Cr-labeled target cells and 5 day–*in vitro*–stimulated splenocytes derived from HSV-1 primed C3H/HeJ mice. Effector cells had been previously treated with complement alone (■) or complement plus monoclonal antibody recognizing the Thy-1.2 alloantigen (▨). Effector cells were then assayed for their cytotoxic potential against autologous L cells (H-2^k), IA$^+$ L cells (H-2^k), or allogeneic A31 (H-2^d) target cells infected with the various viruses. The E/T ratio was 25 : 1, and the results are expressed as the mean of four replicates plus or minus one standard deviation.

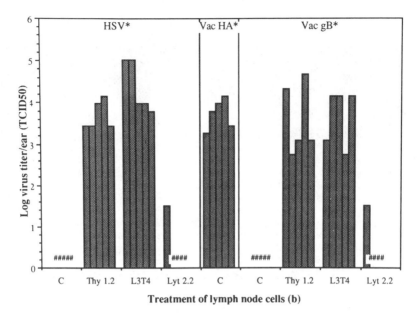

FIGURE 2. Phenotype of immune cells mediating ear clearance. Donor lymphocytes were obtained from the draining lymph nodes of BALB/c mice that had been inoculated in each pinna with 1×10^6 TCID$_{50}$ of virus (*) 10 days previously. After treatment with specific antiserum and complement or complement alone, donor lymphocytes were intravenously inoculated into groups of recipient mice. Each mouse was challenged with 2×10^4 TCID$_{50}$ HSV-1 in the left pinna 24 hr later. Four days after challenge, the infected pinnae were collected, and the infectious virus titer (TCID$_{50}$/ear) was determined on Vero-cell monolayers. Results are shown for individual mice, with animals represented with the symbol ($\#$) as having a virus titer of less than 0.47 logs of virus/ear.

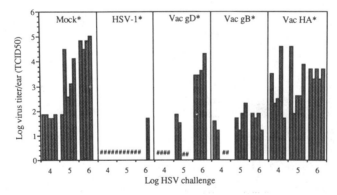

FIGURE 3. Quantitative analysis of ear clearance ability. Twelve days after subcutaneous inoculation (left pinna) with the viruses shown (*), groups of BALB/c mice were challenged in the right pinna with the dose of HSV-1 shown. Four days after challenge, the right pinnae were removed and the infectious virus titers ($\log_{10}$ TCID$_{50}$) determined on Vero-cell monolayers. Results are shown for individual mice, with animals represented with the symbol ($\#$) as having a virus titer of less than 0.47 logs of virus/ear.

To analyze the potential role of HSV-alpha genes in the formation of a CTL-target complex, cells were pretreated with a protein synthesis inhibitor (cyclohex-imide) and infected with HSV-1 for several hours to allow the accumulation of large amounts of alpha-gene mRNA. The cycloheximide was then removed in the presence of a transcriptional inhibitor (actinomycin D), allowing mRNA translation, thus giving rise to a cell that contained large amounts of alpha-gene proteins in the absence of other viral structural and nonstructural proteins (data not shown).

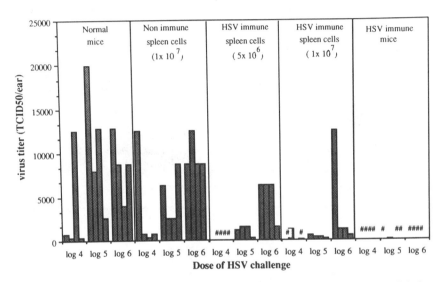

FIGURE 4. HSV-1–specific immune splenocytes enriched for CTL activity-clear high-dose HSV-1 challenges. Spleen cells from HSV-1 immune or noninfected control C3H/HeJ mice were cultured for 5 days *in vitro* in the presence of UV-inactivated HSV-1. The cells were then depleted of L3T4+-bearing T cells and J11.d2-bearing B cells by treatment with the respective monoclonal antibodies and complement. The resulting cell populations were greater than 90% Lyt-2+ cells, with the HSV immune cells exhibiting high levels of CTL killing when analyzed *in vitro*. These cells were then intravenously inoculated into groups of 4 C3H/HeJ mice (1×10^7/mouse), which were challenged 24 hr later in the left pinna with the dose of HSV-1 shown. Four days later, the infected pinnae were removed and the infectious virus titer determined. Results are shown for individual mice, with the animals represented with the symbol (#) as having a virus titer of less than 0.47 logs of virus/ear.

The data in FIGURE 5 show that autologous L cells treated as described and expressing HSV-alpha genes were recognized by C3H-HeJ HSV-specific CTL populations. Because cells pretreated with actinomycin D and then infected with HSV-1 were not lysed (FIG. 5), the recognition of alpha gene–expressing cells cannot be attributed to the CTLs recognition of exogenously acquired input HSV antigens. Moreover, the presence of actinomycin D throughout the assay period prevented any further gene transcription, therefore negating the possibility of beta or gamma gene expression by the alpha targets during the CTL assay period.

A further interesting observation was that alpha gene–expressing targets were recognized almost as efficiently as cells allowed to undergo a fully productive

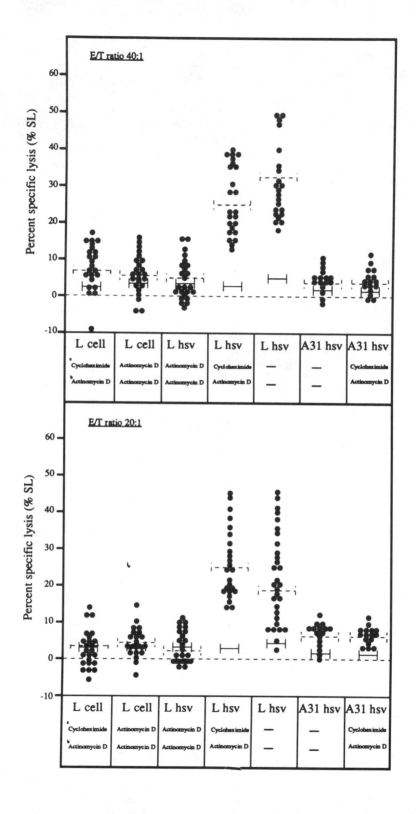

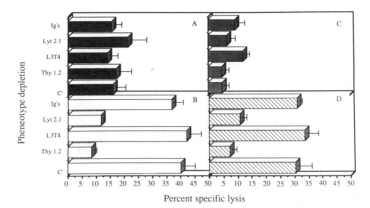

FIGURE 6. The phenotype of the HSV-immune lymphocytes that lyse L cells expressing HSV-1 alpha-gene products. Five-day bulk HSV-specific CTL cultures were split fivefold and the effector cells treated with complement alone, or complement plus one of various antibodies. After depletion, the remaining viable cells from each treatment were assessed for their lytic potential in a 4 hr chromium release assay at an E/T ratio of 32 : 1. The targets were L cells treated with cycloheximide and then Act D (A), L cells infected with HSV-1 at an MOI of 1.0 (B), L cells infected with HSV-1 at an MOI of 1.0 in the presence of Act D (C), or L cells infected with HSV-1 at an MOI of 1.0 after treatment with cycloheximide, followed by Act D (D). Results are expressed as the mean percent specific lysis ± one standard deviation of four replicate wells. The assay was performed with added Act D to prevent further viral transcription.

HSV-1 infection (FIG. 5). Although such data cannot give an estimate of the frequency of alpha gene–recognizing CTL, it does indicate that this population is present at significant levels. The fact that this lysis is not seen against allogeneic A31 (H-2^d) cells expressing HSV alpha genes, and that lysis is the function of Thy-1.2$^+$, Lyt-2.1$^+$, L3T4$^-$ immunoglobulin$^-$ lymphocytes, further supports the notion that this lysis is mediated by class I–restricted CTL (FIG. 6).

DISCUSSION

Our study was designed to achieve the positive identification of gB and gD as targets for HSV-specific CTL and inducers of a CTL response. Accordingly, it

←

FIGURE 5. The recognition of HSV-1 alpha-gene products by HSV-1–specific CTL. CTL were generated as outlined in the legend for TABLE 3 and tested at the E/T ratios shown in a 4 hr chromium release assay. The rationale for the various inhibitor combinations is given in the text. The treatment with inhibitors can be divided into two steps. The first step (a) includes inhibitor addition (1 hr) and infection with HSV-1 at an MOI-1 (6 hr) in the continued presence of the inhibitor. The second step (b) involves the removal of inhibitor (a) by continued washing in the presence of inhibitor (b). Cells are then cultured for 2 hr in the presence of inhibitor (b) before being used in the assay. The solid horizontal bars indicate the 99% tolerance limits of the low control normal distributions, and the dashed horizontal bars mark the median values of the experimental data. The assay was performed with added Act D (5 μg/ml) to prevent further viral transcription.

was disappointing to obtain the negative results we report in this communication. Nevertheless, our observations are of interest for at least two reasons. First, they demand an explanation of why two such prominent surface-expressed large glycoproteins seem not to act as targets and inducers of class I–restricted CTL. Second, because the negative response appeared to be confined to the CTL response, it provided us with a "natural" model to assess the role of CTL in immunity to HSV.

We can consider several explanations for a failure to induce and detect CTL. First among these might be technical difficulties, a seemingly unlikely explanation because of parallel positive responses to HSV and vaccinia virus. Moreover, the absent response appeared limited to class I–restricted CTL because at least with the gD gene–containing vector we have observed class II–restricted CTL using L cells transfected with the IA^k genes. A second explanation might be that CTL development was prevented by a zealous suppressor-cell response. Elsewhere we have shown, with the gD recombinant, that suppressor cells are induced because they are following immunization with infectious HSV.[16] They do not prevent detection of CTL in the latter circumstance, however. Moreover, the inability of HSV immune–memory populations stimulated *in vitro* with virus to generate CTL detectable with Vac-vector–infected targets may be difficult to explain with a suppressor hypothesis, unless gB- and gD-reactive CTL-precursors (CTL-p) are selectively subject to suppressor-cell regulation. Furthermore, inasmuch as mice immunized with either Vac-vectors and subsequently exposed to HSV generate CTL responses and CTL-p frequencies (measurable by limited dilution analysis) to the same extent as mice only infected with HSV, the exuberant suppressor response hypothesis appears unlikely (Martin and Rouse, unpublished data).

We must also consider the possibility that gD and gB represent holes in the repertoire for class I–restricted CTL subsets in mice. Although we have only studied two other strains of mice (BALB/c and C57BL6), neither of these generate detectable CTL (15 and unpublished data). Moreover, we have been unable to detect HSV-specific CTL-p in lymphoid cells from Vac-vector–immunized mice. Because we do not have a target-antigen system, however, that expresses only gB or gD, which can be lysed by HSV-specific CTL, we are unable to examine directly the question of whether CTL-p to gB and gD exists. The failure to observe lysis of gB and gD as targets that express these antigens as a result of gene transfection has been observed by us as well as by others.[20] Recently, Rosenthal and co-workers, however, were able to demonstrate gC-reactive CTL using the transfected target-cell approach,[20] a result that supports previous reports that gC provides a major target for HSV-specific CTL.[9–11] Inasmuch as we lack a recombinant vaccinia virus construct with the gC gene, we cannot establish if such a vector will engender HSV-specific CTL upon *in vivo* immunization.

Even if gC turns out to be a major CTL target, this does not allow us to escape the problem of why gB and gD apparently seem not to act as targets. We are presently considering the possibility that either the type of vector construct we are using does not lead to adequate CTL-p recognition or that neither the gB nor the gD proteins undertake the appropriate processing pathways within infected cells to become CTL recognizable.

It could be argued that the most appropriate target antigens for a protective CTL response would be early antigens. Accordingly, if such antigens were recognized by CTL, infected cells could be killed early in the replication cycle and before infectious progeny virus is produced. In this way infected cells could be sacrificed to the benefit of its uninfected neighbors. If cells were only subject to killing late in the replication cycle, cell disruption by CTL may even serve to further disseminate virus. In herpesvirus systems, where latency is a feature, recognizing early gene products that will be the initial gene products after latency breakdown may serve to maintain the latent state by killing nonlatent infected cells before they replicate virus. Another putative advantage of recognizing alpha-gene products is that their function of gene control may suggest that they have to maintain a conserved structure. Therefore, different strains of virus should be recognized by such CTL. The idea that early proteins synthesized during HSV replication might act as targets is not appealing inasmuch as such proteins are not considered to be expressed at the infected cell surface (Roizman, personal communication). Nevertheless, as recently shown in the influenza A system, proteins can act as CTL targets even when they are not detectable, at least serologically, at the cell surface.[27] Evidence that early gene products act as CTL targets and that CTL precursors reactive with early antigens occur at high frequency in immune populations has been reported previously for the herpesvirus cytomegalovirus.[28]

The results of our present communication demonstrate that target cells infected with HSV and treated with inhibitors so that they only synthesize immediate early gene products act as targets for HSV-specific CTL. These were shown to be class I–restricted and T cell in nature; on the basis of bulk-culture evidence, such CTL may represent a major component of CTL. The notion, however, needs substantiation by limited dilution analysis. Moreover, we do not know which of the early proteins act as targets, whether or not they occur at the cell surface, or if they can be incorporated into a suitable vector system to engender a CTL response *in vivo*. These topics are currently under investigation.

Our failure to demonstrate CTL following immunization with gB- and gD-containing vectors provided us with a valuable means of indirectly assessing the putative role of CTL in recovery from infection. This became possible because as far as could be determined, all other components of the immune response appeared to be induced following immunization. Consequently, cell populations from vector-immunized mice expressed all major aspects of immunity but not CTL activity. Because from other HSV systems[4,5] the suspicion has developed that CTL function becomes particularly necessary for recovery when the load of infection is high, we used a system in which the efficiency of viral clearance was measured after a local epithelial infection that mimics the HSV-1 natural situation. Using this approach, we showed that Vac-vector–immunized mice readily cleared minimal infections, but unlike HSV-immunized mice, could not clear a high-challenge dose of virus. Although we need to prove that the lack of CTL activity is responsible for partial immunity, our results add substantive support for an *in vivo* role for CTL in herpetic infections particularly when infection loads are high. We are currently attempting to support our observations more directly by adoptive cell-transfer approaches, as well as by measuring the efficiency of immunity following immunization with vectors that do induce CTL activity.

SUMMARY

We have used recombinant vaccinia viruses expressing the cloned genes coding for glycoprotein B (gB) or glycoprotein D (gD) of HSV-1 to analyze the role of HSV-1–specific cytotoxic T lymphocytes (CTL) in antiviral immunity. Various studies in mice revealed that either vector could stimulate some aspects of HSV-1–specific immunity, but surprisingly, HSV-specific CTL were not induced. Even though gD appeared to be a target antigen for class II-MHC–restricted CTL, neither the gB or the gD vector was capable of forming a target-cell complex that was recognized by class I-MHC–restricted HSV-specific CTL. The inability of these major extracellular glycoproteins to act as CTL–target antigens was even more unusual in light of the ability of CTL to apparently recognize the immediate early genes of HSV, none of which are considered to be expressed on the surface of infected cells.

The selective failure of either the gB or gD vector to induce numerous aspect of anti-HSV immunity in the absence of a CTL response allowed us to assess the consequence of this failure in terms of the level of protective immunity against HSV challenge seen in vector-immunized mice. These studies suggest that this failure to induce HSV-specific CTL appears to minimize the protective response to only efficiently protecting against low-challenge doses of HSV-1. These findings are discussed with relevance to the role of CTL in the control of herpesvirus infections.

ACKNOWLEDGMENTS

We would like to thank Dr. B. Moss (NIH, Bethesda, MD) for supplying the recombinant vaccinia gD and HA viruses, Dr. P. Berman and Dr. L. Lasky (Genentech, Inc., San Francisco, CA) for providing the gD L cell, Dr. B. Malissen (Division of Biology, California Technical College, Pasadena, CA) for contributing the IA$^+$ L cell, and Dr. M. Trousdale (Estelle-Doheny Eye Institute, Duarte, CA) for the kind gift of the monoclonal anti-gB and -gD antibodies.

REFERENCES

1. ZINKERNAGLE, R. M. & P. C. DOHERTY. 1979. Restriction of *in vitro* T cell mediated cytotoxicity in lymphocytic choriomenigitis within a syngeneic or semiallogenieic system. Nature (London) **248:** 701–702.
2. WILDEY, P. & P. G. H. GELL. 1985. The host response to herpes simplex virus. Br. Med. Bull. **41:** 86–91.
3. ROUSE, B. T., S. NORLEY & S. MARTIN. 1988. Antiviral cytotoxic T lymphocytes induction and vaccination. Rev. Infect. Dis. **10:** 16–33.
4. HOWES, E. L., W. TAYLOR, N. A. MITCHINSON & E. SIMPSON. 1979. MHC matching shows that at least two T-cell subsets determine resistance to HSV. Nature (London) **277:** 66–68.
5. COBBOLD, S. P., A. JAYASURIYA, A. A. NASH, T. D. PROSPERO & H. WALDMANN. 1984. Therapy with monoclonal antibodies by elimination of T cell subsets *in vivo.* Nature **312:** 548.
6. LAWMAN, M. J. P., B. T. ROUSE, R. J. COURTNEY & R. D. WALKER. 1980. Cell mediated immunity against herpes simplex virus: Induction of cytotoxic T lymphocytes. Infect. Immun. **27:** 133–139.
7. MORRISON, L. A., A. E. LAKACHER, V. L. BRACIALE, D. P. PAN & T. G. BRACIALE. 1986. Differences in antigen presentation to MHC class I- and class II-restricted influenza virus-specific cytolytic T lymphocyte clones. J. Exp. Med. **163:** 903–921.
8. BENNINCK, J. R., J. W. YEWDELL, G. L. SMITH, C. HOLLER & B. MOSS. 1984. Recombinant vaccinia virus primes and stimulates influenza haemagglutinin-specific cytotoxic T cells. Nature **311:** 578.

9. LAWMAN, M. J. P., R. J. COURTNEY, R. EBERLE, P. A. SCHAFFER, M. K. O'HARA & B. T. ROUSE. 1980. Cell-mediated immunity to herpes simplex virus: Specificity of cytotoxic T cells. Infect. Immun. **30:** 451–461.
10. CARTER, V. C., P. L. RICE & S. S. TEVETHIA. 1982. Intratypic and intertypic specificity of lymphocytes involved in the recognition of herpes simplex virus glycoproteins. Infect. Immun. **37:** 116–121.
11. GLORIOSO, J., V. KEES, G. HUME, H. KIRCHNER & P. KRAMMER. 1985. Identification of herpes simplex virus type I (HSV-I) glycoprotein C as the immunodominant antigen for HSV-I-specific cytotoxic T lymphocytes. J. Immunol. **135:** 575–582.
11a. ADA, G. L. & P. D. JONES. 1986. The immune response to influenza infection. Curr. Top. Micro. Immunol. **128:** 1.
12. BONE, D. R. & R. J. COURTNEY. 1974. A temperature sensitive mutant of herpes simplex virus type I defective in the synthesis of the major capsid polypeptide. J. Gen. Virol. **24:** 17.
13. CREMER, K. J., M. MACKETT, C. WOHLENBERG, A. L. NOTKINS & B. MOSS. 1985. Vaccinia virus recombinant expressing HSV-I type I glycoprotein D prevents latent herpes in mice. Science **228:** 737.
14. CANTIN, E. M., R. EBERLE, J. L. BALDICK, B. MOSS, D. WILEY, A. L. NOTKINS & H. OPENSHAW. 1987. Expression of herpes simplex virus I (HSV-1) glycoprotein B by a recombinant vaccinia virus and protection of mice against lethal HSV-1 infection. Proc. Natl. Acad. Sci. USA **84:** 5908–5912.
15. MARTIN, S., B. MOSS, P. W. BERMAN, L. LASKY & B. T. ROUSE. 1987. The mechanisms of antiviral immunity induced by a vaccinia virus recombinant expressing herpes simplex virus type I glycoprotein D: 1. Cytotoxic T cells. J. Virol. **61:** 726–733.
16. MARTIN, S. & B. T. ROUSE. 1987. The mechanisms of antiviral immunity induced by a vaccinia virus recombinant expressing herpes simplex virus type I glycoprotein D: Clearance of local infection. J. Immunol. **138:** 3431–3437.
17. PFIZENMAIER, K., A. STARZINSKI-POWITZ, M. ROLLINGHOF, D. FACKE & H. WAGNER. 1977. T-cell mediated cytotoxicity against herpes simplex virus-infected target cells. Nature (London) **265:** 630–632.
18. BURNS, W. H., C. BILLUPS & A. L. NOTKINS. 1975. Thymus dependence of viral antigens. Nature (London) **256:** 654–655.
19. BRUIE, J., F. W. SYMINGTON, T. J. MCKEARN & J. SPRENT. 1981. A monoclonal antibody discriminating between subsets of T and B cells. J. Immunol. **127:** 2496–2501.
20. ROSENTHAL, K. L., J. R. SMILEY, S. SOUTH & D. C. JOHNSON. 1984. Cells expressing herpes simplex virus glycoprotein gC but not gB, gD, or gE are recognized by murine virus-specific cytotoxic T lymphocytes. J. Virol. **61:** 2438–2447.
21. FINBERG, T., M. MESCHER & S. J. BURAKOFF. 1978. Induction of virus-specific cytotoxic T lymphocytes with solubilized viral and membrane proteins. J. Exp. Med. **148:** 1620–1627.
22. TOWNSEND, A. R. & J. J. SKEHEL. 1984. The influenza virus nucleoprotein gene controls the induction of both subtype specific and cross-reactive T cells. J. Exp. Med. **160:** 552–563.
23. BENNINK, J. R., J. W. YEWDELL & W. GERHARD. 1982. A viral polymerase involved in recognition of influenza virus-infected cells by a cytotoxic T cell clone. Nature (London) **296:** 75–76.
24. BANGHAM, C. R. M., P. J. M. OPENSHAW, L. A. BALL, A. M. Q. KING, G. W. WERTZ & B. A. ASKONAS. 1986. Human and murine cytotoxic T cells specific to respiratory syncitial virus recognize the viral nucleoprotein (N), but not the major glycoprotein (G) expressed by vaccinia virus recombinants. J. Immunol. **137:** 3973–3977.
25. REDDEHASE, M. J., G. M. KEILL & V. H. KOSZINOWSKI. 1984. The cytolytic T lymphocyte response to the murine cytomegalovirus. II. Detection of virus replication stage-specific antigens by separate populations of in vivo active cytolytic T lymphocyte precursors. Eur. J. Immunol. **14:** 56–61.

26. SPEAR, P. G. & B. ROIZMAN. 1980. *In* DNA Tumour Viruses. Molecular Biology of Tumour Viruses, part 2. T. Tooze, Ed.: 615. Cold Spring Harbor Monographs 10.
27. BENNINK, J. R., J. W. YEWDELL, G. L. SMITH & B. MOSS. 1987. Anti-influenza cytotoxic T lymphocytes recognize the three viral polymerases and a nonstructural protein. Responsiveness to individual viral antigens is MHC controlled. J. Virol. **61:** 1098–2005.
28. REDDEHASE, M. J. & V. H. KOSZINOWSKI. 1984. Significance of herpesvirus immediate early gene expression in cellular immunity to cytomegalovirus infection. Nature (London) **312:** 369–371.

Virus-Specific Cytotoxic T Cells in Multiple Sclerosis

HENRY F. McFARLAND, ANDREW GOODMAN, AND
STEVEN JACOBSON

Neuroimmunology Branch
Intramural Research Program
National Institute of Neurological and Communicative
Disorders and Stroke
National Institutes of Health
Bethesda, Maryland 20892

INTRODUCTION

Multiple sclerosis (MS) is a demyelinating disease of the central nervous system of unknown cause and pathogenesis. An immunological process possibly related to a viral infection has been suggested as a mechanism for the disease.[1] In support of an immunological process are the inflammatory responses associated with acute lesions and elevations of cerebrospinal fluid (CSF) immunoglobulin found in most patients with MS. Various abnormalities of T cells have been reported, including a reduction in the number of $CD8^+$ T cells and abnormalities in nonspecific assays of suppression. An environmental factor, such as a viral infection is supported by the geographic distribution of the disease, with higher prevalences being found in the more northern regions of North America and Europe. Epidemics have also been reported. Studies of the Faroe Islands indicate that the disease did not exist in this population until after World War II when British troops were stationed on the island. Increased CSF antibody to several viruses includes measles virus, mumps virus, and Epstein Barr virus (EBV); more recently, and controversially, a retrovirus has been reported. When studied, the antiviral antibody has represented only a small fraction of the total CSF immunoglobulin.

In addition to the immunological and environmental factors, genetic influences appear to be important with respect to susceptibility to disease. Certain histocompatibility leukocyte antigen (HLA) determinants, especially DR2 and DQwl, are over represented in North American and North European patients with MS. Studies of twins have shown that the concordance rate is significantly greater among monozygotic twins than among dizygotic twins.[2,3] This is true even in comparison to dizygotic twins who are HLA-identical, suggesting that the inheritable influence may be multigenic with one or more significant genes outside of the major histocompatibility complex (MHC).[4]

Although there have been many reports of immunological abnormalities in MS, these have generally failed to examine function or have measured antigen-nonspecific cell functions such as mitogen-induced suppressor cells. Consequently, the generation of virus-specific cytotoxic T lymphocytes (CTL) has been studied in patients with MS in order to examine components of the immune system that are both antigen-specific and functionally defined. Measles virus was selected for study because of the frequent finding of increased anti-measles virus–

antibody levels in serum and CSF of MS patients. For comparison, influenza virus was studied because of the good understanding of the immunological mechanisms involved in the generation of an influenza virus–specific CTL.

GENERATION OF MEASLES VIRUS–SPECIFIC CTL

In order to perform these studies, it was first necessary to establish the optimal conditions for generating and measuring measles virus–specific CTL. Techniques similar to those for influenza virus were first tested. When phytohemagglutinin (PHA) blasts infected with measles virus were used as targets, significant lysis could be demonstrated in only a small portion of individuals. By contrast, when EBV-transformed autologous B lymphoblasts infected with measles virus were used as targets, substantial lysis could be shown with peripheral blood leukocytes (PBL) from most individuals following a 7 day *in vitro* sensitization with measles virus. This lysis was found to be viral-specific and HLA-restricted. Subsequent studies demonstrated that the measles virus–specific lysis was largely mediated by CD4+ T cells and restricted by HLA-class II molecules.[5]

REDUCTION IN MEASLES VIRUS–SPECIFIC CTL IN MULTIPLE SCLEROSIS

Initially, the generation of measles virus and influenza virus–specific CTL were studied in 16 MS patients in comparison with healthy controls and patients with other neurological or inflammatory diseases.[5] This study showed that there was a significant reduction in the ability to generate measles virus–specific CTL from patients with MS. In distinction, the generation of anti-influenza virus–specific CTL or natural killer (NK) activity, as measured by lysis of K562 cells, was similar in the three groups.

Following this initial observation, several important questions concerning these findings became apparent. First, although these initial studies suggested an abnormality specific for measles virus, the possibility that this finding was due to a more general defect in the generation in CD4+, HLA class II–restricted CTL remained, because influenza virus–specific CTL are predominantly HLA class I–restricted. Next, in the initial studies, several of the MS patients were found to have no measurable measles virus–specific CTL activity. This raised the question as to whether this functionally defined population of cells was totally or relatively reduced. The possibility of either specific or nonspecific suppression as a mechanism for this finding also required examination. Finally, the relationship between the reduced CTL activity and characteristics of the patients, such as degree of disability and genetic makeup, needed to be examined.

In order to address these questions, the generation of measles virus–specific CTL has now been reexamined in a larger group of clinically well-defined MS patients with chronic progressive disease and healthy controls. The specificity of the reduced measles virus–specific CTL has been extended by examining the generation of mumps virus–specific CTL. Mumps virus belongs to the paramyxovirus family along with measles virus, and previous studies in this laboratory have shown that a portion of the mumps virus–specific CTL are CD4+, class II-HLA–restricted. The magnitude of the reduction in measles virus–specific CTL has been studied using precursor-frequency analysis. Finally, possible correlations between measles virus–specific CTL abnormalities and HLA makeup or degree of disability have been examined.

Twenty-seven patients with clinically definite MS in an active chronic progressive course have been studied (FIG. 1). Their mean lysis of measles virus–infected B lymphoblasts was 14.8 ± 12.3 at an E:T ratio of 40:1. By comparison, PBL from 22 healthy controls produced a mean lysis of 26.8 ± 10.4. The difference between these groups continues to be statistically significant ($p = .001$). The large standard deviation reflects the range of values in both groups. Within the MS sample there is a grouping of patients with very low lytic activity and a small number of patients with high normal activity. Over half of the MS patients produced values below the mean of the normals minus 1 SD, and 26% were below the mean minus 2 SD. Thus, whereas a reduction in the generation of measles virus–

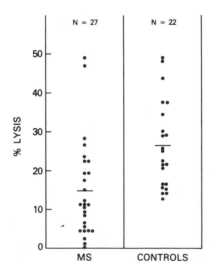

FIGURE 1. Percent of measles viral-specific lysis was calculated as described.[5] Effectors were stimulated with measles virus for seven days in 24-well plates at a cell concentration of 4×10^6 per well. Autologous EBV-transformed lymphoblastoid lines infected with measles virus were used as targets. Effector/target ratio was 40:1. Bars indicate means.

specific CTL is not found in all MS patients, it is observed in a significant portion of these patients.

This reduction has been examined further by performing precursor-frequency analysis of measles virus–specific CTL in healthy controls and MS patients (TABLE 1). PBL were cultured at concentrations from 2×10^5 to 1×10^4 with a constant number of irradiated feeder cells with or without measles virus. Based on these experiments, the precursor frequency of measles virus–specific CTL in healthy controls ranged from 22 to 2.9 and a mean of 10.7 ± 2.4 per 1×10^6 cells. The precursor frequency in 8 MS patients was 3.8 to 1.1, with a mean of $2.1 \pm .3$ per 1×10^6 cells. These results indicate that the reduction or absence of measles virus CTL seen in many MS patients when the CTL are generated in bulk cultures

TABLE 1. Precursor Frequency of Measles Virus–Specific CTL

Health Controls	Precursor Frequency/10^6 Cells[a]	MS Patients	Precursor Frequency/10^6 Cells
1	11.9	1	1.8
2	8.8	2	1.8
3	10.6	3	1.9
4	7.9	4	1.1
5	22.2	5	2.1
6	2.9	6	3.8
Mean ± SD	10.7 ± 2.4		2.1 ± 0.3

[a] Precursor frequency was calculated using the minimal X^2 method.[6] PBL were cultured at various concentrations in microtiter wells with 1×10^5 irradiated feeder cells with or without measles virus. Cell concentrations varied from 2×10^5 to 1×10^4 per well. Following seven days of culture, 1×10^4 ^{51}Cr-labeled–infected or–uninfected B lymphoblasts were added to each well. ^{51}Cr release was measured after four hours of incubation. Negative wells were less than the mean percent lysis, in addition to 3 SD obtained with the unstimulated cultures.

represents a relative reduction of approximately 5- to 10-fold in precursor frequency of the CTL. When plotted on a semilog scale, the fraction of negative cultures produced a straight line passing through the origin. There was no evidence of an unusually high number of positive wells at lower cell concentrations. It seems unlikely, therefore, that the low precursor frequency is due to a suppressor cell, although the possibility of a suppressor cell present in higher frequency than the effector population cannot be eliminated.

Next, the possibility that the observed reduction in measles virus–specific CTL could reflect a general reduction in the subset of CD4$^+$ T cells that mediate HLA class II–restricted cytolysis was examined. This was done by studying the generation of CTL specific for mumps virus (TABLE 2). Using B-cell lymphoblasts infected with mumps virus, it was first demonstrated that both HLA class I– and class II–restricted CTL could be generated. The ability to generate mumps virus–specific CTL using PBL from patients with MS was tested. It was found that the mean percent lysis did not differ from that obtained in a group of healthy controls.

TABLE 2. CD4+ Cell-Mediated HLA Class II–Restricted Virus-Specific Cytotoxicity

Donors[a]	Donor No.	Percent Specific Lysis[b]	
		Mumps[c]	Measles[c]
MS	1	67 ± 9	5 ± 3
	2	15 ± 2	5 ± 1
	3	21 ± 2	4 ± 2
	4	33 ± 1	0 ± 0
Normal	1	14 ± 1	21 ± 2
	2	42 ± 3	22 ± 3
	3	20 ± 2	15 ± 3
	4	42 ± 1	45 ± 5

[a] Effectors are purified populations of CD4+ mumps or measles virus–specific CTL.

[b] Values are percent specific lysis ± SD for 40 : 1 effector : target ratio.

[c] Targets are mumps or measles virus–infected B cells that are only HLA class II–matched with effectors.

In order to address the possibility of a generalized reduction in class II–restricted CTL, mumps virus–specific cytolysis was examined by measuring the ability of CD4$^+$ T cells stimulated *in vitro* with mumps virus to lyse a mumps virus–infected target cell matched for only class II–HLA determinants. PBL were stimulated *in vitro* for 7 days with mumps virus. CD4$^+$ cells were then isolated by negative selection panning. Each experiment was performed using one MS patient and one healthy control matched for at least one class II determinant. As shown in TABLE 2, CD4$^+$ T cells from both the MS patients and healthy controls lysed class II–matched B cells infected with mumps virus. By contrast, following *in vitro* stimulation with measles virus, only low levels of lysis of measles virus–infected B-cell targets were obtained with CD4$^+$ T cells from the MS patients, whereas those from the healthy donors produced normal levels of lysis. These experiments indicate that these MS patients with low measles virus–specific HLA class II–restricted cytolysis generated normal levels of CD4$^+$-mediated mumps-specific HLA class II–restricted CTL. These findings suggest that the reduction observed in the generation of measles virus–specific CTL are specific for measles virus.

As indicated previously, not all MS patients show this reduction in measles virus–specific CTL. One possibility is that this reduction is associated with the

TABLE 3. Correlation between Disability and Antimeasles Viral CTL

Disability (EDSS)	Number of Patients	Mean Percent Lysis
Mild (3–3.5)	6	11.5 ± 3.6
Moderate (4–5.5)	13	17.5 ± 15.9
Severe (5.5)	7	15.2 ± 8.2

severity of the disease as various immunological abnormalities have been associated with extensive disability regardless of its cause. In the initial study of measles virus–specific CTL in MS patients, a reduction was not observed in patients with other neurological or inflammatory disorders and with similar degrees of disability. The patients examined in the current study have been carefully rated for degree of disability using the most commonly employed rating scale, the extended disability status scale (EDSS), as described by Kurtzke.[7] This is a ten point scale. Grades up to 3.5 represent minimal disability. Grade 5.5 represents the need for varying degrees of ambulatory assistance. The correlation between the EDSS score and cytolytic activity is shown in TABLE 3. The generation of measles virus–specific CTL is not reduced in patients with more severe disability. In fact, patients with mild disease have the lowest mean cytolytic value, although the differences are not great enough to be significant. In order to determine if the level of measles virus–specific cytolytic activity varies with time or in relationship to disease activity, four patients have been studied at six month intervals for up to two years. These four patients have had remarkably stable levels of cytolytic activity. Only one of these patients had significant worsening during the study period, however, and this was not associated with measurable differences in cytolytic activity.

Another possible factor that could contribute to differences in the generation of measles virus–specific CTL is HLA makeup. There is a strong association between MS and certain HLA–class II determinants, particularly DR2 and DQwl. Inasmuch as class II molecules serve as the restriction elements for measles virus–specific CTL, the reduction in measles virus–specific cytolysis could be associated with HLA class II makeup. Sixty-three percent of the patients were DR2, and 90% of those typed were DQwl. No correlation was found, however, between cytolytic activity and DR2 or DQwl (TABLE 4.).

TABLE 4. Correlation between HLA Makeup and Measles Virus–Specific CTL

Sample Subset	Number of Patients	Mean Percent Lysis[a]
MS patients		
Total series	27	14.8 ± 12.3
DR2+	17 (63%)	14.7 ± 11.9
Non-DR2	10	16.6 ± 12.4
Normal controls		
Total series	22	26.3 ± 10.5
DR2+	6 (27%)	30.9 ± 11.7

[a] Mean percent lysis ± SD. Cytolysis for each patient at E : T ratio 4 : 1. CTL were stimulated with measles virus for seven days in bulk culture.

CONCLUSION

The findings presented above provide further evidence for a reduction in measles virus–specific CTL activity in patients with MS. The reduction is found in only a portion of patients, approximately half, and does not appear to be correlated with either the degree of disability or with HLA makeup. The reduction in measles virus–specific cytolytic activity is specific for measles virus at least in comparison to influenza virus and mumps virus. The reduction in CTL activity seen in bulk culture assays is due to a 5- to 10-fold reduction in the precursor frequency of the measles virus–specific CTL.

The explanation for this immunological abnormality in MS is unknown. It is possible that differences in the initial infection due to either the virus, the age at the time of infection, or possibly the genetic makeup of the individual, could result in a diminished cellular immune response to the virus. This would suggest that these same circumstances may be related to development of MS. Although this does not necessarily indicate that the reduction in measles virus–specific CTL is directly related to the cause of the disease, the possibilities that infection with measles virus could result in either autosensitization or a persistent infection require consideration. Autosensitization could occur through antigenic mimicry or enhanced immunogenicity of host antigens following infection of cells of the nervous system. It is extremely unlikely that MS is directly related to the effect of virus on the nervous system. A persistent infection resulting even in only partial transcription of the viral genome could provide a target for subsequent immune-mediated damage by measles virus–reactive T cells. A similar mechanism has been postulated in the experimental model of demyelination induced by Theiler's virus. Under these conditions, measles virus–specific CTL could be directly related to disease, and their reduction in the peripheral blood a result of sequestration. The stability of the levels of cytolytic activity over time would argue against this. An alternative hypothesis is that persistent infection could result in increased HLA–class II expression in cells such as astrocytes in the nervous system.[8] This, in turn, could allow presentation of self antigens resulting in autoimmune disease. In support of this is experimental evidence in the rat demonstrating that the presence of viral antigens in astrocytes can induce class II–HLA expression in these cells. Isolation and characterization of T cells from MS lesions will probably be needed to adequately evaluate these possibilities.

Although the mechanism(s) involved in the reduced measles virus–specific CTL is not known, it is believed that this antigen-specific abnormality of a functionally defined T-cell population may provide a means for dissecting the immunological events involved in at least a portion of the patients with MS.

ACKNOWLEDGMENT

The authors express their thanks to Miss Marjorie L. Flerlage for her excellent technical help and to Mrs. Diane Maisel for help in the preparation of this manuscript.

REFERENCES

1. McFARLIN, D. E. & H. F. McFARLAND. 1982. Multiple sclerosis. N. Engl. J. Med. **307:** 1183.
2. WILLIAMS, A., R. ELDRIDGE, H. McFARLAND, S. HOUFF, H. KREBS & D. McFARLIN. 1980. Multiple sclerosis in twins. Neurology **30:** 1139–1147.
3. EBERS, G. C., D. E. BULMAN, A. D. SADOVNICK, D. W. PATY, S. WARREN, W. HADER, T. J. MURRAY, T. P. SELAND, P. DUQUETTE, T. GREY, R. NELSON, M. NICOLLE & D. BRUNET. 1986. A population-based study of multiple sclerosis in twins. N. Engl. J. Med. **315:** 1638–1642.
4. McFARLAND, H. F., J. GREENSTEIN, D. E. McFARLIN, R. ELDRIDGE, X.-H. XU & H. KREBS. 1985. Family and twin studies in multiple sclerosis. Ann. N.Y. Acad. Sci. **436:** 118–124.
5. JACOBSON, S., M. L. FLERLAGE & H. F. McFARLAND. 1985. Impaired measles virus-specific cytotoxic T cell responses in multiple sclerosis. J. Exp. Med. **162:** 839–850.
6. TASWELL, C. 1981. Limiting dilution for the determination of immunocompetent cell frequencies. J. Immunol. **126:** 1614–1619.
7. KURTZKE, J. F. 1983. Rating neurological impairment in multiple sclerosis: An expanded disability status scale (EDSS). Neurology **33:** 1444–1452.
8. MASSA, P. T., R. DORRIES & V. TER MEULEN. 1986. Viral particles induce Ia antigen expression on astrocytes. Nature **320**(6062): 543–546.

Dendritic Cells and Antigen Presentation in the Regulation of Cytotoxic T Lymphocyte Responses against Viruses and Transplantation Antigens

CORNELIS J. M. MELIEF, CLAIRE J. P. BOOG,
WIES L. E. VASMEL, JOLANDE BOES,
ARIE C. VOORDOUW, AND W. MARTIN KAST

Division of Immunology
The Netherlands Cancer Institute
Antoni van Leeuwenhoek Huis
1066 CX Amsterdam, the Netherlands

INTRODUCTION

Failure of T lymphocytes to respond to stimulation by foreign antigen is classically explained by a number of mechanisms that are not necessarily mutually exclusive, namely defective antigen presentation, T cell–repertoire defects, and suppressor (T) cells.[1] In this report, we shall briefly review the evidence, largely derived from studies with major histocompatibility complex (MHC) mutants, that allelic MHC differences (MHC polymorphism) crucially orchestrate T-cell responses in the sense that CD4+ T-helper cell (T_h) responses are regulated by class II–MHC molecules and CD8+ cytotoxic T lymphocyte (T_c) responses by class I–MHC molecules.[1-4] We shall largely limit ourselves to a discussion of only those T_h responses that are required for optimal T_c responses. Next, we shall summarize our recent data indicating the biological consequences of T_h or T_c response regulation for disease induction by murine leukemia virus and Sendai virus, respectively. In the case of Sendai virus, genetic control of natural killer activity also determines disease outcome, and T_h and T_c cooperate in protection against lethal Sendai virus infection. We found that dendritic cells (DC), already proven to be highly effective in the presentation of various antigens,[5] are also superior in the presentation of viral antigens to T lymphocytes. As a result, stimulation with dendritic cells decreases or obviates the CD4+ T_h cell requirement in CD8+ T_c responses.

Finally we observed that approximately half of the specific T_h or T_c response defects investigated thus far can be restored by immunization and/or restimulation with DC. Thus, defective antigen presentation appears to be responsible for these instances of MHC-determined T cell–response failure. The contribution of T cell–repertoire defects remains uncertain, and for suppressor T cells no evidence was obtained in the T-cell responses studied. The superior antigen-presenting capacities of DC is at least partly due to their expression of a large quantity of both class I– and class II–MHC molecules and to fewer sialic acid moieties attached to their MHC molecules. Below we shall deal with each of these points in some detail and summarize the implications in the epilogue at the end.

CYTOTOXIC T LYMPHOCYTE–RESPONSE DEFECTS IN CLASS I– AND CLASS II–MHC MUTANTS

The series of murine MHC (H-2) mutants, detected by graft rejection, has proven a gold mine for structure/function relationship studies of MHC molecules. By virtue of their mode of detection, the MHC molecules of mutant mice were likely to show changes in sites crucial for T-cell recognition.[4,6] This indeed turned out to be the case, not only in allospecific T-cell responses, but also in MHC-restricted T-cell responses to foreign antigens.[4,6] Although many class I–MHC mutants were found, only one class II mutant was detected (the B6C-H-^{bm12} mouse). Extensive studies on the nature of the structural alterations in the mutant MHC molecules has shown that all structural alterations occur in the two NH_2-terminal domains of these molecules and consist of 1–4 amino acid substitutions derived from other class I or class II genes in the same haplotype by a genetic recombination event.[7,8] A great stride forward in understanding the impact of these structural changes on T-cell function was made by the elucidation of the

TABLE 1. Structural Alterations in K^b and I-A^b Mutant H-2 Molecules and Their Consequences for T_c Responses to Foreign Antigens

Mouse Strain	Abbrev-iation	Affected H-2 Molecule (Class)	Structural Alteration[a] (Position)	Defect in T_c Response to Antigen
C57BL/6	B6	—	—	—
B6.C-H-2^{bm1}	bm1	K^b (I)	Glu → Ala (152) Arg → Tyr (155) Leu → Tyr (156)	Sendai virus (refs. 11, 12)
B6.C-H-2^{bm12}	bm12	I-A^b_β (II)	Ile → Phe (67) Arg → Gln (70) Thr → Lys (71)	male antigen H-Y (refs. 13, 14)
B6.C-H-2^{bm13}	bm13	D^b (I)	Leu → Gln (114) Phe → Tyr (116) Glu → Asp (119)	male antigen H-Y (ref. 15)
B6.C-H-2^{bm14}	bm14	D^b (I)	Gln → His (70)	male antigen H-Y (ref. 15) Moloney leukemia virus (ref. 16)

[a] According to Nathenson *et al.*,[7] for the bm1; Hemmi & Nathenson (unpublished observations) for the bm13 and bm14 mutants; and McIntyre & Seidman[8] for the bm12 mutant.

crystal structure of an MHC–class I molecule, HLA-A2.[9,10] MHC molecules on the basis of this study consist of a platform of antiparallel β-strands on top of which two α-helices of the two most external domains form a large groove. The groove is considered to provide a binding site for processed foreign antigens (antigenic peptides). Strikingly, the structural changes in the class I–H-2 mutants have all occurred at positions in the molecule that point into the groove and thus are expected to alter binding of antigenic peptide, and that point up or away from the groove and therefore could affect interaction with the T-cell receptor.[10]

TABLE 1 provides a list of H-2 mutants in which we have detected defects in the T_c response to foreign antigens. The T_c response to Sendai virus is restricted by the H-2K^b molecule in the B6 mouse, the strain of origin of the mutants. This T_c response is defective in the bm1 K^b mutant. The T_c response to the H-Y antigen and to Moloney virus is restricted by the H-2D^b molecule in B6 mice. The T$_c$ response to H-Y is defective in both the bm13 and bm14 D^b mutants. The anti-Moloney virus T$_c$ response is only defective in the bm14 strain. The T$_c$ response against the H-Y antigen is completely dependent on proper class II–restricted T$_h$ activation. In the bm12 class II–MHC mutant, this specific T$_h$ response is defective. As a result, the anti-H-Y T$_c$ response is also defective in this mutant (TABLE 1).

H-2 CLASS II-REGULATED IMMUNITY AGAINST MURINE LEUKEMIA VIRUS PROTECTS AGAINST EARLY T-CELL LYMPHOMAS, BUT NOT LATE B-CELL LYMPHOMAS

In earlier work, we had established that the H-2 I-A class II locus regulates the antibody response to murine leukemia virus (MuLV).[17,18] We had also found, in agreement with observations of many others (reviewed in reference 18), that the MHC controls susceptibility to lymphomagenesis following inoculation of MuLV.[19] The H-2 influence on tumor induction, however, was not mapped in that study. We have now ascertained that the major H-2 influence on both tumorigenesis and antiviral antibody production, following neonatal inoculation of mice with a cloned isolate of mink-cell focus (MCF) inducing MuLV, maps to the H-2 I-A region.[35]

Mice carrying the I-A^b allele are resistant to early T-cell tumors; mice of non-I-A^b types (I-A^d, I-A^k) are susceptible. Resistant mice, in contrast to susceptible mice, are able to clear infectious virus from their thymus between 4 and 10 weeks of age. Surprisingly, a similar number of late B-cell lymphomas (> 45 weeks of age) arose in T-lymphoma resistant and susceptible strains. Interestingly, the few T-cell lymphomas that arose in resistant strains, in contrast to the many T-cell tumors in susceptible strains, showed lack of cell-surface expression of viral gag and/or env antigens detected by cytofluorometry with polyspecific and monoclonal antibodies (W. L. E. Vasmel, A. Sijts & C. J. M. Melief, unpublished observations). Thus in order for lymphomas in resistant strains to escape from immunosurveillance, it seems necessary to turn off viral-antigen expression.

RELATIVE IMPORTANCE OF T$_h$, T$_c$, AND NATURAL KILLER (NK) CELLS IN PROTECTION AGAINST LETHAL SENDAI VIRUS INFECTION. BIOLOGICAL RELEVANCE OF H-2 CLASS I–DETERMINED T$_c$ RESPONSE DEFECT

We determined the *in vivo* susceptibility to virulent Sendai virus infection in four strains of mice; each has a unique combination of immune faculties to cope with virulent Sendai virus. Three of the strains have identical background genes (C57BL). B6 and K^b mutant bm1 mice only differ for three amino acids in the K^b molecule. B6 and B6 nu/nu mice only differ with respect to the nu/nu trait, which causes profound T-cell deficiency. The fourth strain, 129/J, like B6 and B6 nu/nu mice, carries the H-2^b haplotype, but has a different non-H-2 genome. One peculiarity of 129/J mice is their selective deficiency of NK cell activity. The immune responses of these mouse strains have been described in detail elsewhere.[20,21] The results of immune responses against Sendai virus and the susceptibility to lethal pneumonia induction in the four strains are summarized in TABLE 2.

TABLE 2. Summary of Immune Responses against Sendai Virus

	Mouse Strain			
	B6	bm1	B6 nu/nu	129/J
Specific immune responses				
In Vitro				
T$_c$	+	−	−	+
T$_h$	+	+	−	+
In Vivo				
T$_h$ ⎰delayed hypersensitivity	+	+	−	+
⎱antibody production	+	+	−	+
Nonspecific immune response				
NK	+	+	+ +	−
Susceptibility of unprimed mice to lethal pneumonia induction by Sendai virus	150^a	15	0.5	0.2

^{a} LD$_{50}$, lethal dose for 50% of animals, expressed as TCID$_{50}$, tissue culture infectious dose for 50% of cultures.

It is clear from this TABLE that all forms of immunity contribute to antiviral immunity. 129/J mice in these experiments have been immunized with a nonvirulent strain of Sendai virus. If inoculated with virulent Sendai virus, they die before specific T-cell immunity has developed, presumably due to breakdown at the first line of defense against Sendai virus, NK cells. The importance of T$_h$ follows from the difference in susceptibility between bm1 mice and B6 nu/nu mice, which both lack virus-specific T$_c$ but differ with respect to T$_h$ immunity (delayed hypersensitivity, helper activity for specific antibody formation). The importance of T$_c$ can be deduced from the difference in susceptibility between B6 and bm1 mice, that only differ for the specific T$_c$ response and are identical for all other immune parameters.

The importance of virus-specific T$_h$ and T$_c$ was further proven by protection experiments in nude mice with T$_h$ and T$_c$ clones. Indefinite survival of B6 nu/nu mice given a 10-fold lethal dose of Sendai virus was only achieved by simultaneous intravenous (i.v.) injection of an interleukin-2 (IL-2)–producing T$_h$ clone and a non-IL-2–producing T$_c$ clone and not by injection of either clone alone.[20] The *in vivo* effect of the T$_h$ clone was mainly IL-2 production for the T$_c$ clone, because treatment with T$_c$ clone and recombinant IL-2 (rIL-2) was as effective as treatment with the clone mixture.[20] rIL-2 by itself had no protective effect.

RESTORATION OF CLASS II- AND CLASS I-MHC–DETERMINED SPECIFIC T CELL–RESPONSE DEFECTS BY IMMUNIZATION AND/OR RESTIMULATION WITH DENDRITIC CELLS

DC are highly effective in stimulating allogeneic or syngeneic mixed lymphocyte reactions, T-cell reactions against soluble antigens, lymphokine production by T cells and oxidative mitogenesis in T cells. In addition, DC support antibody response to sheep red blood cells, induce a T-cell dependent antibody response against tobacco mosaic virus, and function as efficient antigen-presenting cells (APC) for the generation of T$_c$ against TNP cells (reviewed in references 5 and 22). DC lack T-, B-cell, and macrophage markers, do not bear Fc receptors and do not phagocytose particles.[5] Recently we showed that DC are also superior in the presentation of viral antigens to T cells in comparison with various other types of APC, including normal spleen cells, lipopolysaccharide-induced B-cell blasts (LPS blasts), and concanavalin A–induced T-cell blasts (Con A blasts).[22] On a per cell basis, DC were approximately 100 times more efficient, LPS blasts were 4 times more efficient, and Con A blasts were 0.4 times as efficient as normal spleen cells in the presentation of Sendai virus to responding T_c from primed animals.[22]

In view of the superior APC function of DC in a variety of T-cell responses, we investigated whether these cells could be used to overcome specific immune response defects based on MHC allelic differences such as those seen in the MHC mutants discussed above (TABLE 1). The first specific immune response defect that we tried to restore in this manner was the failure of the bm12 class II mutant to generate a T_c response against the male antigen H-Y, associated with failure to reject male skin grafts. It turned out that it is indeed possible to abolish this specific immune response defect by immunization with DC. Following priming *in vivo* and restimulation *in vitro* with male bm12 DC, female bm12 mice generated strong H-Y–specific T_c. Female bm12 mice primed with male DC also reject male skin grafts.[23] In this class II–response reversal, we found evidence for an essential role of T_h, activated by DC in changing H-Y nonresponder bm12 mice into H-Y responders.[23]

Next we explored whether priming and/or *in vitro* restimulation with antigen-bearing DC was also capable of restoring the other T_c response defects listed in TABLE 1. The results of our combined efforts to restore specific T_c response defects of MHC mutants are shown in TABLE 3. Specific T_c response defects could be restored by immunization and/or restimulation with DC in three out of five instances tested. Priming *in vivo* with antigen-bearing DC was only required to overcome the response defect in the bm12 class II mutant. In the class I–mutant T_c response defects, restoration was also achieved by priming *in vivo* with Moloney virus or with H-Y–bearing spleen cells. Antigen-bearing DC were only required during restimulation *in vitro*.[22–24] Strikingly, however, in the bm14 anti-H-Y T_c response restoration (by restimulation of primed female responder cells with male DC), a marked difference in T_c repertoire was noted between mice primed with male spleen cells (SC) or with DC.[24] The data are briefly summarized in TABLE 4.

TABLE 3. Failure or Success in the Restoration of Specific Cytotoxic T Lymphocyte Response Defects by Immunization and/or Restimulation with Dendritic Cells

H-2 Mutant Mouse Strain	Site of Mutation	T_c Response Defect[a]	Restoration of Defect by Immunization and/or Restimulation with Dendritic Cells	Reference
bm12	I-Aβ	male antigen H-Y	yes	23
bm13	D^b	male antigen H-Y	no	24
bm14	D^b	male antigen H-Y	yes	24
bm14	D^b	Moloney leukemia virus	yes	22
bm1	K^b	Sendai virus	no	22

[a] In mice bearing the H-2^b haplotype, the T_c response against Sendai virus is exclusively K^b-restricted, the T_c response against the H-Y antigen is exclusively D^b-restricted, and the T_c response against Moloney virus is largely D^b-restricted.

TABLE 4. Difference in Target-Cell Specificity of the H-Y–Specific T_c Response of bm14 D^b-Mutant Mice Dependent on the Type of APC Used for *in Vivo* Immunization

		Destruction of Target Cell			
Priming	Restimulation *in vitro*	bm14♂ K^b D^{bm14}	bm14♀ K^b D^{bm14}	B6♂ K^b D^b	B6♀ K^b D^b
♂SC[a]	♂DC[b]	+	−	−	−
♂DC	♂DC	+	−	+	−

[a] SC = spleen cell.
[b] DC = dendritic cell.

It is obvious from TABLE 4 that priming of female bm14 mice with male DC allows the arousal following restimulation with DC of a repertoire not seen after priming with male spleen cells. This suggests the expression of "wild-type D^b-like" epitopes on the D^{bm14} molecule of DC not accessible to T cells on the D^{bm14} molecule of spleen cells. Such wild-type D^b-like epitopes were also detected by D^b-specific monoclonal antibodies on the surface of bm14 DC but were hardly demonstrable on the surface of bm14 spleen cells.[24] Thus, "native D^b" epitopes recognizable by either T_c or monoclonal antibodies appear to be unmasked on bm14 DC. This suggests the possibility of qualitatively altered class I–MHC expression on DC in comparison with spleen cells and other types of APC.[27] Biochemical studies showed that DC indeed not only express quantitatively more class I MHC, but also qualitatively altered class I MHC (see below).

QUANTITY AND QUALITY OF MHC EXPRESSION ON DENDRITIC CELLS IN RELATION TO APC FUNCTION

Binding studies with radiolabeled MHC specific–monoclonal antibodies had already shown that DC on a per cell basis bind more MHC class I– and class II–specific monoclonal antibodies than other types of APC.[27] We recently showed this is due to a larger quantity of MHC class I and II on dendritic cells than on other types of APC and to a better accessibility of MHC class I and II to MHC specific–monoclonal antibodies due to a lower extent of MHC sialylation in DC (C. J. P. Boog, J. J. Neefjes, J. Boes, H. L. Ploegh & C. J. M. Melief, submitted for publication). The larger quantity of MHC class I on DC was proven by quantitative immunoprecipitation of cell surface–iodinated class I–MHC antigens with a polyclonal highly specific rabbit anti-mouse class I–MHC serum. This method of quantitation proved independent of the number of sialic acid molecules attached to class I molecules, in contrast to fluorescence-activated cell sorter (FACS) analysis with monoclonal antibodies. Using two-dimensional gel electrophoresis and isoelectric focusing, the average number of sialic acids attached per MHC–class I molecule was found to be two to three for DC, four for LPS blasts, and more than four for spleen cells. Treatment of normal spleen cells with neuraminidase (NANAse), which removes sialic acids from cell-surface molecules, for only 30 minutes led to markedly enhanced binding of MHC class I– and II–specific monoclonal antibodies. Similar treatment of DC did not increase the (already very strong) binding of such antibodies in FACS analysis. Moreover, treatment of bm14 male spleen cells with NANAse restored their capacity to stimulate an H-Y–specific T_c response in responding T cells from primed bm14 female mice.

Likewise, both bm6 (K^b mutant, Tyr 116 → Phe; Cys 121 → Arg, reference 7), DC, and NANAse-treated bm6 spleen cells were capable of restoring the defective allospecific T_c response of purified CD8$^+$ (CD4 depleted) B6 T cells against bm6, as reported by Rosenberg et al.[25] and confirmed by us. These findings indicate that the superior APC function of DC is due to both qualitative and quantitative aspects of MHC expression on these cells. They have the largest quantity of MHC of all types of APC tested, and, due to a low extent of sialylation, their MHC molecules are better accessible to the T-cell receptor.

The recent elucidation of the three-dimensional structure of a human class I molecule[9,10] provides a rational explanation for the importance of MHC sialylation in antigen presentation. The N-linked glycosylation sites present in K^b and D^b heavy chains include attachment sites at amino acid positions 86 and 176. These residues occur at the extremities of the two α-helices that make an essential contribution to the formation of the putative binding site for (processed) antigen. The close proximity of these two glycans to the site that binds antigen suggests the possible interference of sialic acids with binding of processed antigen to MHC molecules, and/or with the recognition by the T-cell receptor of the complex between the MHC molecule and processed antigen. Our findings of increased binding of class I—specific monoclonal antibody, in the face of constant amounts of total class I antigen as determined biochemically, show that removal of sialic acid can indeed improve accessibility of the class I molecule to "receptors" (immunoglobulin or T-cell receptors) that recognize them. Increased binding of MHC class I-specific monoclonal antibodies to mouse lymphoblasts following influenza virus infection was attributed to viral NANAse and likewise proven to be due to an increase in affinity rather than to an increase in the number of binding sites.[26] The mutations in the bm6 and bm14 mutants occur at positions 70, 116, and 121, respectively. The mutations at positions 70 and 116 involve residues that point into the antigen-binding site. They could lower the affinity of binding for processed antigen in such a way that this reduced affinity could be compensated for by removal of net negative charges carried by sialic acids in the vicinity of the antigen-binding site. This would explain why DC, carrying less negatively charged and a larger quantity of MHC molecules are superior APC. NANAse treatment of nonresponder spleen cells would result in class I molecules more like those on DC and thus restore the ability to present antigen.

That the lower degree of sialylation of MHC products is directly related to the excellent APC function of DC follows from the following considerations. (1) MHC class I and class II antigens are the only known abundant cell-surface molecules on DC, next to T200,[27] and the only known ones to be directly involved in antigen presentation. (2) We have obtained results equivalent to these reported for NANAse but using an inhibitor of N-linked oligosaccharide processing (Swainsonine, manuscript in preparation). This inhibitor only affects N-linked carbohydrates (as found on MHC molecules) that probably contribute to total cell-surface charge in a minor way. A majority is contributed by sialic acids on glycolipids and O-linked sugars. (3) As discussed in the previous section, native D^b-like epitopes are serologically demonstrable on bm14 DC by monoclonal antibody binding at the same very high binding level as on B6 DC. On bm14 spleen cells, in contrast to B6 spleen cells, these epitopes are hardly detectable.[24] Thus on the D^{bm14} molecule of DC, D^b-like determinants are accessible to D^b-specific monoclonal antibodies and D^b-restricted T_c that are not accessible on bm14 spleen cells.[24]

Restoration of MHC-linked specific T cell–response defects by DC is not always achieved (TABLE 3). Defects not restored by DC could be based on complete failure of the available class I (or class II) molecules to associate with processed antigenic peptides or on a true T_c repertoire defect due to, for example, self tolerance requirements.

STIMULATION WITH DENDRITIC CELLS DECREASES OR OBVIATES THE CD4$^+$ HELPER-CELL REQUIREMENT IN CYTOTOXIC T LYMPHOCYTE RESPONSES

We investigated the need for CD4$^+$ T_h cells in the induction of murine T_c responses across minor or major histocompatibility antigenic differences with either normal spleen cells or purified DC as APC. Generation of a secondary *in vitro* class II MHC–specific T_c response was absolutely CD4$^+$ T_h cell–dependent with both types of APC. Likewise, male antigen (H-Y)-primed class II–mutant bm12 T cells, which do not respond to H-Y presented on normal spleen cells, do respond to H-Y presented on DC in an absolutely CD4$^+$ T_h cell–dependent fashion.[28] All other T_c responses, including primary anti-class I MHC, primary anti-class I and II MHC plus anti-minor H, and secondary C57BL/6 (B6) anti-H-Y, although not completely CD4$^+$ T_h-dependent, were greatly augmented in the presence of CD4$^+$ T_h-dependent cells, but only with normal spleen cells as APC. By contrast, with DC as APC, these responses were entirely or largely CD4$^+$ T_h-independent,[28] confirming a recent report.[29] Similarly H-Y—primed class I–MHC mutant bm14 T cells, which do not respond to H-Y presented on normal spleen cells, do respond to H-Y presented on DC in a completely CD4$^+$ T_h cell—independent fashion. The combined results indicate that DC can directly present class I–MHC alloantigen or class I–MHC plus nominal antigen (*e.g.* minor H) to CD8$^+$ cells and generate a T_c response by these cells without the requirement for CD4$^+$ T_h cells. The direct activation of H-Y–specific CD8$^+$ T cells without requirement for CD4$^+$ T_h cells seems at odds with the classical concept[2–4] that for the generation of this T_c response the involvement of class II–restricted T_h is required. We previously showed, however, that with responding cells from primed animals and spleen cells as APC, the requirement for CD4$^+$ T_h could be bypassed with IL-2.[14] In addition, as discussed in the previous section, DC have quantitatively and qualitatively superior class I–MHC expression. Because of this, but perhaps also due to other properties, such as their unique ability to induce cluster formation with T cells,[30] DC are probably more efficient in triggering CD8$^+$ cells to secrete IL-2, thereby bypassing the requirement for CD4$^+$ cells. Recent studies by Heeg *et al.*[31] indicate that the vast majority of class I–MHC–reactive CD8$^+$ T cells clonally segregate into two functionally distinct subsets: IL-2 producing or cytolytic cells. Only a minor subpopulation ($< 10\%$) of class I–reactive CD8$^+$ cells was bifunctional in these studies. The authors concluded that the induction of a primary CTL response in class I–MHC—alloreactive CD8$^+$ T cells reflects T–T interaction between the two major functionally distinct subsets: IL-2–producing noncytolytic cells and non-IL-2–producing cytolytic cells. T–T cooperation between IL-2–producing and non-IL-2–producing cells within the CD8$^+$ population is also apparent from the studies of Golding *et al.*[32] and Rosenberg *et al.*[25] On the basis of these findings, we hypothesize that DC either more efficiently activate the IL-2–secreting noncytolytic subset of CD8$^+$ T cells or induce IL-2 secretion in CD8$^+$ T cells that do not secrete IL-2 upon conventional stimulation, namely in the cells with actual lytic ability. Cluster formation of DC with collaborating cells within the CD8$^+$ population may further promote efficient T–T interaction. We hypothesize that presentation of class I alloantigen or self-class I plus nominal antigen by DC lowers the threshold for IL-2 production by $CD8^+$ cells, either of a potentially cytolytic or noncytolytic $CD8^+$ cell.

The importance of the $CD8^+$ T_h-independent subset in overall *in vivo* T_c immunity was very recently illustrated by the finding that mice, when functionally depleted of $CD4^+$ cells, respond to ectromelia virus infection by developing a strong *in vivo* virus-specific T_c response.[33] These results confirm the existence of two alternative pathways,[33,34] for T_c induction. The first pathway requires the participation of $CD4^+$ T_h cells, for example, in the generation of class II–specific T_c, or in the generation of maximal T_c responses to various other antigenic differences under suboptimal stimulation conditions. The second pathway requires only $CD8^+$ cells (*e.g.* the K^{bm1}-specific T_c response stimulated by DC).[28] DC not only restore specific immune response defects but also decrease the requirement for $CD4^+$ T_h cells in the induction of class I–specific or –restricted T_c responses.

SUMMARY AND EPILOGUE

The cellular interactions required to generate specific $CD8^+$ T_c reactions against foreign antigens are schematically depicted in FIGURE 1. Under conditions of conventional antigen presentation, most $CD8^+$ T_c responses, including those across minor or major histocompatibility differences, are greatly augmented by $CD4^+$ T_h cells. These T_h cells largely operate by secreting IL-2 upon recognition of antigen in the context of class II–MHC molecules (or allospecific class II molecules). Certain MHC types do not permit effective antigen-presenting cell–T-cell interactions, resulting in specific T cell–response defects. In the case of T-cell responses against viruses, such response defects are associated with a marked increase in disease susceptibility, as illustrated by class II-MHC–controlled susceptibility to T-lymphoma induction by murine leukemia virus and class I–MHC—controlled susceptibility to lethal pneumonia induction by Sendai virus.

Certain class I– or class II–determined T_c response defects (three out of five tested by us) can be restored by immunization and/or restimulation *in vitro* with DC. DC are the most effective APC. Their superior APC capacity is due to a very high absolute number of class I– and class II–MHC molecules and to a low degree of MHC sialylation, reducing negative charge and facilitating access of the T-cell receptor to the MHC groove presenting the antigenic peptide. The more effective antigen presentation by DC allows a more prominent role for a $CD4^+$ T_h cell—independent pathway of $CD8^+$ T_c activation (FIG. 1). It is postulated that the more effective direct triggering of $CD8^+$ T_c precursors lowers the threshold for IL-2 production by $CD8^+$ cells, reducing the requirement for IL-2 production by the $CD4^+$ cells. Immunization with DC can be used to arouse dormant T-cell repertoires against weak immunogens, such as tumor antigens. On the other hand, DC are very strong stimulators of the autologous mixed lymphocyte reaction and can be considered, if unchecked, to incite autoimmune disease. This is perhaps the reason why DC are only present in very low numbers in lymphoid tissue and why not all nucleated cells in the body possess the superior MHC expression of DC. The driving force in the direction of autoimmunity might become too strong if too many cells with superior APC capacity were around. Clearly MHC class I on other cells is required to serve as an attachment site for destruction of foreign antigen-infested cells by class I–restricted T_c. The MHC expression requirements for target-cell destruction, however, are much less stringent than for induction of T-cell responses. Failure of DC to overcome certain MHC-linked–specific T_c-

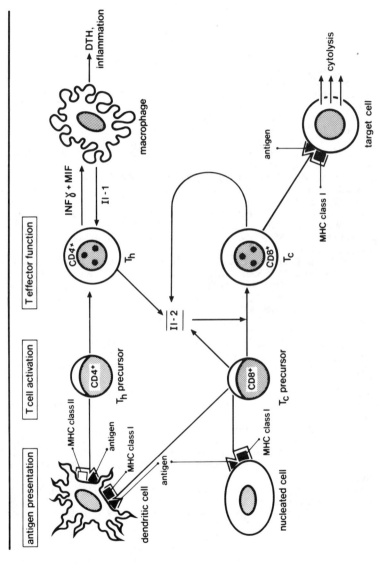

FIGURE 1. Cell–cell interactions in the induction of murine T_c responses.

response defects probably reflects complete failure of any foreign peptide derived from the processed antigen to interact efficiently with the MHC or a true T_c-repertoire defect.

REFERENCES

1. PAUL, W. E. 1984. *In* Fundamental Immunology. W. E. Paul, Ed.: 439–477. Raven Press. New York.
2. SIMPSON, E. & R. D. GORDON. 1977. Immunol. Rev. **35:** 59–75.
3. VON BOEHMER, H., C. G. FATHMAN & W. HAAS. 1977. Eur. J. Immunol. **7:** 443–447.
4. MELIEF, C. J. M., M. J. STUKART, L. P. DE WAAL, W. M. KAST & R. W. MELVOLD. 1983. Transplant. Proc. **15:** 2086–2089.
5. STEINMAN, R. M. & M. C. NUSSENZWEIG. 1980. Immunol. Rev. **53:** 127–147.
6. MELIEF, C. J. M. 1983. Immunology Today **4:** 57–61.
7. NATHENSON, S. G., J. GELIEBTER, G. M. PFAFFENBACH & R. A. ZEFF. 1986. Annu. Rev. Immunol. **4:** 471–502.
8. MCINTYRE, K. R. & J. G. SEIDMAN. 1984. Nature **308:** 551–553.
9. BJORKMAN, P. J., M. A. SAPER, B. SAMRAOUI, W. S. BENNETT, J. L. STROMINGER & D. C. WILEY. 1987. Nature **329:** 506–512.
10. BJORKMAN, P. J., M. A. SAPER, B. SAMRAOUI, W. S. BENNETT, J. L. STROMINGER & D. C. WILEY. 1987. Nature **329:** 512–518.
11. DE WAAL, L. P., W. M. KAST, R. W. MELVOLD & C. M. J. MELIEF. 1983. J. Immunol. **130:** 1090–1096.
12. KAST, W. M., L. P. DE WAAL & C. J. M. MELIEF. 1984. J. Exp. Med. **160:** 1752–1766.
13. MICHAELIDES, M., M. SANDRIN, G. MORGAN, I. F. C. MCKENZIE, R. ASHMAN & R. W. MELVOLD. 1981. J. Exp. Med. **153:** 464–469.
14. DE WAAL, L. P., J. DE HOOP, M. J. STUKART, H. GLEICHMANN, R. W. MELVOLD & C. J. M. MELIEF. 1983. J. Immunol. **130:** 665–670.
15. DE WAAL, L. P., R. W. MELVOLD & C. J. M. MELIEF. 1983. J. Exp. Med. **158:** 1537–1545.
16. STUKART, M. J., A. VOS, J. BOES, R. W. MELVOLD, D. W. BAILEY & C. J. M. MELIEF. 1982. J. Immunol. **128:** 1360–1364.
17. VLUG, A., H. J. SCHOENMAKERS & C. J. M. MELIEF. 1981. J. Immunol. **126:** 2355–2360.
18. ZIJLSTRA, M. & C. J. M. MELIEF. 1986. Biochim. Biophys. Acta **865:** 197–231.
19. MELIEF, C. J. M., A. VLUG, R. DE GOEDE, C. DE BRUYNE, W. BARENDSEN & P. DE GREEVE. 1980. J. Natl. Cancer Inst. **64:** 1179–1189.
20. KAST, W. M., A. M. BRONKHORST, L. P. DE WAAL & C. J. M. MELIEF. 1986. J. Exp. Med. **164:** 723–738.
21. KAST, W. M., A. C. VOORDOUW & C. J. M. MELIEF. 1988. *In* Major histocompatibility genes and their role in immune function. C. S. David, Ed. Plenum Publishing Corp. In press.
22. KAST, W. M., C. J. P. BOOG, B. O. ROEP, A. C. VOORDOUW & C. J. M. MELIEF. 1988. J. Immunol. In press.
23. BOOG, C. J. P., W. M. KAST, H. TH. M. TIMMERS, J. BOES, L. P. DE WAAL & C. J. M. MELIEF. 1985. Nature **318:** 59–62.
24. BOOG, C. J. P., J. BOES & C. J. M. MELIEF. 1988. J. Immunol. In press.
25. ROSENBERG, A. S., T. MIZOUCHI & A. SINGER. 1986. Nature **322:** 829–831.
26. LIBERTI, P. A., C. J. HACKETT & B. A. ASKONAS. 1979. Eur. J. Immunol. **9:** 751–757.
27. NUSSENZWEIG, M. C., R. M. STEINMAN, J. C. UNKELESS, M. D. WITMER, B. GUTCHISON & Z. A. COHN. 1981. J. Exp. Med. **154:** 168–187.
28. BOOG, C. J. P., J. BOES & C. J. M. MELIEF. 1988. Eur. J. Immunol. **18:** 219–223.
29. INABA, K., J. W. YOUNG & R. M. STEINMAN. 1987. J. Exp. Med. **166:** 182–194.
30. INABA, K. & R. M. STEINMAN. 1986. J. Exp. Med. **163:** 247–261.
31. HEEG, K., C. STEEG, C. HARDT & H. WAGNER. 1987. Eur. J. Immunol. **17:** 229–236.

32. GOLDING, H., T. MIZOUCHI, S. A. McCARTHY, C. A. CLEVELAND & A. J. SINGER. 1987. J. Immunol. **138:** 10–17.
33. GUIMEZANES, A. & A.-M. SCHMITT-VERHULST. 1985. Eur. J. Immunol. **15:** 1187–1191.
34. SINGER, A., A. M. KRUISBEEK & P. M. ANDRYSIAK. 1984. J. Immunol. **132:** 2199–2209.
35. VASMEL, W. L. E., M. ZIJLSTRA, T. LEUPERS, T. RADASZKIEWICZ & C. J. M. MELIEF. 1988. J. Virol. In press.

Function of Granule Perforin and Esterases in T Cell–Mediated Reactions

Components Required for Delivery of Molecules to Target Cells[a]

ECKHARD R. PODACK,[b] DAVID M. LOWREY,

MATHIAS LICHTENHELD, AND ARIF HAMEED

New York Medical College
Valhalla, New York 10595

INTRODUCTION

A unique property of T cells is the specificity of recognition restricted by both antigen and the major histocompatibility complex (MHC).[1] Many T-cell effector functions, such as B-cell help, suppression, and cytotoxicity require cognate, that is, antigen and MHC restricted contact. It is known that the secretory apparatus of T cells is involved in the cognate delivery of cytotoxic effector molecules[2–4] for target-cell killing and in the cognate delivery of help for antibody-producing B cells.[5] We postulate a common mechanism for cognate T-cell effector functions involving directed secretion of perforins (P1)[6–8] and esterases[9–12] into the interstitial space of effector target conjugates. The function of perforin is to mediate uptake of T-cell products by way of formation of perforin-induced Ca channels, Ca-influx, and Ca-induced endocytosis by the target cell. Endocytotic activity of the target membrane at the effector-target conjugation site inevitably results in the endosomal uptake of molecules located at this site, including effector cell–secreted components. One of the roles of esterases, on the other hand, may be to detach the target from the effector cell, thus enabling the effector cell to undergo a new effector cycle. This concept is compatible with the secretory model for lymphocyte-mediated cytotoxicity elaborated previously.[13,14] In addition, as outlined below, it takes into account new information demonstrating the presence of esterases and P1 in T-helper cells. This, together with evidence for an effect of esterases on effector-cell recycling, lends support to a unified mechanism for T cell–mediated, cognate effector functions in cytotoxicity, help, and suppression.

We wish to emphasize that these considerations are purely hypothetical, based on a number of observations that would allow alternative interpretations. The pertinent observations, described in more detail below, are the following: (1) Not all granules containing P1 have hemolytic activity. This may suggest a function for P1 other than direct cytolysis. (2) Both P1 and granzymes are found in helper T cells. This implies a function of these components not restricted to cytotoxicity. (3) Cytolytic granules contain P1-independent cytolytic activity. Considering

[a] These studies were supported by a Grant from the American Cancer Society, IM396, and by USPHS Grants AI 21999 and CA 39201. David Lowrey is a fellow of the Cancer Research Institute.

[b] Present address: Department of Microbiology and Immunology, University of Miami School of Medicine, P.O. Box 016960 (R. 138), Miami, FL 33101.

these pieces of evidence together seems to suggest a broader role for P1 and esterases in T cell–effector function than previously thought.

PROPERTIES OF GRANULES ISOLATED FROM MURINE, HUMAN-KILLER, AND HELPER-KILLER LYMPHOCYTES: LACK OF HEMOLYTIC ACTIVITY DESPITE PRESENCE OF PERFORIN

The now classical examples of cytolytically and hemolytically active killer cell granules were obtained with a few cell lines: CTLL2[15] and HY3AG3,[8] a rat NK-lymphoma.[16] Subsequently the results were confirmed with other cell lines and bulk cultures.[17] Granules showing the highest level of hemolytic activity were derived from cells that are antigen-independent, MHC-unrestricted T-killer cells usually derived from originally MHC-restricted CTL (TABLE 1).

We and others have since isolated granules from various other T-cell clones and cultures. Our general experience is that strong hemolytic activity of isolated granules containing P1 is the exception rather than the rule. TABLE 1 lists the properties of granules obtained from various cells.

TABLE 1. Properties of Granules from Various Cells

Name	Type	Antigen Dependent	Hemolysis	P1-Antigen	P1-Message	P1-Independent Esterase Cell Lysis	
CTLL2	CTL-NK	No	+++	+++	ND[b]	+	+++
HY3AG	CTL-NK	No	+++	+++	+++	+	+++
8-10	CTL	Yes	+	+	++	ND	ND
21C11	Helper Killer	Yes	—	+	++	ND	++
LANK[a]	NK	No	—	+	+	++	+++

[a] IL-2–activated human-killer cells. Bulk cultures after 2 weeks of IL-2 activation, approximately 60% Leu 11 positive. All other cells are cloned cells of murine origin.

[b] ND = not determined.

It should be noted, however, that the absence of hemolytic activity cannot be equated with the absence of perforin as has been done previously.[18] As shown in TABLE 1, hemolytically inactive granules from murine helper-killer cells and human interleukin-2 (IL-2)–activated (LANK) cells contain P1 antigen by Western blot analysis. In addition, as shown below, these cells contain P1 message when analyzed in Northern blot using P1-cDNA as probe. Thus, granules from these cells contain P1 at levels insufficient to cause direct target-cell lysis. The P1 level may well be high enough, however, to insert Ca channels in the target membrane.

In addition to P1, all granules of all cells in TABLE 1 contain esterases, as revealed by their activity of cleavage of the synthetic substrate $N\alpha$-CBZ-L-lysine thiobenzyl ester (BLT).[9] Finally, the granules of cytotoxic factors (CTL) and natural killer cells (NK) contain cytolytic activity for nucleated cells, but not for erythrocytes, that is, independent of P1. The molecular identity of this activity is not known. Functionally, this activity requires cytotoxicity assay periods 3 to 18 hr in length, and thus is distinctly different from the rapid action (<5 min) of P1. This activity, isolated from human IL-2–activated cells, lyses both NK-sensitive and resistant targets (see below).

We conclude from these studies that all cloned or longterm (>10 days) cytotoxic lines contain granules containing P1, esterases, and other cytotoxic factors. The relative quantity of individual components, however, varies at least with regard to P1, such that the lack of hemolytic activity cannot be equated with the absence of P1.

EXPRESSION OF P1 MESSAGE

We have recently obtained cDNA clones from a murine CTL-expression library coding for murine P1. The identity of this clone was confirmed by the predicted amino acid sequence that is homologous to C9, as expected;[19,20] the staining of granule P1 by antipeptide antiserum, made against predicted P1-peptide sequences; and the expression of a 2.8 kb mRNA species in appropriate cells, for example, CTL and NK, but not other cells. TABLE 2 summarizes some of the properties of P1.

TABLE 3 lists the results of P1 expression. P1-mRNA has been found in all cytotoxic lymphocyte clones and lines analyzed to date. P1 message is also found in class II–specific, L3T4-positive–helper-killer cells as well as in one helper cell whose cytolytic activity is not known (OVA7). In addition, 8 out of 12 helper T-cell clones secreting various T- and B-cell lymphokines are positive for P1 message. Using spleen cells that are negative for P1 message, its expression can be induced by concanavalin A (Con A) or IL-2 stimulation. Similarly, in alloreactive or virus-specific mixed-lymphocyte reactions, P1 message is induced concomitantly with the observation of cytotoxicity. No P1 message is detected in B cells and lipopolysaccharide (LPS) blasts, in various lymphoma-cell lines, in macrophages, or in fibroblasts. Murine P1-cDNA probes cross-hybridize with a message of identical size in human-cytotoxic cells.

The expression experiments demonstrate that P1 synthesis is not restricted to MHC-class I–restricted killer cells, but is also found in class II–restricted killers that also have helper activity. The question at the present time has to remain open as to whether all differentiated helper cells requiring contact to mediate help, also express P1. In preliminary experiments, we have found P1 message in many of the helper T-cell clones tested. It appears not to be uncommon that cloned helper T cells under appropriate conditions can also mediate cytotoxic activity.

TABLE 2. Properties of Perforin 1

Parameter	Murine P1	Human P1
Molecular weight	70–75 kDa	70–75 kDa
Charge	anionic	?
Cross-reactivity with C9	yes	yes
Intracellular storage	granules	granules
Expression		
CTL	++	+(?)
T_h	++	?
NK	?	+(?)
mRNA length	2.8 kb	2.8 kb
Homology to $C9_H$	27%	?
EGFP[a] domain	+	?
LDL-R-domain	+(?)	?

[a] EGFP = epithelial growth factor receptor precursor.

TABLE 3. Expression of P1 mRNA

Name	Type	Specificity	Content of P1 mRNA
HY3AG3	CTL-NK	NK-like	+++
3A2	CTL	allo	+++
8-10-2	CTL	hapten (AED)	++
50.1	CTL	LCMV[a]	++
MLC (1)	bulk	allogeneic	++
MLC (2)	bulk	vaccinia	+
Con A blast	T cells	polyclonal	+
LPS blast	B cells	polyclonal	+
21C11	T helper	ovalbumin	++
OVA7	T helper	ovalbumin	(+)
macrophage	bone marrow	NA	—
MC 57	fibroblast	NA	—
EL 4	T lymphoma	NA	—

[a] LCMV = lymphocytic choriomeningitis virus.

GRANULE ESTERASES

Esterases associated with cloned cytolytic T cells were originally discovered by Pasternack and Eisen.[9] In the murine system, three different serine esterases have been described at the cDNA level[21-23] and eight at the protein level.[10,11,29] The sequence of these enzymes is homologous to typical serine esterases, and some of them bind radiolabeled diisopropyl fluorophosphate (DFP) at their active site serine. The esterases are localized in the cytoplasmic granules of T cells. It appears probable that the same granule contains esterases as well as P1 and other proteins. The possibility that different granules may contain different proteins, however, has not formally been excluded.

In further discussing these esterases, we will follow the nomenclature proposed by Tschopp[10] and designate the granule-associated esterases as granzymes 1, 2 . . . n. Granzymes were originally believed to be restricted to cytotoxic lymphocytes. It has more recently become clear, however, that T-helper cells also may contain esterases. Similar to the situation with P1, class II–restricted helper cells also expressing cytotoxic activity contain esterase and P1-positive granules (TABLE 1). Whether all helper cells or only those providing cognate help, (that is, requiring contact) contain esterases remains to be established.

We have investigated human IL-2 activated killer cells with regard to their content of esterases. TABLE 4 summarizes the properties of three human granzymes. Granzyme 1 and 2 of the human system appear to be homologous to granzyme A and B of murine cells. Granzyme 1(A) is identical to H factor (HF). Granzyme 2(B) may be identical with CCP1,[21] CTLA1. Human granzyme 3 has not as yet been described in the murine system. Granzyme 4 and 5 are minor DFP-labeled components comigrating with granzyme 3 on cation-exchange chromatography. Whether they are independent esterases or cleavage products is not presently clear.

The natural substrates of the granzymes are not known. Granzyme 1 and 3 cleave the synthetic substrate BLT and seem to have relatively broad tryptic activity. No substrate has been found for granzyme 2, which, in the murine system, is predicted to be chymotrypsin-like. Many potential functions for granzymes can be envisaged and have been discussed. Here we will consider only one possibility, namely the role of esterases in the detachment of effectors from the

TABLE 4. Properties of Human Esterases (Granzymes)

Name	Native Molecular Weight	Subunit Molecular Weight	Cationic Nature	DFP Binding	BLT Cleavage	Murine Analogue	Cloned Sequence	Remarks
Granzyme 1	60 kDa	30 kDa	+	+	Yes	Granzyme A	HF	Disulfide-linked subunits; disulfide-linked oligomers
Granzyme 2	60 kDa	32 kDa	++	+	No	Granzyme B	CCP2?[a]	
Granzyme 3	60 kDa	28 kDa	+++	+	Yes	?	?	
Granzyme 4	60 kDa	~20 kDa	+++	+	?	?	?	Minor component or cleavage product
Granzyme 5	60 kDa	~16 kDa	+++	+	?	?	?	

[a] See ref. 21.

target cell. This hypothetical function is consistent with the presence of esterases both in cytotoxic cells and in T-helper cells mediating cognate signal delivery. In addition, the finding of multiple enzymes in T-cell granules may have its explanation in the requirement for cleavage of multiple adhesion molecules known to participate in the recognition and conjugation of effector T cells with their targets.

DELIVERED MOLECULES: NUCLEOLYTIC FACTORS AND OTHER FACTORS

CTL and NK in addition to forming pores in target membranes cause also degradation of target cell–nuclear DNA.[25–27] It is known that the final enzyme-cleaving DNA between the nucleosomes in the target is a target enzyme. How this endonuclease is activated or, alternatively, how its substrate becomes susceptible is not known. Studies by Ruddle *et al.*[24] indicate that lymphotoxin, produced by many, if not all, CTL clones, can cause rapid DNA-degradation when taken up by

TABLE 5. Properties of Nucleolytic Factor (NF)

Parameter	Murine NF	Human NF
Source	CTL	IL-2–activated cells (LANK)
Target	L929	K562, Daudi, Raji
Time course	>18 hr	>3 hr
P1 dependence	No	No
Ca dependence	ND[a]	Yes
DNA degradation	+(?)	ND
Inhibition by:		
anti-TNF	10–40%	ND
anti-LT[b]	No	ND
anti-granules	Yes	ND

[a] ND = not determined.
[b] LT = lymphotoxin.

target cells through pinocytosis. Our own studies suggest that cytolytic granules contain factors that mediate cytotoxic activity that does not require participation of P1. This activity appears to be distinct from lymphotoxin or tumor necrosis factor (TNF) because it is only partly inhibited by antibodies to these factors (TABLE 5). The statement that this cytotoxic activity is independent of P1 is derived from two observations: (1) In hemolytically active murine-cytolytic granules, the P1 activity can be eliminated by preincubation of isolated granules with 1 mM Ca at 37°. The loss of P1 activity is easily monitored by the loss of hemolytic activity of the granules. P1-inactivated granules, however, are still cytotoxic for L929 cells in 24 hr assays. (2) Several cell lines with cytotoxic activity contain granules that, in isolated form, are not hemolytically active even though they contain P1 detectable on Western blots (TABLE 1). It seems evident that levels of P1 insufficient for the lysis of red cells are also insufficient for the lysis of nucleated cells. Yet granules that are not able to lyse erythrocytes, efficiently lyse nucleated targets within 3 hr, such as K562, Raji, and Daudi cells. We postulate that this cytolytic activity may be caused by the factor(s) responsible for DNA-degradation in target cells and that it may be delivered to the target cell by a process involving pore formation by low levels of P1 and subsequent target-cell endocytosis (FIG. 1).

DISCUSSION

Recent advances in the examination of the molecular mechanism of lympho-cyte-mediated target-cell lysis revealed the following pertinent observations: The killer cell delivers the lethal hit by way of a secretory process. The products to be secreted are stored in cytoplasmic granules. The granules contain pore-forming

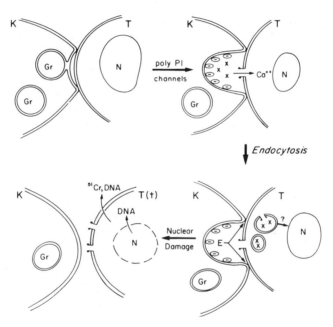

FIGURE 1.

proteins, esterases (proteinases), nucleolytic factors, and other factors (pro-teoglycans and chemotaxins). These findings can be compiled in a hypothetical model for lymphocyte-mediated cytolysis as has been done previously.[13,14]

More recently, however, it was shown that helper T cells, whose primary function is not believed to involve target-cell killing, have very similar mecha-nisms in delivering help. They also appear to secrete products directly onto conju-gated target cells, they often contain granules, and they can express P1 and esterases. In this regard, they contain the same molecular machinery that is believed to be responsible for the delivery of the lethal hit by CTL. How universal is the content of these molecules in helper T cells? And what is their function, assuming they are not primarily used for target-cell killing by helper T cells?

The answer to these questions may be a second function of P1, as a molecule necessary for the direct delivery of T-cell effector molecules to conjugated target cells. TABLE 6 summarizes a hypothetical model for the delivery of help, suppres-

TABLE 6. Steps and Molecules in Cognate T Cell–Mediated Delivery of Signal Molecules to Target Cells

Effector

Contact ⟶ Granule secretion ⟶ Detachment ⟶ Effector Cell Recycling

LFA1, CD2, CD4, CD8, Ti   Esterases   Esterase cleavage
                           Perforin   of
                                        adhesion molecules

ICAM1, LFA3, MHCII, MHCI, MHC-Ag   Other factors ⟶ Uptake of factors

Target

Contact ⟶ Perforin Channels Ca influx ⟶ Local endocytosis ⟶ Detachment ⟶ Target effects: cell death, helper function, suppressor function

sion, and cytotoxicity. FIGURE 1 shows a schematic view of the delivery of the lethal hit. The essential components in the schemes are P1 and esterases (granzymes). Upon effector target-cell contact and engagement of the T-cell receptor, the granule contents of effector T cells are secreted directionally towards the target. P1 will insert and polymerize in the target membrane, resulting in the formation of a Ca-permeable transmembrane channel. Provided the P1 concentration is not too high, these channels will not kill the targets but rather stimulate them to active endocytotic activity due to the Ca influx. This activity by the target cell in turn will inevitably lead to the uptake in endosomes of components previously contained in the granules of the T cell and now located in the interstitial space between the two cells (FIG. 1). Depending on the nature of these products the effect may be target-cell death, help for the target function, or target suppression.

A precedent for this type of reaction sequence may be the underlying mechanism of the observation by Duke *et al.*[28] that NK at high killer-target ratios kill without attendant DNA degradation, whereas at low killer-target ratios, DNA degradation seems clearly important. The most obvious interpretation for this finding is the following: at high killer-target cell ratios, leading to the simultaneous conjugation of several killer cells with a single target, the secretion of P1 by multiple killers is sufficient to cause the immediate demise of the target cell due to the formation of many transmembrane poly-P1 channels and cell lysis. In this situation, the triggering of target nucleases to cause DNA degradation cannot take place, due to the sudden death of the target and dilution of cytoplasmatic components upon perforation of the membrane. At low killer-target ratios, on the other hand, the perforation of the membrane by P1 does not appear to be sufficient to kill the cell. The pores that are undoubtedly formed in this situation allow Ca flux and stimulate endocytosis, resulting in the uptake of the factors responsible for triggering DNA degradation.

T cells thus seem to possess a mechanism by which they can deliver molecules directly into the endosomal compartment of targets recognized and conjugated in an antigen–MHC-restricted manner. The essential components for this pathway are a directional secretory mechanism, Ca pore-forming proteins, and a detachment process. T-cell granules contain these essential factors and T cells can thus be considered as contact-requiring, directionally secreting cells. How widespread this mechanism of molecular signal delivery by T-effector cells is, remains to be determined.

SUMMARY

Cognate T cell–mediated functions require antigen and MHC-restricted recognition of target cells. T-effector functions comprise the delivery of signals for help, for suppression, or for cell death of the target cell. In the case of the delivery of cytotoxicity and of help for B-cell antibody production, it is known that the secretory apparatus of the effector cell participates. Prior to secretion, many components of the effector cell are stored in cytoplasmic granules. Among the important and apparently constant constituents of granules are pore-forming proteins (perforins) and proteinases (granzymes). The putative role of perforin has been thought to mediate direct cytotoxicity. It is postulated here that, in addition, perforin at low concentrations may induce target-cell endocytosis through the formation of Ca channels. Localized endocytosis of the target at the contact site in turn may lead to the uptake of locally secreted effector-cell factors, such as cytotoxic factors (CTL), lymphokines (helper cells), or suppressor factors (suppressor cells). The potential importance of such a mechanism is the delivery and uptake of secreted effector-cell components into the endosomes of target cells, bypassing the need for appropriate target-cell receptors. Perforin thus may subserve two functions depending on its intragranular concentration: one, as a killer molecule, and two, as a delivery system for additional granule factors.

One of the roles of esterases in T cell–mediated cognate-effector functions may be to allow recycling of the effector cell. This apparently is achieved by an active process of detachment of the effector T cell from the target cell, possibly by way of the proteolytic cleavage of adhesion molecules. Esterases are secreted, together with perforin and other factors, during granule release at the effector target-contact site, where they can cleave intercellular adhesion molecules and thus allow effector-cell recycling and attachment to new target cells. Other roles of esterases, not discussed here, may include participation directly in the cytotoxic process through uptake into the target cell.

The evidence for a common intercellular molecular delivery mechanism of cognate effector T-cell function involving perforin and esterases is summarized. This concept represents a unifying hypothesis for MHC-restricted, contact-requiring, intercellular T cell–signal delivery as well as for the delivery of cytotoxicity by non-MHC-restricted T cells and natural killer cells.

ACKNOWLEDGMENTS

We wish to acknowledge the expert assistance of Kristin O. Penichet and Laurie Fulton.

REFERENCES

1. ZINKERNAGEL, R. M. & P. C. DOHERTY. 1979. Adv. Immunol. **27:** 52.
2. GEIGER, B., D. ROSEN & G. BERKE. 1982. J. Cell. Biol. **95:** 137.
3. KUPFER, A., G. DENNERT & S. J. SINGER. 1983. Proc. Natl. Acad. Sci. USA **80:** 7224.
4. PODACK, E. R. 1986. J. Cell. Biochem. **24:** 30.
5. KUPFER, A., S. L. SWAIN, C. A. JANEWAY, JR. & S. J. SINGER. 1986. Proc. Natl. Acad. Sci. USA **83:** 6080.
6. MASSON, D. & J. TSCHOPP. 1985. J. Biol. Chem. **260:** 9069.
7. PODACK, E. R., J. D. E. YOUNG & Z. A. COHN. 1985. Proc. Natl. Acad. Sci. USA **82:** 8629.
8. YOUNG, J. D. E., H. HENGARTNER, E. R. PODACK & Z. A. COHN. 1986. Cell **44:** 849.
9. PASTERNACK, M. S., C. REYNOLDS-VERRET, M. A. LIN & H. N. EISEN. 1986. Nature **322:** 21.
10. MASSON, D., M. NABHOLZ, C. ESTRADE & J. TSCHOPP. 1986. EMBO J. **5:** 7.
11. YOUNG, J. D. E., L. G. LEONG, C. C. LIN, H. DAMIANO, D. A. WALL & Z. A. COHN. 1986. Cell **47:** 183.
12. SIMON, M. M., H. HOSCHUETZKY, U. FRUTH, H. G. SIMON & M. D. KRAMER. 1986. EMBO J. **512:** 3267.
13. HENKAR, P. A. 1985. Annu. Rev. Immunol. **3:** 31.
14. PODACK, E. R. 1985. Immunology Today **6:** 21.
15. PODACK, E. R. & P. KONIGSBERG. 1984. J. Exp. Med. **160:** 695.
16. MILLARD, P. J., M. P. HENKART, C. W. REYNOLDS & P. A. HENKART. 1984. J. Immunol. **132:** 3197.
17. MASSON, D., P. CORHESY, M. NABHOLZ & J. TSCHOPP. 1985. EMBO J. **4:** 2533.
18. GARCIA-SANZ, J. A., G. PLAETNICK, F. VELOTTI, D. MASSON, J. TSCHOPP, H. R. MACDONALD & M. NABHOLZ. 1987. EMBO J. **6:** 933.

19. YOUNG, J. D. E., Z. A. COHN & E. R. PODACK. 1986. Science **233:** 184.
20. PODACK, E. R. 1987. *In* Membrane Mediated Cytotoxicity. Alan R. Liss. New York. p.
     339
21. LOBE, C. G., B. B. FINLEY, W. PARACHYCH, V. H. PAETKAU & R. C. BLEACKLY.
     1986. Science **232:** 858.
22. GERSHENFELD, H. K. & I. L. WEISSMANN. 1986. Science **232:** 855.
23. BRUNET, J. F., M. DOSSETO, F. DENIZOT, M. G. MATTEI, W. R. CLARK, T. M. HARRI,
     P. FERRIER, M. NABHOLZ, A. M. SCHMITT-VERHULST, M. F. LUCIANI & P. GOL-
     STEIN. 1986. Nature **322:** 268.
24. SCHMID, D. S., T. P. TITE & N. H. RUDDLE. 1986. Proc. Natl. Acad. Sci. USA **83:**
     1881.
25. RUSSEL, J. H., V. R. MASAKOWSKI & C. B. DOBOS. 1980. J. Immunol. **124:** 1100.
26. DUKE, R. C., R. CHERVENAK & J. J. COHEN. 1983. Proc. Natl. Acad. Sci. USA **80:**
     6361.
27. HOWELL, D. M. & E. MARTZ. 1987. J. Immunol. **138:** 3695.
28. DUKE, R. C., J. J. COHEN & R. CHERVENAK. 1986. J. Immunol. **137:** 1422.
29. MASSON, D. & J. TSCHOPP. 1987. Cell **49:** 679.

Early Events in Target-Cell Lysis by Cytotoxic T Cells[a]

VICTOR H. ENGELHARD,[b] JAMES R. GNARRA,[b]
JAMES SULLIVAN,[c] GERALD L. MANDELL,[c]
AND LLOYD S. GRAY[d]

Departments of [b]Microbiology, [c]Medicine, and [d]Pathology
University of Virginia School of Medicine
Charlottesville, Virginia 22908

INTRODUCTION

The early phases in the process of target-cell lysis by cytolytic T lymphocytes (CTL) consist of target-cell adhesion, followed by programming for lysis.[1] Whereas the cell-surface components involved in adhesion have been described, it has been unclear how target-cell recognition and binding is translated into the lytic event. Programming for lysis was initially defined as a process occurring with a half time of 7–10 minutes after contact, that resulted in the irreversible commitment of the target cell to lysis. This process is dependent upon external Ca^{2+} and significantly inhibited at temperatures lower than 37°. More recently, granules with a diameter of approximately 0.4 μm were isolated from CTL[2] and large granular lymphocytes[3] and shown to be capable of directly mediating target-cell lysis in a Ca^{2+}-dependent manner. Such granules were shown to contain cytolytically active proteins, as well as serine esterase activity that could also be detected in the medium after CTL contact with appropriate target cells. Accordingly, a model for CTL-mediated lysis has been proposed in which these granules or their contents are secreted by the CTL during the programming for lysis phase.[4,5]

More direct information in support of this model has come from microscopic evaluation of CTL–target cell conjugates. The microtubule-organizing center and Golgi apparatus of CTL were found to be preferentially located in the cytoplasmic space adjacent to the zone of contact with the target cell, and this has been proposed to reflect a reorientation process within the cytoplasm.[6,7] Cinemicrographic examination of CTL–target cell interactions has provided direct evidence that a reorganization of the cytoplasm occurs within 2–10 minutes of target-cell contact.[8,9] In particular, granules morphologically similar to those isolated previously were seen to move from their initial position in the tail of the CTL to a region near the CTL-target interface, and apparent fusion between these granules and the inner surface of the CTL membrane was detected. These morphological events were proposed to represent a likely correlate of the programming for lysis step.

Recently, considerable progress has also been made in delineating the signals that occur in response to occupancy of the antigen receptor on T cells. Antibodies to the T3 component of this receptor induce the breakdown of phosphatidyl

[a] This work was supported by Grants AI20963 (V. H. Engelhard), AI21393 (V.H.E.), AI09504 (G. L. Mandell), AI07046 (G.L.M.), and RR05431 (L. S. Gray) from the U.S. Public Health Service.

303

inositol biphosphate to diacylglycerol and inositol triphosphate.[10-14] Diacyl-glycerol causes the activation of protein kinase C, whereas inositol 1,4,5 triphos-phate has been associated with increases in intracellular Ca^{2+} ($[Ca^{2+}]_i$) mediated by release from intracellular stores[14,15] and by influx.[16] Increases in $[Ca^{2+}]_i$ in response to anti-T3 antibodies[17-19] and specific antigen[20-22] have been measured directly by several groups.

Recent data suggests that the movement of ions may also be important for T-cell function. Gray and Russell showed that a transmembrane influx of Cl^- into the CTL was important during the programming for lysis phase of killing.[23] Occu-pancy of the T-cell receptor by antibody or lectins leads to hyperpolarization of the membrane,[24,25] most probably mediated by an efflux of intracellular K^+. Most recently, it has been shown that interaction of CTL with relevant target cells resulted in an influx of Ca^{2+} into the CTL, which was linked to and apparently regulated by an efflux of K^+.[25]

Through the use of both spectrofluorometric and cinemicrographic methods, the nature of the signal induced in CTL in response to target-cell binding, and how such signals correlate with lethal hit delivery, have been investigated. Such meth-ods allow analysis of the relationship between ion flux and morphological changes leading to the delivery of the lethal hit. Additionally, microscopic examination of single cells can give information regarding the time course, spatial distribution, and magnitude of intracellular ionic concentration changes. Examination of single cells is important in determining the temporal sequence of antigen-induced changes in CTL, which is often obscured during the examination of bulk cell suspensions. This report describes the direct observation of single CTL–target cell interactions in order to examine the subcellular distribution of Ca^{2+} during lethal hit delivery, and to correlate temporal changes in $[Ca^{2+}]_i$ in response to target-cell binding with changes in granule distribution in the CTL. We have also examined the changes in $[Ca^{2+}]_i$ in the presence and absence of external Ca^{2+}, which is generally required for lethal hit delivery. Finally, the effects of K-chan-nel blockade on the time course and magnitude of Ca^{2+} influx have been assessed.

MATERIAL AND METHODS

The murine CTL clone, III12-2, was derived and maintained as previously described and is specific for HLA-A2.[8] The HLA-A2–positive lymphoblastoid cell line, JY, was used as a target cell in all experiments. Viable CTL were isolated by centrifugation on a Ficoll-Hypaque density gradient, washed with RPMI-1640 containing 5% heat-inactivated fetal bovine serum (assay medium), and incubated at 1×10^7 cells/ml for 30 min at 37°C with 1 μM fura-2/AM[26] in assay medium. CTL and JY cells were washed three times and resuspended at 1×10^7 cells/ml in assay medium. Ten μl aliquots of each cell type were placed on a clean glass microscope slide and mixed well. In experiments examining the effect of K-channel blockade, 4-aminopyridine (4-AP) was added at a final concentration of 5 mM following mixing of the cell suspension. A clean glass coverslip was applied, and a thin preparation was made as previously described.[8] The coverslip was sealed with a 1 : 2 mixture of hot paraffin and petroleum jelly, and the prepa-ration was examined immediately.

The microscope (Leitz Orthoplan) was equipped with a 100 W mercury vapor lamp, quartz optical epifluorescence pathway, and a 100 $\times$ glycerine immersion objective (Nikon, UV-CF). The microscope stage was maintained at 37°C by a thermostatically controlled infrared lamp. Cells were located with bright-field illumination, and CTL–target cell interactions were recorded on 3/4 inch video tape using a silicon-intensified target camera (Model 65, DAGE-MTI Inc., Michigan City, IN). Fura-2 fluorescence ratios were obtained from sequential images during excitation at 340 nm and 380 nm using bandpass filters. Fluorescence emission was recorded using a 475 nm longpass filter. Ratios of emission intensity at the two excitation wavelengths were obtained from an average of eight video frames by conversion to a $640 \times 480 \times 8$ bit pixel array using an image-processing computer (Quantex 9210, Quantex Corp., Sunnyvale CA). A pixel-by-pixel logarithmic transformation was performed with subsequent subtraction of the image obtained following excitation at 380 nm from the image obtained following excitation at 340 nm. The antilog of this difference in log emission intensity was then converted to a pseudocolor display to provide a visual representation of the subcellular distribution of Ca^{2+}. The resulting images were photographed directly from a video display monitor.

RESULTS AND DISCUSSION

In previous work, CTL and target cells were prepared as slide specimens with an average thickness of less than 5 μm, allowing visualization of the cytoplasmic contents of the cells in considerable detail, while still allowing the CTL to remain motile.[8] CTL exhibit a morphological asymmetry, with a broad leading edge and a narrower, granule-containing tail. Following target-cell contact, these granules reoriented into the vicinity of the CTL–target cell interface. This reorientation was antigen-specific and occurred with a time course of 2–10 minutes. Using differential interference contrast (Nomarski) optics, apparent fusion between a granule and the inner surface of the CTL membrane was seen. These results were interpreted to indicate that granule reorientation and exocytosis were strongly correlated with programming for lysis.

This method has now been extended through the use of the fluorescent dye Fura-2, which allows the measurement of $[Ca^{2+}]_i$. The results reported here are representative of several independent experiments carried out over nine months. As detected by an increase in the 340 nm/380 nm fluorescence ratio, the binding of a CTL to a specifically recognized target cell caused a rapid increase in $[Ca^{2+}]_i$. This increase was visible within 45 seconds of the estimated time of contact with the target (FIG. 1, panel C). $[Ca^{2+}]_i$ continued to increase for some time, reaching a peak value about 1.5 minutes after contact (FIG. 1, panel E). Thereafter, $[Ca^{2+}]_i$ declined slowly and was often still elevated as long as 20 minutes after contact. CTL interacting with each other or with nonspecific target cells did not show increases in $[Ca^{2+}]_i$.

The magnitude of the increase in $[Ca^{2+}]_i$ was approximately sixfold over the resting value. Spectrofluorometric measurements on suspensions of CTL labeled with another Ca^{2+}-sensitive dye, indo-1, showed a fourfold increase in $[Ca^{2+}]_i$ in response to target cells.[22,25] This difference may reflect the fact that cells in suspension are unlikely to respond simultaneously to the initial stimulus, and therefore the peak increases observed in individual CTL will be averaged with CTL that have either not yet peaked or are past their peak.

The level of detail afforded by the thin-mount technique allowed examination of the subcellular distribution of Ca^{2+} during the early stages of the lytic process. The antigen-induced increase in $[Ca^{2+}]_i$ occurred throughout the cytoplasm, but

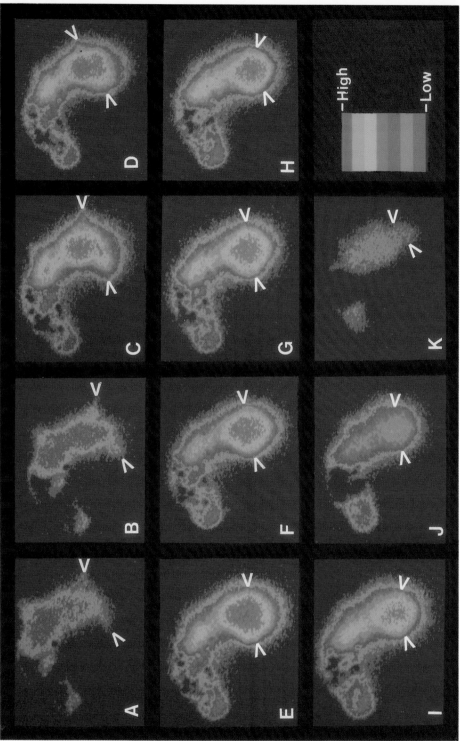

was clearly highest near the area of contact with the target cell. The boundaries of target-cell contact were between the arrowheads along the lower right portion of the CTL shown in FIGURE 1. This distribution was evident as soon as an increase in $[Ca^{2+}]_i$ was evident, and did not change significantly during the course of observation. This points to an increase in $[Ca^{2+}]_i$ mediated either by mobilization from intracellular stores or by influx from the outside that is enhanced in proximity to the target cell. Interestingly, the initially flat surface of the CTL that was in contact with the target became progressively more rounded during this sequence, and it appeared as though the CTL were pushing into the target cell. This type of pushing movement could also be seen in bright-field images, but the extent of the distortion of the shape of the CTL in the area of target-cell contact could not be as clearly visualized. Both the shape change and the preferential increase in $[Ca^{2+}]_i$ in the vicinity of the target cell may be important in directing subsequent reorientation events.

Although the majority of the cytoplasm showed an increase in 340 nm/380 nm fluorescence ratio during the interaction, the granules that were initially located in the tail of the CTL showed either no change or a significantly lower increase. This did not appear to be due to an absence of dye in the granules because they were visible as fluorescent structures in original images. Rather, it appeared to be due to a lack of influx of Ca^{2+} into these organelles. The ability to visualize granules as areas of low Ca^{2+} concentration was important in determining the relationship of the antigen-induced increase in $[Ca^{2+}]_i$ to granule reorientation.

As noted above, the increase in $[Ca^{2+}]_i$ that occurred in CTL following target-cell contact was not restricted to a particular cytoplasmic region. This increase was polarized, however, with the greatest increase seen at the leading edge of the CTL. This would be in agreement with our previous hypothesis that CTL Ca channels are directly ligand-gated.[25] Of importance is the time course of the antigen-induced Ca^{2+} increase and its decay. Estimates of the time required for the delivery of the lethal hit after target-cell binding are 7 to 10 minutes.[1] These estimates are in excess of the time required to achieve maximal $[Ca^{2+}]_i$ and place delivery of the lethal hit at a point when Ca^{2+} levels have decreased to near resting levels. Indeed, as indicated in the sequence in FIGURE 1, and in data to be published elsewhere,[9] the initial target cell–induced increase in $[Ca^{2+}]_i$ had largely declined to a value only slightly above the normal resting level prior to any detectable granule movement towards the region of target-cell contact. Thus, maintenance of $[Ca^{2+}]_i$ at a very high level does not appear to be necessary for lysis to proceed. If an increase in intracellular Ca^{2+} is important in cytolysis, its role must be to initiate intracellular processes that will lead to granule reorientation and secretion of cytolytic components.

The images in FIGURE 1 were selected to show the overall time frame of changes in $[Ca^{2+}]_i$. Detailed examination of several sequences, however, sug-

---

FIGURE 1. Spatial distribution of the increase in $[Ca^{2+}]_i$ induced in CTL by cellular antigen. Fura-2–loaded CTL were prepared and examined by ratio image fluorescence microscopy as described in MATERIAL AND METHODS. The images were obtained at the indicated times following bright-field determination of target-cell contact: A, 15 s; B, 30 s; C, 45 s; D, 60 s; E, 1.5 min; F, 2 min; G, 2.5 min; H, 3 min; I, 3.5 min; J, 4 min; and H, 8 min. Because the target cell was not labeled with Fura-2, it cannot be seen in this sequence of images. The area of contact, however, between the CTL and target cell as determined by bright-field observation is indicated by the arrowheads in each panel. Although not shown in this FIGURE, several granules were noted to move from the tail region of the CTL to the vicinity of the CTL : target-cell interface within approximately 15 minutes.

gested that more subtle and rapid changes in $[Ca^{2+}]_i$ were superimposed on this dominant variation. This was quantified, as shown in FIGURE 2, by averaging the fluorescence in an area of the CTL image representing approximately 80% of the total, and calculating the ratio of 340 nm/380 nm fluorescence as previously described. This allows a numerical value, rather than a color representing a range of fluorescent values, to be assigned to each image. As shown in FIGURE 2, the $[Ca^{2+}]_i$ induced by contact with a target cell did not increase and decrease mono-

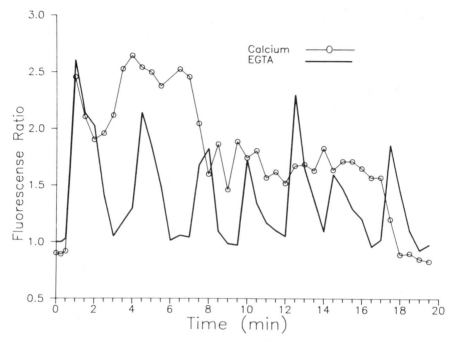

FIGURE 2. Temporal alterations in antigen-induced $[Ca^{2+}]_i$ observed in CTL in the presence and absence of extracellular Ca^{2+}. Fura-2–loaded CTL were examined by ratio image–fluorescence microscopy either in the presence or absence of 3.6 mM EGTA as described in MATERIAL AND METHODS. EGTA was added to the CTL : target-cell suspension prior to placement of the coverslip, and the preparation was examined immediately. Average fluorescence intensities after excitation at 340 and 380 nm were determined from a rectangular area drawn within the CTL and representing approximately 80% of the area of the fluorescent image. Fluorescent ratios were calculated based on these intensity values. Open circles indicate CTL incubated in the presence of extracellular Ca^{2+}; solid lines indicate CTL incubated in the presence of EGTA.

tonically, but instead showed several broad pulses. Although there was a decline after each pulse, $[Ca^{2+}]_i$ did not return to the resting value. Each peak in $[Ca^{2+}]_i$ was distributed in the head region of the CTL with a pattern that was similar to that shown in FIGURE 1.[9] As the overall magnitude of $[Ca^{2+}]_i$ decreased, the pulses also decreased in amplitude. Although the periodic increases in $[Ca^{2+}]_i$ at later times were small, they were not due to fluctuation in illumination intensity or the recording system, inasmuch as ionomycin-treated CTL showed a constant fluorescence ratio under these conditions.

Increases in $[Ca^{2+}]_i$ are generally the result of two components: release of Ca^{2+} from intracellular stores, and an influx of Ca^{2+} from the extracellular medium. Both processes seem to participate in the increase of $[Ca^{2+}]_i$ in T cells.[14,22,27] In order to gauge the relative magnitude of these contributions, and the effect of extracellular Ca^{2+}, thin mounts of CTL and targets were prepared in medium to which 3.6 mM EGTA had been added. This concentration of EGTA was calculated to reduce the extracellular Ca^{2+} concentration to less than 100 nM, which is roughly equivalent to resting $[Ca^{2+}]_i$. CTL-mediated cytolysis was abolished under these conditions as measured by a standard ^{51}Cr release assay,[22] although CTL still exhibited motile behavior and bound to target cells. Target-cell binding was accompanied by an increase in $[Ca^{2+}]_i$, which was presumably due to mobilization from intracellular stores. Interestingly, although the increase was again distributed over most of the cell cytoplasm, it was highest near the nucleus opposite the target cell–contact region, and not in the vicinity of the target cell.[9] As seen in FIGURE 2, under these conditions the kinetics of the initial increase paralleled those seen when extracellular Ca^{2+} was present. In addition, when averaged over the entire cell, the magnitude of the increase was similar to that observed in the presence of extracellular $[Ca^{2+}]_i$. The increase, however, was of shorter duration than in the presence of extracellular Ca^{2+} and was followed by a rapid return to the resting value. This may reflect Ca^{2+} release followed by subsequent sequestration. Alternatively, because antigen binding appears to open CTL plasma membrane Ca channels, it is possible that the rapid decrease in $[Ca^{2+}]_i$ following mobilization resulted from Ca^{2+} efflux into the EGTA-containing medium. This explanation, however, seems less likely because subsequent increases in $[Ca^{2+}]_i$ were observed. These results suggest that the influx of Ca^{2+} from the external medium is necessary for the maintenance of an elevated level of $[Ca^{2+}]_i$ after target-cell contact.

CTL incubated with target cells under these conditions exhibited several consecutive increases and decreases of roughly equal duration, but gradually decreasing intensity (FIG. 2). If these extreme variations in $[Ca^{2+}]_i$ have the same basis as the more moderate pulsations detected in the presence of extracellular Ca^{2+}, then the latter may be due to contributions from intracellular stores. It is also possible that signal transduction in the absence of a Ca^{2+} influx is in some way incomplete and that this results in repeated triggering of the signal for Ca^{2+} release. This would suggest that each pulse occurs after the resetting of an initial signaling mechanism.

Because the lytic capacity of the CTL clone used in these experiments is dependent on extracellular Ca^{2+} and associated with an increase in $[Ca^{2+}]_i$,[22] it is intriguing that $[Ca^{2+}]_i$ increased under conditions in which lysis is inhibited, and that the peak increase observed was very similar to that seen in the presence of extracellular Ca^{2+}. Thus, although mobilization of Ca^{2+} from intracellular stores occurs in response to target-cell binding, it is not sufficient for lysis. Taken together with the results seen in the presence of extracellular Ca^{2+}, these observations suggest that a prolonged elevation of $[Ca^{2+}]_i$ over the resting level is important to enable lysis to occur, but that this level need not be sustained at the peak achieved within the first minutes after target-cell contact. Whether different levels of $[Ca^{2+}]_i$ are associated with the triggering of different intracellular processes is also unclear.

The decay in $[Ca^{2+}]_i$ in the CTL occurred while it was still bound to the target. Inasmuch as it has previously been demonstrated that the initial influx of Ca^{2+} is directly ligand-gated,[16] this implies that regulatory mechanisms must exist to restore $[Ca^{2+}]_i$ to resting levels while ligand is still bound. There are several possible mechanisms by which this might occur. If the antigen receptor were the Ca channel, then it might be modified during target-cell binding to allow it to close even though it is still occupied. Alternatively, the antigen receptor could dissociate from its ligand shortly after binding while contact was maintained through accessory binding molecules. In this case, some mechanism would presumably exist to alter the affinity of the receptor for its ligand following binding and Ca^{2+} influx. It is also possible that the antigen receptor is associated with some other integral membrane protein that serves as the CTL Ca channel. Antigen binding could then trigger Ca^{2+} influx indirectly by a change in the interaction between the antigen receptor and the Ca channel. As described below, subsequent closing of the Ca channel would be mediated by secondary events such as K^{+} efflux, which

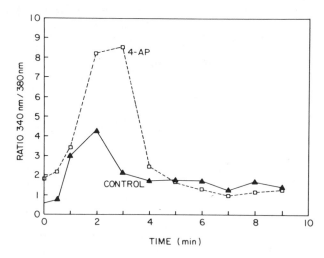

FIGURE 3. The effect of K-channel blockade on the increase in $[Ca^{2+}]_i$ induced in CTL by cellular antigen. CTL were prepared for ratio image–fluorescence microscopy as described in MATERIAL AND METHODS, and examined either in the presence or absence of 5 mM 4-AP. Average fluorescence intensities after excitation at 340 and 380 nm were determined from a rectangular area drawn within the CTL and representing approximately 40% of the area of the fluorescent image. Each rectangle was placed to include the area of the cell with the largest increase in $[Ca^{2+}]_i$. Fluorescent ratios were calculated based on these intensity values. Data were obtained immediately prior to contact between the CTL and target cell, at 30 s following contact and every 60 s thereafter.

could act either directly or activate a pathway leading to Ca channel closing. Regardless of the mechanism, further experimentation will be required to dissect this interesting observation.

In previous work, it was demonstrated that treatment of CTL with the K channel–blocking agent, 4-AP, markedly augmented the increase in $[Ca^{2+}]_i$ induced by occupancy of the T cell–antigen receptor.[25] These experiments, however, were performed in bulk cell suspensions in which it is not possible to accurately examine alterations in the kinetics of increase and decay of $[Ca^{2+}]_i$. When visualized by the techniques described here, the presence of 4-AP markedly augmented the increase in $[Ca^{2+}]_i$ in single CTL stimulated by target-cell contact as compared to the control (FIG. 3). This response is not due to alteration of the fluorescent properties of the sample, inasmuch as the small difference in the initial fluorescence ratio cannot account for the much greater difference in the ratios following stimulation. In addition, the elevated level of $[Ca^{2+}]_i$ achieved in the 4-AP–treated cell was not maintained over the entire period of observation. Indeed, the decay of $[Ca^{2+}]_i$ in these cells showed kinetics that were comparable to those of the control, and this decay was initiated at a comparable time after target-cell contact. This suggests that blockade of K channels by 4-AP does not alter the ability of the CTL to restore $[Ca^{2+}]_i$ to levels only slightly above resting following target-cell contact. It seems more likely that the effect of K-channel blockade is on the early events leading to the initiation of increased $[Ca^{2+}]_i$.

These observations are consistent with our earlier data on cell suspensions,[25] but we have extended our observations by demonstrating the effect of 4-AP on the kinetics of the antigen-induced increase in $[Ca^{2+}]_i$. It should be emphasized that the resting membrane behaves as if it were selectively permeable to K^+, resulting in the dominance of the resting potential of this ion. Thus, K channel–blocking agents may result in membrane depolarization, which could activate voltage-gated Ca channels. It has been directly demonstrated, however, that CTL do not possess a Ca channel that can be activated by depolarization.[25] FIGURE 3 also shows that the augmentation of antigen-induced increase in $[Ca^{2+}]_i$ by 4-AP only occurs following target-cell binding. Therefore, it is unlikely that 4-AP directly induces a depolarization that can account for the augmentation of the antigen-specific increase in $[Ca^{2+}]_i$. Finally, depolarization induced by K-channel blockade would reduce the electromotive driving force for Ca^{2+} influx, resulting in reduction of the antigen-specific influx. The observation that K-channel blockade augments this influx provides additional indirect evidence that K channel controls the function of a CTL Ca channel.

Due to the relatively crude temporal resolution of these observations, the precise mechanism by which K-channel blockade exerts its effects cannot be determined. It is possible that the blockade of K channels momentarily prevents the cells from extruding or sequestering Ca^{2+}. Alternatively, an increase in single-channel open time or lengthening of a period of increased open-state probability would both result in the change in macroscopic kinetics observed here. Regardless of the molecular mechanism, this observation demonstrates that K-channel function and the consequent membrane re- or hyper-polarization are responsible for regulating the magnitude and perhaps the time course of the antigen-specific influx of Ca^{2+} in CTL.

SUMMARY

Using ratio-imaging fluorescence microscopy, we have investigated the changes in intracellular Ca^{2+} ($[Ca^{2+}]_i$) that occurred in cytotoxic T lymphocytes (CTL) upon target-cell binding. This process resulted in a rapid increase in $[Ca^{2+}]_i$, which was localized in the region of the CTL in contact with the target cell. This increase was mediated both by influx from the external medium as well as by release from intracellular stores. Although the magnitude of the initial increase in $[Ca^{2+}]_i$ was not dependent upon the presence of extracellular Ca^{2+}, influx was necessary for sustained elevation of $[Ca^{2+}]_i$. Inasmuch as target-cell lysis by the CTL clone used is dependent on extracellular Ca^{2+}, this suggests that a prolonged elevation of $[Ca^{2+}]_i$ is necessary for lytic function. It was also shown that the increase in $[Ca^{2+}]_i$ and its subsequent decay show several pulsations. The mechanism by which these variations are generated and their possible function is not known. Finally, a role for K^+ efflux in the control of the antigen-induced increase in $[Ca^{2+}]_i$ was demonstrated. Thus it is becoming clear that signal transduction in CTL is remarkably complex, involving several ionic species and second messengers.

REFERENCES

1. MARTZ, E. 1977. Mechanism of specific tumor cell lysis by alloimmune T lymphocytes: Resolution and characterization of discreet steps in the cellular interaction. Contemp. Top. Immunobiol. **7**: 301–361.
2. PODACK, E. R. & P. J. KONIGSBERG. 1984. Cytotoxic T cell granules: Isolation, structural, biochemical, and functional characterization. J. Exp. Med. **160**: 695–710.
3. HENKART, P., P. MILLARD, C. REYNOLDS & M. HENKART. 1984. Cytolytic activity of purified cytoplasmic granules from cytotoxic rat LGL tumors. J. Exp. Med. **160**: 75–93.
4. HENKART, P. 1985. Mechanism of lymphocyte-mediated cytotoxicity. Annu. Rev. Immunol. **3**: 31–58.
5. YOUNG, J. D.-E. & Z. COHN. 1986. Cell-mediated killing: A common mechanism? Cell **46**: 641–642.
6. GEIGER, B., D. ROSEN & G. BERKE. 1982. Spatial relationships of MTOC and the contact area of CTLs and target cells. J. Cell. Biol. **95**: 137–143.
7. KUPFER, A. & G. DENNERT. 1984. Reorientation of the MTOC and the Golgi apparatus in cloned cytotoxic T lymphocytes triggered by binding to lysable target cells. J. Immunol. **133**: 2762–2766.
8. YANNELLI, J. R., J. A. SULLIVAN, G. L. MANDELL & V. H. ENGELHARD. 1986. Reorientation and fusion of cytotoxic T lymphocyte granules after interaction with target cells as determined by high resolution cinemicrography. J. Immunol. **136**: 377–382.
9. GRAY, L. S., J. A. SULLIVAN, G. L. MANDELL & V. H. ENGELHARD. 1988. Spatial and temporal characteristics of the increase in intracellular Ca^{2+} in cytolytic T lymphocytes induced by cellular antigen. Submitted.
10. ISAKOV, N., M. I. MALLY, W. SCHOLZ & A. ALTMAN. 1987. T-lymphocyte activation: The role of protein kinase C and the bifurcating inositol phospholipid signal transduction pathway. Immunol. Rev. **95**: 89–111.
11. STEWART, S., V. PRPIC, F. POWERS, S. BOCCKINO, R. ISAACKS & J. EXTON. 1986. Perturbation of the human T cell antigen receptor-T3 complex leads to the production of inositol tetrakisphosphate: Evidence for conversion from inositol triphosphate. Proc. Natl. Acad. Sci. USA **83**: 6098–6102.
12. KOZUMBO, W., D. HARRIS, S. GROMKOWSKI, J.-C. CEROTTINI & P. CERUTTI. 1987. Molecular mechanisms involved in T cell activation. II. The PI signal-transducing mechanism mediates antigen-induced lymphokine production but not IL-2 induced proliferation in cytotoxic T lymphocytes. J. Immunol. **138**: 606–612.
13. IMBODEN, J. B., C. WEYAND & J. GORONZY. 1987. Antigen recognition by a human T cell leads to increases in inositol phosphate. J. Immunol. **138**: 1322–1324.
14. IMBODEN, J. B. & J. D. STOBO. 1985. Transmembrane signalling by the T cell antigen receptor. Perturbation of the T3-antigen receptor complex generates inositol phosphates and releases calcium ions from intracellular stores. J. Exp. Med. **161**: 446–456.
15. PUTNEY, J. W. 1987. Formation and actions of calcium-mobilizing messenger, inositol 1,4,5-triphosphate. Am. J. Physiol. **252**: G149–G157.
16. KUNO, M. & P. GARDNER. 1987. Ion channels activated by inositol 1,4,5-triphosphate in plasma membrane of human T-lymphocytes. Nature **326**: 301–304.
17. WEISS, A., J. B. IMBODEN, D. M. SHOBACK & J. D. STOBO. 1984. Role of T3 surface molecules in human T cell activation: T3 dependent activation results in a rise in cytoplasmic free calcium. Proc. Natl. Acad. Sci. USA **81**: 4169–4173.

18. OETTGEN, H. F., C. TERHORST, L. C. CANTLEY & P. M. ROSOFF. 1985. Stimulation of the T3-T cell receptor complex induces a membrane potential sensitive calcium influx. Cell **40:** 583–590.

19. IMBODEN, J. B., A. WEISS & J. D. STOBO. 1985. The antigen receptor on a human T cell line initiates activation by increasing cytoplasmic free calcium. J. Immunol. **134:** 663–665.

20. NISBET-BROWN, E., R. CHEUNG, J. LEE & E. GELFAND. 1985. Antigen-dependent increase in cytosolic free calcium in specific human T lymphocyte clones. Nature **316:** 545–547.

21. SHAPIRO, D., B. ADAMS & J. NIEDERHUBER. 1985. Antigen-specific T cell activation results in an increase in cytoplasmic free calcium. J. Immunol. **135:** 2256–2261.

22. GRAY, L. S., J. R. GNARRA & V. H. ENGELHARD. 1987. Demonstration of a calcium influx in cytolytic T lymphocytes in response to target cell binding. J. Immunol. **138:** 63–69.

23. GRAY, L. S. & J. H. RUSSELL. 1986. Cytolytic T lymphocyte effector function requires plasma membrane chloride flux. J. Immunol. **136:** 3032–3037.

24. TSIEN, R. Y., T. POZZAN & T. J. RINK. 1982. T cell mitogens cause earlier changes in cytoplasmic free calcium and membrane potential in lymphocytes. Nature **295:** 68–71.

25. GRAY, L. S., J. R. GNARRA, J. H. RUSSELL & V. H. ENGELHARD. 1987. The role of K^+ in the regulation of the increase in intracellular Ca^{2+} mediated by the T lymphocyte antigen receptor. Cell **50:** 119–127.

26. GRYNKIEWICZ, G., M. POENIE & R. Y. TSIEN. 1985. A new generation of Ca^{2+} indicators with greatly improved fluorescence properties. J. Biol. Chem. **260:** 3440–3450.

27. LEDBETTER, J. A., L. E. GENTRY, C. H. JUNE, P. S. RABINOVITCH & A. F. PURCHIO. 1987. Stimulation of T cells through the CD3/T-cell receptor complex: Role of cytoplasmic calcium, protein kinase C translocation, and phosphorylation of pp60c-src in the activation pathway. Mol. Cell. Biol. **7:** 650–656.

Lymphocyte-Mediated Cytolysis

Effectors, Lytic Signals, and the Mechanism whereby Early Membrane Derangements Result in Target-Cell Death[a]

GIDEON BERKE

Department of Cell Biology
The Weizmann Institute of Science
Rehovot, 76100, Israel

INTRODUCTION

The cytolytic T lymphocyte (CTL) and its related natural cytocidal (NC), natural killer (NK), large granular lymphoid (LGL), and lymphokine-activated killer (LAK) cells are important effectors relevant to virus infection, allograft rejection, and possibly to tumor immunity and certain autoimmune diseases. Recent observations of complement (C)-like lesions following lymphocyte-induced lysis, and the documentation of cytolytic granules and a lytic protein(s), perforin/cytolysin (Perf/Cyto), therein, in certain cytocidal lymphocytes, have lead to the proposition of a unified mechanism in lymphocytotoxicity involving granule exocytosis resulting in the formation of Perf/Cyto-lined, transmembrane "channels" (internal diameter (ID), 10–20 nm) in the target membrane.[1-4] An alternative pathway to the onset of lysis is suggested by studies on the mode of action of peritoneal exudate CTL (PEL) obtained directly from mice after allograft rejection, and of cytocidal hybridomas derived from PEL.[5-7] These highly potent, specific cytotoxic cells[8,9] produce neither C-like lesions, nor possess greater-than-background amounts of lytic granules, Perf/Cyto, nor N-α-benzyloxycarbonyl-L-lysine thiobenzyl ester (BLT)-esterase activity. Interestingly, when stimulated *in vitro* in the presence of interleukin-2 (IL-2), these *in vivo*-primed PEL (but not their hybridomas) transform into large dividing T lymphoblasts, which, unlike their forebears, possess massive quantities of lytic granules and BLT-esterase activity as well as nonspecific lytic activity.[7,7a] These results would thus suggest that high levels of lytic granules and BLT-esterase activity are preferably IL-2–dependent lymphocyte-differentiation markers rather than essential constituents of the cytocidal apparatus in at least the *in vivo*–primed, specific CTL.

Experiments suggest that the progressively increasing changes in target-membrane permeability induced by cytocidal lymphocytes of either type are, in fact, initiated by derangements of integral membrane components (including ion pumps), rather than by the formation of specific, protein-lined transmembrane "holes" (ID, 10–20 nm). Lymphocyte-mediated cytolysis, not unlike membrane

---

[a] This work was supported by Grants from the Israel Cancer Association and Bio-Yeda Ltd. G. Berke is the incumbent of the Bourla Professorial Chair in Cancer Research.

damage inflicted by low levels of chemically nonrelated cytotoxic agents, such as detergents, poly-L-lysins, activated C, and toxins like mellitin and α-toxin, appears to result from a lymphocyte-bound (possibly the T_i–T_3 complex) or secreted effector molecule(s) that affects the interaction of membrane lipids with transmembrane proteins (possibly MHC determinants) of the target, thus creating functional, submicroscopic disturbances in membrane permeability to ions ("leaky patches") (FIG. 4). Small membrane perturbations, rather than formation of specific transmembrane channels, which can be viewed by electron microscopy (EM) as "rings," "pits," or "holes," are sufficient to allow K^+/Na^+ flux down-concentration gradients normally maintained by Na^+/K^+-ATPase. This results in membrane depolarization and prelytic Ca^{2+} (and Cl^-) influx, or Ca^{2+} mobilization, from internal stores.[10,11] Persistent depolarization and elevation of cytosolic Ca^{2+} above a critical cytosolic level appears to be responsible for distinct (catastrophic) prelytic events in the target, namely, adenosine triphosphate (ATP)/creatine-phosphate exhaustion, blebbing, and DNA disintegration. Eventually the failure of ATP-fueled ion pumps to reestablish ion (Na^+/K^+ and Cl^-) gradients bring about net water influx ultimately leading to "colloid osmotic" lysis.

THE NATURE OF IMMUNOLOGICALLY INDUCED LETHAL LESIONS

The Complement Lesion

The formation of protein-lined, hollow transmembrane channels that often appear as rings (ID 100 Å) in negative-staining EM (see FIG. 2, D–I), has been proposed to be the transmembrane mechanism through which lysis occurs.[11a,b] Although a water-filled cylindrical structure of that dimension offers a simple (and intuitive) lytic mechanism enabling free leakage of ions and macromolecules through the hole, this supermolecular interpretation of the C-lesion has been questioned in recent years, and alternatives to the conventional structure/function relationship of C-rings have been proposed. For example, Dankert and Esser[12] have suggested that C-induced rings are only incidental to lysis. They tested the lytic activity and ring formation by thrombin-cleaved C_9 (C_9^n), and by intact C_9, and found that only the latter produced both lysis (with C_{5b}-C_8) and rings; the former (C_9^n) although as lytic as C_9, produced no rings! Further, sequential release of cellular constituents upon C- (and CTL-) induced lysis, showing a clear progression in the molecular size of secreted cellular constituents (first an immediate efflux of $^{86}Rb^+$, a potassium analog, and an influx of Ca^{2+}, followed by the release of ATP, and then of ^{51}Cr-labeled compounds and proteins), is incompatible with the formation of a transmembrane pore of a distinct large size at the outset of lysis. Critically important patch-electrode measurements of ion fluxes through the activated C-lesion[13] yielded ion conductivities accounted for by channel sizes of only 10 Å, versus the proposed 100 ± 20 Å deduced from EM. Furthermore, prelytic influx of Ca^{2+} [14] and depletion of high-energy phosphates (ATP and creatine phosphate) under low level Ab+C attack on nucleated cells (FIG. 1)[15] are difficult to explain with C-induced lysis initiated and completed by the infliction of 100 Å transmembrane holes. The alternative, viewing C-lesions, which appear as rings by negative-staining EM, merely as indicators of submicroscopic membrane derangements (leaky patches),[16] operationally like those inflicted by a wide range of chemicals and toxins (*vidae infra*),[17] is more consistent with the above observations.

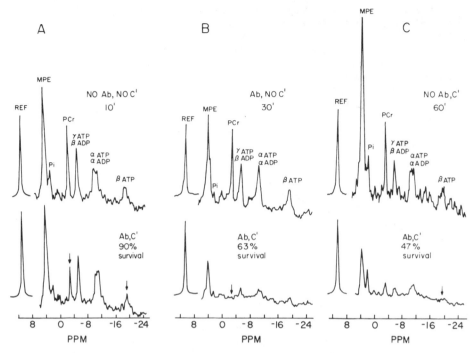

FIGURE 1. ^{31}P-nuclear magnetic resonance (NMR) spectra at 121.1 MHz of leukemia EL4 cells under low level Ab+C attack. Cells were obtained from the peritoneal cavities of syngeneic C57BL/6 mice 4–7 days after intraperitoneal inoculation, by washing with phosphate-buffered saline supplemented with newborn calf serum (10%). Cells (20×10^6/ml) were exposed to BALB/c (H-2^d) anti-EL4 (H-2^b) hyperimmune serum (Ab) diluted 1/100 for 30 min at 4°C with constant shaking. Complement (C'), guinea pig serum, was added diluted 1/10 in **A** and 1/15 in **B** and **C**. The cell suspension was reincubated at 37°C with shaking; survival was determined microscopically by eosin dye exclusion, counting 100–200 cells. For NMR measurements, 4×10^8 treated cells were washed twice with cold phosphate-free Krebs-Ringer buffer solution containing 140 mM NaCl, 5.6 mM KCl, 3.0 mM $CaCl_2$, 1.4 mM $MgSO_4$, 1 mg/ml glucose, and 20 mM HEPES buffer, pH 7.4. Cell pellets were resuspended in 1 ml of a 30% (v/v) D_2O in Krebs Ringer HEPES buffer to a total volume of about 1.5 ml and then transferred to a 10 mm NMR glass tube. The tube contained, in addition, a coaxial capillary with 10 μl reference of 1 M H_3PO_4, 1 M HCl, and 115 mM $PrCl_3$. Spectra were recorded with a Bruker CXP-300 spectrometer, at 4°C. 1000 to 6000 transients of 400 pulses were applied with an interval of 0.69 sec between transients using exponential multiplication with a line broadening of 15 Hz. The external reference signal (REF) in all spectra was recorded with a 10× lower gain. 0 PPM refers to 85% H_3PO_4; REF, reference solution; MPE, monophosphoesters; Pi, inorganic phosphate; PCr, phosphocreatine; ATP, adenosine triphosphate; ADP, adenosine diphosphate. By integrating the various peaks, approximate values can be obtained for intracellular concentration of various phosphate compounds, taking into account 10 micromoles of the reference solution and 1800 cubic microns as the average volume of EL4 cells. For example, from the spectrum of control cells (FIG. 1**A**), MPE = 4.2 mM, PCR = 1.6 mM, ATP = 0.7 mM, and ADP = 0.9 mM. (Tirosh *et al.*[15] With permission from *Complement*.)

The CTL Lesion

Although the notion that C-like factors are involved in CTL-mediated lysis was far from popular, it was Dourmashkin[1] who first showed, by negative-staining EM, C-like lesions following lysis in antibody-dependent cell-mediated cytotoxicity (ADCC) and NK. Interestingly, structurally similar lesions have been observed by these authors in lysis mediated by lymphocytes, monocytes, and neutrophils.[b] Later, lytic lysosomal granules of effector-cell origin were suggested to be the origin of the C-like rings observed.[2,18] Our own search for similar C-like rings in lysis induced by highly lytic, *in vivo*–primed CTL from the peritoneal cavity of the alloimmunized mice (PEL)[8,9] ended with negative results[5,6] (FIG. 2, A–C). Repeated experiments and extended incubation periods of up to 19 hr, resulted in massive cytolysis of the target but failed to reveal ring-shaped structures comparable to those detected after Ab+C or NK attack on the same target cells (FIG. 2, G–I). Membranes isolated following NK-induced lysis, of both mouse or human origin, showed C-like rings (FIG. 2, D–F), but their origin and function remain to be determined.

Although the precise lytic nature of C-rings is still not fully understood, failure to detect them following lysis induced by PEL argues against pore formation in lysis induced by *in vivo*–primed CTL, such as PEL, and suggests an alternative mechanism for the onset of lysis. Importantly, these results do not support or exclude involvement of a secreted CTL molecule that is cytocidal without forming rings. The latter possibility is reminiscent of lysis induced by thrombin-cleaved C_9 (C_9^n) in the absence of rings.[12] The following findings are consistent with the observation that lysis induced by *in vivo*–primed CTL is not initiated by inflicting huge transmembrane pores (ID, 10–20 nm):[2,3] (1) progressive rather than simultaneous release of constituents from affected targets, starting with efflux of ^{86}Rb, followed by ATP release, then by ^{51}Cr-labeled components,[19–21] (infliction of 10–20 nm transmembranal channels would be expected to result in close to simultaneous release of all these molecules); (2) prelytic events inside the target including the sudden prelytic increase in cytosolic Ca^{2+},[10,11,12] and DNA disintegration into 190 bp units (nucleosomes) preceding ^{51}Cr-release,[23,24] (these are difficult to reconcile with a lytic mechanism that starts by inflicting 10–20 nm holes); (3) colloid-osmotic lysis of affected target cells,[21] (the osmotic pressure of a cell perforated with such holes should not rise at all); and (4) strong temperature dependence of ^{51}Cr-release from CTL-damaged target cells, and its complete, yet reversible, arrest upon cooling,[25] (leakage through protein-lined holes should be only minimally affected by temperature, if at all).

WHAT IS THE ALTERNATIVE TO A LYTIC MECHANISM INVOLVING A PROTEIN-LINED TRANSMEMBRANE CHANNEL (ID 10–20 nm) IN IMMUNE CYTOLYSIS?

Recent studies on the mode of action of lytic agents show a sigmoidal-shaped dose response, suggesting positive cooperation in lysis induced by each of the various cytotoxic agents (hemolytic viruses, toxins, detergents), as well as syn-

---

[b] Formation of identical circular lesions would indicate a common molecular mechanism for lymphocytes, monocytes, and neutrophils. Yet lytic granules and Perf/Cyto have been reported to be an exclusive component of cytolytic lymphocytes.[18] This discrepancy will have to be resolved.

ergy when two chemically unrelated lytic agents are presented together, each at sublytic concentration[17] (schematically represented in FIG. 3). Positive cooperation on one hand, and synergy between unrelated agents on the other, strongly argue against formation of a unique channel by monomers of each lytic agent, through which lysis occurs, for synergistic channel formation of chemically distinct monomers is not to be expected. It suggests, instead, a common membranolytic mechanism triggered similarly by the various toxins.[17] Namely, the dose

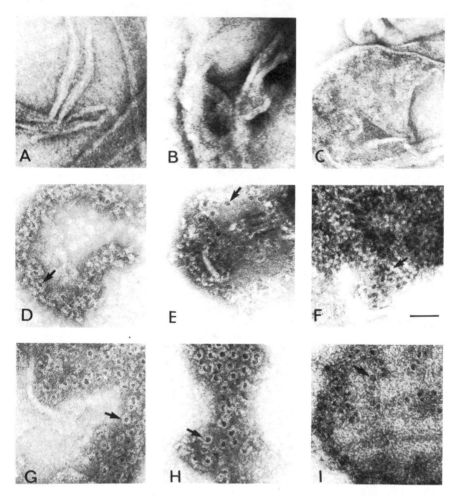

FIGURE 2. Ring structures in immune cytolysis. **A, B, C,** negatively stained membrane isolated after CTL-induced lysis (**A,** BALB/c anti-EL4 PEL plus EL4; **B,** C57BL/6 anti-P815 PEL plus P815; **C,** C57BL/c anti-L1210 PEL plus L1210). No rings are seen. **D, E, F,** membranes following NK induced lysis (**D,** CBA/J NK + YAC-1; **E,** human LGL + K562; **F,** CBA/J plus L1210). Typical rings are seen. **G, H, I,** membranes following lysis induced by hyperimmune serum (Ab) plus complement (C), (**G, H;** BALB/c anti-EL4 serum plus EL4 target cells; **I,** C57BL/6J anti-L1210 serum plus L1210). Typical rings are seen. Bar represents 47.6 nm (**A, B**), 43.8 nm (**C, D, F, H**), and 55.5 nm (**E, G, I**).

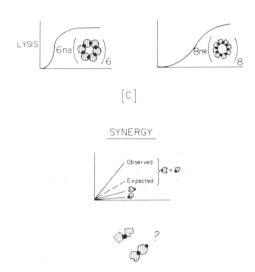

FIGURE 3. Schematic representation of positive cooperation and synergy in the lytic action of cytocidal agents. [C], concentration. Whereas buildup of specific multimeric channels explains satisfactorily the sigmoidal behavior and sudden rise in lytic activity beyond the threshold level, it is incompatible with the synergy observed between chemically unrelated agents at subthreshold concentration. A common critical membrane mechanism affected similarly by widely different lytic agents is more compatible with the results.

response of cell lysis by most toxins is S-shaped, not because of failure to assemble channels at low toxin concentration (see FIGURE), but because it is more likely to be due to compensating ion (primarily Na^+/K^+ and Ca^{2+})-pump activities that reverse subthreshold perturbations inflicted by the toxin. The steep rise is due to membrane potential collapse at higher toxin concentrations. Enhanced ion-flux concentration gradients, induced by interaction of lytic agents with membrane lipids (phospholipase, detergents), or with transmembrane proteins (lectins, poly-L-lysine), and direct damage to ionic pumps or channels (particularly ouabain-sensitive Na^+/K^+-ATPase) appear to be a common initial membrane perturbation ultimately leading to lysis. Prelytic events such as Ca^{2+}-influx[10,23] (prior to ^{14}C-sucrose release,[26] but subsequent to ^{86}Rb influx), as well as prelytic depletion of high energy compounds[15] (FIG. 1) may all be common events resulting from initially submicroscopic derangement(s) induced by a wide range of chemically unrelated lytic agents including activated C and CTL.[c]

SECRETED VERSUS CELL-BOUND LYTIC MECHANISM

Although it is rather easy to envisage a secreted toxin of CTL/NK origin that perturbs membrane permeability by creating hollow transmembrane channels, or by membrane derangements (see below), it is more difficult to conceive of lytic

---

[c] Although closely resembling C_9 both structurally and functionally, P_1 and C_9 have been reported to be molecularly distinct entities;[3] yet the recent successful isolation of P_1 by an anti-C_9 affinity column[61] implies closer similarity and perhaps identity!

effects induced by a putative CTL surface-membrane-bound molecule, as previously suggested.[27] Although less popular, this is not impossible particularly with the membrane derangement model of lysis described below. The obvious advantages of a putative CTL-lytic mechanism that is bound to, or inserted in, but not fully transferred to, the target-cell membrane are that it can be reused by the effector cell, thus enabling their recycling,[28,29] probably in the absence of protein synthesis;[19] and that it obviates the problem of effector self-killing, which one would expect to occur with a secreted toxin like Perf/Cyto, yet which is usually not observed with *in vivo*–primed CTL.[29,30] CTL bound–effector molecules may be located at the tips of finger-like structures shown to penetrate membrane foldings of the target cell during effector/target interaction[20,30] (see Fig. 8). Indeed, earlier studies have shown close proximity and intimate contact of the opposing killer/target membranes, enabling transfer of membrane (though not cytoplasmic)[30] probes such as 1,6-diphenyl 1,3,5-hextriene (DPH) from effector to target and vice versa.[31]

FROM EARLY MEMBRANE DAMAGE TO CELL LYSIS

The function of biological membranes as semipermeable barriers that maintain considerable ion gradients depends on their composition, structure, appropriate interaction of the lipids with each other, and with integral (trans)membrane proteins, as well as their ion pumps and channel activities. Perturbation of the transmembrane–protein/lipid interaction by the external binding of a ligand (cross-linking or not), or its insertion into the bilayer, creates an energetically unstable protein/lipid interface that may enable ion leakage around the transmembrane proteins, including membrane pumps or channels.[27] Indeed, permeability changes as a result of membrane-lipid derangements induced by inserted proteins have been demonstrated in numerous simple membrane systems; for example, incorporation of glycophorin into synthetic lipid vesicles causes a dramatic increase in their permeability.[32] Similarly lysozyme, cytochrome C, and poly-L-lysine increase the permeability of lipid vesicles to Na^+.[33]

Ion Fluxes and Membrane Depolarization

According to the membrane derangement model for immune cytolysis (FIG. 4), leakage from the membrane of an affected target occurs initially through submicroscopic perturbations in membrane structure (leaky patches) induced either by the binding of C_{5b}-C_8-$C_{9(n)}$ or of a secreted lymphocyte effector molecule(s) (Perf/Cyto/NKCF/lymphotoxin), or of an intact CTL through its T_i–T_3 complex. Hence, ring-like structures, where observed, represent sites of membrane perturbation rather than transmembrane pores of ID 10–20 nm. Sequential permeability changes (both lymphocyte and Ab+C induced) probably reflect progressively failing ionic pumps, which are only initially capable of controlling K^+ efflux (depolarization) and Na^+ and Ca^{2+} influx through the deranged membrane. In the red cell, hemoglobin release due to cell rupture is initiated by relatively little damage, which allows Na^+ influx. This relatively minor damage, however, is sufficient to override the outward Na^+ pumping ability of the affected cells and leads to its lysis. Nucleated cells, on the other hand, probably require considerably more damage to initiate lysis, for they possess greater repair mechanisms than erythrocytes and higher energy resources to support ion-pump activity against concentration gradients. The growing lesion is thus considered to be the result of progressively collapsing systems, these systems being stimulated but also exhausted by the lytic signal.[10]

Prelytic Effects of Ca^{2+}

An important early event in CTL-induced lysis is the sudden prelytic increase in cytosolic Ca^{2+} in the target (and the effector), initially observed in this laboratory[10,11] and more recently by Tsien and Poenie.[22] A sudden (prelytic) influx of Ca^{2+} into cells under C attack has been reported earlier.[14,26] Prelytic increase in

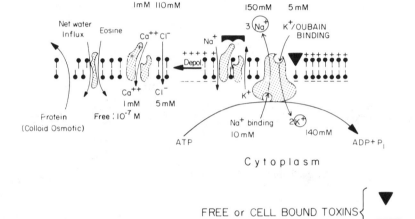

FIGURE 4. Schematic representation of common membrane events in the lytic action of cytocidal agents (free or cell bound). Submicroscopic membrane perturbations, rather than formation of microscopic pores, induce depolarization, Ca^{2+} influx, and metabolic exhaustion ultimately leading to lysis. For Ca^{2+}-mediated effects resulting in cellular injuries, see text.[36]

cytosolic Ca^{2+} occurs through the deranged target-cell membrane or through voltage-dependent gates of the depolarized membrane down a 10,000-fold Ca^{2+} concentration gradient, or by (pH-mediated) release from internal stores.[10,11] Intracellular Ca^{2+} is a well-appreciated factor in cell injury induced by a wide range of molecularly unrelated toxic agents.[26,34] Lysis induced by the Ca^{2+}-ionophore A23187 (FIG. 5) provides a good example for the primary relationships among increase in cytosolic Ca^{2+}, temperature, and cell damage. In the absence of Ca^{2+} (Mg_2 EGTA), certain cells tolerate up to 100 μM A23187; the inclusion of Ca^{2+} but not Mg^{++} brings about suddent cell death. Hence A23187 in itself is not toxic to the cell; its toxicity is Ca^{2+}-mediated. It is of interest to note that CTL-, Perf/Cyto-, and A23187-induced killing are similarly temperature and external Ca^{2+}-dependent, (FIG. 5) although the Ca^{2+}-dependence of Perf/Cyto is attributed to a putative Perf polymerization phase,[3] rather than to an effect on the target proper. Clearly, both are likely and possible.

Under normal physiological conditions, cytosolic free Ca^{2+} is maintained at a submicromolar concentration (total Ca^{2+} concentration is 1 mM). Controlled Ca^{2+} influx or its release from internal-bound stores is a well-recognized signal, including the induction of the repair mechanism after low-level Ab+C attack.[26,35] When damage to the membrane is considerable, but not massive, prelytic elevation of cytosolic (and probably nuclear) Ca^{2+} may account for distinguishable prelytic effects observed during CTL-induced lysis, such as DNA disintegration, blebbing, cytoplasmic streams, membrane damage, and finally, zeiosis.[20,23] The mechanism whereby a persistent increase in cytosolic Ca^{2+} brings about cytolysis is not fully understood, but it is probably many-faceted.[10,11,14,35] Ca^{2+} effects on phospholipase A_2, resulting in cleavage of phospholipids and production of lyso-derivatives, may account for terminal damage to the membrane. Direct Ca^{2+} effects on mitochondria may suppress energy production, hence exacerbating the depletion

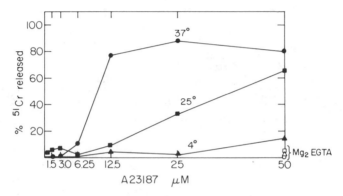

FIGURE 5. Ionophore-induced cytolysis—Ca^{2+} and temperature-dependent. ^{51}Cr-L1210 cells were incubated with the Ca^{2+} ionophore A23187 at 4, 25, and 37°C for 30 min at which time the percent of ^{51}Cr released was assessed. The medium, phosphate-buffered saline, contained 1 mM Ca^{2+}. Medium containing Mg_2EGTA, pH 7.4, gave no lysis at either temperature.

of ATP-dependent ion pumps. Ca^{2+} activation of a major cellular ATPase such as actomysin could lead to major ATP depletion, and consequently to the additional suppression of ATP-fueled Na^+/K^+-ATPase (pump) activity,[10,36] already compromised by the depolarization of the membrane. Ca^{2+}-activated proteases may be responsible for damage to cytoskeleton, culminating in bleb formation.[36a]

Cell Lysis

The outcome of any low-level chemical, physical, and immunological (C- or CTL-induced) assault rests heavily on the target's ability to compensate for and/or repair the inflicted damage. Small perturbations in ion fluxes are dealt with by enhanced ion (mostly Na^+ and Ca^{2+})-pumping activity, energy metabolism, and O_2 consumption by the affected cell. Considerable, or small but persistent, derangements of the cell membrane can exhaust energy resources that normally enable outward pumping of Na^+ and Ca^{2+}, as well as other repair mechanisms. Cessation of outward Na^+ pumping leads to net water influx and (colloid-osmotic) cell rupture. Massive derangements of the membrane, such as those inflicted by detergents above critical micellar concentration, by high doses of Ab+C, or by hypotonic shock, would obviously lead to immediate membrane dissolution and cell death and are not relevant in this discussion.

HETEROGENEITY OF CTL: COMMON DENOMINATORS AND DISTINCT CHARACTERISTICS PERTINENT TO THEIR LYTIC MECHANISM

CTL procured from the rejection site of an ascites tumor allograft (PEL) are nondividing $Ly2^+$, small lymphocytes, exhibiting highly potent, specific binding and lytic activity,[8,29,37] whereas their precursors or lymphocytes growing *in vitro* following activation with mitogen, alloantigen, or IL-2 are large lymphoblastoid cells, some exhibiting heavy granulation, adherence to surface and often to third-party target cells, as well as broader NK-like binding and killing activity.[38–40] Therefore, equating the mechanism whereby *in vitro*–growing CTL, LGL, or LAK kill with that of *in vivo*–primed mature CTL, such as PEL, must be done with caution because potentially distinct killing mechanisms observed with a given population may merely reflect the state of activation or differentiation of the said population. For example, whereas PEL recycle after lytic attack,[28,29] LGL do not, unless they are reactivated by interferon.[41] This constitutes a major, but not isolated, difference between the mode of action of NK and CTL. CTL propagated in IL-2 *in vitro,* unlike *in vivo*–primed CTL, exhibit bystander and even autologous killing, probably through a soluble mediator.[42] Even *in vivo*–primed PEL precursors, in sharp contrast to mature PEL, exhibit considerable nonspecific binding and killing activity.[38] Differences in the mechanisms of lysis induced by CTL and Cyto (a lytic component isolated from granules of NK cells)[18] are shown by the failure of cytolysin-antibody to inhibit CTL-mediated lysis while effectively blocking NK-induced lysis and ADCC.[18,43] The failure of cytolysin antibody to block CTL-induced lysis, has been explained by the inability of the antibody to penetrate the intercellular space of CTL/target conjugates. This explanation is difficult to accept, however, in view of the similar intercellular structure of NK and CTL conjugates.

Lysis induced by CTL involves a multistep process initiated by a Mg^{++}-dependent binding step[44] resulting in specific conjugate formation,[37,45,46] followed by a Ca^{2+}- and temperature-dependent delivery of the lethal hit,[25,46,47] a killer-independent lytic phase[46] and recycling of the effector to start a new lytic interaction.[28,29] A basically similar sequence of events has since been shown to operate in NK-induced lysis (reviewed in reference 43). Importantly, although there are shared features of lymphocyte (CTL, NK, and LAK)-induced cytolysis, most of them are common to a wide range of molecularly distinct cytocidal factors, such as low levels of Triton X-100, hemolytic viruses, α-toxin of *S. aureus,* activated C, mellitin, and poly-L-lysine.[26] Therefore extrapolating from the lytic effects of granules extracted from certain effector cells to the mode of action of *in vivo*–primed CTL merely because of a common denominator such as Ca^{2+} and temperature dependence may be misleading.

In Vivo–*Primed PEL*

Most, if not all, recent work on secretory cytocidal granules and their lytic protein(s) Perf(s)/Cyto and enzymes has been carried out with LGL, LGL-like tumors, and IL-2–dependent CTL/NK lines. Therefore, we sought to investigate the involvement of lytic granules in killing induced by *in vivo*–primed CTL, by their hybridomas, and by IL-2–dependent CTL lines derived from such CTL. In the course of earlier studies on the rejection of ascites tumors (allogeneic and syngeneic[8,9,25,48]), we observed a population of small-to-medium–sized PEL that exhibited highly potent, specific cytocidal activity (TABLE 1). The effector in this system, resulting from a dividing *in vivo* pool[38] is a small-to-medium–sized Thy-1.2[+], L3T4[-], SIg[-], Ly2[+] lymphocyte that exhibits specific binding to target cells,[45] resulting in conjugate formation[37,45] and lysis[9] (TABLE 1). Electron microscopy of PEL conjugated to target cells reveals a well-developed Golgi zone, membrane-bound lysosome-like granules, mitochondria, and many free ribosomes.[29] Up to 50% of all nonadherent cells recovered from the peritoneal cavity shortly after tumor allograft rejection can bind and form conjugates of which up to

TABLE 1. The Lytic Activity and Specificity of BALB/c Anti-EL4 PEL, the PEL-Hybridoma, and IL-2–Dependent PEL Blasts[a]

	75 Min			240 Min		
[51]Cr-Target (H-2)	PEL	PEL-Hybridoma	PEL Blasts	PEL	PEL-Hybridoma	PEL Blasts
	(Percent of ^{51}Cr released)					
EL4 (K[b]D[b])	23.4	6	51.7	70	46	100
BW (K[k]D[k])	0.9	—	2.5	4.3	0	3.5
YAC (K[k]D[d])	4.6	0	1.6	7.1	0	59.2
L1210 (K[d]D[d])	0.6	—	5.2	1.9	—	36.2

[a] BALB/c anti-EL4 PEL[8], their activated PEL-hybridomas,[50] or IL-2–dependent PEL-blasts[7] were mixed with ^{51}Cr-labeled target cells, and the mixture was cocentrifuged to promote conjugate formation.[37] The release of ^{51}Cr into the medium was determined after 75 and 240 min incubation at 37°C. BALB/c mice are of the H-2[d] haplotype. The percent of spontaneous ^{51}Cr release was under 10% at 75 min and less than 25% after 240 min.

85% can kill.[9,29,45] The unidirectional killing exhibited by CTL may be related to the polar orientation of its developed Golgi zone[29] and microtubule organizing center (MTOC),[49] both of which tend to localize at the target contact zone, and probably play a role in binding or in the delivery of the lethal signal.

IL-2–*Dependent PEL Blasts*

When *in vivo*–primed PEL are cultivated in IL-2, they transform into dividing PEL blasts (Thy-1.2[+], Thy-1.1[-], L3T4[-], Ly2[+], Sig[-], Ti α+ β m-RNA transcripts) that express PEL-like, broadly reactive nonspecific killing activity in a short-term assay (75 min), but exhibit NK-like–specific killing in a 4 hr assay[7,7a] (TABLE 1).

PEL Hybridomas

Early attempts to somatically hybridize CTL and form CTL hybridomas were unsuccessful, the failure being attributed to polyethylene glycol–mediated lysis of the fusion partner (usually BW lymphoma) induced by the CTL. In 1981, our laboratory reported successful PEL-BW fusions, resulting in production of lytic CTL hybridomas[50,51] that grow in culture and exhibit considerable, specific lytic activities (TABLE 1) in the absence of IL-2. These characteristics are augmented upon *in vitro* stimulation by mitogenic lectins, concanavalin A (Con A), or phytohemagglutinin (PHA), or by specific antigenic cells, but not by IL-2.

LYTIC GRANULES AND LYTIC PROTEINS OF THE VARIOUS CTL: INFLUENCE OF IL-2

Based on these and other observations that CTL contain a well-developed Golgi apparatus and related lysosomes,[29] it has been suggested that lysosomal enzymes of the effector cell are involved in the induction of lysis.[52] The isolation of potent (lysosomal) cytocidal granules from certain IL-2–dependent LGL/NK cells and NK/CTL lines[3,4,53] supports the proposal that secretory (lysosomal) cytocidal granules are involved in both NK- and CTL-induced lysis. Yet considerable amounts of lytic granules have been detected in nonlytic lymphocytes and, again contrary to expectations, lytic granules have not been isolated from some potent effector cells.[18] Hence, the correlation between cytocidal activity of lymphocytes and lytic granules is not clear. Furthermore, as most studies on lytic granules have been conducted with LGL tumors or IL-2–dependent NK/CTL/LAK/mixed lymphocyte culture (MLC) cells, we chose to examine the presence of lytic granules both in *in vivo*–primed PEL where we have already observed only a few lysosomal granules by EM[29] in their *in vitro*–growing hybridomas, and in IL-2–dependent lines of PEL blasts. While confirming considerable amounts of (Ca^{2+}-dependent) cytolytic granules in the formerly lytic CTLL-2 cells, employed as positive control,[3] only background lytic activity has been observed in high-density granules released by N_2–decavitation from highly potent PEL fractionated on Percoll (TABLE 2).[6,d] Furthermore, and in agreement with previous results of Henkart *et al.*,[18] only background levels of lytic granules have been found in PEL hybridomas either before or after activation with Con A (5 μg/ml) or antigen (x-irradiated EL4 cells), with or without IL-2 (TABLE 2). In sharp contrast to PEL and PEL hybridomas, massive quantities of Ca^{2+}-dependent lytic granules have been detected in IL-2–dependent PEL blasts, derived from PEL by cultivation in IL-2 (TABLE 2).[7,7a] On the other hand, normally noncytocidal cells, such as the T_h-cell clone Z1, capable of inducing experimental allergic encephalomyelitis (EAE) in rats[54] possess considerable amounts of lytic granules (Berke and Ben-Nun, in preparation).

Evidence supporting the presence of (cytocidal) granules in IL-2–dependent PEL blasts but not in *in vivo*–primed PEL comes from immunological studies. Granules extracted from PEL blasts or from CTLL-2–positive controls, but not

---

[d] Low levels of granule-mediated cytocidal activity against sheep red blood cells have been observed with granules from nonlytic cells.[18] Hence, the detection of control-level, Ca^{2+}-dependent lytic activities with granules from PEL, EL4, (TABLE 2), and those mentioned in reference 60 must be dealt with cautiously. Detection may be due to small contamination with blood LGL or with PEL lymphoblastoid precursors during the isolation of PEL (1/1000 is sufficient), or due to background activity of lysosomal granules present in all cells. Similar considerations apply to BLT-esterase activity (TABLE 4).

TABLE 2. Cytolytic Activity of Percoll Isolated–CTL Granules and Postnuclear Extracts[a]

Cell Source and Material Tested		Lysis of ^{51}Cr-SRBC[b]	
		+ Ca	− Ca
		(mean percent ^{51}Cr release)	
Formerly CTL			
CTLL-2	pn	91.6	0
CTLL-2	gr	84.7	0
CTL *in vivo*			
PEL anti-EL4	pn	2.1	0
PEL anti-EL4	gr	0.6	0
Spleen anti-EL4	pn	0	0
Spleen anti-EL4	pn	0.7	0
CTL *in vitro*			
PEL-hybridoma + IL-2	pn	1.8	nm[c]
PEL-hybridoma + EL4	pn	1	nm
PEL-blasts (IL-2–dependent)	pn	97	0
Con A blasts day 1	gr	0.4	0
Con A blasts day 2	gr	16	0
Con A blasts day 4	gr	67.8	0
Non-CTL controls			
EL4	pn	1.7	0
EL4	gr	0.9	0
P815	pn	0	0
P815	gr	0	0

[a] ^{51}Cr-labeled SRBC (2.5×10^6) were incubated in triplicate with either Percoll-fractionated granules (gr) isolated and fractionated as described[18] or postnuclear extracts from homogenized cells (pn) both diluted 1/10–1/25 for 30 min at 37°C in the presence of Ca^{2+} or, in its absence, Mg_2EGTA.

[b] SRBC = sheep red blood cells.

[c] nm, not measured.

from PEL, reacted with a rabbit anti-Perforin 1 serum (anti-P_1) generously provided by Dr. E. Podack. Postnuclear extracts, tested instead of isolated granules, gave nonspecific results. Immunofluorescence of permeabilized PEL/EL4 conjugates and Western blots confirmed the above results (FIGURES 6 and 7). A summary of some pros and cons for secretory granule involvement in lymphocyte-mediated cytolysis is presented in TABLE 3.

FIGURE 6. Dot-blot analysis of Perf1 in PEL, PEL blasts (PEL-B1) and CTLL-2. Four twofold serial dilutions (**A–D**, 10–1.25 µg protein, respectively) of Percoll-isolated granules (gr) and postnuclear fractions of homogenized cells (pn) were blotted onto a nitrocellulose filter. After quenching with 2% BSA in Ca-free PBS plus 0.02% azide, the filters were reacted with rabbit anti-perforin 1 (P_1) serum (kindly provided by Dr. E. Podack), washed, then reacted with [^{125}I]protein A, and finally exposed to X-ray film at −80°C. EL4 and P815 postnuclear supernatants were used as negative controls. As can be seen, granules from CTLL-2 and PEL blasts were positive, whereas those of PEL were negative. Postnuclear fractions of all cells, including the control EL4 and P815 cells showed reactivity, probably due to nonspecific reaction.

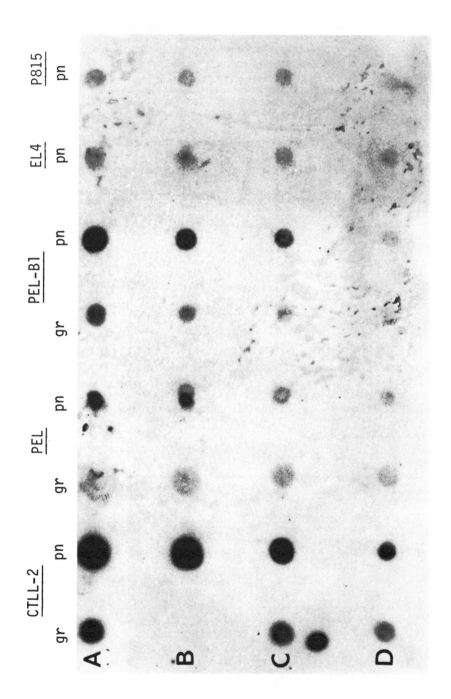

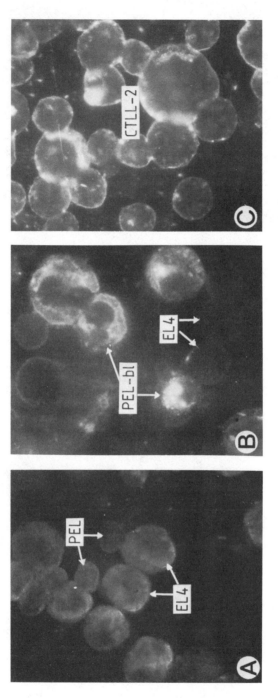

FIGURE 7. P_1 immunofluorescence staining of PEL, PEL-blasts, and CTLL-2. BALB/c anti-EL4-PEL and PEL-blasts were mixed with EL4, cocentrifuged to promote conjugation, and incubated at 37°C for 15 min. Fixed and permeabilized preparations of PEL/EL4 (**A**), PEL-blasts/EL4 (**B**), and of CTLL-2 controls (**C**) were reacted with rabbit anti-P_1 antibodies followed by a rhodamine-labeled goat anti-rabbit IgG.

TABLE 3. Involvement of Lytic Granules and of Perf/Cyto thereof in CTL-Mediated Lysis: Pros and Cons

Pros	Cons
1. Lytic granules and Perf/Cyto are present in cytocidal lymphocytes.	1. Some cytocidal lymphocytes possess only background levels of cytocidal granules.
2. Perf/Cyto is(are) lytic to various target cells, including RBC and killer cells.	2. How are killers spared as targets?
3. Lysis induced by Perf/Cyto is Ca^{2+}-dependent. (Ca^{2+} in excess is inhibitory.)	3. CTL induced lysis of certain targets in the absence of external Ca^{2+}; granule-induced lysis of these targets requires Ca^{2+}.
4. Perf/Cyto antibodies inhibit lytic granules, NK and ADCC.	4. Granule and Perf/Cyto antibodies do not inhibit CTL-mediated lysis.
5. Perf is released into the medium upon stimulation of certain CTL/NK with A23187+TPA.	5. Direct evidence for granule and for Perf/Cyto exocytosis and deposition on the target membrane is lacking.
6. Ring structures in lysis are induced by certain cytocidal lymphocytes, but also by monocytes and neutrophils (implies Perf/Cyto in nonlymphoid cells).	6. *In vivo*–primed CTL, such as PEL, lyse effectively without producing rings.

ROLE OF LYTIC LYSOSOMAL GRANULES IN LYMPHOCYTE DIFFERENTIATION

Even though a general correlation between the presence of lytic granules and lytic protein in lymphoid cells and the cytocidal activity of these cells has been observed in some systems,[18] distinct exceptions exist. PEL and PEL hybridomas, as mentioned above, provide outstanding negative examples, but these are not the only ones (TABLE 2). An interesting possibility, consistent with the above results, may be that lytic lysosomal granules are part and parcel of the T-cell response to IL-2, eventually playing a role in self-destruction of responding lymphocytes. Thus, dividing, granule-containing T cells of the $T_{c/s}$ (and perhaps even T_h) lineage continue to proliferate as long as IL-2 is supplied, but differentiate into small effector/memory-type cells, such as PEL, or disintegrate when IL-2 becomes limiting (FIG. 8). This model basically proposes competition between the response

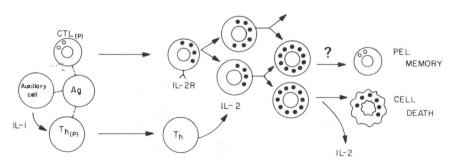

FIGURE 8. Schematic representation of IL-2 regulation of lysosomal-lytic granules expressed in T cytotoxic suppressor lymphocytes; ●, lytic granules; ○, lysosomal granules. See also ref. 54a.

of granulated cells to IL-2 and granule-induced self-destruction. IL-2 thus appears to play a dual role: inducing production and proliferation of granulated lymphocytes, preventing self-annihilation by endogenous granules. Accordingly, the primary role of these lytic lysosomal granules may be to eliminate proliferating lymphocytes upon removal from IL-2; their proposed function in target killing induced by granulated lymphoblasts CTL/NK/LAK may only be secondary.

SERINE (BLT) ESTERASE IN CTL: INFLUENCE OF IL-2

CTL-specific serine (BLT) esterases have been reported by Pasternack and Eisen[55] and shown to be a component of cytolytic granules; their release during CTL/target interaction has been implicated in the lytic process. Examination of

TABLE 4. Serine-Protease (BLT-Esterase) Activity in Various Cells[a]

Cells	BLT-Esterase Activity Optical Density, 412 nm/1 × 10⁶ Cells/15 min
PEL-blasts—B	40.5
PEL-blasts—E	47.0
CTLL-2	53.4
BALB/c anti-EL4 PEL	0.228
Normal spleen	0.222
PEL hybridoma	0.329
EL4	0.220
P815	0.386
L1210	0.018

[a] Cells were lysed in 0.5% NP40 in phosphate-buffered saline (PBS) without Ca for 30 min on ice, except for PEL hybridomas, from which a postnuclear extract was prepared. One hundred microliters lysate of appropriate dilution were reacted with 900 μl reaction mixture (0.2 M Tris-HCl, pH 8.1, 0.2 mM BLT, 0.2 mM dithiobis-2-nitrobenzoic acid (DTNB)) for 15 min at room temperature before the absorbance at 412 nm was recorded, using 100 μl PBS-Ca in 900 μl reaction mixture as blank as described before.[55]

BLT-esterase activity in PEL hybridomas (TABLE 4) revealed only background enzyme levels comparable to those observed in control noncytocidal cells, such as EL4 and P815 or normal lymphoid cells. In sharp contrast to PEL and their hybridomas, however, as has been observed with the lytic granules (TABLE 2), massive quantities of enzyme activity have been detected in the IL-2–dependent PEL blasts growing *in vitro*,[7a] comparable to that observed (as expected) in another IL-2–dependent (formerly lytic) lymphoblastoid line, CTLL-2. Hence BLT-esterase activity appears in cells that also possess cytocidal granules; BLT-esterase activity also appears to correlate with the level of granule activity. Only background levels of BLT-esterase activity, however, are found in highly potent PEL and in PEL hybridomas, indicating that elevated BLT-esterase levels are not a requisite part of the lytic machinery.

Cloning of CTLA-1 (CCP-1) and CTLA-3 (H factor) serine esterase transcripts[56,57] revealed the presence of such transcripts in various CTL, including PEL, but also in mast cells and some noncytotoxic cells shown to contaminate purified PEL preparation,[8] and may account for the detection of serine esterase transcripts in PEL preparations exhibiting background enzyme levels only.[7] Finding serine esterase in CTL, coupled with the demonstration of their release during certain lymphocyte/target interactions, and during lymphocyte stimulation,[55,58] suggests a possible role in lysis induced by granulated lymphoblasts (CTL/NK), perhaps through a protease cascade. Firm evidence, however, is lacking.

SECRETORY PROCESSES IN CTL-INDUCED LYSIS

The intuitive notion that CTL (including PEL)-induced lysis involves secretion of an effector molecule is shared by many;[29,53] yet unequivocal evidence for functional secretion of an effector molecule, its delivery to, and effect on the target, is still not fully at hand.

Early claims of transfer of informational macromolecules from effector to target as well as of formation of intercellular cytoplasmic bridges, allowing intercytoplasmic transfer of fluorescent probes have not been substantiated. Attempts to demonstrate transfer of isotopically or fluorescently labeled markers were all negative;[20,30] on the other hand, membrane-to-membrane transfer of a fluorescent probe, DPH, preferentially during specific CTL–target-cell interaction,[31] is consistent with very close membrane contacts established between the effector and its target. Zagury's demonstration[52] of extracellular lysosomal enzymes at an effector/target contact site did not establish their origin, namely, effector or the lysed target. Although followed microscopically,[59] actual (lytic) granule fusion and exocytosis of the granule content and its deposition on the target membrane in the course of CTL/target interaction remain to be shown. Repeated EM analyses of PEL/target conjugates[20,30] revealed finger-like structures pushing against the target as well as close intercellular contacts; yet no osmophilic, lysosomal-like granules were seen, either free, membrane-bound, or fused, at the contact site of PEL/target conjugates (FIG. 9). Hence, definitive evidence for granule exocytosis during lysis mediated by in vivo–primed CTL such as PEL is still elusive.

Release of BLT-esterase activity during CTL-induced lysis has been shown in a number of systems, for the most part employing IL-2–dependent cytocidal lymphoblast (CTL/NK) effectors.[53,58] A recent report from Henkart's laboratory,[60] claimed BLT-esterase release during PEL-induced lysis, inferring a secretory lytic mechanism. The results presented in TABLE 4, showing comparable and low BLT-esterase activity in PEL and in target cells employed by Munger et al.[60] (EL4, P815), cast doubt on the interpretation that the enzyme is released from the effector upon specific lysis of the target; the data are equally compatible with enzyme release (if any) from the target upon its demise, rather than from the specific killer (PEL). In sharp contrast to PEL and PEL hybridomas, which contain control levels of the enzyme, the IL-2–dependent PEL blasts possess and secrete BLT-esterase activity.

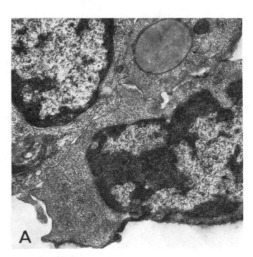

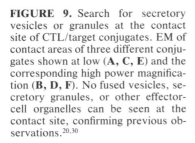

FIGURE 9. Search for secretory vesicles or granules at the contact site of CTL/target conjugates. EM of contact areas of three different conjugates shown at low (**A, C, E**) and the corresponding high power magnification (**B, D, F**). No fused vesicles, secretory granules, or other effector-cell organelles can be seen at the contact site, confirming previous observations.[20,30]

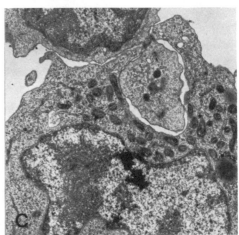

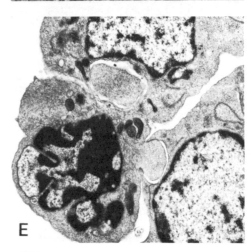

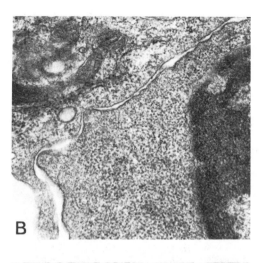

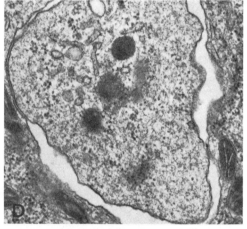

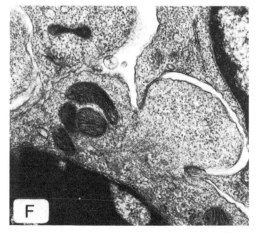

333

ACKNOWLEDGMENTS

I would like to thank Dr. Paul Sondel, Dr. Joseph Gardyn, Dr. Dalia Rosen, and Dr. Reuven Tirosh for reading the manuscript, and Pamela Rubinstein for proficient help in its preparation.

REFERENCES

1. DOURMASHKIN, R. R., P. DETEIX, C. B. SIMONE & P. HENKART. 1980. Clin. Exp. Immunol. **42:** 554–560.
2. HENKART, M. P. & P. A. HENKART. 1982. In Mechanisms of Cell-Mediated Cytotoxicity. W. R. Clark & P. Golstein, Eds.: 227–242. Plenum Press. New York.
3. PODACK, E. R. 1986. J. Cell. Biochem. **30:** 133–170.
4. YOUNG, J. D.-E., Z. A. COHN & E. R. PODACK. 1986. Science **233:** 184–190.
5. BERKE, G. & D. ROSEN. 1987. In Membrane Mediated Cytotoxicity. B. Bonavida & R. J. Collier, Eds.: 357–378. Alan Liss. New York.
6. BERKE, G. & D. ROSEN. 1987. Transplant. Proc. **XIX:** 412–416.
7. BERKE, G. & D. ROSEN. 1987. Proc. 18th Leucocyte Culture Conference, 1987. Immunobiology Suppl. **3:** 145.
7a. BERKE, G. & D. ROSEN. 1988. J. Immunol. In press.
8. BERKE, G., K. A. SULLIVAN & B. D. AMOS. 1972. J. Exp. Med. **135:** 1334–1350.
9. BERKE, G. 1980. Prog. Allergy **27:** 69–133.
10. TIROSH, R. & G. BERKE. 1985. In Mechanisms of Cell-Mediated Cytotoxicity II. P. Henkart & E. Martz, Eds.: 473–492. Plenum Press. New York.
11. TIROSH, R. & G. BERKE. 1985. Cell. Immunol. **95:** 113–123.
11a. MAYER, M. M. 1972. Proc. Natl. Acad. Sci. USA **69:** 2954.
11b. MULLER-EBERHARD, H. J. 1986. Annu. Rev. Immunol. **4:** 503–528.
12. DANKERT, J. R. & A. F. ESSER. 1985. Proc. Natl. Acad. Sci. USA **82:** 2128–2132.
13. JACKSON, M. B., C. L. STEPHENS & H. LECAR. 1981. Proc. Natl. Acad. Sci. USA **78:** 6421.
14. CAMPBELL, A. K., R. A. DAW, M. B. HALLETT & J. P. LUZIO. 1981. Biochem. J. **194:** 551–560.
15. TIROSH, R., H. DEGANI & G. BERKE. 1984. Complement **1:** 207–212.
16. ESSER, A. F. 1982. In Biological Membranes. D. Chapman, Ed.: 277. Academic Press. New York.
17. BASHFORD, C. L., G. M. ALDER, G. MEMESTRINA, K. J. MICKLEM, J. J. MURPHY & C. A. PASTERNAK. 1986. J. Biol. Chem. **261:** 9300–9308.
18. HENKART, P., M. HENKART, P. MILLARD, P. FREDERIKSE, J. BLUESTONE, R. BLUMENTHAL, C. YUE & C. REYNOLDS. 1984. In Mechanisms of Cell-Mediated Cytotoxicity II. P. Henkart & E. Martz, Eds.: 121–138. Plenum Press. New York.
19. HENNEY, C. S. 1977. In Contemporary Topics in Immunobiology. O. Stutman, Ed. Vol. 7: 245–272. Plenum Press. New York.
20. SANDERSON, C. J. 1982. In Mechanisms of Cell-Mediated Cytotoxicity. Advances in Experimental Medicine and Biology. W. R. Clark & P. Golstein, Eds.: 3–21. Plenum Press. New York.
21. MARTZ, E. S., J. BURAKOFF & B. BENACERRAF. 1974. Proc. Natl. Acad. Sci. USA **71:** 177.
22. POENIE, M., R. Y. TSIEN, A.-M. SCHMITT-VERHULST. 1987. EMBO J. **6:** 2223–2232.
23. RUSSEL, J. H. 1983. Immunol. Rev. **72:** 97–118.
24. DUKE, R. C., J. J. COHEN & R. CHERVENAK. 1986. J. Immunol. **137:** 1442–1447.
25. BERKE, G., K. A. SULLIVAN & D. B. AMOS. 1972. J. Exp. Med. **136:** 1594–1604.
26. MORGAN, B. P., J. P. LUZIO & A. K. CAMPBELL. 1986. Cell Calcium **7:** 399–411.
27. BERKE, G. & W. R. CLARK. 1982. In Mechanisms of Cell Mediated Cytotoxicity. W. R. Clark & P. Golstein, Eds.: 57–69. Plenum Press. New York.
28. BERKE, G., K. A. SULLIVAN & D. B. AMOS. 1972. Science **177:** 433–434.

29. ZAGURY, D., J. BERNARD, N. THIERNESS, M. FELDMAN & G. BERKE. 1975. Eur. J. Immunol. **5:** 818–822.
30. KALINA, M. & G. BERKE. 1976. Cell. Immunol. **25:** 41–45.
31. BERKE, G., R. TZUR & M. INBAR. 1978. J. Immunol. **120:** 1378–1384.
32. KIMELBERG, H. K. & D. PAPAHADJOPOULOS. J. Biol. Chem. 1971. **246:** 1142–1148.
33. VAN ZOELEN, E., P. VAN DIJCK, F. DE KRUIJFF, A. VERKLEIJ & L. VAN DEENEN. 1979. Biochem. Biophys. Acta **514:** 9.
34. CAMPBELL, A. K. 1987. Clin. Sci. **72:** 1–10.
35. PASTERNAK, C. A. 1986. Cell Calcium. **7:** 387–397.
36. BERKE, G. 1985. Microbiol. Sci. **2:** 44–48.
36a. NICOTERA, P., P. HARTZELL, G. DAVIS & S. ORRENIUS. 1986. FEBS Lett. **209:** 4254.
37. BERKE, G., D. GABISON & M. FELDMAN. 1975. Eur. J. Immunol. **5:** 813–818.
38. DENIZOT, F., A. WILSON, F. BATTYE, G. BERKE & K. SHORTMAN. 1986. Proc. Natl. Acad. Sci. USA **83:** 6089–6092.
39. BROOKS, C. G., D. L. URDAL & C. S. HENNEY. 1983. Immunol. Rev. **72:** 43–72.
40. HAVELE, C., R. C. BLEACKLEY & V. PAETKAU. 1986. J. Immunol. **137:** 1448–1454.
41. ABRAMS, S. I. &. Z. BRAHMI. 1986. Cell. Immunol. **101:** 558–570.
42. FLEISCHER, B. 1986. Eur. J. Immunol. **16:** 1021–1024.
43. HERBERMAN, R. B., C. W. REYNOLDS & J. R. ORTALDO. 1986. Annu. Rev. Immunol. **4:** 651–680.
44. STULTING, R. D. & G. BERKE. 1973. J. Exp. Med. **137:** 932–942.
45. BERKE, G. 1985. Eur. J. Immunol. **15:** 337–340.
46. MARTZ, E. 1977. *In* Contemporary Topics in Immunobiology. O. Stutman, Ed.: Vol. 7: 301–361. Plenum Press. New York.
47. GOLSTEIN, P. &. E. T. SMITH. 1977. *In* Contemporary Topics in Immunobiology. O. Stutman, Ed.: Vol. 7: 273–300. Plenum Press. New York.
48. BERKE, G. & B. SCHICK. 1980. Contemp. Top. Immunobiol. **10:** 297–315.
49. GEIGER, B., D. ROSEN & G. BERKE. 1982. J. Cell Biol. **95:** 137–143.
50. KAUFMANN, Y., G. BERKE & Z. ESHHAR. 1981. Proc. Natl. Acad. Sci. USA **78:** 2502–2506.
51. KAUFMANN, Y. & G. BERKE. 1983. J. Immunol. **131:** 50–56.
52. ZAGURY, D. 1982. *In* Mechanisms of Cell-Mediated Cytotoxicity. Advances in Experimental Medicine and Biology. W. R. Clark & P. Golstein, Eds.: 149–163. Plenum Press. New York.
53. HENKART, P. A. 1985. Annu. Rev. Immunol. **3:** 31–58.
54. BEN-NUN, A. & I. R. COHEN. 1982. J. Immunol. **129:** 303–308.
54a. KRAMER, M. D. & M. M. SIMON. 1987. Immunology Today **8:** 140–142.
55. PASTERNACK, M. S. & H. N. EISEN. 1985. Nature **314:** 743.
56. LOBE, C. G., B. B. FINAL, W. PARANCHYCH, V. H. PAETKAU & R. C. BLEAKLEY. 1986. Science **232:** 858.
57. BRUNET, J.-F., F. DENIZOT, M. SUZAN, W. HAAS, J.-M. MENCIA-HUERTA, G. BERKE, M.-F. LUCIANI & P. GOLSTEIN. 1987. J. Immunol. **138:** 4102–4105.
58. TAKAYAMA, H., G. TRENN, W. HUMPHREY, JR., J. A. BLUESTONE, P. A. HENKART & M. V. SITKOVSKY. 1987. J. Immunol. **138:** 1–4.
59. YANELLI, J. R., J. A. SULLIVAN, G. L. MANDELL & V. H. ENGELHARD. 1985. J. Immunol. **136:** 377.
60. MUNGER, W. E., G. BERREBI & P. A. HENKART. 1987. Ann. Immunol. Inst. Pasteur. **138:** 301–304.
61. LIU, C.-C., B. PERUSSIA, Z. A. COHN & J. D.-E. YOUNG. 1986. J. Exp. Med. **164:** 2061–2076.

Mechanism of Natural Killer Cell–Mediated Cytotoxicity[a]

BENJAMIN BONAVIDA

Department of Microbiology and Immunology
UCLA School of Medicine
University of California
Los Angeles, California 90024

Since the first description of the existence of a subpopulation of lymphocytes termed natural killer cells (NK) several years ago, many reports in the literature described various characteristics of these cells.[1] Little is known, however, on the biochemical and molecular basis of the NK mediated–cytotoxic mechanism. Our laboratory has initiated studies to investigate possible underlying mechanisms of the natural killer cell–mediated cytotoxic (NKCMC) reaction and the adaptation of methodology for the preparation of highly purified cytotoxic cells for study.

PURIFICATION OF CYTOTOXIC NK

Studies on the molecular mechanism of cell-mediated cytotoxicity require the usage of a highly purified cytolytic-cell population. Due to the absence of specific markers, however, that distinguish lytic from nonlytic cells, new methods for purification have to be developed. Most reported studies used heterogeneous cell populations containing NK, and cytotoxicity was determined by ^{51}Cr released from radiolabeled target cells. Regardless of whether these cell populations were derived from *in vivo* models, *in vitro* cultures, or clones, the actual fraction of cytolytic cells present in these populations is rather small. Studies at the single-cell level enabled us to determine the frequency of killer cells and to demonstrate that such frequencies are small. Therefore, studies characterizing cytotoxic cells must take into consideration the significant contribution made by nonlytic cells present in the cell mixture.

Our laboratory has developed a methodology to enrich and purify cytolytic cells from noncytolytic cells. These studies were based on known stages of the cell-mediated cytotoxic (CMC) reaction and adaptation of flow cytometric techniques. Our initial investigations were done with *in vivo*–derived cytolytic T cells and subsequently were successfully applied to NK and other killer-cell populations.

Conventional techniques have defined three discrete sequential phases that take place during a CMC reation: target-cell recognition and adhesion between target and lymphocyte, resulting in the formation of stable lymphocyte-target conjugates; delivery of a lethal hit to the target; and dissociation and recycling of the lymphocyte while the target undergoes lymphocyte-independent lysis.[2] The adaptation of flow cytometry to study adhesion was concurrently initiated by Segal and Stephany.[3] Our first studies investigated *in vivo*–derived CTL in mice.[4]

[a] This work was supported by Grant CA-35791 awarded by the National Cancer Institute, DHHS.

The protocol used is shown in FIGURE 1. FIGURE 2 shows a representative experiment of separating conjugates from nonconjugates (FIG. 2A) and identification of killer cells (FIG. 2B). These studies demonstrated that it is possible to adapt multiparameter flow–cytometric analysis to identify single and multiple effector-target conjugates, to enumerate total conjugates and conjugates containing killer cells, and to sort selected CTL–target-conjugate subpopulations. Using these techniques, it is now possible to sort killer-cell populations for further analysis of mechanisms.

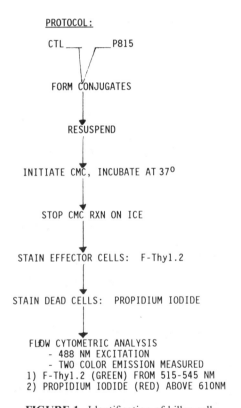

PROTOCOL:

CTL ———— P815

FORM CONJUGATES

RESUSPEND

INITIATE CMC, INCUBATE AT 37°

STOP CMC RXN ON ICE

STAIN EFFECTOR CELLS: F-Thy1.2

STAIN DEAD CELLS: PROPIDIUM IODIDE

FLOW CYTOMETRIC ANALYSIS
 - 488 NM EXCITATION
 - TWO COLOR EMISSION MEASURED
1) F-Thy1.2 (GREEN) FROM 515-545 NM
2) PROPIDIUM IODIDE (RED) ABOVE 610NM

FIGURE 1. Identification of killer cells.

MECHANISM OF NATURAL KILLER CELL–MEDIATED CYTOTOXICITY

Several mechanisms have been postulated by which natural killer cells mediate their cytolytic reaction. The molecular basis of lysis, however, is not known. This is not surprising because little is known about the mode of target cell–recognition, and adhesion and signal transduction. Circumstantial evidence postulated a stimulus-secretion model of NK cytolysis in which the target cell stimu-

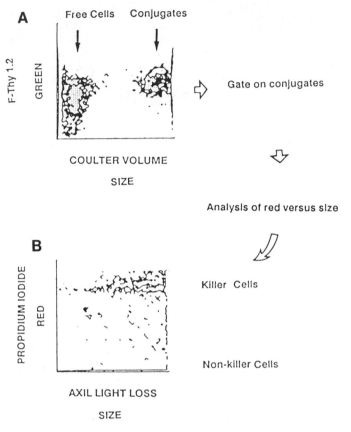

FIGURE 2.

lates the NK effector cell to release cytolytic factors that bind and lyse the sensitive target.[5]

Our laboratory was the first to describe a specific soluble cytotoxic factor produced by NK and shown to be implicated in the NKCMC reaction.[6–8] These characteristics of natural killer–derived cytotoxic factors (NKCF) correlated well with the known characteristics of the NK. Based on numerous studies, we have developed a working multistage model of the NKCMC reaction. In this model, the first step of the lytic pathway involves the recognition by the NK of the target cell

TABLE 1. Neutralization of NKCF Fractions

	Anti-TNF
Chromatofocusing	
pH 5–6	+
pH 7–8	−
NKCMC	−
Macrophage CMC	+

through putative receptor-ligand interactions. Following this interaction and adhesion, the target cell signals the effector NK to activate its secretory system, and soluble NKCF is secreted by the NK. These NKCF then bind to specific binding sites on the target cell, resulting in target-cell death. Many of the biochemical and molecular structures participating in this NKCMC mechanism have not been examined.

The biochemical nature of NKCF is not clear. Several purification procedures have been used and indicate that NKCF exhibit a MW ranging between 15–40,000.[9] More recent studies indicate that NKCF containing supernatant fractionated on a chromatofocusing column, performed with a pH gradient from 8 to 5, result in two biologically active fractions in the pH range 5–6 and 7–8.[10] Thus, it appears that the NK may secrete more than one biologically active molecule. The relationship of these fractions to known recombinant molecules such as lymphotoxin (LT) and tumor necrosis factor (TNF) was compared (TABLE 1). It was found that LT does not contribute to the lytic activity mediated by NKCF. A relationship between NKCF and TNF was revealed, however. Anti-TNF antibody inhibited the acidic form of NKCF but not the neutral form. These studies suggested that NKCF activity may be mediated in part by TNF or antigenically related molecules, as well as some other distinct factor(s). Current studies are being undertaken to delineate the structural basis and identity of the NKCF fractions.

Other investigators have reported the presence of cytolytic granules in NK clones. Such granules and a protein derived from such granules were shown to be lytic to all types of target cells.[11,12] Although these cytolytic molecules form pores on the target-cell membranes, NKCF or TNF do not form pores. We used synthetic lipid vesicles to study pore formation and could not demonstrate pores under conditions whereby pores are formed and their diameters measured.[13]

We also examined factors that dictate sensitivity and resistance to NK. The first approach investigated whether the sensitivity of a target cell to NK lysis is a property of the target-cell membrane. This was tested by liposome-fusion studies. The studies demonstrated that NK resistant–tumor cells acquired sensitivity to lysis by NK after fusion with reconstituted vesicles containing membranes derived from NK sensitive–target cells. The conversion from resistance to sensitivity was specific and species-specific.[14] The second approach investigated whether target cells resistant to NKCF can be rendered sensitive if fused with liposome-encapsulated NKCF. Our preliminary studies indicate that NK resistant–target cells become lysed following fusion with NKCF containing liposomes.[15]

The studies on the mechanism of NKCMC suggest to us that it involves a soluble cytotoxic mediator that is not a pore-forming protein. Sensitive target cells must process these factor-receptor complexes in an unknown and complex manner that will ultimately result in target-cell death. Target-cell death may or may not be the direct consequence of the cytotoxic factor. The role played by non-pore-forming cytolytic molecules and pore-forming molecules in the mechanism of NKCMC may represent distinct pathways. Further studies are required to address this issue.

ACKNOWLEDGMENTS

The author acknowledges the various investigators that performed the reported work in his laboratory: most notably, Dr. Roozemond, Dr. Wright, Dr. Graves, and Laura Lebow.

REFERENCES

1. HERBERMAN, R. B. 1983. NK cells and other natural effector cells. Academic Press. New York.
2. MARTZ, E. 1977. Contemp. Top. Immunobiol. **7:** 301.
3. SEGAL, D. M. & D. A. STEPHANY. 1984. Cytometry **5:** 169.
4. LEBOW, L. T., C. STEWART, A. S. PERELSON & B. BONAVIDA. 1986. Natural Immun. Cell Growth Regul. **5:** 221.
5. KIYOHARA, T., R. LANZON, T. HALIOTIS & J. C. RODER. 1986. *In* Immunobiology of Natural Killer Cells. E. Lotzova & R. B. Herberman, Eds.: vol. 1: 108. CRC Press. Boca Raton, Florida.
6. BONAVIDA, B. & S. C. WRIGHT. 1986. J. Clin. Immunol. **6:** 1.
7. BONAVIDA, B. & S. C. WRIGHT. 1986. *In* Immunology of natural killer cells. E. Lotzona & R. B. Herberman, Eds.: vol. 1: 125. CRC Press. Boca Raton, Florida.
8. BONAVIDA, B. & S. C. WRIGHT. 1987. Adv. Cancer Res. **49:** 169.
9. WRIGHT, S. C., S. M. WILBUR & B. BONAVIDA. 1985. Natural Immun. Cell Growth Regul. **4:** 202.
10. WRIGHT, S. C. & B. BONAVIDA. 1987. J. Immunol. **138:** 1791.
11. DENNERT, G. & E. R. PODACK. 1983. J. Exp. Med. **157:** 1483.
12. MILLARD, P. J., M. P. HENKART, W. REYNOLDS & P. A. HENKART. 1984. J. Immunol. **132:** 3197.
13. BALDWIN, R. C., M. P. CHANG, J. BRAMHALL, S. C. GRAVES, B. BONAVIDA & B. WISNIESKI. 1988. J. Immunol. Submitted.
14. ROOZEMOND, R. C., P. VAN DE GEER & B. BONAVIDA. 1986. J. Immunol. **136:** 3921.
15. ROOZEMOND, R. C., D. C. URLI, S. C. WRIGHT, S. C. GRAVES & B. BONAVIDA. 1988. Immunobiology. In press.

Inhibition of Lytic Programming by Pharmacologic Agents[a,b]

MARSHALL PLAUT AND ROBERT P. SCHLEIMER

Division of Clinical Immunology
Department of Medicine
Johns Hopkins University School of Medicine
The Good Samaritan Hospital
Baltimore, Maryland 21239

INTRODUCTION

A wide variety of pharmacologic agents modulate lytic programming. Such agents have been used for two reasons: to identify potentially useful therapeutic agents and to define the mechanism of killing. The latter studies are particularly useful when complemented by biochemical studies on purified cytotoxic cells that unequivocally identify the site of action of a drug. Even in the absence of direct biochemical studies, inferences can be made from studies of drug effects on mixed cell populations containing only a small percentage of CTL. For example, inasmuch as colchicine and vinblastine inhibit cytotoxic T lymphocyte (CTL)-mediated killing, then microtubules, the cellular target of the pharmacologic agents, must be involved in the killing process.[1,2] Moreover, chelators of divalent cations inhibit CTL-mediated killing, and Ca^{++} (or Mg^{++} and Ca^{++}) reverses the inhibition.[3] Because intact microtubules and Ca^{++} are required for killing to occur, then killing is probably a secretory event. Because protein, DNA, and RNA synthesis inhibitors do not inhibit killing, cell differentiation is not required.

Much of our work on CTL has focused on the effects of receptor-mediated hormones and autacoids or locally active hormones. One of us has recently reviewed this subject.[4] Many hormones modulate lymphocyte differentiation and proliferation, and they also modulate CTL killing, and presumably the secretory events involved in this killing process. A summary of the effects of several receptor agonists is found in TABLE 1.[4-22]

Some hormones act on cell-surface receptors to stimulate adenylate cyclase. Hormone-receptor complexes are linked, through a series of regulatory guanosine triphosphate (GTP)-binding or G proteins, to enzyme systems that generate several distinct intracellular "second messengers." For the agonists listed in TABLE 1A, such as histamine (acting on histamine type 2 receptors), β adrenergic-receptor agonists like isoproterenol, prostaglandin E_2, and adenosine (by way of R_a receptors), the G proteins associated with the receptor stimulate adenylate cyclase and result in increases in intracellular levels of cAMP. The increased cAMP levels are associated with inhibition of CTL activity. The neuropeptide, vasoactive intestinal peptide, appears to act in the same manner, and it has been shown to inhibit NK-mediated killing.

[a] This work was supported in part by Grants AI 21722, AI 12810, and AR 31891 from the National Institutes of Health.

[b] This is publication #727 of the O'Neill Research Laboratories of The Good Samaritan Hospital.

TABLE 1. Hormone Receptors on Cytotoxic Cells and the Functional Effects of Receptor Activation[a]

| Receptor | Effect on Lytic Programming by[b] | | | | References |
	Mouse CTL[c,d]	Mouse NK	Human NK	Human K	
A. Receptors that are linked to stimulation of adenylate cyclase					
1. Adenosine (R_a[e])	inhibit				5,6
2. β-adrenergic	inhibit		inhibit		7,8
3. Histamine (H2[f])	inhibit		$\pm$[g], variable		4,9
4. Prostaglandin E_2	inhibit	inhibit	inhibit	inhibit	10,11
5. Vasoactive intestinal peptide			inhibit		12
B. Receptors that are not linked to stimulation of adenylate cyclase					
6. Glucocorticoid[h]	inhibit		$\pm$inhibit		13,14
7. Insulin	enhance[i]	no effect			15,16
8. Leukotriene B_4			enhance[j]		17
9. Muscarinic cholinergic	enhance[k]	$\pm$enhance	$\pm$enhance		8,18–20
10. Opiate (beta-endorphin, enkephalin)			enhance		21,22

[a] We have listed only those receptors that have been reported to modulate cytotoxic activity.

[b] All the effects listed are for direct addition of receptor agonist to lymphocyte–target cell mixtures. Some agonists when preincubated with killer cells induce opposite effects. For example, preincubation with some cAMP agonists enhances cytotoxicity.

[c] Abbreviations: CTL, cytotoxic T lymphocytes; NK, natural killer cells; K, killer cells (antibody-dependent cytotoxicity)

[d] As discussed in the text, the inhibitory effects of many receptor agonists vary among different CTL populations. For example, the effects are much greater on splenic CTL from mice immunized *in vivo* with allogeneic cells than on CTL generated *in vitro* (in a mixed lymphocyte culture).

[e] Two adenosine receptors are described, with opposite effects. Only the R-site receptor that activates adenylate cylase (R_a receptor) has been identified on CTL.

[f] Two histamine receptors are described, with opposite effects. Only the histamine-type 2 (H2) receptor has been identified on CTL.

[g] $\pm$denotes weak effect.

[h] Glucocorticoid receptors are in a separate category. Whereas the other receptors described here are apparently on the cell surface, glucocorticoid receptors are probably cytoplasmic receptors that transmit signals to the nucleus. Although glucocorticoids activate adenylate cyclase, this activation probably is not the mechanism by which glucocorticoid signals are transmitted.

[i] Rat and mouse CTL.

[j] Human NK and human natural cytotoxic (NC) cells.

[k] Rat CTL.

Glucocorticoids apparently act on cytoplasmic receptors, and the glucocorticoid-receptor complexes translocate to the nucleus where they stimulate production of new mRNA and new proteins. Other hormone receptors in TABLE 1B are linked by way of different G proteins, which activate phospholipase C (PLC) and/or inhibit adenylate cyclase and/or activate guanylate cyclase, thereby producing other intracellular second messengers. The second messengers generated by these hormones are still under investigation. These latter hormones do not inhibit, but are reported to enhance CTL- or NK-mediated killing.

Activation of T cells may stimulate PLC (compare reference 23). We have no information about whether signals (*e.g.*, lymphokines) other than the hormones we have discussed activate adenylate cyclase in CTL and thereby inhibit CTL activity.

In this paper, we will not discuss all hormones, but will focus on the effects on murine anti-alloantigenic CTL of glucocorticoids and of histamine and other hormones that increase intracellular levels of cAMP.

GLUCOCORTICOIDS

Glucocorticoids do not inhibit the effector function of *in vitro*–generated IL-2–dependent CTL clones.[24] We determined whether glucocorticoids would inhibit *in vivo*–generated splenic CTL.[13] Glucocorticoids when added directly to CTL–target cell mixtures did not inhibit lysis. When glucocorticoids were preincubated with spleen cells for 24 hours prior to addition of target cells, however, low concentrations of these agents were potent inhibitors of lysis (FIG. 1). The magnitude of inhibition was dependent on both the concentration of glucocorticoid and the duration of preincubation. The concentration of dexamethasone acetate that inhibited cytolysis by 50% was 1.4×10^{-10} M. Because the relative potency of a series of glucocorticoids on inhibiting cytotoxicity was identical to their relative potency in a standard *in vivo* assay, the agents must act on specific lymphocyte glucocorticoid receptors. Inasmuch as glucocorticoids inhibit the production of lymphokines like IL-2,[24] we determined whether IL-2–containing supernatants reversed the inhibitory effects of dexamethasone. The inhibitory effects of low concentrations of dexamethasone (10^{-10} M–10^{-9} M) were reversed by human or mouse IL-2–containing supernatants, whereas the inhibitory effects of higher concentrations of dexamethasone (10^{-8} M–10^{-7} M) were not reversed.[13] High concentrations of dexamethasone also induced increased death of lymphocytes, which was not reversed by IL-2. Thus, glucocorticoids appear to have two distinct effects on splenic CTL populations. It is likely that low concentrations of

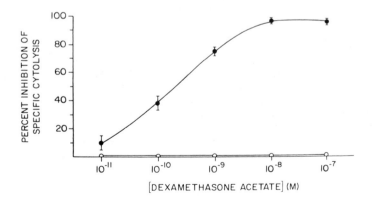

FIGURE 1. Inhibition of T cell–mediated cytotoxicity by dexamethasone acetate. C57BL/6 anti-P815 spleen cells were cultured in the presence of the indicated concentrations of dexamethasone acetate for 24 h (closed circles) or 23.75 h and then dexamethasone acetate for 15 min (open circles). ^{51}Cr-labeled P815 cells were then added and cytotoxicity was assessed in a 3 h assay. Control cytotoxicity (in cells never exposed to drug) was 34%. (R. P. Schleimer *et al.*[13] With permission of the Williams and Wilkins Co.)

glucocorticoids inhibit CTL activity by blocking the production of lymphokines, presumably because endogenous lymphokines must be produced for CTL activity to persist in culture. Higher concentrations of glucocorticoids act directly on the CTL to inhibit activity, and also kill the CTL.

Glucocorticoids inhibit CTL generated *in vivo*,[13] but not cloned CTL.[24] Although cloned CTL are cultured in the presence of exogenous IL-2, their unresponsiveness to glucocorticoids is probably independent of IL-2. High concentrations (10^{-6} M) of dexamethasone, which, as just stated, inhibit *in vivo* CTL even in the presence of exogenous IL-2,[13] have no effect on either cloned CTL, or CTL generated in a primary mixed lymphocyte culture when dexamethasone was added on day 2.[24] Thus, *in vivo*–generated CTL are sensitive to glucocorticoids, whereas some cultured CTL are not.

ADENYLATE CYCLASE-STIMULATING HORMONES AND AUTACOIDS

Early studies by Sutherland and others on the role of cAMP as a second messenger emphasized that cAMP was a positive secretory signal (reviewed in reference 4). In contrast to the activating effects of cAMP on many tissues, elevated levels of cAMP inhibit the effector functions of CTL, NK cells, and other inflammatory leukocytes. Most of the early studies of the role of cAMP on CTL activity did not define the cellular target of the cAMP agonist because CTL were a minor fraction of the cell populations that were studied, and because two cells, CTL and target cells, were interacting during the killing process. Cholera enterotoxin, an irreversible stimulator of adenylate cyclase, inhibited when preincubated with effector cells but not when preincubated with target cells, establishing that cAMP inhibited the effector cell and not the target cell.[25] Biochemical studies have become possible because of the availability of cloned CTL. Recent studies by Sitkovsky and colleagues[26,27] have assessed the secretion of CTL-derived N-α-benzyloxycarbonyl-L-lysine thiobenzyl ester (BLT) esterases that are triggered by a solid phase anti-T-cell receptor antibody, a secretory process that appears to be parallel to the lytic process itself. They have demonstrated that cAMP analogues (8-bromo-cAMP and N^6-benzoyl-cAMP) as well as a direct stimulator of adenylate cyclase (forskolin) and an inhibitor of cAMP phosphodiesterase (isobutyl-methylxanthine, IBMX) not only inhibit killing of targets, but also inhibit anti-T-cell receptor antibody-mediated secretion of esterase. IBMX inhibits esterase secretion induced not only by the antibody, but also by the combination of the phorbol ester, phorbol myristic acetate (PMA) and the calcium ionophore A23187. Thus, cAMP may act on a pathway common to T-cell receptor–dependent and T-cell receptor–independent (by PMA/A23187) triggering, so it must work on a common postreceptor pathway, possibly a relatively late event in CTL activation. IBMX also inhibits antibody-induced phosphatidylinositol turnover, so cAMP may also inhibit early events in CTL activation. A cAMP-dependent protein kinase may be important in regulating CTL-mediated killing.

MODULATION OF RESPONSIVENESS TO cAMP AGONISTS

Different CTL populations vary widely in their capacity to be modulated by agonists that increase cAMP levels (which we will call cAMP agonists). The cAMP agonists, including histamine, prostaglandin E_2 (PGE$_2$), and dibutyryl cAMP, inhibited the activity of splenic CTL obtained 14 days following intraperitoneal immunization with alloantigen, but were much less potent inhibitors of splenic CTL obtained 8–11 days following immunization.[28] The cAMP agonists were weak inhibitors of peritoneal CTL obtained throughout the immune response. Moreover, cAMP agonists were extremely weak inhibitors of in vitro–generated primary or secondary CTL.[11] When spleen cells from in vivo–immunized mice were cultured for 1–3 days, the responsiveness of the CTL to cAMP agonists fell progressively, and antigen accelerated the loss of responsiveness.[29] The effects of agonists on cloned CTL were different from their effects on CTL in short-term culture: PGE$_2$ and dibutyryl cAMP were potent inhibitors of the activity of cloned CTL, whereas histamine had no inhibitory effect[30] (FIG. 2, discussed below).

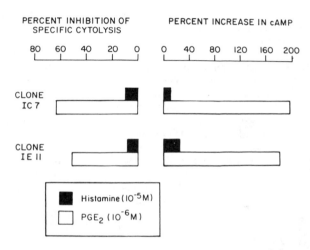

FIGURE 2. Effect of histamine (10^{-5} M) and PGE$_2$ (10^{-6} M) on inhibition of activity of, and cAMP levels of, CTL clones. Two C57BL/6 anti-P815 CTL clones (IC 7 and IE 11) were tested in a 4 hour cytolyic assay (10^4 CTL, 2×10^3 ^{51}Cr-P815) with or without drugs, or 10^6 CTL were incubated for 10 minutes with or without drugs and cAMP levels determined. The percent specific cytolysis (no drug) for clone IC 7 was 11.9%, for clone IE 11, 8.8%. The cAMP levels (mean ± SEM, no drug) for clone IC 7 were 4.6 ± 0.5 pM/10^6 cells, for clone IE 11, 4.1 ± 0.3 pM/10^6 cells.

The physiologic significance of the changes in responsiveness to cAMP agonists are unknown. We have speculated on the possible significance of changes in responsiveness to histamine, because we believe that a physiologic inhibitory effect of histamine depends on the magnitude of both the CTL responsiveness to histamine and of the endogenous levels of histamine. Endogenous histamine production appears to be due to new synthesis and secretion of histamine, probably by mast cell precursors in lymphoid tissue. The inducers of synthesis are lymphokines, both IL-3 and granulocyte-macrophage colony-stimulating factor (GM-CSF). Alloantigen-triggered histamine production is increased in lymphoid tissues from alloimmune mice relative to those from nonimmune mice.[31-33] Thus, both histamine responsiveness and histamine production are increased late in the immune response. We predict that an enhanced physiologic effect of histamine will occur only late in the immune response, when responsiveness and production are both high. One piece of evidence in favor of our prediction is that, following *in vivo* immunization with alloantigen, splenic CTL activity was twice as high in W/W^v mice (which are deficient in mast cells and mast cell precursors) as control mice, but only on about day 20 after immunization.[6]

Different CTL populations vary in their responsiveness not only to cAMP agonists, but also to many other agents. We have already mentioned that glucocorticoids inhibit *in vivo*–generated splenic CTL, but not *in vitro*–generated CTL. The capacity of cholinergic agonists and insulin to enhance cytotoxicity occurs only with CTL early after immmunization.[15,18] The agent 2-deoxyglucose inhibits the CTL activity of *in vitro*–generated CTL from 4 day cultures more than the activity of CTL from *in vitro*–generated 11 day cultures and of CTL from *in vivo* immunization.[34] The response to azide may also be variable.[35] Responsiveness to colchicine appears to be relatively constant.[11]

The mechanisms that regulate changes in responsiveness are not fully understood. For agents that interact with receptors, the altered responsiveness can be due to changes in both receptor numbers and/or affinity, and to changes in biochemical pathways distal to the receptors, such as receptor-adenylate cyclase coupling and post-cAMP events.[29] Such alterations in cAMP responsiveness have been described in other cell types. We have determined whether the cAMP responses to histamine and PGE$_2$ explain the effects of these agents on the activity of several CTL clones (FIG. 2). Histamine did not increase cAMP levels (but compare reference 36) and did not inhibit cytotoxicity, although PGE$_2$ induced a marked increase in cAMP levels and inhibited cytotoxicity. Thus, CTL clones probably lack histamine receptors but have intact cAMP pathways that link increased cAMP levels (stimulated by PGE$_2$ or (not shown) dibutyryl cAMP) to inhibition of killing. Indirect evidence, assuming that cAMP responses in mixed spleen cell populations represent cAMP responses in the CTL themselves, suggest that CTL populations cultured with antigen for one day are deficient in receptor-adenylate cyclase coupling,[29] and that CTL generated in a primary mixed lymphocyte culture are poorly responsive to dibutyryl cAMP because of a deficiency in post-cAMP pathways.[11] Thus, CTL may lack functional histamine receptors or be deficient in components of the biochemical events that link increased cAMP levels to inhibition of killing, yet be quite effective at killing appropriate targets. The biochemical pathways in cloned CTL or other *in vitro* CTL populations may differ markedly from those in physiologic *in vivo* CTL.

We next determined whether the variation of cAMP responsiveness of CTL was an intrinsic property of the CTL, or whether intrinsic factors regulate responsiveness.[28,32] We transferred CTL populations into nonimmune syngeneic recipients. Forty-eight hours after transfer, we tested peritoneum and spleen in individual recipients. We proposed that inasmuch as cAMP agonists inhibited splenic CTL more than peritoneal CTL, the environment of the spleen versus peritoneum might differentially regulate inhibition by the agonists. Indeed, following intraperitoneal (or intravenous) transfer, the responsiveness to cAMP agonists of CTL in recipient peritoneal exudate and recipient spleen was partially or completely determined by the organ in which they resided. Results of a single experiment are illustrated in TABLE 2. The inhibition by histamine and PGE$_2$ of CTL in recipient peritoneum was much less than inhibition of CTL in recipient spleen. When results of many experiments were averaged, we observed that the activity of CTL in recipient spleen was inhibited 25%, 45%, and 75% by 10^{-5} M histamine, 10^{-6} M PGE$_2$, and 10^{-3} M dibutyryl cAMP, respectively. These levels of inhibition were independent of the inhibition of the transferred population. The activity of CTL in recipient peritoneal exudate was inhibited 10–21%, 11–20%, and 38–65% by the same three cAMP agonists, and was partly defined by the responsiveness of the starting population. Thus, the inhibitory effects of histamine, PGE_2, and other agonists are not intrinsic properties of a CTL population but are determined by the local environment.

The factors in the local environment that regulate cAMP responsiveness are unknown. T cell–derived lymphokines are one possibility. T cells make lymphokines that regulate levels of histamine and PGE_2,[31] so they might make lymphokines that regulate responsiveness. Indeed, T cells regulate insulin receptor expression on B cells,[37] so they might regulate other receptors. Moreover, subpopulations of T cells (i.e., T_h1 and T_h2 cells) appear to produce distinct lymphokines,[38] so it is conceivable that T cells in distinct environments would regulate cAMP responsiveness differentially.

TABLE 2. Effect of Intraperitoneal Transfer of Ten Day Immune Cells into Syngeneic Recipients on Inhibition of CTL Activity in Recipient Spleen and Peritoneum[a]

| | | Percent Inhibition by | |
Cells	Percent Specific Lysis[b]	Histamine 10^{-5} M	PGE_2 10^{-6} M
Donor	33.0	16.2	27.8
Recipient peritoneum	25.1	10.3 ± 1.8	21.1 ± 1.8
Recipient spleen	3.5	26.9 ± 4.5	51.2 ± 2.4

[a] 1×10^8 spleen cells from C57BL/6 mice, 10 days after immunization with P815 cells, were transferred intraperitoneally into 4 recipients. 48 hours later, recipients were killed, and peritoneal and spleen cells from individual mice were tested separately. Results are expressed as mean ± SEM inhibition of specific cytolysis.

[b] Results are expressed as percent specific lysis in 4 hours, at an effector : target ratio of 50 : 1. Although only the ratio of 50 : 1 is shown, inhibition was calculated as the average inhibition at two ratios. For example, percent specific lysis by the recipient spleen, at an effector : target ratio of 250 : 1, was 5.6%.

REFERENCES

1. PLAUT, M., L. M. LICHTENSTEIN & C. S. HENNEY. 1973. Studies on the mechanism of lymphocyte-mediated cytolysis. III. The role of microfilaments and microtubules. J. Immunol. 110: 771–780.
2. HENNEY, C. S., J. GAFFNEY & B. R. BLOOM. 1974. On the relation of products of activated lymphocytes to cell-mediated cytolysis. J. Exp. Med. 140: 837–852.
3. PLAUT, M., J. E. BUBBERS & C. S. HENNEY. 1976. Studies on the mechanism of lymphocyte-mediated cytolysis. VII. Two stages in the T cell-mediated lytic cycle with distinct cation requirements. J. Immunol. 116: 150–155.
4. PLAUT, M. 1987. Lymphocyte hormone receptors. Annu. Rev. Immunol. 5: 621–669.
5. WOLBERG, G., T. P. ZIMMERMAN, K. HIEMSTRA, M. WINSTON & L. C. CHU. 1975. Adenosine inhibition of lymphocyte-mediated cytolysis: Possible role of cyclic adenosine monophosphate. Science 187: 957–959.
6. PLAUT, M. 1987. Unpublished data.
7. HENNEY, C. S. 1973. On the mechanism of T-cell mediated cytolysis. Transplant. Rev. 17: 37–70.

8. KATZ, P., A. M. ZAYTOUN & A. S. FAUCI. 1982. Mechanisms of human cell-mediated cytotoxicity. I. Modulation of natural killer cell activity by cyclic nucleotides. J. Immunol. **129:** 287–296.
9. PLAUT, M., L. M. LICHTENSTEIN & C. S. HENNEY. 1975. Properties of a subpopulation of T cells bearing histamine receptors. J. Clin. Invest. **55:** 856–874.
10. GOODWIN, J. S. & J. CEUPPENS. 1983. Regulation of the immune response by prostaglandins. J. Clin. Immunol. **3:** 295–315.
11. PLAUT, M. 1979. The role of cyclic AMP in modulating cytotoxic T lymphocytes. I. *In vivo*-generated cytotoxic lymphocytes, but not *in vitro*-generated cytotoxic lymphocytes, are inhibited by cyclic AMP-active agents. J. Immunol. **123:** 692–701.
12. ROLA-PLESZCZYNSKI, M., D. BOLDUC & S. ST.-PIERRE. 1985. The effects of vasoactive intestinal peptide on human natural killer cell function. J. Immunol. **135:** 2569–2573.
13. SCHLEIMER, R. P., A. JACQUES, H. S. SHIN, L. M. LICHTENSTEIN & M. PLAUT. 1984. Inhibition of T cell-mediated cytotoxicity by anti-inflammatory steroids. J. Immunol. **132:** 166–172.
14. CUPPS, T. R. & A. S. FAUCI. 1982. Corticosteroid-mediated immunoregulation in man. Immunol. Rev. **65:** 133–155.
15. STROM, T. B., R. A. BEAR & C. B. CARPENTER. 1975. Insulin-induced augmentation of lymphocyte-mediated cytotoxicity. Science **187:** 1206–1208.
16. RODER, J. C. & M. KLEIN. 1979. Target-effector interaction in the natural killer cell system. IV. Modulation by cyclic nucleotides. J. Immunol. **123:** 2785–2790.
17. ROLA-PLESZCZYNSKI, M. 1985. Immunoregulation by leukotrienes and other lipoxygenase metabolites. Immunology Today **6:** 302–307.
18. STROM, T. B., M. A. LANE & K. GEORGE. 1981. The parallel, time-dependent, bimodal change in lymphocyte cholinergic binding activity and cholinergic influence upon lymphocyte-mediated cytotoxicity after lymphocyte activation. J. Immunol. **127:** 705–710.
19. STROM, T. B., A. J. SYTKOWSKI, C. B. CARPENTER & J. P. MERRILL. 1974. Cholinergic augmentation of lymphocyte-mediated cytotoxicity. A study of the cholinergic receptor of cytotoxic T lymphocytes. Proc. Natl. Acad. Sci. USA **71:** 1330–1333.
20. HENNEY, C. S. 1974. Relationship between the cytolytic activity of thymus-derived lymphocytes and cellular cyclic nucleotide concentrations. *In* Cyclic AMP, Cell Growth and the Immune Response. W. Braun, L. M. Lichtenstein & C. Parker, Eds.: 195–208. Springer-Verlag. New York.
21. BLALOCK, J. E. 1985. Relationships between neuroendocrine hormones and lymphokines. Lymphokines **9:** 1–13.
22. PAYAN, D. G., J. P. MCGILLIS & E. J. GOETZL. 1986. Neuroimmunology. Adv. Immunol. **39:** 299–323.
23. ISAKOV, N., M. I. MALLY, W. SCHOLZ & A. ALTMAN. 1987. T-lymphocyte activation: The role of protein kinase C and the bifurcating inositol phospholipid signal transduction pathway. Immunol. Rev. **95:** 89–111.
24. GILLIS, S., G. R. CRABTREE & K. A. SMITH. 1979. Glucocorticoid-induced inhibition of T cell growth factor production. II. The effect on the *in vitro* generation of cytolytic T cells. J. Immunol. **123:** 1632–1638.
25. HENNEY, C. S., L. M. LICHTENSTEIN, E. GILLESPIE & R. T. ROLLEY. 1973. *In vivo* suppression of the immune response to alloantigen by cholera enterotoxin. J. Clin. Invest. **52:** 2853–2857.
26. TAKAYAMA, H., G. TRENN, W. HUMPHREY, JR., J. A. BLUESTONE, P. A. HENKART & M. V. SITKOVSKY. 1987. Antigen receptor-triggered secretion of a trypsin-type esterase from cytotoxic T lymphocytes. J. Immunol. **138:** 566–569.
27. TAKAYAMA, H., G. TRENN & M. V. SITKOVSKY. 1988. Locus of inhibitory action of cAMP-dependent protein kinase in the antigen-receptor triggered cytotoxic T lymphocyte activation pathway. J. Biol. Chem. **263:** 2330–2336.
28. PLAUT, M., L. NORDIN, M. C. LIU & A. R. JACQUES. The role of cAMP in modulating cytotoxic T lymphocytes (CTL). III. The local *in vivo* environment determines the cAMP responsiveness of CTL. Submitted.

29. PLAUT, M., G. MARONE & E. GILLESPIE. 1983. The role of cyclic AMP in modulating cytotoxic T lymphocytes. II. Sequential changes during culture in responsiveness of cytotoxic lymphocytes to cAMP-active agents. J. Immunol. **131:** 2945–2952.
30. PLAUT, M. & R. P. SCHLEIMER. 1987. Unpublished data.
31. SCHNEIDER, E., H. POLLARD, F. LEPAULT, D. GUY-GRAND, M. MINKOWSKI & M. DY. 1987. Histamine producing cell stimulatory activity. Interleukin 3 and granulocyte-macrophage colony stimulating factor induce *de novo* synthesis of histidine decarboxylase in hemopoietic progenitor cells. J. Immunol. **139:** 3710–3717.
32. PLAUT, M., A. KAGEY-SOBOTKA & A. R. JACQUES. 1985. Modulation of cytotoxic T lymphocyte responses by histamine. *In* Frontiers in Histamine Research. R. Ganelini & J.-C. Schwartz, Eds.: 379–388. Pergamon Press. Oxford.
33. DY, M. & B. LEBEL. 1983. Skin allografts generate an enhanced production of histamine and histamine-producing cell-stimulating factor (HCSF) by spleen cells in response to T cell mitogens. J. Immunol. **130:** 2343–2347.
34. MACDONALD, H. R. & J.-C. CEROTTINI. 1979. Inhibition of T cell-mediated cytotoxicity by 2-deoxy-D-glucose (2-DG): Differential effect of 2-DG on effector cells isolated early or late after alloantigenic stimulation *in vitro*. J. Immunol. **122:** 1067–1072.
35. REDELMAN, D. 1982. The mechanism of cell-mediated cytotoxicity. II. The apparent biochemical requirements for cytolysis are influenced by the source and frequency of murine cytotoxic T lymphocytes. Cell. Immunol. **74:** 172–181.
36. KHAN, M. M., K. L. MELMON, C. F. FATHMAN, B. HERTEL-WULFF & S. STROBER. 1985. The effects of autacoids on cloned murine lymphoid cells. Modulation of IL-2 secretion and the activity of natural suppressor cells. J. Immunol. **134:** 4100–4106.
37. HELDERMAN, J. H. 1983. T cell cooperation for the genesis of B cell insulin receptors. J. Immunol. **131:** 644–650.
38. MOSMANN, T. R., H. CHERWINSKI, M. W. BOND, M. A. GIEDLIN & R. L. COFFMAN. 1986. Two types of murine helper T cell clones. I. Definition according to profiles of lymphokine activities and secreted proteins. J. Immunol **136:** 2348–2357.

Cyclic AMP–Dependent Protein Kinase as a Part of the Possible Down-regulating Pathway in the Antigen Receptor–Regulated Cytotoxic T Lymphocyte Conjugate Formation and Granule Exocytosis

MICHAIL V. SITKOVSKY, GUIDO TRENN,
AND HAJIME TAKAYAMA

Laboratory of Immunology
National Institute of Allergy and Infectious Diseases
National Institutes of Health
Bethesda, Maryland 20892

It has been suggested that one view CTL screening activities as a cycle of engagements and disengagements with target cells (TC), where every surrounding cell is treated by cytotoxic T lymphocytes (CTL) as a potentially antigen-bearing cell[1] in the first stage of the conjugate formation. Recognition of an antigen on the TC by the CTL antigen receptor (TcR) results in the triggering of the exocytosis of cytolytic granules from CTL and "lethal hit" delivery to the TC.[1–4] It was shown that requirement for TcR cross-linking in the activation of CTL and exocytosis triggering can be bypassed by synergistic action of phorbol ester and Ca^{++} ionophores (reference 3 and Takayama and Sitkovsky, manuscript submitted), implicating protein kinase C and Ca^{++}-regulated proteins in T-cell activation ("on" signal). One of the unexplained features of CTL activation is a biochemical mechanism of an "off" signal, which would result in the termination of the exocytosis of the cytolytic granules (preventing the "exhaustion" of CTL) and allow the disengagement of CTL from the TC and subsequent engagement with, and destruction of, the other TC. The existence of an off signal increases the immunologic efficiency of CTL by preventing their irreversible engagement with the first encountered TC.

Here we review our data on the effect of different cAMP level-raising agents on CTL activation and suggest that cAMP dependent–protein kinase (PK-A) may be a part of such a biochemical pathway, which is involved in the inhibition of TcR-triggered T-cell activation. The possibility of bypassing TcR in CTL activation (exocytosis triggering) by addition of PMA and A23187 (FIG. 1) allowed us to show here that inhibitory action of cAMP dependent–protein kinase is exerted at both early and late stages of the TcR-mediated transmembrane signaling pathway.

EXPERIMENTAL PROCEDURES

CTL clones, monoclonal antibodies, preparation of the wells with solid-phase monoclonal antibodies, measurements of the secretion, and the cytotoxicity assay were described previously.[1,3,5] Ficoll-purified CTL clones were used with ^{51}Cr-labeled target cells in the standard cytotoxicity assay and exocytosis triggering assay.[3]

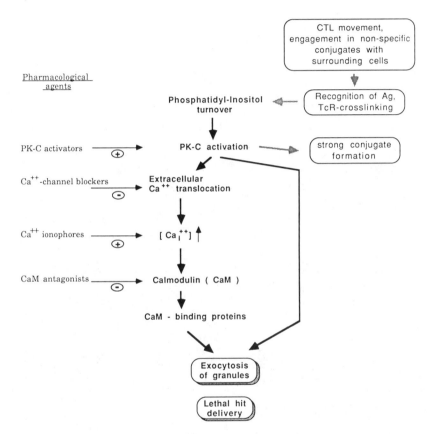

FIGURE 1. Biochemical pathways involved in conjugate formation, granule exocytosis, and cytotoxicity by cytotoxic T lymphocytes. Abbreviations: Ag, antigen; TcR, T-cell antigen receptor; PK-C, protein kinase C; $\ominus$, inhibitory action; $\oplus$, stimulating action.

Pretreatment of CTL with Pertussis or Cholera Toxin

Four $\times$ 10^6 CTL were suspended in 0.7 ml of RPMI-1640/10 mM HEPES/5% FCS in the presence of 0.1 μg/ml cholera toxin or pertussis toxin at 37°C under 5% CO_2 atmosphere. After 2 h incubation, cells were washed with RPMI-1640/10 mM HEPES/5% FCS and counted to evaluate the recovery and cell viability. Viability of CTL was more than 95% after both pretreatments. Cells were then used for the cytotoxicity assay or the BLT-esterase secretion assay.[3]

Determination of cAMP Levels in CTL

CTL were suspended in Hanks' balanced salt solution (HBSS)/1 mg/ml BSA/ 10 mM HEPES pH 7.2 at a concentration of 2×10^7 cells/ml with addition of cAMP-raising reagent. Then, 50 μl of this suspension was mixed with 50 μl of 4 mM EDTA/1 mM IBMX/50 mM Tris-HCl pH 7.4/0.15 M NaCl solution at 100°C. After 5 min heating, the mixture was frozen by liquid nitrogen and thawed at 100°C. This freezing-thawing procedure was repeated twice. The mixture was then spun at 10,000 × g for 5 min, and 50 μl of supernatant was processed for cAMP assay. cAMP content was determined by the assay based on the competition between unlabeled cAMP and a fixed quantity of tritium-labeled cAMP for cAMP-binding protein according to Gilman.[6] Assays were made in duplicates with 10^6 CTL per one point using a cAMP assay kit (Amersham) following the manufacturer's procedure.

Assay of Phosphatidylinositol Degradation

Cloned CTL were purified by Ficoll-Hypaque centrifugation, and after washing with inositol-free medium (DMEM, Biofluids) containing 10% dialyzed FCS, 10–20 × 10^6 CTL were incubated with 100 μCi of myo[2-^{3}H]inositol (14.3 Ci/ mmol, Amersham International) for 6 h in a CO_2 incubator at 37°C and were resuspended in a final volume of 10 ml (inositol-free DMEM (Biofluids), supplemented with 10% of dialyzed FCS). After incubation, cells were washed twice with RPMI-1640 medium containing 5% FCS, supplemented with 10 mM LiCl. Such a procedure for CTL labeling did not have an adverse effect on their viability and responses.

The labeled CTL were stimulated in conditions that in parallel experiments were shown to result in granule exocytosis triggering; 0.75–1.0 × 10^7 CTL were stimulated by solid-phase anti-TcR monoclonal antibody (mAb) or by antigen-bearing target cells at E/T = 0.5:1 by incubating them at 37°C in a humidified atmosphere at 5% CO_2, 95% air for 1 h in polypropylene, round-bottom tubes (for measurements of target cell–induced phosphatidylinositide turnover) (Falcon #2063, 12 × 75 mm style) or in 96-well plate microtiter wells, precoated with immobilized anti-TcR mAb.[9] The incubation medium was RPMI-1640, supplemented with 5% FCS and 10 mM LiCl. Reactions in the tubes were terminated by the addition of 750 μl of $CHCl_3$:methanol:4N HCl (100:200:2 v/v). The supernatant medium was transferred to polypropylene tubes (Falcon #2063).

The assay of total [^{3}H]inositol phosphates was based on the procedure of Berridge et al.[8,10] and Beaven et al.[11]

Reagents

Forskojin, 8-bromo cyclic AMP, N^6-benzoyl cyclic AMP were purchased from Sigma Chemical Company. 3-Isobutyl-1-methylxanthine (IBMX) was purchased from Aldrich. N-α-benzyloxycarbonyl-L-lysine thiobenzyl ester (BLT) and 5,5'-dithiobis(2-nitrobenzoic acid (DTNB) were products of Calbiochem, and cholera toxin and pertussis toxin were products of List Biological Laboratory. 1,9-Dideoxyforskolin (ddFK) and Rp-cAMP were generous gifts of Dr. Ken Seamon (Food and Drug Administration, Bethesda, MD) and Dr. Lynne H. P. Botelho (Sandoz Research Institute, East Hanover, NJ), respectively.

RESULTS

cAMP-Dependent Protein Kinase (PK-A) Is Involved in Inhibition of TcR-Triggered CTL Activation

In an attempt to understand biochemical mechanisms involved in the TcR-triggered activation pathway, we tested the effect of cholera toxin and pertussis toxin on the antigen (Ag) receptor–mediated CTL activation. Two hour pretreatment of cloned CTL with pertussis toxin did not affect ^{51}Cr-release from Ag-bearing target cells, whereas pretreatment of CTL with cholera toxin dramatically inhibited it. A similar result was obtained when a different CTL activation assay was used. It was shown that incubation of CTL with Ag-bearing target cells results in the secretion of granule-associated enzyme, and preincubation of CTL with cholera toxin, but not with pertussis toxin, practically abolished target cell–induced, Ag-specific secretion from CTL at all tested target-cell/effector-cell ratios.

When we tested cAMP levels in CTL, a significant increase in cAMP levels was detected after treatment of CTL with cholera toxin, but not with pertussis toxin. These data suggest that cAMP may be the cause of inhibition of CTL activation by cholera toxin.

Addition of forskolin, which was shown to directly activate the adenylate cyclase, to the incubation medium resulted in the inhibition of CTL-mediated cytotoxicity. In the control experiment, ddFK, which does not activate adenylate cyclase, did not inhibit cytolysis.

Addition of IBMX, which is able to inhibit cAMP phosphodiesterase and to increase intracellular levels of cAMP, causes significant inhibition of Ag specific–CTL cytotoxicity in both tested CTL clones, 0E4 and 2C. Inhibition was also registered when forskolin and IBMX were tested for their effects on TcR-triggered exocytosis. Effect of ddFK was tested as a control for nonspecific action of forskolin and was found to be inefficient in inhibiting TcR-triggered CTL activation. None of these drugs were toxic for CTL or affected basal level of secretion in tested dose. The ability of IBMX and forskolin to increase cAMP levels in CTL was demonstrated in parallel experiments.

These data implicated increases in cAMP levels in the inhibition of the CTL activation and suggested involvement of PK-A in this inhibition. We attempted to investigate the possibility of PK-A involvement in the inhibitory pathway by taking advantage of the availability of two classes of cAMP analogues, which are selective for the two different cAMP-binding sites of type II protein kinase. These cAMP analogues demonstrated synergism in activating PK-A when added together to intact adipocytes.[7] Because 8-Br-cAMP and N[6]-benzoyl-cAMP are specific for site I and II of PK-A regulatory subunit, respectively, and because they synergize in activating protein kinase activity of the catalytic subunit, we expected to detect a synergistic effect of these cAMP analogues in inhibition of TcR-triggered exocytosis. Addition of N[6]-benzoyl-, but not 8-Br-cAMP analogue, into incubation medium significantly inhibited secretion. Although up to 2 mM 8-Br-cAMP did not inhibit secretion alone, it significantly increased the inhibitory action of 0.5 mM N[6]-benzoyl-cAMP. Both analogues were not toxic for CTL and did not change the basal level of secretion in the absence of immobilized anti-TcR mAb. These data strongly implicate PK-A in the inhibitory pathway. Such a conclusion is reinforced by the effect of the cAMP antagonist on the TcR-mediated CTL activation.

(Rp)-diastereomer of adenosine cyclic $3',5'$-phosphorothioate was shown to be specific inhibitor of PK-A.[12] Mixing of CTL with ^{51}Cr-labeled Ag-bearing target cells in the presence of forskolin or IBMX resulted in the decrease of the maximal ^{51}Cr-release and in the shift to the right of E/T ratio curve. Evident reversal of inhibition could be detected, however, if PK-A antagonist was present during assay. The antagonist of PK-A reverses the inhibitory effect of forskolin and IBMX, and it was found that Rp-cAMP is less efficient in the reversal effect of forskolin, than the effect of IBMX.

Similar observations were made when the effect of Rp-cAMP was tested in a TcR-triggered enzyme–secretion assay of CTL activation. The differences in the ability of Rp-cAMP to reverse forskolin- and IBMX-induced inhibition of TcR-triggered exocytosis could be explained if forskolin induced higher levels of cAMP in CTL than IMBX. Indeed, fewer cAMP-binding sites on the regulatory subunit of PK-A could be occupied by a competitive cAMP antagonist, Rp-cAMPS, in the presence of higher concentrations of cAMP.[12] To investigate this issue, we compared levels of cAMP, and the time-course of cAMP levels changes after incubation of CTL with forskolin and IBMX. It was shown that forskolin is much more potent in raising cAMP levels than IBMX. Levels of cAMP in the presence of forskolin and IBMX were compared, up to 60 min of incubation, and it was found that the level of cAMP was significantly elevated above basal level until at least 3 hr of incubation with IBMX.

The results described strongly implicate PK-A in an inhibition of the TcR-triggered transmembrane signaling pathway. Which step(s) of this activating pathway are susceptible to inhibition by PK-A remained to be established, however. To resolve this question, we took advantage of our recent finding that the requirement for TcR cross-linking in exocytosis triggering can be bypassed by synergistic action of protein kinase C activators and Ca^{++}-ionophores.

Locus of the Inhibitory Action of PK-A in the TcR-Triggered Activation Pathway

In an attempt to identify the locus of inhibitory action of PK-A in the TcR-triggered protein kinase C- and Ca^{++}-mediated activating biochemical pathway, we took advantage of the possibility to bypass TcR-cross-linking by protein kinase C activators and Ca^{++} ionophores (Takayama et al., submitted for publication). We studied the effect of the cAMP level-raising compound IBMX on the exocytosis in CTL, which is triggered by the synergistic action of phorbol esters and calcium ionophores. Increases in cAMP levels caused by incubation of both CTL clones 0E4 and BM10-37, in the presence of IBMX, result in the inhibition of PMA/A23187-triggered BLT-esterase secretion in both tested CTL clones. Strong inhibition of PMA/A23187-induced BLT-esterase secretion was also observed when cAMP levels were increased by treatment of CTL with cholera toxin. We did not obtain consistent results, however, when the effect of forskolin on PMA/A23187-triggered secretion was studied. No significant differences in inhibition of PMA/A23187-triggered exocytosis were found when CTL were preincubated with IBMX for 1 h before addition of PMA/A23187 or were mixed with IBMX, PMA, and A23187, simultaneously. Because addition of PMA/A23187 bypasses early stages of TcR-triggered activation, these results suggest that PK-A could inhibit the later stages of exocytosis. Such results, however, do not exclude the possibility of PK-A inhibiting the TcR-triggered pathway simultaneously with earlier stages.

To further investigate the possibility that PK-A may inhibit early events following TcR cross-linking, we tested the effect of cAMP raising agents on the Ag receptor–triggered phosphatidylinositol turnover. To investigate the possibility that PK-A can inhibit the TcR-triggered pathway at earlier stages, which were bypassed by the PMA/A23187, we tested the effect of cAMP raising agents on anti-TcR mAb-triggered phosphatidylinositol 4,5-biphosphate (PI-P₂) metabolism. Cross-linking of TcR on the surface of CTL by antigen on the surface of target cells or by solid-phase anti-TcR mAb results in the triggering of phosphatidylinositol turnover, which we measured by accumulation of inositol triphosphate (InsP₃) as well as its breakdown products. In this experiment, we did not follow separately the changes in the amounts of InsP₃, inositol biphosphate (InsP₂), and inositol

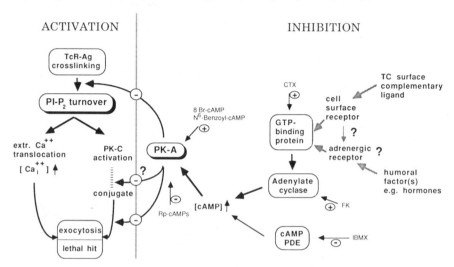

FIGURE 2. Locus of inhibitory action of cAMP dependent–protein kinase (PK-A) in CTL activation pathway. Abbreviations: TC, target cell; cAMP PDE, cAMP phosphodiesterase; PI-P₂, phosphatidylinositol 4,5-biphosphate; FK, forskolin; IBMX, isobuthylmethylxantine; PK-C, protein kinase C; CTX, cholera toxin; ⊕, stimulatory action; ⊖, inhibitory action.

phosphate (InsP) inasmuch as it was shown earlier that in T cells, addition of anti-TcR mAb results in increases in all three inositol phosphates. Forskolin and IBMX significantly inhibited TcR-triggered PI-P₂ turnover when it was induced by incubation of CTL with Ag-bearing target cells or with immobilized anti-TcR mAb. IBMX was more efficient in inhibiting PI-P₂ turnover than forskolin. The ability of cAMP level raising agents to inhibit TcR-triggered PI-P₂ turnover suggest that PK-A may inhibit CTL activation by blocking early events required to trigger a putative PI-P₂ phosphodiesterase and thereby block formation of diacylglycerol and inositol phosphates (FIG. 2).

DISCUSSION

The data presented in this paper strongly suggest that PK-A is involved in the inhibitory pathway, which can counteract TcR-triggered transmembrane signaling in CTL. The existence of such an inhibitory pathway raises the question of how it is regulated in CTL. The logical next step in such studies should be identification of proteins on the CTL surface that are coupled to the cAMP-dependent pathway and if monoclonal Ab to known surface antigens can trigger cAMP accumulation in CTL or can interfere with cAMP level–raising stimuli.

Whereas cholera toxin had a strong inhibitory effect on CTL activation, no inhibition was observed when CTL were pretreated with pertussis toxin. It is possible, although not formally proven, that CTL do not have surface receptors for pertussis toxin, as was shown to be the case in platelets.

The synergistic effects of 8-Br-cAMP and N^6-benzoyl-cAMP in the inhibition of TcR-triggered or PMA/A23187 ionophores were registered. Interestingly, 8-Br-cAMP had little or no effect on CTL, whereas N^6-benzoyl-cAMP was, on itself, inhibitory. It was demonstrated earlier, that these cAMP analogues are selective for cAMP binding sites 1 and 2, respectively, on the monomeric regulatory subunit of PK-A; these analogues synergistically activate protein kinase and demonstrate a synergy of cAMP-mediated lipolytic response in isolated intact adipocytes.[7] The correlation between synergistic action of 8-Br-cAMP and N^6-benzoyl-cAMP in inhibition of CTL activation and their documented ability to synergize in activation of PK-A strongly implicate this enzyme in the inhibitory pathway.

The ability of CTL clones to respond by exocytosis of granules to two such different stimuli as anti-TcR mAb and PMA/A23187 provided an opportunity to investigate the locus of inhibitory action of PK-A in the TcR-triggered pathway of CTL activation. Because PMA/A23187-triggered secretion is inhibited by the cAMP level-raising drug IBMX, it suggests that PK-A inhibits at stages, which are distant from the TcR–cross-linking and early transmembrane signaling pathways. These data did not rule out, however, the ability of cAMP to inhibit both early and late stages of TcR triggered–CTL activation. The ability of PK-A to inhibit early stages of TcR triggered–CTL activation was directly tested in experiments in which the effect of forskolin and IBMX on TcR mediated–PI-P$_2$ turnover was studied. Strong inhibition of inositol phosphates accumulation by forskolin and IBMX suggests that PK-A can also affect the early stages of TcR-transmembrane signaling and block diacylglycerol and inositol-phosphate formation, thereby inhibiting protein kinase C- and Ca^{++}-mediated pathways (FIG. 2).

The existence of more than one locus of inhibitory action of cAMP suggests an important regulatory role of cAMP in lymphocyte regulation. It is still not known which particular events of TcR-triggered exocytosis (protein kinase C translocation, interactions of granule proteins with cytoskeletal proteins, granule movement, granule prepositioning near the plasma membrane, and fusion of granules with plasma membrane) are affected by PK-A. These questions will be addressed in future studies. It is possible that different levels of cAMP are required to inhibit different partial reactions of the exocytosis, thereby providing a mechanism of quantitative regulation by cAMP. Experiments are now under way to correlate mechanical activities of CTL (e.g., shearing-force resistant conjugate formation) and changes in PK-A activity caused by a rise in intracellular levels of cAMP. It could be expected, however, that PK-A will inhibit conjugate formation, as it is inhibiting TcR-triggered exocytosis, inasmuch as the same early, protein kinase C–involving stages are implicated in both conjugate formation[1] and in exocytosis triggering (FIGURES 1, 2).

Results described in this paper form the basis for the hypothetical model of a molecular on and off switch mechanism in CTL activation during engagement with the antigen-bearing target cells. Activation of CTL (studied here in a functional TcR-regulated exocytosis assay) as we demonstrated earlier is mediated by TcR-triggered phosphoinositide turnover, protein kinase C activation, and extracellular Ca^{++} translocation through the plasma membrane Ca^{++} channels, followed by the involvement of Ca^{++}/calmodulin–dependent proteins (FIG. 1). It is postulated here that during CTL interaction with target cells, the number of TcR, which are occupied by the antigen, might be decreased (due to *e.g.*, the proteolytic action of the proteases released from the granules during exocytosis). Subsequently, the intensity of the TcR-triggered transmembrane-signaling pathway is decreased. As a result of this and PK-A activation, CTL disengages from the TC, and exocytosis of granules is terminated.

Levels of cAMP in CTL might be increased[13,14] due to cross-linking of CTL surface proteins by yet unidentified complementary protein ligands on the TC surface. Such an increment of the cAMP level could result in the inhibition of the on signal by the cAMP regulated–inhibitory pathway (FIG. 2), which we consider as part of an off signal. It remains to be established which surface proteins, hormones,[15] or lymphokines can trigger increases of cAMP in CTL.

SUMMARY

Screening activities of cytotoxic T lymphocytes (CTL) are viewed as a cycle of engagements and disengagements with target cells. One of the unexplained features of CTL activation is a biochemical mechanism of an ''off'' signal, which would result in disengagement of CTL from the target cell and termination of exocytosis of granules. Data are presented that suggest that cAMP dependent–protein kinase (PK-A) inhibits both early and late stages of antigen receptor-regulated CTL activation and may be a part of such an off signaling pathway.

ACKNOWLEDGMENTS

Authors wish to thank Dr. Ken Seamon for the preparation of 1.9-dideoxy-forskolin, Dr. Lynn Parker-Botelho for the preparation of Rp-cAMPs, Dr. Michael Bevan for F23.1 mAb, Dr. Jeffery Bluestone for the BM10-37 CTL clone, and Dr. Osami Kanagawa for the 0E4 CTL clone. Excellent editorial help of Ms. Starnes in preparation of this manuscript is greatly appreciated. Helpful discussions with Dr. Michio Ui and Dr. Teruko Ishizaka are greatly appreciated.

REFERENCES

1. BERREBI, G., H. TAKAYAMA & M. SITKOVSKY. 1987. The antigen-receptor requirement for conjugate formation and lethal hit triggering by cytotoxic T lymphocytes can be bypassed by protein kinase C activators and Ca^{++}-ionophores. Proc. Natl. Acad. Sci. USA **84:** 1364–1368.
2. PASTERNACK, M., C. R. VERRET, M. A. LIN & H. N. EISEN. 1986. Serine esterase in cytolytic T lymphocytes. Nature **322:** 740–743.
3. TAKAYAMA, H., G. TRENN, W. HUMPHREY, J. BLUESTONE, P. HENKART & M. SITKOVSKY. 1987. Antigen receptor triggered secretion of a trypsin-type esterase from cytotoxic T lymphocytes. J. Immunol. **138:** 566–569.
4. HASKINS, K., C. HANNUM, J. WHITE, N. ROEHM, R. KUBO, J. KAPPLER & P. MARRACK. 1984. The major histocompatability complex-restricted antigen receptor on T cells. J. Exp. Med. **160:** 452–471.

5. STAERZ, U. D., O. KANAGAWA & M. J. BEVAN. 1985. Hybrid antibodies can target sites for attack by T cells. J. Immunol. **134:** 3995–4000.
6. GILMAN, A. G. 1970. A protein binding assay for adenosine 3',5'-monophosphate. Proc. Natl. Acad. Sci. USA **67:** 305–312.
7. BEEBE, S. J., R. HOLLOWAY, S. R. RANNELS & J. D. CORBIN. 1984. Two classes of cAMP analogs which are selective for the two different cAMP-binding sites of type II protein kinase demonstrate synergism when added together to intact adipocytes. J. Biol. Chem. **259:** 3539–3547.
8. BERRIDGE, M. J. 1984. Inositol trisphosphate and diacylglycerol as second messengers. Biochem. J. **220:** 345–360.
9. STAERZ, U. D., O. KANAGAWA & M. J. BEVAN. 1985. Hybrid antibodies can target sites for attack by T cells. Nature **314:** 628–631.
10. BERRIDGE, M. J., C. P. DOWNES & M. R. HANLEY. 1982. Lithium amplifies agonist-dependent phosphatidylinositol responses in brain and salivary glands. Biochem. J. **206:** 587–595.
11. BEAVEN, M., J. P. MOORE, G. A. SMITH, T. R. HESKETH & J. C. METCALFE. 1984. The calcium signal and phosphatidylinositol breakdown in 2H3 cells. J. Biol. Chem. **253:** 7137–7142.
12. ROTHERMEL, J. P., B. JASTORFF & L. H. PARKER-BOTELHO. 1984. Inhibition of glycogen-induced glycogenolysis in isolated rat hepatocytes by the Rp diastereoisomer of adenosine cyclic 3',5'-phosphorothioate. J. Biol. Chem. **259:** 8151–8155.
13. HENNEY, C. S., H. R. BOURUE & L. M. LICHTENSTEIN. 1972. The role of cyclic AMP in the specific cytolytic activity of lymphocytes. J. Immunol. **108:** 1526–1534.
14. BOURNE, H. R., L. M. LICHTENSTEIN, K. L. MELMON, C. S. HENNEY, Y. WEINSTEIN & G. M. SHEARER. 1974. Modulation of inflammation and immunity by cyclic AMP. Science **194:** 19–28.
15. PLAUT, M. 1987. Lymphocyte hormone receptors. Ann. Rev. Immunol. **5:** 621–669.

A Molecular-Genetic Analysis of Cytotoxic T Lymphocyte Function[a]

R. CHRIS BLEACKLEY, CORRINNE G. LOBE,
CALLIOPI HAVELE, JENNIFER SHAW, BILL POHAJDAK,
MARK REDMOND, MARC LETELLIER,
AND VERNER H. PAETKAU

Department of Biochemistry
University of Alberta
Edmonton, Alberta, Canada, T6G 2H

The molecular basis of cytotoxic T lymphocyte (CTL)–mediated lysis remains a mystery. Over the past few years, however, a number of candidate components of the killing machinery have been identified and characterized. One of the most significant findings was made by Dourmashkin *et al.* in 1980.[1] They observed that cells lysed by cells in an antibody dependent–cellular cytotoxicity (ADCC) reaction contained tubular lesions. Similar ultrastructural studies provided evidence for such lesions in natural killer cells (NK)[2] and, most importantly for this discussion, CTL.[3] These observations stimulated researchers to pursue a biochemical approach to study the mechanism. It was known that similar lesions could be induced by complement components, so it was entirely logical to look for analogous pore-forming proteins in CTL. This was made easier by the discovery of interleukin-2[4] which made it possible to grow large quantities of cloned CTL for biochemical analysis. The protein from CTL, responsible for the ring-like lesions, was isolated and named perforin.[5,6] A similar molecule, cytolysin, was identified in NK.[7] Perforin is located in the electron-dense granules that are present in the cytoplasm of CTL. This has prompted efforts to purify and characterize other granular components, as it is believed that such molecules, acting in concert with perforin, are responsible for lysis of target cells.[8] At this time, however, the identities of, and relationships between, the various granular proteins and the roles they play in the lytic mechanism remain unresolved.

Our approach for studying this intriguing question is based upon the hypothesis that the proteins involved in killing will be expressed only in activated CTL and not in other closely related cells, including precursor CTL. We have adopted a comprehensive strategy to identify such CTL-specific proteins using molecular genetic techniques. The identification of the molecules involved in CTL-mediated lysis will be important in our understanding of how CTL function. Moreover, such precise knowledge could lead to the development of innovative forms of immunotherapy.

[a] This work was supported by Grants from the MRC and the NCI of Canada, and salaries were provided by the Alberta Heritage Foundation for Medical Research and the Terry Fox Special Initiatives Program.

RESULTS AND DISCUSSION

Genes encoding molecules that may be important to CTL function were isolated by a differential approach.[9] This method is based on the assumption that proteins that are required in a cell's specialized function are represented by mRNA present in that cell type, but at a low level or not at all in other types of cells. Thus, cytotoxic T lymphocytes should express a set of mRNA that encode its function-related proteins and that are not present in helper T cells or thymocytes. To isolate such mRNA sequences, a cDNA library was constructed using mRNA from a CTL line as template. This library was sequentially screened with probe generated from CTL, helper T cells, and thymus cells. Several cDNA clones were identified that were positive with the CTL and not the other probes. Two of these, B10 and C11, were characterized in detail.[9]

B10 and C11 are CTL-Specific

The specificity of expression of these two clones was tested in a number of different cell types. Of 12 T-cell lines or cultures tested that had cytotoxic activity, all 12 expressed B10 and C11. These include so-called helper-killer cells, which although they have the helper phenotype and produce lymphokines, also have cytolytic activity.[10]

NK, which do possess granules and are thought to kill their target cells using a similar mechanism to CTL, did not express detectable B10 or C11 transcripts and so possibly use some other B10- or C11-like molecules instead. Other types of lymphoid cells tested included five noncytolytic helper T cell lines, resting and activated splenic B cells and macrophages, all of which were negative for B10 and C11 transcripts. The nonlymphoid cells tested, brain, liver, and fibroblasts, did not express B10 or C11. Thus, these two clones, which were identified by differential hybridization screening, represent CTL-specific mRNA.

B10 and C11 Expression Correlates with Cytolytic Activity

The expression of B10 and C11 was found to be not only CTL-specific, but also to correlate with the activation of cytotoxicity. In time-course experiments, the level of B10 and C11 mRNA increased when antigen-dependent cytotoxic T cell lines or spleen cell cultures were activated by antigen or concanavalin A (Con A). FIGURE 1 shows a bar-graph representation of data taken from an allogeneic cytolytic reaction. Spleen cells were mixed with stimulators on day zero, and on subsequent days the levels of cytolytic activity (chromium release assay, filled in bars) and relative mRNA levels (cytodots hybridized with C11 probe, stippled bars) were measured. The data shown here were obtained with the C11 probe; when the cytodot was reprobed with B10, the pattern of expression was the same. A difference, however, between C11 and B10 expression was revealed by Northern blot analysis. The peak of induction of C11 mRNA occurred first, followed by B10 mRNA, and finally the peak of cytotoxic activity. This order of events occurred regardless of whether the cell's response peaked in a few hours or in a few days. Thus, these two mRNA seem to be sequentially regulated in response to CTL activation. The CTL-specific expression and the correlation with T cell–cytotoxic activity strongly suggest that the B10- and C11-encoded proteins play a key role in CTL function.

B10 and C11 Encode Serine Proteases

Sequence analysis of C11 and B10 revealed that they were related to each other (80% homologous at the nucleotide level). An open reading frame was identified in the C11 sequence and the predicted protein sequence compared to others in the National Biomedical Research Foundation data bank. The C11-predicted protein-designated cytotoxic-cell protein (CCPI) was homologous with a large number of serine proteases, and closer inspection revealed that CCPI contains the residues that form the catalytic triad in the active site of all known proteases (His[57], Asp[102], and Ser[195] in chymotrypsin).[11] The B10 cDNA was not full-length, but an open reading frame was identified and the predicted protein

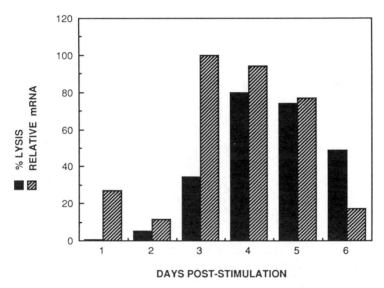

DAYS POST-STIMULATION

FIGURE 1. Expression of C11 during the activation of a cytotoxic T cell response. Murine spleen cells were mixed with mitomycin C–treated EL4 cells on day 0. On subsequent days, the cytolytic activity against EL4 was measured in a chromium-release assay (filled in bars), and the relative level of C11 mRNA expression was quantitated by scanning densitometry of cytodots hybridized with a radioactive C11 cDNA probe (stippled bars).

named CCPII. In the top two lines of FIGURE 2, the protein sequences of CCPI and II are compared. Clearly, they are homologous proteins, but most importantly, they contain the characteristic protein motif Asp-Ser-Gly-Gly, which includes the active-site serine ($). Therefore we predict that both CCPI and II encode serine proteases and suggest that a protease cascade may play a role in the activation of CTL.[12] The protease described by Gershenfeld and Weissman may also be a member of this cascade.[13]

The serine protease with which CCPI shares the greatest homology is rat mast cell–protease II (RMCPII). This protease was thought to be structurally unique; however, CCPI and II also possess the same unusual structural features that are thought to affect substrate binding.[14] These include (see FIG. 2) an alanine (*) six residues upstream from the $. This residue, which lies at the bottom of the substrate-binding site, is a serine in chymotrypsin-like proteases and an aspartic acid in trypsin-like enzymes. In addition RMCPII, CCPI, and CCPII lack the cysteines to form a disulphide bond that is present in all other known proteases. One of the cysteines is replaced by a phenylalanine (**), whereas the other corresponds to an apparent deletion (****). This disulphide is thought to be important in stabilizing the secondary structure of the binding site.[15] Finally, the Ser-Try-Gly sequence of chymotrypsin and trypsin is replaced by Ser-Tyr-Gly (***), again suggesting an unusual substrate specificity. In addition to the features shared with RMCPII, modeling studies (M. Murphy and M. N. G. James, unpublished data)

CCPI	Thr	Val	Gln	Lys	Asp	Arg	Glu	Cys	Glu	Ser	Tyr		Phe	Lys	Asn	Arg	Tyr	Asn	Lys	Thr	Asn	Gln	166
CCPII	Thr	Val	Gln	Lys	Asp	Gln	Val	Cys	Glu	Ser	Gln		Phe	Gln	Ser	Phe	Tyr	Asn	Arg	Ala	Asn	Glu	
RMCPII	Arg	Ile	Met	Asp	Glu	Lys	Ala	Cys	Val	Asp	Tyr	Arg	Tyr	Tyr	Glu		Tyr		Lys	Phe		Gln	165
CHYM.	Pro	Leu	Leu	Ser	Asn	Thr	Asn	Cys	Lys	Lys	Tyr		Trp	Gly	Thr	Lys		Ile	Lys	Asp	Ala	Met	179
TRYP.	Pro	Ile	Leu	Ser	Asn	Ser	Ser	Cys	Lys	Ser	Ala		Tyr	Pro	Gly	Gln	Ile	Thr		Ser	Asn	Met	166

(• •• $)

CCPI	Ile	Cys	Ala	Gly	Asp	Pro	Lys	Thr	Lys	Arg	Ala	Ser	Phe	Arg	Gly	Asp	Ser	Gly	Gly	Pro	Leu	Val	188
CCPII	Ile	Cys	Val	Gly	Asp	Ser	Lys	Ile	Lys	Gly	Ala	Ser	Phe	Glu	Glu	Asp	Ser	Gly	Gly	Pro	Leu	Val	
RMCPII	Val	Cys	Val	Gly	Ser	Pro	Thr	Thr	Leu	Arg	Ala	Ala	Phe	Met	Gly	Asp	Ser	Gly	Gly	Pro	Leu	Leu	187
CHYM.	Ile	Cys	Ala	Gly	Ala	Ser	Gly	Val			Ser	Ser	Cys	Met	Gly	Asp	Ser	Gly	Gly	Pro	Leu	Val	200
TRYP.	Phe	Cys	Ala	Gly	Tyr	Leu	Glu	Gly	Gly	Lys	Asp	Ser	Cys	Gln	Gly	Asp	Ser	Gly	Gly	Pro	Val	Val	188

(••• ••••)

CCPI	Cys	Lys	Lys	Val	Ala	Ala				Gly	Ile	Val	Ser	Tyr	Gly	Tyr	Lys	Asp		Gly	204
CCPII	Cys	Lys	Arg	Ala	Ala	Ala				Gly	Ile	Val	Ser	Tyr	Gly	Gln	Thr	Asp		Gly	
RMCPII	Cys	Ala	Gly	Val	Ala	His				Gly	Ile	Val	Ser	Tyr	Gly	His	Pro	Asp		Ala	203
CHYM.	Cys	Lys	Lys	Asn	Gly	Ala	Trp	Thr	Leu	Val	Gly	Ile	Val	Ser	Trp	Gly	Ser	Ser	Thr	Cys	Ser	Thr	222
TRYP.	Cys	Ser	Gly	Lys	Leu	Gln				Gly	Ile	Val	Ser	Trp	Gly	Ser		Gly	Cys	Ala	Gln	205

CCPI	Ser	Pro		Pro	Arg	Ala	Phe	Thr	Lys	Val	Ser	Ser	Phe	Leu	Ser	Trp	Ile	Lys	Lys	Thr	Met	Lys	225
CCPII	Ser	Ala		Pro	Gln	Val	Phe	Thr	Arg	Val	Leu	Ser	Phe	Val	Ser	Trp	Ile	Lys	Lys	Thr	Met	Lys	
RMCPII	Lys	Pro		Pro	Ala	Ile	Phe	Thr	Arg	Val	Ser	Thr	Tyr	Val	Pro	Thr	Ile	Asn	Ala	Val	Ile	223
CHYM.	Ser	Thr		Pro	Gly	Val	Tyr	Ala	Arg	Val	Thr	Ala	Leu	Val	Asn	Trp	Val	Gln	Gln	Thr	Leu	Ala	243
TRYP.	Lys	Asn	Lys	Pro	Gly	Val	Tyr	Thr	Lys	Val	Cys	Asn	Tyr	Val	Ser	Trp	Ile	Lys	Gln	Thr	Ile	Ala	227

CCPI	Ser	Ser	227
CCPII	His	Ser	
RMCPII	Asn		224
CHYM.	Ala	Asn	245
TRYP.	Ser	Asn	229

FIGURE 2. Comparison of the protein sequences in the carboxy terminal regions of CCPI, CCPII, RMCPII, chymotrypsin, and trypsin. The protein sequences predicted from the cDNA inserts, designated C11 (CCPI) and B10 (CCPII) were compared with the known protein sequences for rat mast cell protease II (RMCPII), bovine chymotrypsin (CHYM.), and bovine trypsin (TRYP.). The numbering for CCPI is based on the full predicted protein sequence,[12] whereas no residue assignment can be given for CCPII, as a full-length cDNA clone has not yet been sequenced. Residues that are homologous to those found in CCPI are boxed, and the active-site serine is designated by $. Residues that are unusual in CCPI, II, and RMCPII are marked with one to four asterixes (*).

suggest that CCPI may have other unusual structural properties that would endow this protease with a novel substrate specificity.

Localization of CCPI to Granules

Synthetic peptides based on the C11 sequence were synthesized and used to generate antibodies against CCPI. These were used to localize CCPI to the characteristic granules of CTL. The antibodies detected a protein in the granules of the CTL clones MTL2.8.2 and MTL2.2.1, which express C11, but not in EL4, S194, or CTL.L16 cells, which do not express C11. On Western blots, either of total cellular protein or of granular-associated proteins, the antibody bound to a protein at ~29 kDa, both in nonreducing and reducing gels.

CTL granules are believed to contain the effector molecules for CTL-mediated lysis. Isolated granules from CTL contain perforin and serine proteases and are capable of nonspecific target-cell lysis.[16,17] Recently, one of these granule-associated proteases was purified to homogeneity and sequenced.[18] The amino acid sequence determined is identical to that predicted for Hanukah Factor, based on the cDNA sequence of AR10.[13] This protein runs at 60 kDa on a nonreducing gel and 35 kDa on a reducing gel. At least one other serine protease has been detected in granules by diisopropyl fluorophosphate (DFP) binding.[17] It is reported to run at 29 kDa on both reducing and nonreducing gels and seems to have an unusual substrate specificity. Therefore it quite likely is CCPI. The existence of CCPI as a monomer was not expected, because an uneven number of cysteine-residues occurred in the derived amino acid sequence. This led to the suggestion that the cysteine at position 74, which has no counterpart in other known serine proteases, is linked by a disulphide bond to another chain.[19] CCPI was therefore predicted to correspond to the serine protease homo- or heterodimer that ran at 60 kDa on a nonreducing gel and 35 kDa on a reducing gel.

The CTL-L16 line is an IL-2–dependent clone that has lost its cytotoxic activity even when incubated with the mitogen, Con A. RNA was prepared from CTL-L16, with and without a 16 hr incubation with Con A, and used to prepare a Northern blot. When probed with B10 and C11, no B10 or C11 mRNA was detected, either in the samples from unstimulated or mitogen-treated cells. The lack of B10 and C11 expression may be the cause of the loss of CTL-L16 cytotoxic activity, although it is possible that other molecules involved in cytolysis are also not expressed. CTL-L16 cells have a high number of the characteristic dense CTL granules. When the granule-associated proteins from CTL-L16 were analyzed on a Western blot by probing with the anti-CCPI antibody, however, no signal was detected. This absence of CCPI in the CTL-L16 granules agrees with the lack of C11 mRNA in the cells.

DOES CCPI PLAY A ROLE IN CTL-MEDIATED LYSIS?

Localization of CCPI to CTL granules provides further support that the proteins are involved in the cytolytic event. Granules have previously been implicated in the mechanism of T cell–mediated lysis.[16] A model of granule-mediated killing is presented in FIGURE 3. Upon interaction of the CTL with its target, cytoplasmic granules polarize to the point of contact between the two cells.[20] By fusing with the cytoplasmic membrane, the granular contents are released into the contact space between the cells. One of these proteins contained inside the granules, perforin, is capable of forming a polymerized complex containing hydrophobic and hydrophilic domains that can be inserted into the target-cell membrane, thus creating a transmembrane channel.[3] The "lytic molecules" could then pass into the target cell and induce its destruction in association with DNA fragmentation.[21]

One of the intriguing aspects of this mechanism is that the killer cells are not killed themselves. In FIGURE 3 one possible explanation for this is represented. The internal membrane of the granules is presumably impermeable to the lytic molecules or else the CTL would be lysed by their own granular components. By the mechanism of exocytosis, this granule membrane transiently becomes the outer membrane of the CTL in the region where the cytolytic effector molecules are released. Therefore in this area the CTL is impermeable and thus resistant to killing.

The nature of the lethal effector molecules is not known, but presumably they are contained within the granules. The fact that CCPI is located in the granules of cytolytically active T cells suggests that it may play a key role in the lytic mechanism. Indeed, inhibitors of serine proteases have been shown to block target-cell lysis even when introduced late in the process.[22] The granules in CTL are acidic, so it is unlikely that CCPI would be active at this pH.[17] Therefore it is concluded that the proteases are active either during or after exocytosis. They could play a

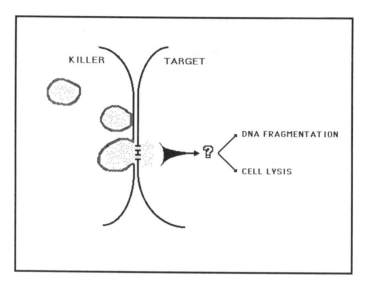

FIGURE 3. A model for the involvement of granular proteins in the lysis of target cells. When the CTL binds to a target cell, the cytoplasmic granules polarize to the contact point, fuse with the cytoplasmic membrane, and exocytose their contents. One of the granular proteins, perforin, polymerizes and inserts into the cytoplasmic membrane of the target cell. This creates a transmembrane channel through which other granule-proteins can pass to induce chromosomal DNA fragmentation in, and eventually lysis of, the target cell.

role in the degranulation process itself by attacking cell-membrane proteins or, in a similar manner, facilitate polyperforin insertion in the target-cell membrane. The analogy with complement-mediated lysis would suggest that the esterases may be involved in activating or assembly of the lytic molecules. Finally, it is possible that one or more of the proteases could pass through the transmembrane channels and, finding their substrate inside the target cell, initiate a chain of events resulting in cell death.

Potential Therapeutic and Diagnostic Uses of CTL-Specific Molecules

Although the precise functions of the B10- and C11-encoded proteins are not yet known, the results presented here demonstrate that they are specifically expressed in cytolytic T cells, their expression correlates with cytolytic activity, and they are located in the CTL granules. Together, this strongly suggests that they play an important role in the lytic mechanism of CTL.

The CTL-specific genes that have been isolated represent useful markers of cell function. Unlike most T-cell markers that are cell-surface antigens of unknown function, B10 and C11 expression appears to be associated with T cell–cytotoxic activity. These markers will be useful, not only in assigning cells to a T-cell subset, but also in determining the role of CTL in immune defense and in autoimmune dysfunction. The identification of molecules that seem to be directly involved in CTL lysis has increased our understanding of how the cells may induce target-cell destruction. Characterization of the molecules involved in the lytic event will allow the development of specific potentiators or inhibitors of CTL function. The novel substrate specificity of CCPI may be useful, for example, in developing synthetic substrates that selectively block the CTL response, without inhibiting other important physiological functions. The ability to monitor the role of CTL in disease, together with a knowledge of how the cells function and are regulated at the molecular level, provides a basis for the development of rational immunotherapy.

SUMMARY

Two genes that are specifically expressed in T cells with cytolytic activity were isolated from a CTL cDNA library by differential screening. Both appear to encode serine proteases, thus suggesting a cascade mechanism, similar to complement, in activated CTL. Both CTL-specific proteases have a number of unusual structural features that suggest that they will have novel substrate specificities. One of the proteins (CCPI) has been oriented to the granules found in the cytoplasm of CTL. Taken together, these data strongly suggest that these molecules play an important role in target-cell lysis by CTL. Furthermore, we believe that the detailed molecular knowledge being accumulated through these studies may lead to the development of innovative forms of immunotherapy.

ACKNOWLEDGMENTS

The authors are most grateful to Brett Finlay, Michael James, and Michael Murphy for their valuable contributions to this work; Nancy Ehrman and Brenda Duggan for providing excellent technical assistance; and to Mae Wylie for preparing the manuscript.

REFERENCES

1. DOURMASHKIN, R. R., P. DETEIX, C. B. SIMONE & P. A. HENKART. 1980. Clin. Exp. Immunol. **42:** 554–560.
2. PODACK, E. R. & G. DEMERT. 1983. Nature **302:** 442–445.
3. DENNERT, G. & E. R. PODACK. 1983. J. Exp. Med. **157:** 1483–1495.

4. MORGAN, D. A., F. W. RUSCETTI & R. C. GALLO. 1976. Science **193**: 1007–1008.
5. PODACK, E. R., J. D. YOUNG & Z. A. COHN. 1985. Proc. Natl. Acad. Sci. USA **82**: 8629–8633.
6. MASSON, D. & J. TSCHOPP. 1985. J. Biol. Chem. **260**: 9069–9072.
7. HENKART, P. A., P. J. MILLARD, C. W. REYNOLDS & M. P. HENKART. 1984. J. Exp. Med. **160**: 75–93.
8. YOUNG, J. D.-E. & Z. A. COHN. 1986. J. Cell. Biochem. **32**: 151–167.
9. LOBE, C. G., C. HAVELE & R. C. BLEACKLEY. 1986. Proc. Natl. Acad. Sci. USA **83**: 1448–1452.
10. TITE, J. P. & C. A. JANEWAY. 1984. Eur. J. Immunol. **14**: 878–886.
11. NEURATH, H. 1984. Science **224**: 350–357.
12. LOBE, C. G., B. B. FINLAY, W. PARANCHYCH, V. H. PAETKAU & R. C. BLEACKLEY. 1986. Science **232**: 858–861.
13. GERSHENFELD, H. K. & I. WEISSMAN. 1986. Science **232**: 854–858.
14. WOODBURY, R. G. & H. NEURATH. 1980. FEBS Lett. **114**: 189–196.
15. WOODBURY, R. G., K. KATUNUMA, K. KOBAYASHI, K. TITANI & H. NEURATH. 1978. Biochemistry **17**: 811–819.
16. PODACK, E. R. & P. J. KONIGSBERG. 1984. J. Exp. Med. **160**: 695–710.
17. MASSON, D., M. NABHOLZ, C. ESTRADE & J. TSCHOPP. 1986. EMBO J. **5**: 1595–1600.
18. MASSON, D., M. ZAMAI & J. TSCHOPP. 1986. FEBS Lett. **208**: 84–88.
19. REID, K .B. M. 1986. Nature **322**: 684–685.
20. YANELLI, J. R., J. A. SULLIVAN, G. L. MANDELL & V. H. ENGELHARD. 1986. J. Immunol. **136**: 377–382.
21. DUKE, R. C., R. CHERVENAK & J. J. COHEN. 1983. Proc. Natl. Acad. Sci. USA **80**: 6361–6365.
22. REDELMAN, D. & D. HUDIG. 1983. Cellular Immunol. **81**: 9–21.

A T Cell– and Natural Killer Cell–Specific, Trypsin-like Serine Protease

Implications of a Cytolytic Cascade[a]

HOWARD K. GERSHENFELD, R. JANE HERSHBERGER,
CHRISTOPH MUELLER, AND IRVING L. WEISSMAN

Department of Pathology
Stanford University School of Medicine
Stanford, California 94305

> The verdict is not suddenly arrived at, the
> proceedings gradually merge into a verdict.
>
> F. KAFKA, *The Trial*

Although no verdict has arrived on the exact mechanism(s) of lymphocyte cytotoxicity, we hope to present one possible view of the process in these proceedings. Inasmuch as many features of cytolytic T lymphocytes (CTL) and natural killer cells (NK) have been reviewed in these proceedings and elsewhere,[1-6] we will briefly introduce the problem of cytotoxic mechanisms, summarize our work on the cloning of a serine protease that possibly is involved in cytolysis, and provide evidence for a proposed "lytic cascade" resulting in target-cell destruction. From this vantage point, we will explore some possible implications of such a cascade for clinical medicine. Finally, we will consider a hypothesis for approaching the etiology of diseases with NK defects.

Both CTL and NK cells possess the remarkable ability to recognize, bind, and lyse specific target cells. FIGURE 1 schematically represents the process of a CTL cell initially adhering and then "strengthening" to a target cell by way of LFA-1 and other accessory molecules.[7,8] At some point, the CTL recognizes the cell bearing its target antigen in the context of self-MHC by way of a T cell–receptor complex, each of which expresses a unique T-cell idiotype (T_i); other molecules in the complex include the accessory molecules implicated in class-specific MHC recognition (CD4 or CD8/Lyt-2) and the multichain T3 molecules.[9,10] The T_i-T3 complex "triggers" the CTL by transmembrane signaling and secondary intracellular messengers, including the metabolism of phosphatidylinositol, and increases in cytosolic calcium ions.[11] Subsequently, the CTL undergoes a rapid reorientation and polarization of its Golgi apparatus, microtubule assembly, and intracytoplasmic granules, aligning these structures towards the bound target cell.[12,13] Then, the dense intracytoplasmic granules are unidirectionally secreted, releasing their components in a temperature-dependent reaction requiring energy and calcium ions. Finally, the target cell is lysed, an event closely correlated with the appearance of membrane lesions and DNA fragmentation, both presumably produced by this "lethal hit–delivery system" without a requirement for the continuous presence of the CTL cell. Although the granule secretion model of cytolysis has received the most experimental support, this pathway of target-cell lysis is

[a] This research was supported by US PHS Grant AI 19512 to I. L. Weissman.

only one of several possible mechanisms of cytolysis (see G. Berke and B. Bonavida for other models, this volume).

This enigmatic lethal hit–delivery system has been intensively studied in the last several years. From a morphologic analysis of CTL-target conjugates, D. Zagury[14] initially proposed that the lethal hit resulted from the secretion of lysosome-like granules containing hydrolytic enzymes at the CTL-target interface. In addition, Henkart and Henkart[15] and Carpen et al.[16] suggested that the secretion

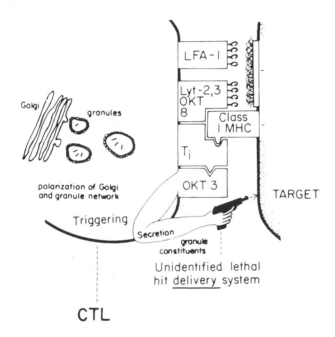

FIGURE 1. A schematic model of cytotoxic T lymphocyte (CTL) killing. After "homing" to and/or finding the target cell, the initial adhesive interaction between CTL and the target cell becomes "strengthened"[7] as symbolized by the hooks and wool, representing molecular "Velcro" (trademark of Velcro Corp., New York, N.Y.). One of the T cell–receptor molecules (T_i- a T-cell idiotype) specifically recognizes an ill-defined class I (MHC) protein-antigen complex on target cells. CD3 (OKT3)-T_i trigger the "killing-cell mechanism" by way of secondary intercellular mechanisms. The secretion of granules containing perforin and serine proteases is involved in one of several proposed killing mechanisms. The FIGURE emphasizes the unidentified nature of the delivery system for the lethal hit. The unidirectionality of the lethal hit and homeostatic factors limiting the cytotoxic mechanism to the site of conjugate formation are further mechanistic problems suggested by the FIGURE.[111,112] (See text for further discussion.)

of intracytoplasmic granules was responsible for the lethal hit, based on morphological evidence and on experiments correlating inhibition of a secretory apparatus with inhibition of cytotoxicity. Several investigators have focused on isolating and subsequently analyzing the contents of these granules from CTL and NK (reviewed in references 17–19).

In an independent approach toward the understanding of cytolytic mechanisms, we used recombinant DNA techniques and a natural history approach, namely, collecting genes preferentially expressed in CTL but absent in noncyto-lytic cells by using an RNA-hybridization competition protocol.[20] The advantage of this method of selecting preferentially expressed genes stems from the paucity of underlying assumptions about how CTL function. A disadvantage is that the harvest from such a method provides no selection for functionally significant genes. Using this approach, however, we cloned a complementary DNA (cDNA) expressed in the C57L murine CTL clone 1E4, but absent in the noncytolytic T cell–tumor line VL3.[21] Recently, using this cDNA, called Hanukah factor (HF) for its sequence similarity to Christmas factor, we cloned the human homologue of this gene from a cDNA library prepared from human peripheral blood leuko-cytes (PBL) stimulated with phytohemagglutinin (PHA) for four days.[22]

T-Cell and NK Specificity of the HF Gene's Expression

On a Northern blot and by S1 endonuclease–mapping analysis, we demon-strated the expression of the murine gene in two CTL cloned lines, but we de-tected no transcripts in normal liver, spleen, kidney, or a variety of B and non-cytolytic T-cell tumors. On S1 endonuclease analysis, a second band was present in the CTL clone 1E4, but not AR1 (another C57L mouse CTL clone). This band, which shares 550 nucleotides with the original cDNA, suggests the possibility of a second related sequence. By dot blot hybridization, we found that the murine HF sequence was also expressed in nu/nu mouse spleen cells, in three sublines of a rat NK-like leukemia, in 11 of 11 CTL clones, and in 2 of 8 T helper–cell lines. Similarly, in the human system, we found the human HF (HuHF) transcripts expressed in allogeneically stimulated CTL, in 3 of 3 CTL cloned lines, in 3 noncytolytic T cell lines, in Jurkat cells, and in 2 purified subsets of NK (*i.e.*, both $CD16^+CD3^-$ and $CD16^-CD3^+$ LGL). We found no transcripts in normal liver, tonsil, thymus, KB cells (a nasopharyngeal carcinoma), or in the B cell and other T cell–tumor lines we tested. The mouse and HuHF poly(A)–containing RNA were detected as 0.95 and 1.3 kilobase bands on a Northern gel, respectively.

Using RNA dot blots, we examined the temporal relationship between the induction of this gene's transcription and the appearance of cytotoxic activity in a culture of murine spleen cells stimulated with interleukin-2 (IL-2) and con-canavalin A (Con A). Although no hybridizing RNA was apparent in the initial cultures, the expression was detected on day 2 and peaked on days 3 and 4, just preceding the appearance of cytotoxicity for allogeneic targets in this culture. The kinetics of expression were consistent with a translated product that might be involved with cytotoxicity.

Both the human and mouse HF genes encode novel serine proteases with trypsin-like activity. FIGURE 2 presents the alignment of the mouse and HuHF proteins derived from their cDNA sequences. Both the mouse and HuHF proteins conserve the amino acids of the serine protease "charge-relay" system, equiva-lent to the His-57, Asp-102, and Ser-195 residues in chymotrypsin. The HF pro-teins both contain an acidic Asp residue at the position six amino acid residues N-terminal to the active site Ser-195 equivalent, which suggests that, like trypsin, the HF proteins cleave C-terminal to basic residues.[23,24] In addition, the two sequences share all ten cysteine residues. The two sequences are 65% similar over their entire lengths, but this can be divided into a 21% sequence similarity over their pre-pro-sequences and a 71% similarity over the active enzyme. The predicted mature pre-pro-mouse and HuHF proteins are 257 and 262 amino acids, respectively. Applying the algorithm developed by G. von Heijne,[25] the mouse

```
HUMAN  Met Arg Asn Ser Tyr Arg Phe Leu Ala Ser Ser Leu Ser Val Val Val
MOUSE  Met Ser Lys Glu Met Asn Glu         Ile Leu Leu Ser Trp Glu Ile

 -12   Ser Leu Leu Leu Ile Pro Glu Asp Val Cys Glu Lys Ile Ile Gly Gly
       Asn Leu Ser     Ser Lys Arg Gly Gly Cys Glu Arg Ile Ile Gly Gly

 +5    Asn Glu Val Thr Pro His Ser Arg Pro Tyr Met Val Leu Leu Ser Leu
       Asp Thr Val Val Pro His Ser Arg Pro Tyr Met Ala Leu Leu Lys Leu

 +21   Asp Arg Lys Thr Ile Cys Ala Gly Ala Leu Ile Ala Lys Asp Trp Val
       Ser Ser Asn Thr Ile Cys Ala Gly Ala Leu Ile Glu Lys Asn Trp Val

 +37   Leu Thr Ala Ala His Cys Asn Leu Asn Lys Arg Ser Gln Val Ile Leu
       Leu Thr Ala Ala His Cys Asn Val Gly Lys Arg Ser Lys Phe Ile Leu

 +53   Gly Ala His Ser Ile Thr Arg Glu Glu Pro Thr Lys Gln Ile Met Leu
       Gly Ala His Ser Ile Asn Lys     Glu Pro Glu Gln Gln Ile Leu Thr

 +69   Val Lys Lys Glu Phe Pro Tyr Pro Cys Tyr Asp Pro Ala Thr Arg Glu
       Val Lys Lys Ala Phe Pro Tyr Pro Cys Tyr Asp Glu Tyr Thr Arg Glu

 +85   Gly Asp Leu Lys Leu Leu Gln Leu Thr Glu Lys Ala Lys Ile Asn Lys
       Gly Asp Leu Gln Leu Val Arg Leu Lys Lys Lys Ala Thr Val Asn Arg

+101   Tyr Val Thr Ile Leu His Leu Pro Lys Lys Gly Asp Asp Val Lys Pro
       Asn Val Ala Ile Leu His Leu Pro Lys Lys Gly Asp Asp Val Lys Pro

+117   Gly Thr Met Cys Gln Val Ala Gly Trp Gly Arg Thr His Asn Ser Ala
       Gly Thr Arg Cys Arg Val Ala Gly Trp Gly Arg Phe Gly Asn Lys Ser

+133   Ser Trp Ser Asp Thr Leu Arg Glu Val Asn Ile Thr Ile Ile Asp Arg
       Ala Pro Ser Glu Thr Leu Arg Glu Val Asn Ile Thr Val Ile Asp Arg

+149   Lys Val Cys Asn Asp Arg Asn His Tyr Asn Phe Asn Pro Val Ile Gly
       Lys Ile Cys Asn Asp Glu Lys His Tyr Asn Phe His Pro Val Ile Gly

+165   Met Asn Met Val Cys Ala Gly Ser Leu Arg Gly Gly Arg Asp Ser Cys
       Leu Asn Met Ile Cys Ala Gly Asp Leu Arg Gly Gly Lys Asp Ser Cys

+181   Asn Gly Asp Ser Gly Ser Pro Leu Leu Cys Glu Gly Val Phe Arg Gly
       Asn Gly Asp Ser Gly Ser Pro Leu Leu Cys Asp Gly Ile Leu Arg Gly

+197   Val Thr Ser Phe Gly Leu Glu Asn Lys Cys Gly Asp Pro Arg Gly Pro
       Ile Thr Ser Phe Gly Gly Glu     Lys Cys Gly Asp Arg Arg Trp Pro

+213   Gly Val Tyr Ile Leu Leu Ser Lys Lys His Leu Asn Trp Ile Ile Met
       Gly Val Tyr Thr Phe Leu Ser Asp Lys His Leu Asn Trp Ile Lys Lys

+229   Thr Ile Lys Gly Ala Val
       Ile Met Lys Gly Ser Val
```

FIGURE 2. Alignment of the complete mouse and human HF proteins derived from the HF cDNA sequences. The thin arrows indicate the predicted signal sequence cleavage sites generating the pro-HF, and the thick arrows indicate the putative cleavage site generating the active enzyme. The amino acids of the serine protease charge-relay system, His, Asp, and Ser are each marked with a solid diamond. The acidic Asp-178 residue, marked by an open diamond, is thought to determine substrate specificity for cleavage after Lys or Arg residues. (See text for details.)

370

and HuHF have predicted signal sequences of 18 and 22 residues and pro-pieces of 7 and 6 amino acids, respectively. The active unglycosylated active mouse and HuHF proteins are 232 and 234 amino acids, with molecular weights of 25,651 and 25,820, respectively.

RELATIONSHIP TO THE FIELD AT LARGE

Using recombinant DNA techniques selecting for CTL-specific transcripts, Lobe *et al.*[26] (Bleackley, this volume) and then Brunet *et al.*,[27] independently, cloned murine cDNAs (CCPI-C11/CTLA-1) with a remarkably similar, but distinct, pattern of expression compared to the murine HF gene. These murine cDNA genes encode a serine protease with chymotrypsin-like specificity. The human homologue has recently been cloned by Schmid and Weissmann;[28] its protein-sequence similarities to the murine CCPI and the HuHF protein are of 68% and 43%, respectively. By a similar method, Koyama *et al.*[29] have cloned a murine CTL–specific cDNA, pT49, which encodes a protein showing similarity to the COOH-terminal half of fibrinogen beta and gamma subunits.

Recently, workers from several laboratories have been analyzing the contents of CTL and NK intracytoplasmic granules. The granules contain the following components: perforin (also known as cytolysin), a chondroitin sulfate A proteoglycan,[30] and several serine proteases. Monomeric perforin is a 60–66 kilodalton monomer protein that can reconstitute cytolytic activity in the presence of calcium by polymerizing into 160 Å tubular pores in the target cell's membrane. Petty *et al.*[31] and Pasternack and Eisen[32] have identified murine NK and CTL specific–serine proteases using a radiolabeled-specific inhibitor of the active-site serine, diisopropylfluorophosphate (DFP). Several groups[33–35] have purified these murine serine esterases, and Masson, Tschopp, and co-workers[36,37] have demonstrated that one of these serine esterases, granzyme A, has an N-terminal sequence identical to the predicted active murine HF. Granzyme A/HF is a disulfide-linked homodimer of 35 kDa subunits that has a trypsin-like substrate specificity. The trypsin-like enzyme activity located in granules can be secreted into the medium after antigen-receptor triggering.[38] Furthermore, Masson and Tschopp[39] have suggested that at least five serine proteases exist, based on N-terminal amino acid–sequence analysis of purified granule-serine proteases. Thus, the identity of the similar serine proteases isolated by other groups to the murine HF cannot confidently be assumed. The granule-serine proteases should be distinguished from a recently defined serine protease involved in an initial step of CTL activation.[40]

EVIDENCE FOR A LYTIC CASCADE

We initially proposed that HF is one of several serine proteases involved in a lytic cascade. Although the verdict has not been decided about the function of these granular-serine proteases, it seems likely that this cascade is functional. What is the evidence for this cascade? First, many independent groups[41–49] have shown that the cytotoxicity of CTL, NK, and antibody mediated–cytotoxic cells has been inhibited with a variety of trypsin and chymotrypsin protease inhibitors. In particular, Lavie *et al.*[50] showed that human NK cytotoxicity was susceptible to serine-protease inhibitors during a short postbinding window of 2–10 minutes, consistent with a model of granule secretion and extracellular activation. Second, the cloning of several different chymotrypsin-like and trypsin-like serine proteases with T cell– and NK-specific expression, and the independent protein purification of these serine proteases from CTL intracytoplasmic granules provide important circumstantial evidence for a cascade in the cytolytic mechanism. Finally, the perforin molecule is immunologically and functionally related to the ninth component of complement cascade (C9).[51–54] Both proteins form ring-like channels in membranes and may be regulated by serine-protease cascades. The ultimate proof of this proposed cascade will result from the formidable task of defining the substrates of each enzyme.

IMPLICATIONS OF A LYTIC CASCADE

The implications of a serine-protease cascade necessary for cytotoxic lymphocyte lysis pose several biological and clinical questions. For instance, what signals activate the cascade? How are these proteins ordered in the cascade, and what are their natural substrates? What factors and membrane-surface molecules, if any, control the unidirectional delivery of the cascade components from the granules to the target cell? What homeostatic mechanisms limit the cytotoxic mechanism to the site of conjugate formation? For this last question, we suggest dilution and lability of factors, protease inactivators, and specific inhibitors (such as lipoproteins for perforin[55] or serine-protease inhibitors, known as serpin molecules[56,57]) as possible contributory mechanisms for controlling this cascade.

Rational Drug Therapy

If such a lytic cascade is responsible for lymphocyte cytotoxicity, these granule-serine proteases provide targets for designing specific serine protease inhibitors as drugs.[58] Through a combination of protein modeling and X-ray crystallographic visualization of enzyme-binding sites, plus an understanding of the enzymatic mechanisms of serine proteases, investigators should be able to find extremely specific and potent active-site titrant or transition-state analogues. The precedent for these types of drugs is best illustrated by the angiotensin-converting enzyme and renin inhibitors.[59,60] Beyond specificity, the requirements for the medicinal use of a synthetic inhibitor include a low incidence of side effects, lack of antigenicity, and pharmacologic bioavailability. FIGURE 3 illustrates the site of action of this type of drug at a CTL and NK post-binding step, contrasting it to the sites of action of the current immunosuppressive agents.[61] These new drugs could be synergistic with current agents and should affect only cytolytic cells. Such inhibitors should have the advantage of inhibiting the disease process (e.g., a transplant graft rejection) immediately, rather than with the lag inherent in immunosuppressives, which prevent the generation of new cytolytic cells. A longer-acting immunosuppressive regimen might be instituted and the specific inhibitor discontinued as the longer-term agents take effect. Similarly, the discontinuation of the drug should permit the rapid return of normal cytolytic function. A potential secondary benefit of this drug may be a natural compensatory immunosuppressive mechanism responding to the proliferating cytotoxic cells with blocked lytic capacity. Hence, the balance between effector cells and target may be reset. Regardless of the eventual toxicity of these drugs, the development of such inhibitors will provide powerful tools for pharmacologically testing and dissecting a lytic cascade. The use of these drugs in animal models will also give clues as to which cell mediated–immune reactions are dependent on cytolytic cells.

HF as a Marker for Cytolytic Cells

Ideally, one could use the HF gene or protein as a marker for defining autoimmune diseases with cytolytic cell involvement. Every cytolytic cell tested to date expresses the HF gene. Some investigators, however, have questioned the presumption that HF is specific to cytolytic cells, because the HF transcripts or

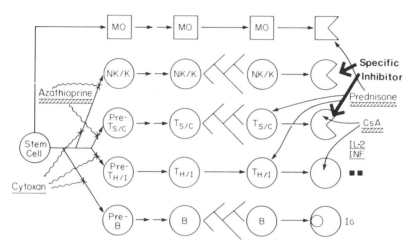

FIGURE 3. Comparison of the sites of action of several immunosuppressive agents and a proposed specific inhibitor to a serine protease, such as HF. This specific serine protease inhibitor would block a postbinding lytic step and inhibit cytolysis of active NK and CTL. Cyclophosphamide (cytoxan, Bristol-Meyers Co.) and azathioprine act on the generation of cells, whereas prednisone and cyclosporine A (CsA) inhibit the function of existing immune cells. Maturation of immune cells is indicated in a left to right flow of the figure. MO = monocytes; K = killer cells active in antibody mediated–cytotoxic reactions; $T_{S/C}$ = T-suppressor/cytotoxic cells; $T_{H/I}$ = T-helper/inducer cells; IL-2 = interleukin-2; INF = interferon; and Ig = immunoglobulin.[61]

enzymatic activity have been found in some helper cells and other IL-2–stimulated noncytolytic cells *in vitro*. Perhaps expression of the HF gene is specific *in vivo* but can be induced in noncytolytic cells by IL-2 stimulation. For example, experiments by Simon *et al.*[62] have demonstrated the expression of trypsin-like enzyme activity in both Lyt-2+,L3T4− and Lyt-2−,L3T4+ *in vitro*, but activity was detected only in cytolytic Lyt-2+,L3T4− cells *in vivo*.

What maladies would benefit from such an HF inhibitor? Allograft transplantations are prime candidates for improved regimens of immunosuppression. After transplantation of an allograft, a massive inflammatory infiltration of mainly mononuclear cells occurs in the unmodified host.[63,64] Most of these cells seem to be attracted nonspecifically to the site of the graft, as only a fraction of these cells has immunological specificity for the allograft.[65–67] This nonspecific recruitment of cells is probably caused by specifically sensitized host cells, presumably T helper/inducer cells. Inasmuch as the majority of the infiltrating cells are attracted nonspecifically to the site of the graft, phenotypic analysis of infiltrating cells is of limited value for the prediction of either survival or rejection of a graft. We have chosen to test the usefulness of HF as a marker for cytolytic cells in an allogeneic mouse model system. A heart muscle graft from a newborn (<24 hr) BALB/c mouse was transplanted under the kidney capsule of adult sex-matched C57BL/ Ka mice and adult BALB/c mice as previously described.[68] Five micrometer cryostat sections were prepared through the graft in two-day intervals after transplantation. These sections were hybridized with a ^{35}S-labeled RNA probe of complementary sequence to the cellular HF mRNA (antisense probe), as described in more detail elsewhere.[69] Control slides were hybridized with a ^{35}S-labeled RNA probe with an identical sequence to the HF mRNA (sense probe). The results are summarized in TABLE 1: the number of HF-positive cells per unit area of inflammatory infiltration increases dramatically between day 4 and 6 in allografts, whereas it remains at a low level in control animals with a syngeneic graft.

TABLE 1. Frequency of Cells with Detectable Levels of HF-mRNA in the Infiltrate[a]

Days Post-transplantation	Allogeneic Graft	Syngeneic Graft
2	+/−	+/−
4	+	+/−
6	+++	+
8	+++	+
10	+++	+
12	+++	+/−

[a] Frequency of cells with HF-mRNA in tissue sections of grafts at various time points after transplantation. The grades are roughly as follows: +/−: <10 positive cells/mm² infiltrate; +: 10–50 positive cells/mm² infiltrate; ++: 50–150 positive cells/mm² infiltrate; +++: 150–300 positive cells/mm² infiltrate.

Interestingly, this time point correlates with earlier findings of increased alloantigen-specific lymphocyte-mediated cytotoxicity around day 4–6 posttransplantation in renal grafts in the rat.[63,64] The observed appearance of HF-positive cells among infiltrating cells in an allograft suggests that expression of this serine esterase may provide a useful marker for an ongoing graft rejection. As monoclonal or polyclonal antisera for HF become available, one may routinely envision staining needle biopsies from organ grafts for the presence of HF.

Cell-mediated cytolysis is not only proposed to be a central effector function in graft rejection and elimination of virally infected cells, but it also may play a role in an increasing number of autoimmune diseases:[70,71] insulin-dependent diabetes mellitus (IDDM), experimental allergic encephalomyelitis, Hashimoto's thyroiditis,[72,73] and chronic hepatitis B.[74,75] We are currently investigating whether serine-esterase genes become expressed during the cellular infiltration of the pancreas that precedes the destruction of B cells and the clinical signs of IDDM in NOD mice and BB rats.

Speculation on Potential Genetic and Acquired Deficits in the Lethal Hit–Delivery System[b]

Eighty years after Garrod's introduction of the concept of inborn errors of metabolism,[76] one can almost axiomatically state that for any given T cell– or

[b] This section represents solely the views of H. Gershenfeld.

NK-specific gene, there may be an inherited malady with a defect or deficiency of this gene (with the exception of lethal mutations). These "experiments of nature" are particularly enlightening as they permit the correlation of a definable genetic lesion with a presumed function. The advantage of human genetics resides in the large population and the powerful selection of nontrivial mutations, in "which physiological stimuli produce abnormal reactions; and conditions of life which are harmless to the majority of members of the human race bring about morbid states."[77]

If one were to postulate an inherited deficiency or complete absence of the HF gene or any other step in the lethal hit–delivery system of NK, what might the resulting phenotype be? Let us suppose such an individual has NK with 10% of the normal cytolytic activity. Although this level of activity may be sufficient for most infectious agents, there may be certain viruses that stress the host's immune system and require the full measure of immunocompetence for regression. Such a virus may produce mild morbidity to the majority of the population, yet overwhelm the host incapable of fighting off viral infections.

Do any diseases fit this phenotype and if so, what does it teach us about NK function? Patients with Chediak-Higashi and Wiskott-Aldrich disease have NK defects,[78,79] but because these patients have similar impairments of other hematopoietic cells, few conclusions about NK functions can be gleaned. Our crude scheme may explain some cases of fatal Epstein-Barr virus (EBV)[80] and near-fatal varicella[81,82] infections. In the case of EBV infections,[83] a spectrum of disease exists from asymptomatic infections, these being the rule in childhood, to the classic infectious mononucleosis of adolescence, to the fatal infections of a well-studied X-linked variety,[81,84,85] and a non-X-linked familial form.[86] The presence of multiple genetic loci, all presenting as a "morbid predisposition" toward fatal EBV, might be explained by the complexity of the immune response. Clearly, a single phenotype such as "bleeding" can present from a defect in platelets, coagulant factors, or a hyperactive fibrinolytic system.[87] As F. W. Andrewes put it, "a chronometer can suffer from a greater variety of defects than an hour glass."[88]

Let us extend our hypothetical case of NK with 10% of normal cytolytic activity, taking EBV as an example. Despite the ability of these NK to recognize the viral stimulus, to bind the appropriate target cells, to trigger appropriately, to release their multiplicity of lymphokines, and to proliferate in response to the viral stimulus, the NK may be unable to lyse a sufficient proportion of virally infected cells (B cells in the case of EBV) to cause a regression of the infection.[89,90] If one views a viral infection as an autologous mixed-lymphocyte reaction,[91,92] these NK would steadily proliferate, stimulated by the persistent presentation of viral antigens from the unabated infection. Suppressor cells may be generated by the host, attempting to restore immunological homeostasis, but suppressor cells may also be capable of causing suppression of many immune responses.[93] NK cultured with HLA-DR$^+$ hematopoietic cells and target cells produce a soluble factor that inhibits bone marrow–colony formation.[94] This factor and other lymphokines (*e.g.*, IFN gamma-suppressing IL-4 activity) may down-regulate the hematopoietic systems during periods of prodigious NK activity.[94,95,96] Thus one may have a case of overwhelming, perhaps fatal, viral infection associated with a panoply of hematologic abnormalities (neutropenia, aplastic anemia, or hypogammaglobulinemia), depending upon how the host's immunological balance is restored. If one imagines a gene in the lethal hit–delivery system shared by NK and CTL, like HF or perforin, then one can easily imagine an exacerbation of the infection due to impairment of CTL function. This CTL impairment has been found in several individuals with the X-linked form of susceptibility to EBV,[80] and it has been postulated to be responsible for the low titers found to the EBV nuclear antigens (EBNA) in immunocompromised individuals.[97]

Why are these individuals predisposed only to EBV infections without suffering extensive sequelae from a variety of other infections? No answer is known, although an X-linked lymphoproliferative immunoregulatory defect has been proposed.[80,85] In fact, the explanation may be different for each of several responsible genotypes. The inherited complement deficiencies provide a precedent for this peculiar type of predisposition, as patients with defects in any one of the complement factors C5-C9 are unusually susceptible to Neisseria infections.[98] I would like to propose that some individuals may be predisposed to severe EBV infections because EBV-infected B cells produce a plasminogen activator (PA) that inhibits normal CTL killing of their targets.[99,100] The concentration of this PA could easily be sufficient to prevent lysis of EBV cells, because at the end of the first week of infection, 6–20% of all B cells are infected with EBV.[91] The efficacy of this PA inhibition may be profound in the patient with a borderline deficiency in our lytic cascade. Similarly, one may view some T gamma–lymphoproliferative disease[101] and T8[+] lymphocytosis syndromes[102] as the reactive proliferations of a cytolytic clone with diminished lytic activity, the acquired equivalent of the above-proposed genetic deficiency. Studies of these conditions should be a foundation for approaching more complicated acquired postbinding lytic-step NK defects[103–106] and normal deficiences secondary to immunosuppression.

Studies of defined inherited genetic mutations in patients suffering from a bleeding diathesis have led to the discovery of coagulation factors, platelet membrane receptors, and the regulatory pathways of thrombosis.[87] One hopes for similar success in studying NK defects, shedding light on the normal lethal hit–delivery system. In particular, if one views the delivery and unidirectionality of CTL and NK action as resulting from membrane receptors, cell lines from individuals with genetic deficiencies in cytolysis may establish this claim. The model for such unidirectionality can be imagined from considering thrombomodulin[107] or the prothrombinase complex,[108] whereby membrane receptors act as necessary cofactors in protease activation. Alternatively, unidirectionality might be analogous with the model of immunity suggested for the yeast killer–toxin system.[109,110]

Despite engendering the risks of explaining the unknown by the even less well-known, the intention of this working hypothesis and these examples is to frame experiments approaching such defects and to focus on the importance of studying the lethal hit–delivery system in CTL and NK. The development of NK and/or CTL lines from such affected individuals would permit reconstitution of function by biochemical or gene transfer techniques. By classical "mixing" experiments, different kindreds with similar phenotypes could be placed in complementation groups.

SUMMARY

A new trypsin-like serine protease was cloned from both a murine cytotoxic T lymphocyte and a human PHA–stimulated peripheral blood lymphocyte cDNA library. In both the mouse and human system, this transcript had a T cell– and NK-specific distribution, being detected in cytotoxic T lymphocytes (CTL), some T-helper clones, and NK, but not in a variety of normal tissues. T-cell activation with Con A plus IL-2 induced mouse spleen cells to express this gene with kinetics correlating with the acquisition of cytolytic capacity. Both the mouse and human nucleotide sequences of this gene encoded an amino acid sequence with 25–40% identity to members of the serine protease family. The active-site "charge-relay" residues (His-57, Asp-102, and Ser-195 of the chymotrypsin numbering system) are conserved, as well as the trypsin-specific Asp (position 189 in trypsin). We reviewed the evidence of this serine protease's role in lymphocyte lysis and proposed a "lytic cascade." We discussed the biological and clinical implications of a cascade, proposing these enzymes as markers for cytolytic cells and as targets for rational drug therapy. Genetic and acquired deficits in the lethal hit–delivery system are considered as a basis for approaching some immunodeficiency states, including severe EBV infections, T-gamma leukemias, and T8[+] lymphocytosis syndromes.

ACKNOWLEDGMENTS

We thank our Stanford colleagues for their contributions and helpful discussions. The senior author is thanked for his forbearance of the first author's floccinaucinihilipilifications on lymphocyte lysis.

REFERENCES

1. HENNEY, C. S. & S. GILLIS. 1984. *In* Fundamental Immunology. W. Paul, Ed.: 669–684. Raven Press. New York.
2. MOLLER, G., Ed. 1983. Immunol. Rev., Vol. 72.
3. HENKART, P. A. 1985. Annu. Rev. Immunol. **3:** 31.
4. HERBERMAN, R., C. REYNOLDS & J. ORTALDO. 1986. Annu. Rev. Immunol. **4:** 651.
5. TRINCHIERI, G. & B. PERUSSIA. 1984. Lab. Invest. **50:** 489.
6. LANIER, L., J. PHILLIPS, J. HACKETT, M. TUTT & V. KUMAR. 1986. J. Immunol. **137:** 2735.
7. MARTZ, E. 1987. Hum. Immunol. **18:** 3.
8. SPRINGER, T. A., M. DUSTIN, T. KISHIMOTO & S. MARLIN. 1987. Annu. Rev. Immunol. **5:** 223.
9. KRONENBERG, M., G. SIU, L. HOOD & N. SHASTRI. 1986. Annu. Rev. Immunol. **4:** 529.
10. ALLISON, J. P. & L. L. LANIER. 1987. Annu. Rev. Immunol. **5:** 503.
11. WEISS, A., J. IMBODEN, K. HARDY, B. MANGER *et al.* 1986. Annu. Rev. Immuol. **4:** 593.
12. YANNELLI, J. R., J. SULLIVAN, G. MANDELL & V. ENGELHARD. 1986. J. Immunol. **136:** 377.
13. KUPFER, A., S. SINGER & G. DENNERT. 1986. J. Exp. Med. **163:** 489.
14. ZAGURY, D. 1982. Adv. Exp. Med. Biol. **146:** 149.
15. HENKART, M. P. & P. A. HENKART. 1982. Adv. Exp. Med. Biol. **146:** 227.
16. CARPEN, O., I. VIRTANEN & E. SAKSELA. 1981. Cell. Immunol. **58:** 97.
17. PODACK, E. R. 1985. Immunology Today **6:** 21.
18. YOUNG, J. D.-E. & Z. COHN. 1986. J. Cell. Biochem. **32:** 151.
19. HENKART, P. A., M. HENKART, P. MILLARD, P. FREDRISKE *et al.* 1985. Adv. Exp. Med. Biol. **184:** 121.
20. MANGIAROTTI, G., S. CHUNG, C. ZUCKER & H. LODISH. 1981. Nucleic Acids Res. **9:** 947.
21. GERSHENFELD, H. & I. L. WEISSMAN. 1986. Science **232:** 854.
22. GERSHENFELD, H., R. J. HERSHBERGER, T. B. SHOWS & I. L. WEISSMAN. 1987. Proc. Natl. Acad. Sci. USA **85:** 1184.
23. HARTLEY, B. S. 1970. Philos. Trans. Roy. Soc. London Ser. B **257:** 77.
24. KRAUT, J. 1977. Annu. Rev. Biochem. **46:** 331.

25. VON HEIJNE, G. 1986. Nucleic Acids Res. **14:** 4683.
26. LOBE, C. G., B. FINLAY, W. PARANCHYCH, V. PAETKAU & R. C. BLEACKLEY. 1986. Science **232:** 858.
27. BRUNET, J., M. DOSSETO, F. DENIZOT, M. MATTEI, W. CLARK *et al.* 1986. Nature **322:** 268.
28. SCHMID, J. & C. WEISSMANN. 1987. J. Immunol. **139:** 250.
29. KOYAMA, T., L. HALL, W. HASER, S. TONEGAWA & H. SAITO. 1987. Proc. Natl. Acad. Sci. **84:** 1609.
30. MACDERMOTT, R. P., R. SCHMIDT, J. CAULFIELD, A. HEIN *et al.* 1985. J. Exp. Med. **162:** 1771.
31. PETTY, H. R., W. HERMANN, W. DERESKI, T. FREY & H. McCONNELL. 1984. J. Cell Sci. **72:** 1.
32. PASTERNACK, M. S. & H. EISEN. 1985. Nature (London) **314:** 743.
33. KRAMER, M. D., L. BINNINGER, V. SCHIRRMACHER, H. MOLL *et al.* 1986. J. Immunol. **136:** 4644.
34. PASTERNACK, M. S., C. VERRET, M. LIU & H. EISEN. 1986. Nature (London) **322:** 740.
35. YOUNG, J. D.-E., L. LEONG, C. LIU, A. DAMIANO *et al.* 1986. Cell **47:** 183.
36. MASSON, D., M. NABHOLZ, C. ESTRADE & J. TSCHOPP. 1986. EMBO J. **5:** 1595.
37. MASSON, D., M. ZAMAI & J. TSCHOPP. 1986. FEBS Lett. **208:** 84.
38. TAKAYAMA, H., G. TRENN, W. HUMPHREY, J. BLUESTONE *et al.* 1986. J. Immunol. **138:** 566.
39. MASSON, D. & J. TSCHOPP. 1987. Cell **49:** 679.
40. UTSUNOMIYA, N. & M. NAKANISHI. 1986. J. Biol. Chem. **261:** 16514.
41. TRINCHIERI, G. & M. DEMARCHI. 1976. J. Immunol. **116:** 885.
42. REDELMAN, D. & D. HUDIG. 1980. J. Immunol. **124:** 870.
43. CHANG, T. & H. EISEN. 1980. J. Immunol. **124:** 1028.
44. HUDIG, D., T. HAVERTY, C. FULCHER, D. REDELMAN & J. MENDELSOHN. 1981. J. Immunol. **126:** 1569.
45. QUAN, P. C., T. ISHIZAKA & B. BLOOM. 1982. J. Immunol. **128:** 1786.
46. PASTERNACK, M. S., M. SITKOVSKY & H. EISEN. 1983. J. Immunol. **131:** 1477.
47. RISTOW, S. S., J. STARKEY & G. HASS. 1983. Immunology **48:** 1.
48. ADES, E. W., A. HINSON, C. CHAPUIS-CELLIER & P. ARNAUD. 1982. Scand. J. Immunol. **15:** 109.
49. BROGAN, M. & S. TARGAN. 1986. Cell. Immunol. **103:** 426.
50. LAVIE, G., Z. LEIB & C. SERVADIO. 1985. J. Immunol. **135:** 1470.
51. MASSON, D. & J. TSCHOPP. 1985. J. Biol. Chem. **260:** 9069.
52. PODACK, E., J. YOUNG & Z. COHN. 1985. Proc. Natl. Acad. Sci. USA **82:** 8629.
53. YOUNG, J. D.-E., E. PODACK & Z. COHN. 1986. J. Exp. Med. **164:** 144.
54. ZALMAN, L., D. MARTIN, G. JUNG & H. MULLER-EBERHARD. 1987. Proc. Natl. Acad. Sci. USA **84:** 2426.
55. TSCHOPP, J., D. MASSON & S. SCHAFER. 1986. J. Immunol. **137:** 1950.
56. TRAVIS, J. & G. SALVESEN. 1983. Annu. Rev. Biochem. **52:** 655.
57. SPRENGERS, E. & C. KLUFT. 1987. Blood **9:** 381.
58. LAWSON, W. B. 1978. Annu. Rep. Med. Chem. **13:** 261.
59. ONDETTI, M. A. & D. CUSHMAN. 1982. Annu. Rev. Biochem. **51:** 283.
60. BOGER, J. 1985. Annu. Rep. Med. Chem. **20:** 253.
61. FAHEY, J. L. 1987. Annu. Intern. Med. **106:** 25.
62. SIMON, M., U. FRUTH, H. SIMON & M. KRAMER. 1986. Eur. J. Immunol. **16:** 1559.
63. STROM, T. B., N. TILNEY, J. PARADYSZ, J. BANCEWICZ & C. CARPENTER. 1977. J. Immunol. **118:** 2020.
64. TILNEY, N. L., T. STROM, S. MACPHERSON & C. CARPENTER. 1975. Transplantation **20:** 323.
65. HOPT, U. T., H. BOCKENHORN, G. MULLER, K. THIEDE & R. SIMMONS. 1983. Transplant. Proc. **15:** 367.
66. OROSZ, C., N. ZINN, L. SIRINEK & R. FERGUSON. 1986. Transplantation **41:** 75.
67. ASCHER, N., R. HOFFMAN, S. CHEN & R. SIMMONS. 1980. Cell. Immunol. **52:** 38.
68. BILLINGHAM, M., R. WARNKE & I. WEISSMAN. 1977. **23:** 171.

69. ANGERER, L. H., M. STOLER & R. ANGERER. 1987. *In In Situ* Hybridization: Applications to the CNS. K. Valentino, J. Eberwine & J. Barchas, Eds.: 42–70. Oxford Press. New York.
70. SELL, S. 1985. *In* Anderson's Pathology. J. M. Kissane, Ed. Vol. **1**: 458–470.
71. COHEN, I. R. 1986. Immunol. Rev. **94**: 5.
72. VOLPE, R. 1986. Mol. Biol. Med. **3**: 25.
73. BAGNASCO, M., S. FERRINI, D. VENUTI, I. PRIGONE *et al.* 1987. Int. Arch. Allergy Appl. Immunol. **82**: 141.
74. HOFFMAN, R. M., G. PAPE, R. RIEBER, J. EISENBERG *et al.* 1986. Eur. J. Immunol. **16**: 1635.
75. PARONETTO, F. 1986. Human Pathol. **17**: 168.
76. GARROD, A. E. 1963. *In* Garrod's Inborn Errors of Metabolism-1908. Oxford University Press. London.
77. HIS, W. 1931. *In* Inborn Factors in Disease. A. E. Garrod. p. 17. Oxford University Press (Clarendon). London.
78. LIPINSKI, M., J. VIRELIZIER, T. TURZ & C. GRISCELLI. 1980. Eur. J. Immunol. **10**: 246.
79. HALIOTIS, T., J. RODER, M. KLEIN, J. ORTALDO *et al.* 1980. J. Exp. Med. **151**: 1039.
80. PURTILO, D. 1985. Biomed. Pharmocother. **39**: 52.
81. VERDER, H., E. DICKMEISS, S. HAAHR, E. KAPPELGAARD *et al.* 1986. Clin. Exp. Immunol. **63**: 367.
82. SULLIVAN, J. L., K. BYRON & C. BIRON. 1985. Clin. Res. **33**: 389.
83. SCHOOLEY, R. T. & R. DOLIN. 1985. *In* Principles and Practice of Infectious Disease. G. Mandell, R. Douglas & J. Bennett, Eds.: 971–982. John Wiley & Sons. New York.
84. SULLIVAN, J. L. 1983. Adv. Pediatr. **30**: 365.
85. GRIERSON, H. & D. T. PURTILO. 1987. Annu. Intern. Med. **106**: 538.
86. FLEISHER, G., S. STARR, N. KOREN, H. KAMIYA *et al.* 1982. J. Pediat. **100**: 727.
87. GRAHAM, J., E. BARROW, H. REISNER & C. EDGELL. 1983. Adv. Hum. Genet. **13**: 1.
88. ANDREWES, F. W. 1926. Lancet **1**: 1075.
89. MASUCCI, M., M. BEJARANO, G. MASUCCI & E. KLEIN. 1983. Cell. Immunol. **76**: 311.
90. KAPLAN, J. & T. SHOPE. 1985. Nat. Immun. Cell. Growth. Regul. **4**: 40.
91. ROBINSON, J. E. 1982. Yale J. Biol. Med. **55**: 311.
92. KONTTINEN, Y. T., H. BLUESTEIN & N. ZVAIFLER. 1985. J. Immunol. **134**: 2287.
93. TOSATO, G. & R. M. BLAESE. 1985. Adv. Immunol. **37**: 99.
94. DEGLIANTONI, G., B. PERUSSIA, L. MANGONI & G. TRINCHIERI. 1985. J. Exp. Med. **161**: 1152.
95. LOTZ, M., C. TSOUKAS, S. FONG, C. DINARELLO *et al.* 1986. J. Immunol. **136**: 3636.
96. RABIN, E., J. MOND., J. OHARA & W. PAUL. 1986. J. Immunol. **137**: 1573.
97. HENLE, W. & G. HENLE. 1981. Cancer Res. **41**: 4222.
98. LACHMAN, P. J. 1984. Philo. Trans. Roy. Soc. London. Ser. B **306**: 419.
99. SUNDAR, S. K., J. BERGERON & J. MENEZES. 1984. Clin. Exp. Immunol. **56**: 701.
100. SUNDAR, S. K., J. BERGERON & J. MENEZES. 1985. Exp. Biol. **43**: 277.
101. FOON, K. A., R. GALE & R. TODD. 1986. Semin. Hematol. **23**: 265.
102. GRILLOT-COURVALIN, C., G. VINCI, A. TSAPIS, M. KOKHELAR *et al.* 1986. Blood **69**: 1204.
103. PEDERSEN, B. K. 1985. Allergy **40**: 547.
104. KATZ, P., A. ZAYTOUN, J. LEE. R. PANUSH & S. LONGLEY. 1982. J. Immunol. **129**: 1966.
105. KATZMAN, M. & M. LEDERMAN. 1986. J. Clin. Invest. **77**: 1057.
106. KLIMPEL, G. R., D. HERNDON, M. FONS, T. ALBRECHT *et al.* 1986. Clin. Exp. Immunol. **66**: 384.
107. ROSENBERG, R. D. & K. A. BAUER. 1987. Human Pathol. **18**: 253.
108. TRACY, P. B. & K. G. MANN. 1987. Human Pathol. **18**: 162.
109. TIPPER, D. J. & K. A. BOSTIAN. 1984. Microbiol. Rev. **48**: 125.
110. BOONE, C., H. BUSSEY, D. GREENE, D. THOMAS & T. VERNET. 1986. Cell **46**: 105.
111. MARTZ, E., W. HEAGY & S. GROMKOWSI. 1983. Immunol. Rev. **72**: 85.
112. YOUNG, J. D.-E. & Z. A. COHN. 1986. Cell **46**: 641.

Lymphokine-Activated Killer Cells

Induction and Function

ELIZABETH A. GRIMM,[a,b] LAURIE B. OWEN-SCHAUB,[a]
WILLIAM G. LOUDON,[a] AND MASATO YAGITA[a]

[a] Department of Tumor Biology
[b] Division of General Surgery
M.D. Anderson Hospital and Tumor Institute
University of Texas System Cancer Center
Houston, Texas 77030

The lymphokine-activated killer-cell (LAK) activity is proposed as a fundamental mechanism involved in regulation of malignant and/or infected cells.[1] This system is deceptively simple, as only interleukin-2 (IL-2)[2] is required for induction of both initial lytic competence[3] and subsequent maintenance of its hallmark oncolytic activity.[4] IL-2 alone maintains this lymphocyte-killing activity for periods as long as one month in serum-free medium and longer when cultures are supplemented with normal human serum (data unpublished).

Multiple lymphocyte types have been identified as responsive to IL-2. In the absence of any added antigen or exogenous factors, it has been reported that positively selected purified subpopulations of T, B, NK, and null lymphocytes directly respond to purified recombinant IL-2 and differentiate into LAK.[5-7] Our own studies indicate that cyclosporine A, which is proposed to prevent all endogenous lymphokine production, does not inhibit LAK activation under conditions that totally ablate CTL generation.[8] Therefore, it is believed that IL-2 alone, interacting directly with any one of several lymphocyte types, induces a program of lytic differentiation followed by a protracted period of cellular proliferation, resulting in an activity we call LAK. We propose that LAK is not a unique cell type, but a function representing only one part of the inducible, antigen-nonspecific amplification mechanism operative in the normal immune response. Depending on the location and quality of each response, discrete lymphocyte subclasses respond to IL-2, with cytotoxic expression toward any form of altered self or tumor.

The studies reported here represent our attempts to approach a more detailed understanding of the mechanisms involved in the generation and regulation of LAK activity. Our goals are to resolve the most minimal and essential requirements for LAK activation, and then to systematically reconstitute components that might be found *in vivo*, either in normal or tumor-bearing individuals, under conditions that would normally be expected to exist during delayed hypersensitivity reactions.

LAK ACTIVATION OCCURS OPTIMALLY IN SERUM-FREE MEDIUM

Serum-free media are sufficient for the generation of LAK in short-term cultures[1,9] (FIG. 1). Although such media was not always comparable to human serum-supplemented media, its use is considered by us to provide a more defined and predictable environment in which to study the mechanism(s) involved in

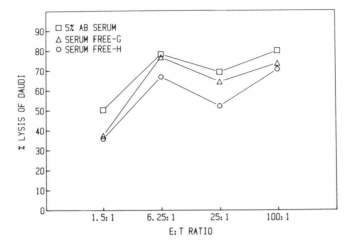

FIGURE 1. LAK activation–media comparisons. Fresh normal peripheral blood leukocytes (PBL) were incubated in parallel in each of three media: the standard 5% AB serum containing RPMI-1640 (Gibco Life Sciences, Grand Island, New York); serum-free medium-G (commercially available as AIM-V from Gibco); or serum-free medium-H (commercially available HB-104, DuPont-NEN, Boston, MA). After 4 days of culture with 2 nM recombinant IL-2 (Cetus Corporation, Emeryville, CA), the cultured cells were harvested, counted, and tested for cytotoxicity of the NK-resistant Daudi cell line. Viable cell recovery was equivalent from each of these three cultures.

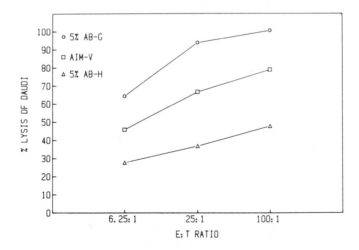

FIGURE 2. LAK activation human serum comparisons, assayed on day 4 of culture. Human AB serum from two commercial sources was tested for support of LAK activation in comparison to serum-free AIM-V medium (Gibco, see FIGURE 1 legend). Serum AB-G is also from Gibco, and serum-H from Hazelton (Hazelton Research Products, Denver, PA). Viable cell recovery from the three culture conditions was equivalent.

LAK-cell activation. Our data has indicated that commercially available human AB serum is quite variable in its ability to support LAK generation, with both augmentation and suppression observed in subsequent serum lots from individual suppliers (FIG. 2), presumably employing standard processing methods.

Although our understanding of the influence of serum on LAK activation is not fully understood, we have performed experiments to determine what essential serum-derived components existed. While screening a variety of proteins, we observed that some activation was evident following culture in basal RPMI medium alone for 3 days. This activity could be increased by the addition of human albumin (TABLE 1). Titration of purified human albumin in RPMI-1640 for short-term LAK activation demonstrated that consistent, optimal activation occurred optimally between 140 to 700 μg/ml. For long-term growth, albumin-only–supplemented media was rather poor for support of LAK, both cytotoxic activity and growth beyond two weeks of culture, whereas commercially available serum-free medium used in concommitant studies supported activity for up to one month (data not shown).

TABLE 1. Titration of Human Albumin for LAK Activation

Addition to RPMI-1640[a]		Percent Lysis Sarcoma[b]			Percent
IL-2	Human Albumin	100 : 1	25 : 1	6 : 1	Recovery
+	—	30	15	9	30
–	—	4	1	0	22
+	70 μg/ml	36	18	8	22
+	140 μg/ml	38	25	11	26
+	700 μg/ml	35	21	8	24
–	1.4 mg/ml	27	19	11	19
+	SF-Medium	41	24	14	22
–	SF-Medium	4	5	0	30

[a] PBL were incubated in basal RPMI medium supplemented with 2 nM recombinant IL-2 (Cetus Corporation, Emeryville, CA) and purified human albumin (Sigma Chemical Corporation, St. Louis, MO) at the concentrations indicated. The serum-free (SF) medium is HB-104, described in detail in the legend for FIGURE 2.

[b] Cells are harvested from these culture conditions and tested for lysis of a fresh sarcoma tumor in our standard 4 hour ^{51}chromium release assay.

EVIDENCE SUGGESTS THAT INITIAL INTERACTION OF THE PRECURSOR LAK WITH IL-2 OCCURS BY WAY OF A NON-TAC, P75 RECEPTOR

Although the experimental evidence demonstrates that exogenous IL-2 alone suffices for LAK activation, elimination of cells expressing the cell-surface receptor for IL-2, named Tac,[10,11] consistently resulted in no decrease in the subsequent generation of LAK activity.[4,12] Therefore, it appeared that Tac-negative cells were IL-2 responsive. Although Tac positive–precursor cells were not necessary for LAK generation, it was interesting that upregulation of Tac expression on the cells in LAK activation cultures closely paralleled the development of oncolytic function (FIG. 3).[12] Furthermore, expression of LAK function at 96 hours could be inhibited by the continuous presence of a monoclonal antibody directed against Tac.[12,13]

In order to determine the potential mechanism(s) by which IL-2 interacts with Tac-negative lymphocytes, we undertook a series of experiments to explore the pathway(s) of IL-2 interaction. First, trypsinization of PBL-cell surfaces rendered them unresponsive to IL-2, although viability was retained.[3] This result suggested that cell-surface protein was involved in the acquisition of lytic function. Subsequent [^{125}I]IL-2 (New England Nuclear, Boston, MA) binding and chemical cross-linking to populations enriched in LAK-precursor function, revealed an IL-2–binding protein of approximately 70,000–75,000 M_r (FIG. 4).[14,15] This binding was inhibited by excess cold IL-2, but was not inhibited by anti-Tac monoclonal antibody. Therefore, we have identified a receptor for IL-2 on Tac-negative PBL populations, which may be responsible for initial LAK activation.[15]

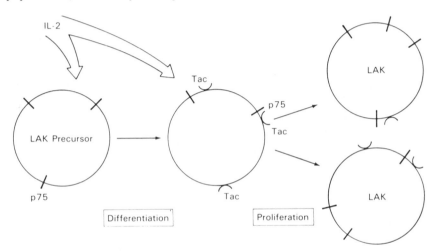

FIGURE 3. IL-2 and LAK: two roles mediated by two distinct receptors. A model for interaction of IL-2 with the receptor, known as p75, for the initial induction of LAK-lytic competence is presented. We propose that the p75–IL-2 interaction is followed by cell-cycle progression and proliferation that correlates with the upregulation of Tac, possibly in combination with p75. Our studies also indicate an upregulation of p75[15] during the stage of proliferation, but it is not yet clear whether this is on a per-cell basis, or merely reflects the relative increase in LAK-cell composition of the cultures.

AUGMENTATION OF LAK ACTIVATION BY INTERFERON (IFN)-GAMMA OCCURS ONLY IN THE PRESENCE OF ADHERENT-MONONUCLEAR CELLS

Conflicting reports exist concerning the potential of IFN-gamma to augment the activation of LAK.[16-19] Thus, we undertook a re-evaluation of the interaction of IFN-gamma and IL-2, using serum-free conditions and well-defined cell populations. Our results consistently demonstrate that IFN-gamma can augment LAK activation, but only when monocytes are present. Furthermore, this augmentation is detectable only when IL-2 is used at suboptimal concentrations (TABLE 2). These findings support the theory that although IL-2 alone is sufficient for optimal LAK activation, alternative pathways may be manifest under limiting IL-2 conditions.

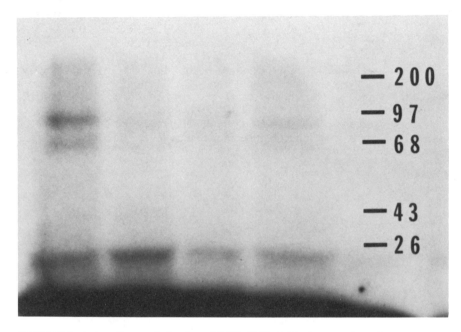

FIGURE 4. Autoradiogram indicating a 75,000 M_r IL-2–binding protein on LAK precursor cells. Percoll-enriched LAK precursor cells were incubated with 5 nM [^{125}I]IL-2 (New England Nuclear, Boston, MA) for 1 hour at 4°C. The cell-surface proteins of the intact cells were then cross-linked using 0.5 mM discuccinimidyl suberate. Cross-linked surface proteins were solubilized with 1% Triton X-100, the cells were pelleted (10,000 g for 10 min), and supernatants were collected. Supernatants were analyzed by electrophoresis under reducing conditions (7.5% SDS–PAGE in the presence of 2-ME) and the dried gel exposed to photographic film for 7 days. Lane 1 is PBL incubated with only [^{125}I]IL-2; lane 2 is PBL incubated with [^{125}I]IL-2 and a 200-fold molar excess of unlabeled IL-2; lane 3 is the same as lane 2, but PBL had been depleted of TAC+ cells; and lane 4 is PBL depleted of TAC+ cells, incubated only with [^{125}I]IL-2.

TABLE 2. Comparison of PBM versus PBL LAK Activation: PBM Selective Augmentation by IFN-Gamma

	Factors added[a]	Percent Lysis of Fresh Sarcoma			
		100:1	25:1	6:1	LU/10^6
PBM	IL-2	43.5	25.6	11.9	6.2
PBM	IL-2 + IFN	54.0	31.4	20.8	12.2
PBM	— IFN	4.1	1.8	0.6	<.1
PBL	IL-2	36.9	17.3	8.0	3.4
PBL	IL-2 + IFN	38.5	21.3	8.5	4.0
PBL	— IFN	3.6	6.0	5.7	<.1

[a] Serum-free HB 104 was used to culture PBM (peripheral blood mononuclear cells) or the macrophage-depleted PBL in the presence or absence of 1 nm rIL-2. Further cultures were supplemented with 200 U/ml of IFN-gamma (Biogen, recombinant interferon gamma, 14 Cambridge Center, Cambridge, MA). On day 5 of incubation, the cells were harvested, counted, and tested for lysis of a fresh human sarcoma in the standard 4 hour assay.

INHIBITION OF LAK ACTIVATION

Preliminary data suggest that LAK activation is susceptible to several types of negative regulation. It is known that high cell concentrations are not supportive for LAK activation, unless monocytes are removed.[20] We have shown that several tumor-derived factors,[21] as well as some fresh and cultured tumors[1] secrete substances that inhibit LAK activation. Our other studies also indicate that hydrocortisone directly inhibits LAK activation.[18]

Our current interest in the cellular regulation has led to two previously unreported observations: separation of T cells from non-T by E-rosetting often results in more total lytic activity than originally observed in the unseparated cells; and secondly, that platelet contamination results in a dose-dependent decrease in LAK activity. An example of our findings is that 40 lytic units of LAK activity are generated from populations containing platelet : lymphocyte ratios of 13 : 1, and only 5 lytic units can be generated from cultures containing ratios of 75:1 (Grimm, Ammann, Durrett, and Hester, to be published elsewhere). Recently we described a reversible, transforming growth factor–beta specific inhibition of IL-2 responsiveness.[22] The mechanisms of inhibition are not understood, but their study is in progress. Nevertheless, it should be appreciated that both humoral and cellular regulation of LAK is evident, and that further understanding of these will contribute significantly to our attempts to resolve both the potential for LAK in tumor therapy as well as in immune homeostasis.

REFERENCES

1. GRIMM, E. A. 1986. Human lymphokine-activated killer cells (LAK cells) as a potential immunotherapeutic modality. Biochim. Biophys. Acta **865:** 267–279.
2. ROSENBERG, S. A., E. A. GRIMM, N. MCGROGAN, M. DOYLE, E. KAWASAKI, K. KOTHS & D. F. MARK. 1984. Biological activity of recombinant human interleukin-2 produced in E. coli. Science **223:** 1412–1415.
3. OWEN-SCHAUB, L., W. G. LOUDON, M. YAGITA & E. A. GRIMM. 1988. Functional differentiation of human lymphokine activated killing (LAK) is distinct from expansion and involves dissimilar interleukin-2 receptors. Cell. Immunol. **48:** 235.
4. GRIMM, E. A., R. J. ROBB, J. A. ROTH, L. M. NECKERS, L. LACHMAN, D. J. WILSON & S. A. ROSENBERG. 1983. The lymphokine activated killer cell phenomenon. III. Evidence that IL-2 alone is sufficient for direct activation of PBL into LAK. J. Exp. Med. **158:** 1356.
5. DAMLE, N. K., L. V. DOYLE & E. C. BRADLEY. 1986. Interleukin 2-activated killer cells are derived from phenotypically heterogeneous precursors. J. Immunol. **137:** 2814.
6. ORTALDO, J. R., A. MASON & R. OVERTON. 1986. Lymphokine-activated killer cells. Analysis of progenitors and effectors. J. Exp. Med. **164:** 1193.
7. PHILLIPS, J. H. & L. L. LANIER. 1986. Dissection of the lymphokine activated killer phenomenon. Relative contribution of peripheral blood natural killer cells and T lymphocytes to cytolysis. J. Exp. Med. **164:** 814.
8. GRIMM, E. A., L. M. MUUL & D. J. WILSON. 1985. Cyclosporine and hydrocortisone exert differential inhibitory effects on the activation of human cytotoxic lymphocytes by recombinant IL-2 versus allospecific CTL. Transplantation **39:** 537.
9. FROELICH, C. J. & S. GUIFFAUT. 1986. Induction of lymphokine activated killer cells in serum-free medium. J. Immunol. Methods **86:** 205–211.
10. UCHIYAMA, T. S., S. BRODER & T. A. WALDMANN. 1981. A monoclonal antibody (anti-Tac) reactive with activated and functionally mature human T cells. I. Production of anti-Tac monoclonal antibody and distribution of Tac (+) cells. J. Immunol. **126:** 1393.

11. LEONARD, W. J., J. M. DEPPER, T. UCHIYAMA, K. A. SMITH, T. A. WALDMANN & W. C. GREENE. 1982. A monoclonal antibody that appears to recognize the receptor for human T-cell growth factor; partial characterization of the receptor. Nature 300: 267.
12. GRIMM, E. A. & S. A. ROSENBERG. 1984. The human lymphokine activated killer cell phenomenon. In Lymphokines. E. Pick, Ed.: 9: 79–310. Academic Press. New York.
13. GRAY, J. D., S. SHAU & S. S. GOLUB. 1985. Functional studies on the precursors of human lymphokine-activated killer cells. Cell. Immunol. 96: 338–342.
14. YAGITA, M., L. B. OWEN-SCHAUB, M. TSUDO, T. A. WALDMANN & E. A. GRIMM. 1987. Detection of a non-Tac IL-2 binding peptide (p75) on fresh peripheral blood lymphocytes as a receptor associated with induction of lymphokine activated killer activity. Submitted.
15. TSUDO, M., C. K. GOLDMAN, K. F. BONGIOVANNI, W. C. CHAN, E. F. WINTON, M. YAGITA, E. A. GRIMM & T. A. WALDMANN. 1987. The p75 peptide is the receptor for interleukin 2 expressed on large granular lymphocytes and is responsible for the interleukin 2 activation of these cells. Proc. Natl. Acad. Sci. USA 84: 5394.
16. ITOH, K., K. SHIIBA, Y. SHIMIZU, R. SUZUKI & K. KUMAGAI. 1985. Generation of activated killer (AK) cells by recombinant interleukin-2 (rIL-2) in collaboration with interferon-gamma (IFN-γ). J. Immunol. 134: 3124.
17. BRUNDA, M. J., D. TARNOWSKI & V. DAVATELIS. 1986. Interaction of recombinant interferon with recombinant interleukin-2: Differential effect on natural killer cell activity and interleukin-2-activated killer cells. Int. J. Cancer 37: 787.
18. BRAAKMAN, E., A. VAN TUNEN, A. MEAGER & J. C. LUCAS. 1986. IL-2 and interferon-gamma enhanced cytotoxic activity: Analysis of the role of different lymphoid subsets and implications for activation routes. Cell. Immunol. 99: 476–488.
19. UENO, Y., T. MIYAWAKI, S. SEKI, A. MATSUDA, K. TAGA, H. SATO & N. TANIGUCHI. 1985. Differential effects of recombinant human interferon-gamma and interleukin-2 on natural killer cell activity of peripheral blood in early human development. J. Immunol. 135: 180–184.
20. HOYER, M., T. MEINEKE, W. LEWIS, B. ZWILLING & J. RINEHART. 1986. Characterization and modulation of human lymphokine (interleukin 2) activated killer cell induction. Cancer Res. 45: 2834–2838.
21. ROTH, J. A., E. A. GRIMM, R. K. GUPTA & R. S. AMES. 1982. Immunoregulatory factors from human tumors. I. Immunological and biochemical characterization of factors that suppress lymphocyte proliferation and cytotoxic responses. J. Immunol. 125: 1955–1962.
22. GRIMM, E. A., W. L. CRUMP III, A. DURETT, J. P. HESTER, S. LAGOO-DEENADALAYAN & L. B. OWEN-SCHAUB. 1988. TGF-beta inhibition of the in vitro induction of lymphokine-activated killing is reversible. Cancer Immunol. Immunother. In press.

Tumor-Infiltrating Lymphocytes in Patients with Renal-Cell Carcinoma

J. H. FINKE,[a] R. TUBBS,[b] B. CONNELLY,[c] E. PONTES,[c]
AND J. MONTIE[c]

[a] Department of Immunology and Cancer
Research Institute
[b] Department of Pathology
Laboratory Medicine
[c]Department of Urology
Cleveland Clinic Foundation
Cleveland, Ohio 44106

INTRODUCTION

In an attempt to define the host-immune response to neoplastic diseases, lymphocytes that infiltrate the tumor (TIL) have been studied.[1–4] The phenotype and functional status of TIL has been examined in a number of tumor types including breast, lung, and melanoma.[4,5] The majority of the infiltrating cells are T lymphocytes with both cytotoxic and helper phenotypes present.[4–6] Only a minor (<5%) portion of the TIL preparation is composed of natural killer cells (NK) and macrophages (MØ).[4–6] Results from most studies show that TIL have little or no cytotoxic activity against autologous or allogeneic tumor targets when freshly isolated.[1,5,7] There have been a few reports, however, that have showed that TIL from colorectal tumors will lyse autologous tumors.[2,8] In addition, there is evidence to suggest that the frequency of proliferating lymphocyte precursors are reduced in TIL preparations.[4] A portion of the TIL population, however, can be activated by interleukin-2 (IL-2) and can be grown out of a single cell suspension of tumor cells.[5,6,9] TIL reactive to melanoma and lung carcinomas have been cultured long-term in the presence of IL-2 with many of these lines maintaining their cytolytic activity.[5,6,9,10]

TIL appear to represent part of the host-immune response to the tumor and may contain an enriched population of cells with reactivity to autologous tumor.[11] TIL cultured in IL-2 display more lytic activity for autologous tumor than is observed with lymphokine-activated killer cells (LAK) cultured from the peripheral blood.[9,10] Moreover, IL-2–activated TIL obtained from some tumors appear to be specifically cytotoxic for autologous tumor cells and do not lyse allogeneic targets.[5,6] In contrast to TIL, peripheral blood lymphocytes cultured with IL-2 lyse a broad spectrum of tumor targets.[12,13] These effectors are distinct from those derived from the tumor and are composed mainly of NK (CD16[+]) with a minor T-cell component.[4–6,12,13] In addition, recent studies have shown that TIL were therapeutically more potent than IL-2–activated spleen cells in several murine tumor models.[14]

We have begun to analyze the phenotype and functional properties of TIL from patients with renal-cell carcinoma. This tumor is of particular interest because it is one of the most responsive types to adoptive immunotherapy with LAK cells plus IL-2.[15] Here we report on the type of mononuclear cells that infiltrate renal-cell tumors, their responsiveness to IL-2, the phenotype of the expanded population, and their ability to lyse autologous tumor cells.

MATERIAL AND METHODS

Tumors

Human renal-cell carcinoma were obtained from patients who underwent nephrectomy at the Cleveland Clinic. The tumors were used to prepare TIL and tumor-targets cells for ^{51}Cr release assay. The cell line K562 was maintained in RPMI-1640 media supplemented with 10% FCS (Hyclone, Logan, Utah) and was used as a target for the cytotoxicity studies.

Human Renal Cell Carcinoma TIL Isolation and Activation

The involved kidney is cut in transverse section, the tumor is excised, and the material is weighed. Blood and necrotic material is removed and tissue is minced under sterile conditions and placed in a 100 ml sterile specimen container containing 20 ml of collagenase (0.1% solution) (CLSIII Worthington-Millipore) with 1 mg of deoxyribonuclease type I (Sigma, St. Louis, MO) for every 10 ml of collagenase solution used. Enzymes were dissolved in Dulbecco's phosphate-buffered saline. The flask is placed in a Blue-M shaker bath at room temperature for two hours. After the incubation period, the tissue slurry is diluted, washed twice in tissue culture media to remove debris plus residual collagenase, and resuspended in complete tissue culture media.

Cell count was performed and viability determined by Trypan blue dye exclusion. This cell preparation was used for expansion of TIL and for tumor targets. Aliquots of the tumor cells were frozen down in complete media containing 90% FCS and 10% DMSO. Additionally, cells were plated in complete media in 24-well plates at a cell concentration of 1.25×10^5/ml. The RPMi-1640 media (complete) was supplemented with 1000 U/ml of human recombinant IL-2 (provided by the Cetus Corp., Emeryville, CA), 5 units/ml of penicillin, 5 μg/ml of streptomycin sulfate, and 10% heat-inactivated human antibody (AB) serum. Cultures were incubated at 37°C in 5% CO_2 and 95% air for 11 to 15 days. In some of the TIL preparations, the cultures were refed on day 10 with fresh media plus IL-2. After the incubation period, cells were harvested, washed, and counted. Aliquots of TIL were either phenotyped or tested for cytotoxic activity.

Cytolytic Assay

Detection of lytic activity was performed using a four hour ^{51}Cr release assay.[16] Various concentrations of cultured cells were added to U-bottom 96-well plates to achieve effector to target cell ratios of 100:1, 50:1, 12:1, 6:1, and 3:1. Prior to cytotoxicity assays, target cells were labeled with 250 μCi of $Na^{51}CrO_4$ (New England Nuclear, Boston, MA), washed three times, and then suspended in media at a concentration of 10^5 viable cells/ml. Thereafter, target cells (10^4/100 μl) were added to 96-well plates. Following a four-hour incubation period, supernatant fluid from each well was harvested with the Skatron harvesting system and the amount of released ^{51}Cr determined in a Beckman Gamma 4000 counter.

Results were presented as percent specific lysis, which was calculated using the following formula:

$$\text{percent specific lysis} = \frac{(\text{experimental cpm}) - (\text{spontaneous cpm})}{(\text{maximum cpm}) - (\text{spontaneous cpm})} \times 100.$$

Maximum ^{51}Cr release was measured by lysing triplicate wells of 1×10^4 target cells with 1% sodium lauryl sulfate. Spontaneous release was measured in target cells to which medium alone was added.

In all the experiments, the autologous targets were greater than 70% tumor as determined by histological examination. In a few cases, the autologous tumor targets were purified ($>90\%$ tumor) using percoll gradients prior to labeling with ^{51}Cr.

Phenotyping of TIL

Immunocytology

Cytocentrifuge preparations was used for immunostaining.[17] Approximately 10^5 (100 μl) cells were mixed with 100 μl of fetal calf serum (FCS) and centrifuged at 100 g for five minutes, air dried, and fixed in acetone prior to immunostaining. Mouse monoclonal antibodies were applied to the cytospins (approximately 1 mcg/ml, dilutions optimized previously with tonsillar cryostat sections). Primary antibodies were allowed to incubate for 15 minutes in a humidified chamber at ambient temperature. The antibodies used were CD3 (Leu4, Beckton-Dickinson [B-D]), CD4 (T4, Coulter), CD8 (T8, Coulter), CD16c (Leu11), CD22 (Leu14, B-D), Leu19 (B-D), and LeuM3 (B-D). The slides were washed with modified phosphate-buffered saline (MPBS) (NaCl 180 gm/liter, NaH$_2$PO$_2$ 32 mg/liter, K2HPO$_4$ 188 gm/liter with 20 mg/liter of merthiolate). Next, the biotinylated affinity-purified human serum–absorbed horse-antimouse IgG (Vector) and the preformed avidin biotinylated peroxidase (Vector Laboratories) were incubated sequentially with the cells, 15 minutes per reagent, with MPBS washes between application. The color-reaction product was developed from the chromogenic substrate 3-amino 9-ethylcarbazole in the presence of .005 H$_2$O$_2$, the slides counterstained with hematoxylin and mounted with water soluble media (Aquamount, Lerner Laboratories).

Immunocytometry (Flow Cytometry)

Immunocytometry of TIL

Direct two-color immunofluorescence with FITC and phycoerythrin (PE)-conjugated murine monoclonal antibodies were used.[18]

Cell suspension aliquots in RPMI were distributed to tubes and two fluorochromes incubated with 1×10^6 cells/ml in each tube. Each group of antigens detected by a monoclonal antibody of a particular immunoglobulin class was preceded by cells incubated with the appropriate fluorochrome-conjugated isotypic controls. Prior to addition of the monoclonal antibody, nonspecific binding sites are blocked with heat aggregated–mouse IgG (Jackson) for five minutes at 4°C. The cell-suspension aliquots were incubated at 4°C in the dark for 30 minutes with vortexing at ten-minute intervals. The FITC-conjugated antibodies were added first and then the PE-conjugated antibodies last inasmuch as PE are the most photolabile reagents. After 30 minutes incubation, the suspensions were washed twice with 2 ml of MHBSS at 300 × g for five minutes at 4°C and fixed in 500 μl cold 2% paraformaldehyde in phosphate-buffered saline.

Cytometric analysis was done using an upgraded fluorescein-activated cell sorter (FACS II). Detection was performed with an Argon ion laser operated at 200 mW with 488 nm excitation. The system included a beam splitter and a 488/10 band pass filter, a 560 dichroic mirror. Results were reported as percentage of individual fractions of total mononuclear cells in suspension.

Preparation of Immunocytometry Compensation Standards

For accurate identification of population subsets, compensation networks were established on a daily in-run basis. For this procedure, heparinized peripheral blood was supplied daily by the primary laboratory center. Isotypic control mouse IgG1-FITC (B-D), HLE1-FITC (B-D), isotypic control mouse IgG1-RD1 (Coulter), and T11-RD1 (Coulter) comprised the reagents used to stain the cells for deriving green and red compensation standards. The use of isotypic controls allowed for the most accurate delineation of positive and autofluorescent populations and controls for nonspecific binding by a particular subclass of immunoglobulin.

RESULTS

Phenotype of Mononuclear Cells That Infiltrate a Renal-Cell Carcinoma

The type of mononuclear cells that infiltrate renal-cell tumors was determined by immunostaining cytospin preparations of single-cell suspensions from the tumor. As seen in TABLE 1, there was considerable variation in the degree of cellular infiltrate among the different patients. In all the patients, however, the infiltrate was composed primarily of T cells and MØ. Immunostaining for T-cell subsets revealed that both CD8$^+$ and CD4$^+$ cells are present. The high value of CD4$^+$ cells observed in a few patients was attributable to the fact that tissue MØ also express this marker. In agreement with others,[4–6] we found that very few of the infiltrates have the phenotype of natural-killer cells (NK) (CD16$^+$). Immunostaining of frozen sections yielded similar results as that generated from the cytospins (data not shown). Thus, the procedures used for dissociation of the tumor did not result in depletion of any subset of cells.

Analysis of the Cellular Expansion and Phenotype of IL-2–Activated TIL

A portion of the infiltrating lymphocytes are responsive to IL-2. Results from dose-response studies revealed that 1000 U/ml of IL-2 induced maximal expansion of lymphocytes. The culture of a tumor-cell suspension with IL-2 leads to significant expansion by day 10 to 12. As seen in TABLE 2, the degree of clonal expansion varies considerably among the patients. With additional TIL cultures completed, the range of expansion is between 0- and a 450-fold increase. The fold-increase calculation was based on the number of CD3$^+$ cells that were present at

TABLE 1. Phenotype of Cells Infiltrating a Renal-Cell Carcinoma

		Percent Positively Stained Cells (Cytocentrifuge Preparations) T Cells			
		Cytotoxic/	Helper/		
	Total	Suppressor	Inducer	NK	Macrophages
Patients	CD3	CD8	CD4^c	CD16	LeuM3
N.D.	14.9	15.3	26.5^c	0	8.9
M.H.	9.4	ND^a	52.4^c	1.0	ND^a
L.J.	30.4	ND^a	0.9	0	14.4
P.B.	16.3	8.1	3.3	1.9	4.6
L.B.	22.8	11.0	4.2	0	5.4
D.D.	8.9	ND^a	ND^a	10.7^b	3.4
J.W.	13.3	ND^a	1.8	0	0.1

^{a} not done.
^{b} Polymorphonuclear leukocytes predominately; no positive mononuclear cells.
^{c} Tissue macrophages also express CD4.

the initiation of culture. TIL had been grown for four weeks *in vitro* by subculturing cells with additional IL-2 every five to seven days (data not shown).

Flow cytometry studies were conducted to analyze the cell types that are expanded by IL-2. In all the patients studied, the predominant cell type that grows out of the tumor-cell suspension expresses the T-cell marker CD3 (73%) (TABLE 3). CD8$^+$ cells were more frequent than CD4$^+$ cells, with a mean CD4:8 ratio of 0.5. The majority of these cells appear to be activated inasmuch as they express markers (*i.e.*, HLA DR) that are normally present on activated lymphocytes. Using the monoclonal antibody to CD16$^+$, only minimal numbers of NK were detected after culture in IL-2. In addition, B cells and MØ were not present at this time.

TABLE 2. TIL Expansion following Culture with IL-2

Patients with Renal-Cell Carcinoma	Cells/Gram of Tissue^a $\times 10^6$	Percent CD3$^+$ Cells^b	Cell Viability^c (Days)	Culture Time^d	Fold Increase^e 1000 U/ml IL-2
P.B.	2.87	16.3	98%	13	50.0
E.C.	3.0	1.2	95%	12	266.6
L.B.	1.0	22.8	90%	15	34.4
L.J.	9.9	30.4	95%	11	14.2
D.D.	1.2	8.9	80%	11	17.6
N.D.	12.6	14.9	95%	13	16.2
M.H.	ND^f	9.4	90%	11	115.1

^{a} The amount of tissue used for TIL represented less than 10% of the total tumor (about 14 grams). The cell (tumor and lymphocytes) yield per specimen ranged from 1.1×10^6 cells to 207×10^6 cells.
^{b} Based on immunostaining of cytospins from the initial tumor-cell preparation.
^{c} Viability was assessed by Trypan blue dye exclusion.
^{d} Single cell suspensions derived from the tumor were plated at 1.25×10^5 cells/ml in the presence of 1000 U/ml of IL-2 for the length of time given in the TABLE. TIL did not expand in the absence of IL-2.
^{e} The fold-increase calculation was based on the number of CD3$^+$ T cells present in the starting tumor population.
^{f} Not done.

TABLE 3. Immunophenotype of TIL[a] Expanded by IL-2

| | | Percent Positively Stained Cells[b] | | | |
| | | T Cells | | | |
Patients	Total CD3	Cytotoxic/ Suppressor CD8	Helper/ Inducer CD4	CD4:8 Ratio	NK CD16
L.B.	89.5	57.4	43.5	0.8	2.7
N.D.	83.2	37.5	ND	—	1.4
L.J.	63.4	54.3	9.9	0.2	0.8
J.W.	40.9	36.5	3.8	0.1	0
M.H.	64.0	52.0	22.1	0.4	0.4
P.B.	74.9	54.4	17.4	0.3	7.2
D.D.	83.2	37.5	44.0	1.2	1.4

[a] TIL were cultured for 10 to 15 days in IL-2 (1000 U/ml). After the incubation period, TIL were washed and immunostained by direct, dual-label immunofluorescence using monoclonal antibodies directed against various subsets of lymphocytes. Thereafter, the number of positive cells was quantitated using four parameter, two-color immunocytometry. Comparable results were obtained by immunostaining a cytospin preparation of TIL.

[b] Results are percent of total cells obtained with immunocytometry.

Cytotoxic Activity of TIL

TIL expanded in IL-2 for 10 to 15 days were tested for their ability to lyse autologous as well as allogeneic tumor targets. In TABLE 4, we show that cultured TIL lysed autologous tumor cells in a dose-dependent manner. Recently we have observed that TIL subcultured with additional IL-2 retained their lytic activity for autologous tumor cells when tested on days 20 and 26 (data not shown).

IL-2–activated TIL from all patients tested displayed strong cytotoxic activity against the NK sensitive–line K562. In a limited number of experiments[3] TIL were found to be cytotoxic for allogeneic renal cell–carcinoma targets (data not shown).

DICUSSSION

A number of studies have shown that the predominant cellular infiltrate in many human solid tumors are T cells and that these cells are not generally acti-

TABLE 4. Cytolytic Activity of TIL

| | Percent Specific Lysis[a] | | | | | | | | | |
| | Autologous RCC[b] | | | | | K562 | | | | |
Patients	50:1[c]	25:1	12:1	6:1	3:1	50:1	25:1	12:1	6:1	3:1
N.D.	31.1	26.3	30.5	18.8	10.9	53.1	34.1	1.2	8.3	3.9
L.J.	44.6	28.5	17.9	16.5	7.7	66.7	46.0	41.1	27.7	21.6
W.S.	10.1	3.5	4.0	4.6	6.2	97.1	60.2	48.0	36.1	15.9
L.B.	24.3	18.8	12.3	5.8	6.0	72.9	74.0	61.1	49.3	37.1

[a] TIL were cultured for 10 to 15 days with IL-2 and then tested for cytolytic activity in a four-hour ^{51}Cr release assay.

[b] RCC = renal-cell carcinoma

[c] Effector: target-cell ratio

vated.[4-6,9] The addition of IL-2 to cultures of TIL, however, leads to the expansion of lymphocytes that have the ability to lyse tumor targets.[5,6,9]

Here we show that primary tumors from patients with renal-cell carcinoma contain a significant infiltrate of T cells and MØ. In agreement with others,[5,9,10] we have found that a portion of the TIL population can be activated and expanded in the presence of recombinant IL-2. The degree of cell expansion varies considerably among the different patients. The level of cellular expansion did not correlate with the number of T cells present at the beginning of culture. Although the reason for the wide variation in expansion of TIL by IL-2 is not known, we will determine if it correlates with tumor type, stage of disease, or the presence of regulatory mononuclear cell types.

The majority of renal-cell TIL expanded by IL-2 were T cells with a predominance of CD8[+] cells over CD4[+] cells. Several studies, however, have shown that CD4[+] cells represent the predominant T-cell phenotype in long-term TIL cultures (one to four months).[5,10] In one study, a sequential analysis of TIL phenotype revealed that with time, the number of CD4[+] cells steadily increased, whereas the number of CD8[+] cells decreased.[5] We have found, however, that after 30 days of culture, TIL from renal-cell patients are still composed primarily of CD8[+] cells (data not shown). Whether continued growth of these TIL would lead to a predominance of CD4[+] cells is not known but is being examined.

TIL from renal cell–carcinoma patients activated by IL-2 had the capacity to lyse autologous tumor targets. In every case tested, the effector cells also lysed allogeneic tumor targets. These results are in contrast to TIL derived from several tumor types, including melanoma[5,9] and lung,[10] where it was reported that TIL cultured from a portion of the patients preferentially lysed autologous tumor targets. Although TIL from all renal cell–carcinoma patients lysed autologous and allogeneic targets, it is possible that TIL represent a heterogenous population of cytotoxic cells, some of which are specific for autologous tumor. Others, however, can lyse a broad spectrum of tumor targets. Our preliminary data suggest that in addition to CD4[+] and CD8[+] cells, a subset of Leu19[+] cells are present in some patients (data not shown). CD3[+] Leu19[+] cells are present in the peirpheral blood and represent a minor component of the LAK activity.[11,12]

A number of issues remain to be resolved that concern the cytotoxic response mediated by TIL. The lytic potency of each subset of TIL expanded in IL-2 has not yet been defined. Such an analysis of IL-2–cultured peripheral-blood lymphocytes demonstrated that multiple sets with varying potencies mediated LAK activity. It is not clear what role the Ti/T3 receptor, the CD8 or CD4 molecules, or other receptors (Leu11) play in TIL effector-cell recognition. Additionally, the *in vivo* homing properties of activated TIL need to be examined, and more effective ways of targeting these cells to metastatic sites need to be developed. Results from these studies should help determine the role TIL play in the host response to tumors and further define their therapeutic potential.

ACKNOWLEDGMENT

The authors thank Mrs. Robbie Martin for typing the manuscript.

REFERENCES

1. VOSE, B. M., F. VANKY & E. KLEIN. 1977. Human tumor-lymphocyte interaction *in vitro*. V. Comparison of the reactivity of tumor-infiltrating, blood, and lymph-node lymphocytes with autologous tumor cells. Int. J. Cancer **20:** 895.

2. WERKMEISTER, J. A., E. PIHL, A. P. P. NID, G. R. FLANNERY & R. C. NAIRN. 1979. Immunoreactivity by intrinsic lymphoid cells in colorectal carcinoma. Br. J. Cancer **40:** 839.
3. HUTCHINSON, G. H., D. HEINEMANN, M. O. SYMES & R. C. N. WILLIAMSON. 1981. Differential immune reactivity of tumor-intrinsic and peripheral blood lymphocytes against autoplastic colorectal carcinoma cells. Br. J. Cancer **44:** 376.
4. WHITESIDE, T. L., S. MIESCHER, J. HURLIMANN, L. MORETTA & V. VON FLIEDNER. 1986. Separation, phenotyping, and limiting dilution analysis of T-lymphocytes infiltrating human solid tumors. Int. J. Cancer **30:** 803.
5. MUUL, L. M., P. J. SPIESS, E. P. DIRECTOR & S. A. ROSENBERG. 1987. Identification of specific cytolytic immune response against autologous tumor in humans bearing malignant melanoma. J. Immunol. **138:** 989.
6. KURNICK, J. T., R. L. KRADIN, R. BLUMBERG, E. E. SCHNEEBERGER & L. A. BOYLE. 1986. Functional characterization of T lymphocytes propagated from human lung carcinomas. Clin. Immunol. Immunopathol. **38:** 367.
7. TOTTERMAN, T. H., P. HAYRY, E. SAKSALA, T. TIMONEN & B. EKLUND. 1978. Cytological and functional analysis of inflammatory infiltrates in human malignant tumors. II. Functional investigation of the infiltrating inflammatory cells. Eur. J. Immunol. **8:** 872.
8. VOSE, B. M., P. GALLAGHER, M. MOORE & P. SCHOFIELD. 1981. Specific and nonspecific lymphocyte cytotoxicity in colon carcinoma. Br. J. Cancer **44:** 846.
9. ITOH, K., A. B. TILDEN & C. M. BALCH. 1986. Interleukin 2 activation of cytotoxic T-lymphocytes infiltrating into human metastatic melanomas. Cancer Res. **46:** 3011.
10. KRADIN, R. L., L. A. BOYLE, F. I. PREFFER, R. J. CALLAHAN, M. BARLAI-KOVACH, H. W. STRAUSS, S. DUBINETT & J. T. KURNICK. 1987. Tumor derived interleukin 2-dependent lymphocytes in adoptive immunotherapy of lung cancer. Cancer Immunother. **24:** 76.
11. VANKY, F. & E. KLEIN. 1982. Specificity of antitumor cytotoxicity exerted by fresh, activated, and propagated human T lymphocytes. Int. J. Cancer **29:** 547.
12. PHILLIPS, J. H. & L. L. LANIER. 1986. Dissection of the lymphokine-activated killer phenomenon. Relative contribution of peripheral blood natural killer cells and T lymphocytes to cytolysis. J. Exp. Med. **164:** 814.
13. ORTALDO, J. R., A. MASON & R. OVERTON. 1986. Lymphokine-activated killer cell analysis of progenitors and effectors. J. Exp. Med. **164:** 1193.
14. ROSENBERG, S. A., P. SPIESS & R. LAFRENIERE. 1986. A new approach to the adoptive immunotherapy of cancer with infiltrating lymphocytes. Science **233:** 1318.
15. ROSENBERG, S. A. *et al.* 1987. A progress report on the treatment of 157 patients with advanced cancer using lymphokine-activated killer cells and interleukin 2 or high-dose interleukin 2 alone. N. Eng. J. Med. **316:** 889.
16. FINKE, J. H., B. YEN-LIEBERMAN, J. W. SCOTT & M. R. PROFFITT. 1985. Phorbol ester-inactivation of cloned cytotoxic T lymphocytes: Restoration of lytic activity by interleukin 2 and induction of interferon production are separable events. Lymphokine Res. **4:** 299.
17. TUBBS, R. R., G. N. GEPHARDT & R. E. PETRAS. 1986. Atlas of Immmunohistology. Am. Soc. Clin. Pathol.
18. JACKSON, A. L. & N. L. WARNER. 1986. *In* Manual of Clinical Laboratory Immunology. N. R. Rose, H. Friedman & J. L. Fakey, Eds.: 226. American Society of Microbiology.

Role of Soluble Cytotoxic Factors in Lymphokine-Activated Killer Cell (LAK)–Mediated Cytotoxicity

JOHN C. HISERODT AND WILLIAM H. CHAMBERS

Pittsburgh Cancer Institute and Department of Pathology
University of Pittsburgh
Pittsburgh, Pennsylvania 15213–2592

Secretion of cytotoxic effector molecules has been described as a means of tumor-cell destruction by lymphoid and monocytoid-effector cells. These include tumor necrosis factor (TNF) produced by monocytes/macrophages,[1–3] natural cytotoxic cells (NC),[4] possibly natural killer cells (NK),[5] lymphotoxin (LT, TNF-beta) produced by cytotoxic T lymphocytes (CTL),[6,7] and natural killer cell cytotoxic factor (NKCF) produced by NK.[8–10] In addition, a class of pore-forming molecules (cytolysin/perforin) has also been described as effector molecules derived from *in vitro* cultured NK and CTL.[11–14] Using cell lines that constitutively secrete cytotoxic molecules, TNF-alpha and -beta have been isolated to purity. They have also been characterized, and the genes for these molecules have been isolated, cloned, and expressed in *Escherichia coli*.[15–20] Cytolysin has now been isolated from the granules of large granular lymphocyte (LGL) leukemias,[13] NK and CTL clones,[11,14,21] and LAK[22] and has also been purified to homogeneity. The isolation of NKCF has remained elusive, as NK represent a very small population (<5%) in peripheral blood, and a cell line or clone that constitutively secretes this molecule has not been identified.

Many observations, at the effector cell level, have suggested that cell-mediated cytotoxicity is a secretory phenomenon. Treatment of NK effector cells with strontium chloride,[23,24] monensin,[25] or compounds that block lysosomal secretions by other cells (cAMP, PGE, theophylline, histamine) block cytotoxicity by NK.[26] Secretion is an energy-dependent phenomenon, and compounds that uncouple oxidative phosphorylation, such as dinitrophenol, block NK cytotoxicity.[25] It has been reported that NK undergo cytoskeletal changes following conjugation with target cells. These changes are associated with the formation of a specific type of junction involving actin and vinculin.[26] Morphologic evidence has also indicated a role for secretion, particularly the release of intracytoplasmic granules in the cytotoxic process. Reorientation of the Golgi apparatus and the microtubule-organizing center in cloned NK following their interaction with target cells was reported by Kupfer *et al.*[27] This reorientation occurred in a directional manner toward the contact zone between killer and target cells. Failure to reorient the Golgi apparatus resulted in an absence of killing. Photomicroscopy, using Nomarski optics, has demonstrated that polarization of intracellular granules of CTL toward the effector cell–target cell interface precedes target-cell lysis.[28] Granule discharge has also been noted in the intracellular space between target cells and effector cells, again suggesting a role for granule components as mediators of cytotoxicity.[29]

In discussing the role of soluble cytotoxic factors in the mechanism of cytotoxicity, it is important to discuss evidence indicating the transfer of materials from killer cells to target cells that is requisite for target-cell lysis. Evidence for the transfer of such material was first obtained using an in vitro–cytotoxicity assay employing phytohemagglutinin (PHA)-coated L-929 target cells and human effector lymphocytes. It was shown that trypsinization of target cells, following a brief exposure to the effector cells, could protect the target cells from lysis.[30] Using a similar system, antibodies against purified alpha-lymphotoxin could also block target-cell lysis during the killer cell–independent (KCIL) phase of the lytic process.[31]

As an alternative approach to studying the role of cytoplasmic components in the lytic mechanism, antibodies were generated against in vivo–elicited CTL or against cytosolic fractions obtained from these cells. These antibodies strongly inhibited NK and CTL cytolytic function without affecting target-cell binding and were able to inhibit cytotoxicity during the operationally defined KCIL phase of the cytotoxic process.[32] As an extension of these studies, Hiserodt et al.[33] showed that the lysis of target cells, physically isolated from NK effector cells, could be blocked by trypsinization of the target or by reducing the temperature to 4°C. Lysis of the lethally hit targets could be reactivated by rewarming them to 37°C. These results were consistent with previous reports that the CTL "lethal hit" could be blocked by reducing the temperature to 4°C and reactivated by warming the lethally hit target to 37°.[34] Cumulatively, these data suggest that cytolytic effector cells contain, within their cytoplasm, material that is released and deposited, at least transiently, on the target-cell membrane, which signals the death of the target cell.

Recently, effector cells termed lymphokine-activated killer cells (LAK) have been described,[35-37] and much interest has been focused on these cells due to their potent antitumor reactivity.[38-40] Cells with LAK activity are generated in vitro by culturing lymphocytes with either supernatants containing interleukin-2 (IL-2)[35-41] or with recombinant IL-2 (rIL-2).[42,43] Whereas cells with LAK activity were originally described as deriving from primitive T cells,[35,38] recent evidence indicates that the majority of LAK activity in short-term cultures (<7 days) is derived from the LGL/NK subset of lymphocytes.[37,44-47]

In purifying populations of activated NK, we have exploited the observation that LGL adhere to plastic or glass following stimulation with rIL-2. Morphologic analysis of the adherent population demonstrated that these cells were greater than 95% LGL, expressed surface markers characteristic of IL-2–activated NK (TABLE 1), and contained very high levels of cytolytic activity. After 3–5 days in culture, the adherent population underwent a high degree of expansion (up to 100-fold) and we could isolate a pure population (>95%) of LAK effector cells possessing exceedingly high levels of cytotoxic activity against a variety of NK resistant–tumor cells, including syngeneic fresh tumor explants (TABLE 2).

Because of their relationship to NK, their rapid expansion and enhanced cytolytic activity, we have employed purified populations of adherent LAK as a useful model for the study of natural cell–mediated cytotoxicity. We have examined several properties of the cytolytic process of these cells and have found that, except for a broader range of target-cell specificities, LAK are qualitatively identical to NK in cytotoxic function (TABLE 3). Lysosomotropic amines, strontium chloride (inducer of degranulation), monensin, and EGTA inhibit cytotoxicity by NK and LAK, again suggesting the involvement of secretory processes. An interesting observation is the ability of charged sugars, particularly mannose-6-sulfate to effectively inhibit NK and LAK cytotoxicity at low concentrations (1–10 mM). Studies on the mechanism of inhibition by sugar sulfates employing target-cell binding and calcium-pulse experiments have indicated that the inhibition is medi-

TABLE 1. Surface Marker Analysis of NK and rIL-2–Stimulated NK Isolated from Spleens of F344 Rats[a]

Cells	Percent LGL	Percent positive cells								Cytotoxic activity[b]		
		OX 8[c]	AsGM$_1$	Laminin	OX 19	R1-3B3	OX 39	OX 6	Ig	YAC-1	P815	MADB106
NK	94 ± 2	96	98	79	2	3	2	3	4	496	<10	<10
rIL-2–NK	98 ± 2	81	98	58	4	3	6	62	9	5790	1200	940

[a] 50×10^6 nylon wool nonadherent F344 spleen cells were plated at 2×10^6 cells/ml in medium containing 10^3U/ml rIL-2. After 2 hours at 37°C, the plastic adherent LGL (NK) were collected and analyzed for surface-marker expression, morphology, and cytotoxic activity on YAC-1 targets. The same cells were placed back into culture for 5 days with rIL-2.

[b] Lytic units, 20/10^7 cells.

[c] Markers: OX 8 = marker for NK and T-suppressors cells; AsGM$_1$ = asialo GM$_1$; OX 19 = pan-T marker; R1-3B3 = pan-T marker; OX 39 = IL-2 receptors (Tac); OX 6 = Ia; Ig = Immunoglobulin.

TABLE 2. Spectrum of Tumor Target Cell–Lysis by rIL-2 Rat-Activated Natural-Killer Cells

Tumor Cells	Histologic Type	Percent Cytotoxicity (4 hr)	
		40 : 1	20 : 1
RNK-16 (rat)	LGL leukemia	66	38
MADB106 (rat)	mammary adenocarcinoma	81	55
M13762 (rat)	mammary adenocarcinoma	72	51
NTD (rat)	T-cell lymphoma	80	60
G1TC (rat)	T-cell lymphoma	88	66
YAC-1 (mouse)	T-cell lymphoma	92	78
P815 (mouse)	mastocytoma	65	46
L5178Y (mouse)	T-cell lymphoma	56	39
MDAY/D2 (mouse)	lymphosarcoma	50	27
B-16 (mouse)	melanoma	48	29
1.0/Anti-B^r (mouse)	fibrosarcoma	61	32

TABLE 3. Similarities in NK and LAK-Mediated Cytotoxicity Regarding Pharmacologic Blockade

Agent	NK	LAK
SrCl$_2$	+[a]	+
Monensin	+	+
EDTA/EGTA	+	+
NH$_4$Cl	+	+
Diphenylamine	+	+
Cadaverine	−[b]	−
Dansylcadaverine	+	+
Charged monosaccharides	+	+

[a] Inhibitory effects.
[b] No effect.

TABLE 4. TNF-Like Activity in LAK Supernatants[a]

Dilution	rIL-2 only	Stimulus		
		P815 + rIL-2	YAC-1 + rIL-2	Con A + rIL-2
1 : 4	41[b]	44	45	50
1 : 8	32	36	40	44
1 : 16	18	24	34	26
1 : 32	14	20	16	22
1 : 64	11	0	13	16
1 : 128	10	0	12	14

[a] P815 and YAC-1 target cells used at 20 : 1 E : T ratio and Con A at 10 μg/ml.
[b] Percent cytotoxicity in an 18 hour neutral red uptake assay versus actinomycin D–treated L-929 target cells.

TABLE 5. Cytotoxic Activity of LAK-Derived TNF-Like Activity

Dilution	− Actinomycin D	+ Actinomycin D[b]
1 : 2	0[a]	66
1 : 4	0	54
1 : 8	0	35

[a] Percent cytotoxicity in an 18 hour neutral red uptake assay versus L-929 target cells.
[b] Actinomycin D at 1.0 μg/ml.

ated at a postconjugation, posttriggering step in the lytic process and operationally during the lethal-hit phase. These results suggest that both NK and LAK lyse tumor target cells using similar lethal-hit mechanisms, which at some point involve sulfated carbohydrates.

Several cytotoxic molecules, with a diverse spectra of cytotoxic/cytostatic activities, have been shown to be released by or extracted from NK. These include TNF-alpha, cytolysin/perforin, and NKCF. TNF has been implicated as a cytotoxic mediator in the killing of certain tumor targets by macrophages[3,48,49] and natural cytotoxic cells (NC).[4,50,51] A recent study indicated that human LGL (35–50% pure) also produced TNF-alpha, but not -beta.[5] We have examined supernatants of highly purified populations of rIL-2–activated NK (LAK) for the presence of TNF and have found substantial amounts of a factor with characteristics similar to TNF. TNF-like activity is secreted constitutively by rIL-2–activated NK, and its release is not enhanced by the treatment of effector cells with lectin, phorbol ester, or target cells (TABLE 4). The activity of this cytotoxin is dependent upon treatment of L-929 target cells with actinomycin D or mitomycin C (TABLE 5). Its activity is partially heat-resistant (56°C for 60 minutes) but is destroyed at 100°C for 10 minutes (TABLE 6). Preliminary evidence using molecular sieve chromatography (HPLC) has indicated that the TNF-like activity was heterogenous in size with a major peak of activity eluting in the 45–60 kDa range. Although these data suggest that this factor is TNF, we have been unable to identify TNF-alpha or -beta mRNA transcripts in the purified A-LAK using cDNA probes for mouse TNF. Because neutralizing antibodies specific for rat TNF-alpha and -beta are not available, we have been unable to identify this factor using immunological approaches.

Although rIL-2–activated NK (LAK) and fresh NK are apparently capable of producing TNF, there is evidence to suggest this factor is not a primary mediator of cytotoxicity by these cells in short-term (4 hour) cytotoxicity assays. First, anti-TNF-alpha and -beta antibodies do not inhibit NK or rIL-2–activated NK cytolysis,[52] (unpublished data). Second, recombinant TNF-alpha and -beta are not cytotoxic for most NK targets in either short-term (4 hour) or long-term (18 hour) assays, with or without actinomycin D treatment, even when used at very high concentrations (1000 U/ml). Third, we have shown that the lethal-hit phase of NK

TABLE 6. Heat Sensitivity of TNF-Like Activity from LAK Supernatants

Dilution	Control	56°C for 60 min	100°C for 10 min
1 : 2	40[a]	32	5
1 : 4	33	12	6
1 : 8	26	8	5

[a] Percent cytotoxicity in an 18 hour neutral red uptake assay versus actinomycin D–treated L-929 target cells.

or rIL-2–activated NK is inhibited by sugar phosphates or sugar sulfates,[53–61] but TNF-alpha and -beta are not inhibited by these sugars. In addition, direct cell-mediated cytotoxicity occurs at a much accelerated rate over that of TNF. Direct cytotoxicity by NK, activated or unactivated, can be demonstrated within 1–2 hours, but TNF cytotoxicity is not evident for at least 12–18 hours, even at high concentrations. Collectively, these data indicate that although TNF may be involved in certain forms of cellular cytotoxicity (*i.e.* macrophage or NC activity), it is most likely not involved as a primary lytic mediator in NK or LAK cytotoxicity.

Although we have identified a TNF-like activity produced by purified rat LAK, for the reasons discussed in the previous paragraph, we do not believe that it is involved in direct LAK cytotoxicity in short-term assays. It is tempting to speculate, however, that the production of such TNF-like factors by adoptively transferred LAK may have important systemic anti-tumor effects *in vivo*. TNF has been shown to cause regression of certain types of tumors *in vivo*[1,62] and can enhance cytotoxicity by monocytes[63] and eosinophils.[64] Interferon and TNF in combination have been shown to strongly synergize in mediating cytotoxic/cytostatic effects against a variety of target cells *in vitro*.[63,65–69] TNF treatment can also enhance class I expression, thereby potentially increasing immunogenicity of tumors *in vivo*.[67] Thus, the constitutive secretion of TNF-like factors by adoptively transferred LAK may have important direct and indirect effects in LAK-mediated antimetastatic activity, and these effects may be important considerations in adoptive immunotherapy.

The membranolytic pore-forming molecules, cytolysin/perforin, have also been suggested as mediators of cytotoxicity by NK and CTL.[11–14] The activity of these molecules fulfill many of the necessary criteria for an effector-cell cytotoxin, but several criticisms to the universality of these molecules in all forms of direct lymphocyte-mediated cytotoxicity have been raised. Cytolysin/perforin is carried within the intracytoplasmic granules of NK, NK leukemias, or IL-2–dependent CTL clones. This form of compartmentalization is compatable with the general hypothesis of the secretory nature of the cytotoxic mechanism. Cytolysin is nonspecific in its lytic activity and is capable of killing any cell that can induce its release. Thus, cytolysin would be an attractive mediator in LAK cytotoxicity inasmuch as LAK are capable of killing virtually any tumor target cell. The nonselective nature of the cytotoxic activity of cytolysin/perforin, however, creates a major problem in explaining how NK or LAK are resistant to their own cytolytic attack because these cells are indeed susceptible to their own purified cytolysin. These effector cells have been shown to remain viable following target-cell lysis and to have the capacity to recycle during the lytic process.[70] This being the case, it is still necessary to explain the directionality of cytotoxicity, that is, the means by which effector cells escape the effects of a totally nonspecific and highly potent membranolytic mediator such as cytolysin/perforin.

As with direct NK cytolysis, cytolysin/perforin–mediated cytotoxicity is very rapid, occurring within minutes.[13,71] On the other hand, if one accepts the argument against TNF involvement, based on disparity of kinetics of killing (>12 hours), it is difficult to dismiss the fact that the kinetics of killing by cytolysin (minutes) also fall outside those established for direct killing by effector cells.

The activity of cytolysin/perforin has an absolute requirement for Ca^{++}.[13,71] Although it is clear that in most instances the overall cytolytic process requires Ca^{++}, there are reports of target cells (EL-4) that are susceptible to direct cytotoxicity in short-term assays in the absence of Ca^{++}.[72] It is also apparent that charged sugars (phosphorylated and sulfated) do not have an inhibitory effect on purified cytolysin, but are potent inhibitors of direct NK- and rIL-2–activated

NK-mediated cytolysis. Although antibody to intracytoplasmic granules (which contain cytolysin) is an effective inhibitor of NK-mediated cytotoxicity, to date there are no reports of the effects of antibody specific for cytolysin on direct cell-mediated cytotoxicity.

We have also investigated whether highly purified rat LAK contain within their granules cytolysin activity. It is clear from the data shown in TABLE 7 that potent cytolysin activity can be extracted from purified LAK granules, which demonstrates the typical Ca^{++} dependency noted previously for NK- or CTL-derived cytolysin.

Finally, another soluble mediator has been suggested as important to the cytotoxic mechanisms of NK. This factor, NKCF, has been defined as a soluble cytotoxin released by NK in response to NK susceptible–target cells, lectin, or phorbol ester, that has cytotoxic activity only for NK-susceptible, but not NK-resistant, cells.[8–10,73–77] This definition, coupled with the evidence that NKCF activity can be partially inhibited with charged monosaccharides,[75,78] has been suggested as evidence that NKCF fits the criteria for the NK cytotoxin, functional in short-term cytotoxicity assays. The kinetics of NKCF cytotoxicity (18–40 hours), however, are also unlike those in direct assays of cytotoxicity. Even more

TABLE 7. Cytolysin Activity in the Postnuclear Extract of Purified LAK

Dilution (Log 2)	$CaCl_2$: 0 mM	2 mM	4 mM
1	10.7[a]	82.7	78.1
2	18.8	79.9	66.8
3	5.6	63.0	17.5
4	5.8	60.8	18.0
5	7.2	66.1	10.9
6	4.6	53.9	4.5
7	1.4	33.2	1.7
8	0.0	14.9	0.0

[a] Percent cytotoxicity versus ^{51}Cr-labeled sheep red blood cells in a 20 minute assay. Activity derived from 10^7/ml LAK.

difficult to explain is the dichotomy between the killing capabilities of NK and LAK. Cells with LAK activity derive from a common precursor of NK or represent NK in a unique state of activation. If, as our results suggest, the cytolytic machinery of NK and LAK is qualitatively indistinguishable, then NK and LAK cytolysis differ only in their receptor/trigger mechanisms. Under these conditions, it would be difficult to envision NKCF, as currently defined, as a primary mediator of direct LAK-mediated cytotoxicity in short-term assays. It must be considered that NK and LAK cytolytic mechanisms may be qualitatively different in a fashion that is undetectable in our experiments. Alternatively, resistance to NK cytolysis may be a quantitative difference in susceptibility of a tumor to a factor like NKCF. If this is the case, then the definition of NKCF as a cytotoxin "specific" for NK susceptible–target cells may need reevaluation.

In summary, we have begun to analyze the role of a variety of soluble factors in direct cellular cytotoxicity mediated by highly purified populations of rIL-2–activated killer cells in rats. In addition, we are addressing questions as to whether these factors may be important in the antimetastatic activity of LAK during adoptive immunotherapy. It is hoped that this will lead to improved strategies for combination therapy using multiple cytokines or cytotoxic factors that could synergize with the already high level of cytotoxic activity in purified populations of adoptively transferred LAK.

REFERENCES

1. CARSWELL, E. A., L. J. OLD, R. L. KASSEL, S. GREEN, N. FIORE & B. WILLIAMSON. 1975. Proc. Natl. Acad. Sci. USA **72:** 3666.
2. GREEN, S., A. DOBRJANSKY, E. A. CARSWELL, R. L. KASSEL, L. J. OLD, N. FIORE & M. K. SCWHARTZ. 1976. Proc. Natl. Acad. Sci. USA **73:** 381.
3. ZEIGLER-HEITBROOK, H. W. L., A. MOLLER, R. P. LINKE, J. G. HAAS, E. R. RIEBER & G. REITHMULLER. 1986. Cancer Res. **46:** 5947.
4. ORTALDO, J. R., A. MASON, T. SAYERS & R. B. HERBERMAN. 1986. Nature **321:** 700.
5. PETERS, P. M., J. R. ORTALDO, M. R. SHALABY, L. P. SVEDERSKY, G. E. NEDWIN, T. S. BRINGMAN, P. E. HASS, B. B. AGGARWAL, R. B. HERBERMAN, D. V. GOEDDEL & M. A. PALLADINO. 1986. J. Immunol **137:** 2592.
6. GRANGER, G. A. & W. P. KOLB. 1968. J. Immunol. **101:** 111.
7. RUDDLE, N. H. & B. WAKSMAN. 1968. J. Exp. Med. **128:** 1267.
8. WRIGHT, S. C. & B. BONAVIDA. 1981. J. Immunol. **125:** 1516.
9. FARRAM, E. & S. R. TARGAN. 1983. **130:** 1251.
10. DEEM, R. L. & S. R. TARGAN. 1984. J. Immunol. **133:** 1836.
11. PODACK, E. R. & G. DENNERT. 1983. Nature **302:** 442.
12. MILLARD, P. J., M. P. HENKART, C. W. REYNOLDS & P. A. HENKART. 1984. J. Immunol. **132:** 3197.
13. HENKART, P. A., P. J. MILLARD, C. W. REYNOLDS & M. P. HENKART. 1984. J. Exp. Med. **160:** 75.
14. PODACK, E. R. & P. J. KONIGSBERG. 1984. J. Exp. Med. **160:** 695.
15. PENNICA, D., G. E. NEDWIN, J. S. HAYFLICK, P. H. SEEBERG, R. DERYNCK, M. A. PALLADINO, J. K. KOHR, B. B. AGGARWAL & D. V. GOEDDEL. 1985. Nature **312:** 724.
16. WANG, A. M., A. A. CREASEY, M. B. LADNER, L. S. LIN, J. STRICKLER, J. N. VAN ARSDELL, R. YAMAMOTO & M. F. MARK. 1985. Science **228:** 149.
17. AGGARWAL, B. B., W. J. HENZEL, B. MOFFAT, W. J. KOHR & R. N. HARKINS. 1985. J. Biol. Chem. **260:** 2333.
18. SHIRAI, T., H. YAMAGUCHI, H. ITO, C. W. TODD & R. B. WALLACE. 1985. Nature **313:** 803.
19. AGGARWAL, B. B., W. J. HENZEL, B. MOFFAT, W. J. KOHR & R. N. HARKINS. 1985. J. Biol. Chem. **260:** 2345.
20. GRAY, P. W., B. B. AGGARWAL, C. V. BENTON, T. S. BRINGMAN, W. J. HENZEL, J. A. JARRETT, D. W. LEUNG, B. MOFFAT, P. NG, M. A. PALLADINO & G. E. NEDWIN. 1985. Nature **312:** 721.
21. DENNERT, G. & E. R. PODACK. 1983. J. Exp. Med. **157:** 1483.
22. HENKART, P. A., C. C. YUE, J. YANG & S. A. ROSENBERG. 1986. J. Immunol. **137:** 2611.
23. NEIGHBOR, P. A. & H. S. HUBERMAN. 1982. J. Immunol. **128:** 1236.
24. NEIGHBOR, P. A., H. S. HUBERMAN & Y. KRESS. 1982. Eur. J. Immunol. **12:** 588.
25. CARPEN, O., I. VIRTANEN & E. SAKSELA. 1981. Cell. Immunol. **58:** 97.
26. RODER, J. C. & M. KLEIN. 1979. J. Immunol. **123:** 2785.
27. KUPFER, A., G. DENNERT & S. J. SINGER. 1983. Proc. Natl. Acad. Sci. USA **80:** 7224.
28. YANELLI, J. R., J. A. SULLIVAN, G. L. MANDELL & V. H. ENGELHARD. 1986. J. Immunol. **136:** 377.
29. HISERODT, J. C. & T. BEALS. 1985. *In* Mechanisms of Cytotoxicity by NK Cells. R. B. Herberman, Ed.: 195. Academic Press. Orlando, FL.
30. KRAMER, S. & G. A. GRANGER. 1976: J. Immunol. **116:** 562.
31. HISERODT, J. C. & G. A. GRANGER. 1977. J. Immunol. **119:** 379.
32. HISERODT, J. C. & B. BONAVIDA. 1981. J. Immunol. **126:** 256.
33. HISERODT, J. C., L. J. BRITVAN & S. R. TARGAN. 1984. Cell. Immunol. **83:** 43.
34. MARTZ, E. 1987. *In* Contemporary Topics in Immunobiology. O. Stutman, Ed.: **7:** 301. Plenum. New York.
35. GRIMM, E. A., A. MAZUMDER, H. Z. ZHANG & S. A. ROSENBERG. 1982. J. Exp. Med. **155:** 1823.

36. KEDAR, E. & D. W. WEISS. 1983. Adv. Cancer Res. **38**: 171.
37. ITOH, K., A. B. TILDEN, K. KUMAGAI & C. M. BALCH. 1985. J. Immunol. **134**: 502.
38. ROSENBERG, S. A. 1984. Cancer Treat. Rep. **68**: 233.
39. ROSENBERG, S. A. 1986. *In* Important Advances in Oncology. V. Devita, S. Hellman & S. Rosenberg, Eds.: 55. J. B. Lippincott. Philadelphia.
40. FEFER, A., M. A. CHEEVER & P. D. GREENBERG. 1982. *In* Immunologic Approaches to Cancer Immunotherapy. E. Mihich, Ed.: 333. Plenum. New York.
41. LOTZE, M. T., E. A. GRIMM, A. MAZUMDER, J. L. STRAUSS & S. A. ROSENBERG. 1981. Cancer Res. **41**: 4420.
42. ROSENBERG, S. A., E. A. GRIMM, M. MCGROGAN, M. DOYLE, E. KAWASAKI, K. KOTHS & D. F. MARK. 1984. Science **223**: 1412.
43. GRIMM, E. A., R. J. ROBB, J. A. ROTH, L. M. NEIKERS, L. B. LACHMAN, D. J. WILSON & S. A. ROSENBERG. 1983. J. Exp. Med. **158**: 1356.
44. VUJANOVIC, N. L., R. B. HERBERMAN & J. C. HISERODT. 1988. Cancer Res. **48**: 878.
45. PHILIPS, J. H. & L. L. LANIER. 1986. J. Exp. Med. **164**: 814.
46. ORTALDO, J. R., A. MASON & R. OVERTON. 1986. J. Exp. Med. **165**: 1193.
47. HISERODT, J. C., N. L. VUJANOVIC, R. B. HERBERMAN, C. W. REYNOLDS & D. V. CRAMER. 1987. *In* Cellular Immunotherapy of Cancer. R. Truitt, R. Gale & M. Bortin, Eds.: 137. A. R. Liss. New York.
48. CHEN, A. R., K. P. MCKINNON & H. S. KOREN. 1985. J. Immunol. **135**: 3978.
49. URBAN, J. L., H. M. SHEPARD, J. L. ROTHSTEIN & B. J. SUGARMAN. 1986. Proc Natl. Acad. Sci. USA **83**: 5233.
50. STUTMAN, O., M. STEFFEN, K. WELTE & E. C. LATTIME. 1987. Fed. Proc. **46**: 476.
51. LATTIME, E. C., A. KAHN & O. STUTMAN. 1987. Fed. Proc. **46**: 476.
52. ORTALDO, J. R., J. R. RANSOM, T. J. SAYERS & R. B. HERBERMAN. 1986. Immunol. **137**: 2857.
53. STUTMAN, O., P. DIEN, R. E. WISUN & E. C. LATTIME. 1980. Proc. Natl. Acad. Sci. USA **77**: 289.
54. FORBES, J. T., R. K. BRETTHAUER & T. N. OELTMANN. 1986. Proc. Natl. Acad. Sci. USA **78**: 5797.
55. ADES, E. W., A. HINSON & J. M. DECKER. 1981. Immunobiology **160**: 248.
56. VOSE, B. M., M. HARDING, W. WHITE, M. MOORE & J. GULLAGHER. 1983. Clin. Exp. Immunol. **51**: 517.
57. WERKMEISTER, J. A., J. C. RODER, C. CURRY & H. F. PROSS. 1983. Cell. Immunol. **80**: 172.
58. WEITZEN, M. L., E. INNINS, R. S. YAMAMOTO & G. A. GRANGER. 1983. Cell. Immunol. **77**: 42.
59. ORTALDO, J. R., T. T. TIMONEN & R. B. HERBERMAN. 1984. Clin. Immunol. Immunopathol. **31**: 439.
60. KORNBLUTH, J., S. S. RAAB & D. B. WILSON. 1984. Cell Immunol. **88**: 162.
61. CHAMBERS, W. H. & T. N. OELTMANN. 1986. J. Immunol. **137**: 1469.
62. HARANAKA, K., N. SATOMI, A. SAKURAI & R. HARANAKA. 1984. Int. J. Cancer **34**: 87.
63. PHILIP, R. & L. B. EPSTEIN. 1986. Nature **323**: 86.
64. SILBERSTEIN, D. S. & J. R. DAVID. 1986. Proc. Natl. Acad. Sci. USA **83**: 1055.
65. TRINCHIERI, G., M. KOBAYASHI, M. ROSEN, R. LOUDEN, M. MURPHY & B. PERUSSIA. 1986. J. Exp. Med. **164**: 1206.
66. WONG, G. H. W. & D. V. GOEDDEL. 1986. Nature **323**: 819.
67. COLLINS, T., L. A. LAPIERRE, W. FIERS, J. L. STROMINGER & J. S. POBER. 1986. Proc. Natl. Acad. Sci. USA **83**: 446.
68. BEUTLER, B., I. W. MILSARK & A. CERAMI. 1985. J. Immunol. **135**: 3972.
69. BEUTLER, B., D. GREENWALD, J. D. HULMES, M. CHANG, Y. C. E. PAN, J. MATHISON, R. ULEVITCH & A. CERAMI. 1985. Nature **318**: 522.
70. ULLBERG, M. & M. JONDAL. 1986. J. Exp. Med. **153**: 615.
71. PODACK, E. R., J. D.-E. YOUNG & Z. A. COHN. 1985. Proc. Natl. Acad. Sci. USA **82**: 8629.
72. TIROSH, R. & G. BERKE. 1985. Cell. Immunol. **95**: 113.
73. DEEM, R. L. & S. R. TARGAN. 1984. J. Immunol. **133**: 1836.

74. STEINHAUER, E. A., A. T. DOYLE & A. S. KADISH. 1985. J. Immunol. **135:** 294.
75. WRIGHT, S. C. & B. BONAVIDA. 1982. J. Immunol. **129:** 433.
76. WRIGHT, S. C. & B. BONAVIDA. 1983. J. Immunol. **130:** 2960.
77. ORTALDO, J. R., I. BLANCA & R. B. HERBERMAN. 1985. Adv. Exp. Med. Biol. **184:** 203.
78. SAYERS, T. J., J. H. RANSOM, A. C. DENN, R. B. HERBERMAN & J. R. ORTALDO. 1986. J. Immunol. **137:** 385.

Direct and Indirect Modes of Action of Cyclosporine on Cytotoxic T Lymphocytes[a]

VERNER PAETKAU, CALLIOPI HAVELE, AND
JENNIFER SHAW

Department of Biochemistry
University of Alberta
Edmonton, Alberta, Canada T6G 2H7

INTRODUCTION

There is extensive evidence to show that the immunosuppressive agent, cyclosporine A (CsA), inhibits immune responses by blocking the induction of a number of cytokines. Factors whose generation is inhibited by CsA, and which might be involved in immune responses, include interleukin-2 (IL-2),[1-5] interferon gamma,[4,5] and colony-stimulating factors.[6,7] Inhibition of IL-2 synthesis could account for the ability of CsA to block cytotoxic T lymphocyte (CTL) responses, and could also be at least partly responsible for its ability to inhibit the appearance of IL-2 receptors in peripheral blood cells (PBL),[8] inasmuch as IL-2 up-regulates its own receptor.[9] On the other hand, in cultures of cloned cells, CsA has little effect on the expression of IL-2 receptor.[3,5,7] Overall, CsA affects the expession of only a small subset of genes in T lymphocytes, and this subset includes several known lymphokines.[10] The proliferation and cytotoxicity of IL-2–dependent, antigen-independent CTL lines is typically insensitive to CsA.[1,11]

The inhibition of lymphokine synthesis by CsA can account for many of its suppressive effects on cellular and humoral immunity. Besides inhibiting lymphokine production and response, however, CsA exhibits other modes of immunosuppression. Inhibition of antigen presentation by macrophages to induce T cells to produce IL-2 has been observed.[12] In another study,[13] activation of resting B lymphocytes by BSF-1 was found to be resistant to CsA, but stimulation with BSF-1 in conjunction with anti-immunoglobulin was sensitive. In addition, the effect of BCGF-II on preactivated B lymphocytes was also CsA-sensitive. One of the difficulties in assessing the precise modes of action of CsA in many studies is the use of uncloned cell populations. In this paper, we describe a direct effect of CsA on a class of cloned CTL that is not mediated by an inhibition of IL-2 synthesis. In these cells, CsA blocks both the antigen-dependent activation and the resulting cytotoxic activity.

[a] This work was supported by Grants from the Medical Research Council and National Cancer Institute of Canada, and the Alberta Heritage Trust Fund for Medical Research.

INDIRECT EFFECTS OF CsA

The ability of CsA to inhibit cellular immune responses indirectly is illustrated in FIGURE 1, in which the phorbol myristate acetate (PMA)-induced synthesis of IL-2 mRNA by the T lymphocyte–cell line EL4.E1 is inhibited by pharmacologically relevant concentrations of CsA. In this cell line, transcription of granulocyte-macrophage colony-stimulating factor (GM-CSF) is induced coordinately with that of IL-2, and as can be seen in the FIGURE, is also coordinately suppressed by CsA. It was shown earlier that the action of CsA in inhibiting IL-2 production is mediated by an inhibition of induction of mRNA synthesis.[3] In addition to blocking the induction of IL-2 mRNA synthesis, CsA also interrupts ongoing transcription of this gene,[7] as seen in FIGURE 2. This effect can account for the loss of cytoplasmic mRNA, because the half-life of IL-2 mRNA is relatively short.[13a]

The number of cytokines whose synthesis is affected by CsA includes interferon gamma, IL-3 (at least in some T cells), lymphotoxin, and TRF/IL-5. There are also cases in which a given cytokine is suppressible by CsA in one cell but not in another. For example, IL-3 expression is blocked in T helper–cell lines,[14] but not in WEHI-3 cells.[15] The reason for the resistance in the latter case is the presence of an intracisternal A-particle sequence just upstream of the IL-3 gene in WEHI-3 cells.[15] There are at least two subsets of inducible genes in T lymphocytes, one of which is suppressible by CsA, the other not. The IL-2 receptor gene in the human T leukemia–cell line Jurkat, for example, is inducible by mitogens, but this induction is not directly suppressed by CsA.[3,7] The majority of genes in a cell line such as EL4.E1 are not affected by either PMA, the inducing agent for lymphokine synthesis, or CsA.[10]

TYPE I AND TYPE II CTL

Cloned CTL that are independent of antigen often exhibit a degenerated cytotoxicity, in terms of both specificity and potency. Previous work has shown that

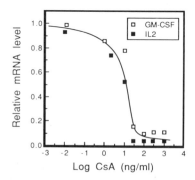

FIGURE 1. Inhibition of lymphokine production by CsA. Cells of the mouse-T lymphoma line EL4.E1 were stimulated with 15 ng/ml PMA for 12 hours, at which time the cytoplasmic contents of IL-2 and GM-CSF mRNA were determined by cytodot analysis, essentially as described earlier.[7] Oligonucleotide probes described in the earlier reference were used. The maximum values obtained by densitometry of autoradiograms were set to 1.0 for each mRNA.

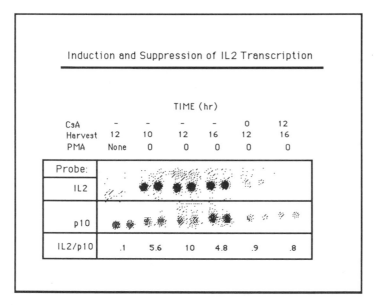

FIGURE 2. CsA interrupts IL-2 gene transcription. The transcription rate of IL-2 mRNA in EL4.E1 cells was determined by nuclear run-on analysis. Nuclei were harvested from cells exposed to the agents indicated, added at the times shown in the FIGURE. Nascent transcripts were labeled by exposure to alpha-[32P]UTP.[20,3] The FIGURE shows a digitized representation of the data. The numerical values of relative densities of IL-2 and the invariant marker mRNA p10[21] were obtained by densitometry of the original autoradiogram. The results indicate that Il-2 transcription peaked at 12 hours, and that addition of 100 ng/ml CsA at 0 time or at 12 hours blocked transcription almost completely. Lane 1 is a control of unstimulated cells.

highly specific CTL can be converted to less-specific cytotoxic forms. Thus, a transient conversion to NK-like cells in response to interferon was described by Brooks and colleagues.[16] Antigen-dependent, and highly specific CTL can be converted to a form that is antigen-independent and that grows in response to IL-2 alone. In our own work, we refer to the specific, antigen-dependent population as type I CTL, and the conversion products as type II.[17] The relevant properties of type I and II CTL are given in FIGURE 3. Type I cells require IL-2 for survival, but in the absence of antigen, go to a quiescent state showing neither growth nor cytotoxicity. It should be noted that the quiescent type I cells do indeed respond to IL-2, and do so at concentrations that reflect high-affinity receptors;[17] in the absence of IL-2, type I cells rapidly die, and this occurs whether or not antigen is present. Type I cells are activated to growth and specific killing by antigen, or by the phorbol diester PMA. They undergo a burst of activity and then again drift toward quiescence.

The relationship of type I CTL to CTL generated from mixed leukocyte cultures is not entirely clear. For example, long-term CTL cultures can be reactivated by IL-2 alone.[18] Those results, however, were obtained with uncloned cells and could have resulted from indirect effects. In addition, it is difficult to entirely exclude effects of antigen remnants in the earlier work, although there was some evidence that the response differed in kind from that induced by adding back intact antigenic cells.

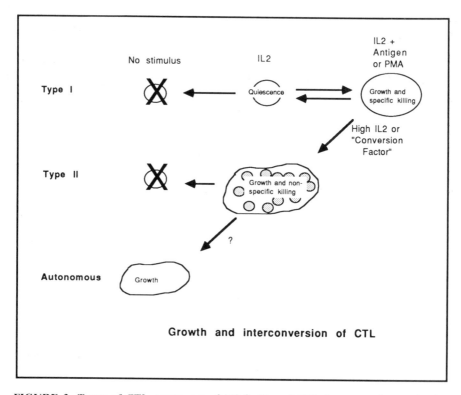

Growth and interconversion of CTL

FIGURE 3. Types of CTL grown out of MLC. Type I CTL become quiescent in the presence of IL-2, but without antigen. They slowly decline in numbers, but can rapidly be restimulated to grow by exposure to either the appropriate antigen or PMA. In the absence of IL-2, type I and type II cells die within 48 hours. Type II cells are larger, adherent, and visibly granular. They grow in response to IL-2 alone and are indifferent to antigen. They kill a variety of target cells, although they kill the nominal target more efficiently than others. Autonomous cells arising from type II cells through unknown mechanisms grow in the absence of added factors. The conversion from type I to type II is induced with high efficiency by exposure of activated type I cells to high levels of IL-2 ($>$100 U/ml). It can also be induced at low levels of IL-2 by exposure to a lymphokine preparation from PMA-activated EL4.E1 cells (fraction 3, reference 22). Detailed properties of type I and II CTL are described elsewhere.[17]

The cells typically used for an IL-2 bioassay are like the type II cells described in FIGURE 3. Their properties include a highly granular appearance, relatively large size, adherence, and nonspecific cytotoxicity (but with a superimposed specific cytotoxicity toward the nominal antigen). Most importantly, they are independent of, and indifferent to, antigen.[17] As for type I cells, they rapidly die in the absence of IL-2. FIGURE 3 also includes autonomous cells, which occasionally grow out of IL-2–dependent (type II) cells.

The conversion of specific to less-specific CTL has been effected by interferons.[16] In our work, we have found two mechanisms for converting type I to type II cells. These are very-high IL-2 concentrations and an as-yet undefined "conversion factor" that is present in cytokine-rich supernatants of EL4.E1 and some T helper–cell lines. Conversion requires activation by antigen (or PMA); thus, the conversion factor, which works at moderate IL-2 levels, is without effect if the cells are not simultaneously activated by exposure to antigen or PMA.

THE DIRECT EFFECT OF CsA ON TYPE I CTL

The proliferation of IL-2–dependent, antigen-independent T lymphocyte–cell lines is generally found not to be sensitive to CsA. By contrast, we observed that the proliferation of type I CTL stimulated by the addition of antigen in the presence of IL-2 was profoundly inhibited by CsA at concentrations over 10 ng/ml. This was seen as a lack of [³H]TdR-incorporation into DNA (FIGURE 4) and also as a lack of increase in cell number (data not shown). The level of IL-2 present in this experiment, 100 U/ml, was high enough to stimulate maximal proliferation upon addition of antigen, although there was no response (<2% of the maximum) in the absence of antigen. The level of CsA required for >80% inhibition, several hundred ng/ml, was higher than is normally required for inhibiting cytokine production by EL4.E1 or other cell lines.[7] A similar inhibitory effect was observed when type I CTL clones were stimulated with PMA instead of antigen; CsA inhibited growth as measured by DNA synthesis or cell counting (data not shown).

Quiescent type I cells slowly lose their cytotoxic activity toward the target. Exposure to the appropriate antigen restores cytotoxicity as well as proliferation.[17] In TABLE 1, we show evidence that CsA also blocks the reacquisition of cytotoxic activity in type I CTL exposed to antigen. The residual activity at the time of the assay was 9.8% ⁵¹Cr release, at an effector to target ratio of 0.5. The

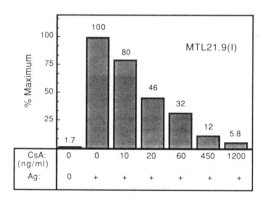

FIGURE 4. CsA blocks the stimulation of proliferation of a cloned type I CTL line by antigen. Cells of the MTL21.9(I) cloned line, which is of H-2ᵏ origin (CBA/J mice) and is stimulated by H-2ᵈ alloantigen, were allowed to come to quiescence by incubation in IL-2 alone for 15 days after the last exposure to antigen. The cells were harvested and recultured in 96-well microtiter trays at 10⁴ per well in the presence of 100 U/ml recombinant human IL-2. Antigen was added as 5 × 10⁵ cells per well of irradiated spleen cells from CBA/J × BALB/c mice, and CsA was present where indicated in the FIGURE. Proliferation was measured by incorporation of [³H]TdR at 72 hours after the start of reculture (addition of antigen). As seen in column 1, proliferation in the absence of antigen was less than 2% of the maximum seen with antigen.

TABLE 1. CsA Blocks the Activation of Cytotoxicity in Type I CTL[a]

State of Type I CTL Cells MTL22.2(I)	Percent [51]Cr Release
A. Quiescent	9.8
B. Antigen-activated	24.6
C. Antigen-exposed in the presence of CsA	7.5

[a] Cells of type I CTL line MTL22.2(I) (H-2^k anti-H-2^b) were allowed to reach quiescence by incubation in Il-2 without antigen for 15 days. They were harvested, and equal numbers were cultured in the three groups. All groups received 10 U/ml recombinant human IL-2. Group B also was given antigen in the form of irradiated spleen cells from C57BL/6 mice. Group C was given antigen plus 300 ng/ml CsA. After 3 days, the cells were harvested and recultured for 24 hours in IL-2 alone (10 U/ml). Group C was also given CsA (300 ng/ml) during this time. Cytotoxicity was tested on day 4 by ^{51}Cr release from EL4 cells.

response to antigen in the absence of CsA was 24.6% killing. In the presence of 300 ng/ml CsA plus antigen, however, the level of killing was only 7.5%; overall, the data show that CsA blocks the activation of quiescent type I CTL by antigen. Morphologically, the cells remained small in the presence of antigen plus CsA, in contrast to the rapid blastogenic appearance attained with antigen alone.

The results described above were obtained by having CsA present during the reactivation of type I CTL. In a separate series of experiments, CsA was added at the beginning of the chromium-release assay, which was 4 hr long. As can be seen in FIGURE 5, CsA inhibited the effector phase directly, with 100 ng/ml inhibiting by 70–75% over 4 hours.

In separate experiments, a number of type II CTL, derived from the clonal lines used above, were examined. CsA had no effect on the IL-2–dependent growth of these cell lines, as already noted for a number of IL-2–dependent, but antigen-independent, lines. Thus, only the antigen-dependent stimulation of type I CTL was sensitive. In terms of direct effect on the CTL assay, CsA inhibited killing by type II CTL only slightly.

Addition of CsA to mixed leukocyte cultures inhibits the generation of CTL.[1] One reason for this is the block in IL-2 production that this causes. We have found the five day CTL response of mouse splenic lymphocytes, however, to be inhibited by CsA even when the cultures were flooded with optimal levels of IL-2 (C. Havele and V. Paetkau, unpublished). This inhibition was seen when CsA was added at the outset of the cultures, but not if it was present only from 48 hours. Thus, the activation of primary CTL, similar to that of type I CTL lines, is sensitive to CsA, and this sensitivity is not related to IL-2.

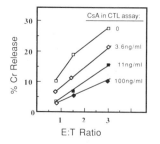

FIGURE 5. CsA inhibits the cytotoxic effect of type I CTL directly. The type I CTL line MTL21.9(I) was reactivated with antigen as described in FIGURE 4, and cytotoxicity was tested 8 days later. CsA was added, at the concentrations indicated, at the beginning of the 4 hr assay for ^{51}Cr release.

DISCUSSION

Our results indicate that, in addition to inhibiting the production of cytokines, CsA can have direct effects on the activation of cloned CTL by antigen, and on the effector phase of certain types of CTL activity. The levels of CsA required for these effects are higher than those that inhibit cytokine production, although this is difficult to interpret because different cells are involved, and the uptake may differ among cells. Perhaps the most surprising result was the direct inhibition of the effector phase of type I CTL. Further kinetic analysis suggests that a portion of the activity is blocked almost instantaneously. It seems unlikely that this effect is mediated by an effector of the cytokine type, inasmuch as cells are typically washed just before the assay, and any soluble mediator would have to accumulate. Rather, it seems likely that completely distinct, as yet undefined, sets of genes expressed in T lymphocytes may be the target of CsA inhibition. In contrast to the cytokine genes, their products may function intracellularly. The functions inhibited by CsA would include transduction of the antigen-induced signal for reactivation of quiescent CTL and the generation of "killing signals" to targets. Whether target recognition is affected remains to be determined.

Given that conventionally generated CTL activity in primary cultures is only minimally sensitive to CsA at the effector stage, it is germane to ask what the relationship is between type I CTL and CTL generated in primary cell cultures. Whether the difference is due to the presence of ancillary cells in the primary mixed leukocyte culture, or to the fact that the type I CTL represent an unrelated type of cytotoxicity, remains to be established. Recently, it was found that the IL-2–driven proliferation of human alloactivated CTL cells was inhibited by CsA, with the concentration required for 50% inhibition being about 100 ng/ml.[19] The cloning efficiency and frequency of cytotoxic clones obtained after eight days of limiting dilution culture were also both reduced by the same concentration of CsA. This behavior is almost exactly like that of our type I clones.

In cultures of human peripheral blood leukocytes (PBL), CsA inhibited the expression of the IL-2 receptor by about 50%, as did dexamethasone.[8] Addition of recombinant IL-2 largely overcame the dexamethasone inhibition of a mitogenic T-cell response, but did not significantly ameliorate the CsA effect. Although the cell system studied was complex, the results do indicate that CsA inhibits the proliferative response to mitogens by a mechanism other than simply blocking the expression of IL-2 and its receptor. This is the same general point made by our data showing an inhibitory effect of CsA on the restimulation of type I CTL by antigen in the presence of IL-2. The unifying theme of CsA effects on T lymphocytes may be the existence of similarly regulated sets of genes that are responsible for the unique, specific properties of T lymphocytes.

REFERENCES

1. BUNJES, D., C. HARDT, M. ROLLINGHOFF & H. WAGNER. 1981. Cyclosporin A mediates immunosuppression of primary cytotoxic T-cell responses by impairing the release of interleukin-1 and interleukin-2. Eur. J. Immunol. **11:** 657–661.
2. ELLIOTT, J. F., Y. LIN, S. B. MIZEL, R. C. BLEACKLEY, D. G. HARNISH & V. PAETKAU. 1984. Induction of interleukin-2 messenger RNA inhibited by cylosporin A. Science **226:** 1439–1441.
3. KRONKE, M., W. J. LEONARD, J. M. DEPPER, S. K. ARYA, F. WONG-STAAL, R. C. GALLO, T. A. WALDMANN & W. C. GREENE. 1984. Cyclosporin A inhibits T cell growth factor gene expression at the level of mRNA transcription. Proc. Natl. Acad. Sci. USA **81:** 5214–5218.

4. WISKOCIL, R., A. WEISS, J. IMBODEN, R. KAMIN-LEWIS & J. STOBO. 1985. Activation of a human T cell line: A two-stimulus requirement in the pretranslational events involved in the coordinate expression of IL-2 and gamma interferon genes. J. Immunol. **134:** 1599–1603.
5. GRANELLI-PIPERNO, A., L. ANDDRUS & R. M. STEINMAN. 1986. Lymphokine and non-lymphokine mRNA levels in stimulated human T cells. J. Exp. Med. **163:** 922–937.
6. KAUFMANN, Y., A. E. CHANG, R. J. ROBB & S. A. ROSENBERG. 1984. Mechanism of action of cyclosporin A: Inhibition of lymphokine secretion studied with antigen-stimulated T cell hybridomas. J. Immunol. **133:** 3107–3111.
7. SHAW, J., K. MEEROVITCH, J. F. ELLIOTT, R. C. BLEACKLEY & V. PAETKAU. 1987. Induction, suppression and superinduction of lymphokine mRNA in T lymphocytes. Mol. Immunol. **24:** 409–419.
8. REED, J. C., A. H. ABIDI, J. D. ALPERS, R. G. HOOVER, R. J. ROBB & P. C. NOWELL. 1986. Effect of cyclosporin A and dexamethasone on interleukin 2 receptor gene expression. J. Immunol. **137:** 150–154.
9. DEPPER, J. M., W. J. LEONARD, C. DROGULA, M. KRONKE, T. A. WALDMANN & W. C. GREENE. 1985. IL-2 augments transcription of the IL-2 receptor gene. Proc. Natl. Acad. Sci. USA **82:** 4230–4234.
10. PAETKAU, V. 1985. Molecular biology of interleukin 2. Can. J. Biochem. Cell Biol. **63:** 691–699.
11. LARSSON, E.-L. 1980. Cyclosporin A and dexamethasone suppress T cell responses by selectively acting at different sites of the triggering process. J. Immunol. **124:** 2828–2833.
12. PALAY, D. A., C. W. CLUFF, P. A. WENTWORTH & H. K. ZIEGLER. 1986. Cyclosporine inhibits macrophage-mediated antigen presentation. J. Immunol. **136:** 4348–4353.
13. O'GARRA, A., D. J. WARREN, M. HOLMAN, A. M. POPHAM, C. J. SANDERSON & G. G. KLAUS. 1986. Effects of cyclosporine on responses of murine B cells to T cell-derived lymphokines. J. Immunol. **137:** 2220–2224.
13a. SHAW, J., K. MEEROVITCH, R. C. BLEACKLEY & V. PAETKAU. 1988. Mechanisms regulating the level of IL-2 mRNA in T lymphocytes. J. Immunol. **140:** 2243–2248.
14. HEROLD, K. C., D. W. LANCKI, R. L. MOLDWIN & F. W. FITCH. 1986. Immunosuppressive effects of cyclosporin A on cloned T cells. J. Immunol. **136:** 1315–1321.
15. YMER, S., W. Q. J. TUCKER, C. J. SANDERSON, A. J. HAPEL, H. D. CAMPBELL & I. G. YOUNG. 1985. Constitutive synthesis of interleukin 3 by leukaemia cell line WEHI-3B is due to retroviral insertion near the gene. Nature **317:** 255–258.
16. BROOKS, C. G., M. HOLSCHER & D. URDAL. 1985. Natural killer activity in cloned cytotoxic T lymphocytes: Regulation by interleukin 2, interferon, and specific antigen. J. Immunol. **135:** 1145–1152.
17. HAVELE, C., R. C. BLEACKLEY & V. PAETKAU. 1986. Conversion of specific to non-specific cytotoxic T lymphocytes. J. Immunol. **137:** 1448–1454.
18. LEFRANCOIS, L., J. R. KLEIN, V. PAETKAU & M. J. BEVAN. 1984. Antigen-independent activation of memory cytotoxic T cells by interleukin 2. J. Immunol. **132:** 1845–1850.
19. BUURMAN, W. A., T. J. M. RUERS, I. A. J. J. M. DAEMEN, C. J. VAN DER LINDEN & G. GROENEWEGEN. 1986. Cyclosporin A inhibits IL2-driven proliferation of human alloactivated T cells. J. Immunol. **136:** 4035–4039.
20. MCKNIGHT, G. S. & R. D. PALMITER. 1979. Transcriptional regulation of the ovalbumin and conalbumin genes by steroid hormones in chick oviduct. J. Biol. Chem. **254:** 9050–9058.
21. PAETKAU, V., R. C. BLEACKLEY, D. RIENDEAU, D. G. HARNISH & E. W. HOLOWACHUK. 1985. Toward the molecular biology of IL2. *In* Contemporary Topics in Molecular Immunology. S. Gillis & F. P. Inman, Eds.: Vol. **10:** 35–61. Plenum Press. New York.
22. RIENDEAU, D., D. G. HARNISH, R. C. BLEACKLEY & V. PAETKAU. 1983. Purification of mouse interleukin 2 to apparent homogeneity. J. Biol. Chem. **258:** 12114–12117.

Failure and Success in Abolition of Virus-Specific CTL-Response Defects by Dendritic Cells

W. M. KAST, C. J. P. BOOG, B. O. ROEP,
A. C. VOORDOUW, AND C. J. M. MELIEF

Division of Immunology
The Netherlands Cancer Institute
1066 CX Amsterdam, the Netherlands

C57BL/6 (B6, H-2^b) mice can generate cytotoxic T lymphocyte (CTL) responses against Sendai virus and Moloney virus (TABLES 1 and 2, and reference 1). H-2K^b mutant bm1 mice, however, fail to generate a major histocompatibility complex (MHC) class I–restricted CTL response against Sendai virus when normal spleen cells (NSC) are used as antigen-presenting cells (APC) (TABLE 1 and reference 1). This CTL-response failure is due to a mutation in the H-2K^b molecule, which is the class I–MHC restriction element used by H-2^b mice in the response against Sendai virus.[1-4] Other CTL responses such as the Moloney virus–specific CTL response are unimpaired in bm1 mice (not shown). H-2D^b mutant bm14 mice fail to generate an MHC class I–restricted CTL response to Moloney virus when lipopolysaccharide (LPS) blasts are used as APC (TABLE 2). This CTL response failure is due to a mutation in the H-2D^b molecule, which is the MHC-restriction element used by H-2^b mice in the response against Moloney virus.[5] Other immune responses like the generation of Sendai virus–specific CTL are unimpaired in bm14 mice (not shown). We previously demonstrated that dendritic cells (DC), compared to NSC a̱d LPS blasts, are superior in the presentation of antigens to T-helper cells.[6] We even demonstrated that with the use of DC, an MHC class II–determined CTL-response defect against the male antigen H-Y can be restored in H-2 I-A^b–mutant bm12 mice.[6]

In attempting to overcome the Sendai virus–specific CTL-response defect of bm1 mice, we immunized bm1 mice with highly potent Sendai virus–infected syngeneic DC and used Sendai virus–infected syngeneic DC *in vitro* as stimulator cells to stimulate the spleen cells of the immunized mice (responder cells) (TABLE 1). The Sendai virus–specific CTL-response defect of bm1 mice was not restored by this protocol, however.

In attempting to restore the Moloney virus–specific CTL-response defect of bm14 mice, we stimulated the spleen cells of immunized mice (responder cells) *in vitro* with Moloney virus–infected syngeneic DC (stimulator cells). In contrast to our findings regarding the Sendai virus–specific CTL-response defect of bm1 mice, DC can overcome the Moloney virus–specific CTL-response defect of bm14 mice. The reason why DC are superior as APC and are sometimes capable of abolishing MHC-determined T cell–response defects is not known. Qualitative properties of DC may play a role, such as their morphology with large thin and

TABLE 1. Dendritic Cells Fail to Overcome the Sendai Virus–Specific CTL-Response Defect of bm1 Mice

Responder Cells[a]	Stimulator Cells[b]	Target Cells[c]			
		B6 S	B6	bm1 S	bm1
B6 S	B6 NSC S	45[d]	3	6	4
B6 DC S	B6 DC S	47	9	8	7
B6 DC S	bm1 DC	5	8	65	67
bm1 S	bm1 NSC S	0	2	4	1
bm1 DC S	bm1 DC S	4	4	8	4
bm1 DC S	B6 DC	45	48	0	1

[a] 10^7 spleen cells from Sendai virus–primed (S) mice or Sendai virus–infected DC-primed (DC S) mice.

[b] 10^7 Sendai virus–infected NSC (NSC S), 10^5 DC, or 10^5 Sendai virus–infected DC (DC S) (irradiated with 25 Gy).

[c] 5×10^3 Sendai virus–infected (S) or uninfected concanavalin A–induced blasts.

[d] Mean percentage–specific ^{51}Cr release of four experiments at an effector-to-target ratio of 16.

smooth cytoplasmic veils and large surface area. This morphology can facilitate close contact with cells to which antigens are presented, and it might allow the expression of a large number of antigenic particles per cell. It is also known that DC express large numbers of MHC–class II molecules.[7] Moreover, the amount of MHC–class I molecules is also very high on DC (C. J. P. Boog et al., submitted for publication). In cases of poor fit between antigen and MHC molecules, it is conceivable that for productive antigen/MHC interaction, high numbers of MHC molecules and antigen particles on the cell surface are necessary for T-cell activation. Nevertheless, DC were incapable of restoring the Sendai virus–specific CTL-response defect of bm1 mice (TABLE 1). This indicates that the defect of bm1 mice may lie at the level of a CTL-repertoire defect or alternatively that a productive Sendai virus/K^{bm1} interaction is completely impossible.

We conclude that DC through their very effective presentation of viral antigens can overcome those virus-specific CTL-response defects due to poor association between MHC molecules and viral antigens. DC, however, cannot be used to overcome virus-specific CTL nonresponsiveness in cases of T cell–repertoire defects or complete failure of MHC molecules and viral antigens to associate.

TABLE 2. Dendritic Cells Can Overcome the Moloney Virus–Specific CTL-Response Defect of bm14 Mice

Responder Cells[a]	Stimulator Cells[b]	Target Cells[c]			
		B6 M	B6	bm14 M	bm14
B6 M	B6 LPS M	41[d]	6	7	7
bm14 M	bm14 LPS M	3	2	3	0
bm14 M	bm14 DC M	36	5	30	0

[a] 10^7 spleen cells from Moloney virus–primed (M) mice.

[b] 10^6 Moloney virus–infected lipopolysaccharide (LPS) stimulated–spleen cells (LPS M), or 10^5 Moloney virus–infected DC (DC M), irradiated with 25 Gy.

[c] 5×10^3 Moloney virus–infected (M) or uninfected LPS blasts.

[d] Mean percentage–specific ^{51}Cr release of three experiments at an effector-to-target ratio of 32.

REFERENCES

1. DE WAAL, L. P. *et al.* 1983. J. Immunol. **130:** 1090.
2. KAST, W. M. *et al.* 1984. J. Exp. Med. **160:** 1752.
3. KAST, W. M. *et al.* 1986. J. Exp. Med. **164:** 723.
4. KAST, W. M. *et al.* 1987. Eur. J. Immunol. **17:**471.
5. STUKART, M. J. *et al.* 1982. J. Immunol. **128:** 1360.
6. BOOG, C. J. P. *et al.* 1985. Nature **318:** 59.
7. NUSSENZWEIG, M. C. *et al.* 1981. J. Exp. Med. **154:** 168.

Suppression of Hapten-Specific Cell-Mediated Lympholysis by Oral Administration of Hapten Is Reversed *in Vitro* by Normal Helper T Cells or Helper Factors[a]

S. C. GAUTAM AND J. R. BATTISTO

Department of Immunology and Cancer
The Research Institute
The Cleveland Clinic Foundation
Cleveland, Ohio 44106

Immunologic tolerance is an induced state of selective inability to respond to a specific antigen, although responses to unrelated antigens remain normal. Whereas antigen given through most parenteral routes usually results in a humoral or cell-mediated immune response, antigen given by the oral route usually induces a state of unresponsiveness or tolerance.[1–3] We have previously reported that intragastric administration of trinitrochlorobenzene (TNCB) prior to sensitization with the hapten epicutaneously abrogated development of systemic contact sensitivity (CS).[4,5] Suppression of CS in hapten-fed mice was attributable to the production of an efferently acting suppressor T cell (T_s eff) and an acceptor T cell (T_{acc}). These two T_s were found to act in tandem to inhibit CS.[4] We have extended the examination of this phenomenon of orally induced tolerance to understand the development of cytotoxic T lymphocytes (CTL) to hapten-modified "self" antigens. Now we report that a profound state of specific immunologic tolerance for the production of CTL may be induced in adult mice by pre-exposing them to the hapten intragastrically. The CTL development in draining popliteal lymph nodes following immunization with hapten-altered syngeneic spleen cells (modified self) was significantly reduced in animals that had been fed TNCB three times at weekly intervals prior to immunization for the CTL (TABLE 1, experiment 1). In addition, splenic cells from hapten-fed mice were found to be incapable of producing CTL *in vitro* when stimulated with hapten-modified, irradiated-syngeneic spleen cells (experiment 2).

In order to determine whether suppression of the CTL response in hapten-fed mice resulted from production of suppressor cells, we adoptively transferred spleen cells from hapten-fed mice into normal recipients just prior to immunizing them for CTL. The injection of spleen cells from hapten-fed mice intravenously or locally at the site of immunization for CTL did not abrogate generation of CTL (experiment 3), indicating that the suppression of CTL response in hapten-fed mice probably is not due to production of suppressor cells. This observation is especially noteworthy, because we have previously shown that the suppression of CS in hapten-fed mice results from production of T_s that are capable of transferring suppression adoptively.[4,5] Likewise, determination of frequencies of hapten-specific precursors of CTL (P-CTL) by limiting-dilution analysis revealed no

[a] This work was supported by NIH Grant AI 20748.

TABLE 1. Intragastric Administration of TNCB Causes Nontransferable Suppression of Hapten-Specific CTL Response[a]

Experiment No.	Fed TNCB Three Times	Injected i.v. with Spleen Cells from TNCB Fed Mice[b]	Injected in Hind Paws with Spleen Cells from TNCB-Fed Mice[c]	Sensitized for TNP-Specific CTL in vivo	in vitro	Percent Lysis of TNP-Coupled Target Cells	Percent Suppression
1.	−	−	−	+	−	24	NA[d]
	+	−	−	+	−	11	54
2.	−	−	−	−	+	23	NA
	+	−	−	−	+	2	91
3.	−	−	−	+	−	37	NA
	+	−	−	+	−	8	78
	−	+	−	+	−	36	3
	−	−	+	+	−	37	0

[a] Groups of mice were fed TNCB, dissolved in olive oil, three times at weekly intervals. Mice were rested for 8 to 10 days after last feeding before sensitizing for TNP-specific CTL or using them as donors of spleen cells for adoptive transfer of suppression.
[b] Seventy million splenic cells from TNCB-fed mice were injected i.v. into normal mice one hour before sensitization for CTL.
[c] Twenty million splenic cells from TNCB-fed mice were injected subcutaneously into hind paws one hour before sensitization for CTL.
[d] Not applicable.

decrease in the frequency of P-CTL in spleens of mice fed TNCB, suggesting that the suppression of CTL response cannot be attributed to a decrease in P-CTL either. Our recent findings indicate that the inhibition of development of CTL in hapten-fed mice may result from abrogation of helper T-cell functions inasmuch as unresponsiveness to CTL production *in vitro* was partially reversed by adding supernatant from cultures of spleen cells of rats stimulated with concanavalin A. Partial reversal of the inability of spleen cells of hapten-fed mice to generate CTL *in vitro* was also achieved by adding Lyt-1$^+$ cells from normal mice to cultures (data not shown). This information reinforces our original belief that the suppression of contact sensitivity and cell-mediated lympholysis by oral administration of hapten is caused by different mechanisms.

ACKNOWLEDGMENT

The authors thank Ms. Robbie Martin for excellent secretarial support.

REFERENCES

1. CHASE, M. W. 1946. Proc. Soc. Exp. Biol. Med. **61:** 257.
2. RICHMAN, L. K., J. M. CHILLER, W. R. BROWN, D. G. HANSON & M. VAZ. 1978. J. Immunol. **120:** 861.
3. TOMASI, T. B., JR. 1980. Transplantation **29:** 353.
4. GAUTAM, S. C. & J. R. BATTISTO. 1985. J. Immunol. **135:** 2975.
5. GAUTAM, S. C. & J. R. BATTISTO. 1983. Cell. Immunol. **78:** 295.

Prevention of Cytotoxic T Lymphocyte Generation by an Induced Suppressor T Cell That Cooperates with I-A⁻ Macrophages[a]

KAI-PING N. CHOW AND JACK R. BATTISTO

Department of Biology
Case Western Reserve
and
Department of Immunology and Cancer
The Research Institute
Cleveland Clinic Foundation
Cleveland, Ohio 44106

Work from this laboratory has established that hapten-specific cytotoxic T lymphocytes (CTL) can be generated *in vivo* toward hapten-conjugated syngeneic splenic cells provided that a concomitant stimulus is given to the host animal's helper T cells.[1-3] The stimulus is an Mls-disparate antigen on CBA/J splenic cells that are otherwise H-2–compatible with C3H/HeN hosts. Furthermore, inducing tolerance to the Mls^d antigen in host mice (Mls^c) prior to immunizing the latter for hapten-specific CTL abrogated the response.[1,2]

In newer experiments the tolerizing antigen was shown to induce a suppressor T cell (T_s) that appeared in the spleens within seven days. The T_s proved to be cyclophosphamide-insensitive and was readily transferable to naive hosts where it functioned to prevent CTL development.[4]

More recent work has identified the T_s as bearing Lyt-1.1. In addition, it appears among peritoneal exudate cells (PEC) as well as in spleens. In experiments intended to detect it *in vitro*, we have added T cells and macrophages separated from PEC of normal and tolerized mice in various combinations or alone to cultures of cells capable of developing CTL. PEC were derived from normal and tolerized mice 24 hours after an intraperitoneal injection of Mls^d-bearing inactivated splenic cells. This was intended to evoke peritoneal exudates as well as trigger T_s. To develop CTL, cultures consisted of splenic T cells as responders and heat-treated trinitrophenylated (TNP) syngeneic thymocytes as stimulators plus exogenously produced helper factors. After five days, the cultures were assayed for TNP–H-2^k–specific CTL at an effector-to-target ratio of 40:1. We have observed that when T cells and macrophages from tolerized mice were present together in culture there was marked suppression of CTL generation (TABLE 1, line 6). By contrast, T cells and macrophages derived from PEC of tolerized mice, when present separately in culture, had no suppressive effect. In like manner, the T cells and macrophages from PEC of normal mice were not suppressive regardless of whether they were put separately or together into cultures (TABLE 1, lines 1–3). Additionally, the macrophages of normal mice were

[a] This work was supported by Grants AI 18305 and AI 17657 from the National Institutes of Health.

found to prevent CTL development *in vitro* in conjunction with T_s from PEC or spleens of tolerized mice (data not shown). Finally, the macrophages that were found to be functional in this regard were those that lack I-A surface markers (data not given).

Thus, CTL can be nonspecifically prevented from developing in culture when an Mls^d-induced T_s is made to interact with $I-A^-$ macrophages. These data, in conjunction with additional information, suggest that generation of CTL toward altered self antigens can be down-regulated at the level of helper signals.

TABLE 1. T Cells and Macrophages from Peritonea of Mls^d-Tolerized Mice Synergize to Inhibit the Generation of CTL *in Vivo*

Types and Sources of Cells Added to *in vitro* Cultures[a]		Percent TNP–H-2^k–Specific Lysis (±SD) (40:1)
T^b	Macrophage $(M\emptyset)^c$	
Normal	0	18 (0.6)
0	Normal	16 (2.1)
Normal	Normal	24 (1.5)
Tolerant	0	23 (1.4)
0	Tolerant	16 (1.4)
Tolerant	Tolerant	8 (1.5)

[a] *In vitro* cultures containing responders (C3H/HeN splenic T cells (5×10^6 cells/well)), and stimulators (heat-treated TNP coupled–syngeneic thymocytes (5×10^6 cells/well)), and exogenously produced helper factor (HF; Con A supernatant (with 10 U of IL-2 activity)). The positive control (with HF) was 17% (0.7). The negative control (without HF) was 0% (0.6).

[b] Enriched PEC-T (5×10^5 cells/well) were obtained from the petri-dish nonadherent population followed by treatment with anti-Mac-1 + C'.

[c] PEC-M$\emptyset$ (3.8×10^5 cells/well) were enriched by treating PEC with anti-Thy-1.2 + C'.

ACKNOWLEDGMENT

The authors thank Ms. Robbie Martin for excellent secretarial support.

REFERENCES

1. BUTLER, L. D. & J. R. BATTISTO. 1979. *In vivo* generation of hapten-specific killer T cells without elimination of suppressor cells. J. Immunol. **122:** 1578.

2. BATTISTO, J. R., L. D. BUTTLER & H. L. WONG. 1980. Use of hapten-altered self-moieties to probe the cell mediated lympholytic response and immuno-tolerance interface. Immunol. Rev. **50:** 47.

3. GAUTAM, S. C., M. L. HILFIKER & J. R. BATTISTO. 1983. *In vivo* development of cytolytic T lymphocytes to hapten-altered self: Mls-disparate cells facilitate the response by neutralizing IL-2 inhibitor. J. Immunol. **130:** 533.

4. VARGO, P. M. & J. R. BATTISTO. 1984. Tolerance to Mls-disparate cells induces suppressor T cells that act at the helper level to prevent *in vivo* generation of cytolytic lymphocytes to hapten-altered self. J. Immunol. **132:** 2796.

A Novel Form of T-T Collaboration Requiring the Active Participation of the Antigen-Presenting Cell

RONALD G. GILL AND KEVIN J. LAFFERTY

Barbara Davis Center for Childhood Diabetes
University of Colorado Health Sciences Center
Denver, Colorado 80262

We recently developed a simple mathematical model describing antigen-triggered lymphokine release from activated T cells (T').[1] This analysis can be used to determine the antigenic requirements for the triggering of T' cells by plotting lymphokine release ($\log_{10}$ lymphokine titer) as a function of target-cell number under assay conditions of T' excess. The slope of this plot, n_A, defines the intrinsic number of target cells, A, required to trigger lymphokine release from a single T'. That is, n_A is the order of reaction for a given T'-A interaction.[1] In this report, we describe a case where class I major histocompatability complex (MHC)-reactive T cells (class I T cells) can modulate the nature of lymphokine release from class II MHC-reactive T cells (class II T cells) as detected by an alteration in the value of n_A.

When T cells are activated against either class I (C57BL/6 anti-bm1) or class II (C57BL/6 anti-bm12) antigens, independently, the ensuing T' exhibit second-order kinetics when triggered for lymphokine release by their priming antigen; that is, n_A approximates a value of two for each case (FIG. 1A). When T cells are activated against a mixture of class I and class II MHC-disparate stimulator cells, C57BL/6 anti-[bm1 + bm12], the lymphokine-triggering requirements remain unchanged; that is, n_A has a value of two in response to either class I- or class II-bearing target cells (FIG. 1B). When these same T cells, however, are activated against stimulators bearing both class I and class II alloantigens, C57BL/6 anti-(bm1 × bm12)F1, a modulation event occurs whereby the lymphokine-triggering requirements of the ensuing T' are altered. Specifically, the class II-reactive component of the T' triggering response to antigen is altered from a second-order reaction, n_A of 2, to a first-order reaction, n_A of 1 (FIG. 2A). Further, this modulation event requires a metabolically active antigen-presenting cell (APC) population; when the stimulating population is ultraviolet (UV)-irradiated and cultures are supplemented with factors from Con A–stimulated spleen-cell supernatants, the resulting class II T' is not modulated (FIG. 2B); that is, n_A has a value of two. The addition of exogenous factors has no effect on the modulation event observed in response to gamma-irradiated F1 stimulator cells (data not shown).

Taken together, these results show that the effector function of class II T cells can be qualitatively changed by a simultaneous response to class I alloantigens during primary activation. Two significant requirements for this modulation event are linked recognition/presentation of class I and class II alloantigens (that is, class I and class II alloantigens must be presented on the same APC during activation); and active participation of the APC in this process (metabolic inactivation of the APC abrogates the modulation of the class II T cell). These results suggest a novel form of T-T collaboration that involves the active participation of

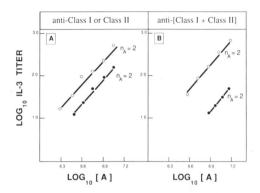

FIGURE 1. Dose response of C57BL/6 T'. Panel **A**: C57BL/6 (B6) lymph node cells were activated against either B6.C-H-2^bm1 (bm1) or B6.C-H-2^bm12 (bm12) gamma-irradiated spleen cells. After 4 days of primary culture, activated cells were clonally expanded by growth in medium supplemented with supernatants from Con A–stimulated spleen cells (CS). After 7 days total culture, cells were harvested and washed, and 2×10^5 T' were triggered for lymphokine release with UV-irradiated spleen-cell targets. B6 T' activated against bm1 stimulators were triggered with bm1 targets, (○-○); B6 T' activated against bm12 stimulators were triggered with bm12 targets, (●-●). There was no cross-reactivity observed between bm1- and bm12-reactive T' (data not shown). Panel **B**: B6 lymph node cells were activated against a mixture of bm1 and bm12 gamma-irradiated spleen cells and propagated as described above. The resulting T' then were triggered for lymphokine release with bm1 (○-○) or bm12 (●-●) targets. Titers of IL-3 activity were calculated as previously described.[1]

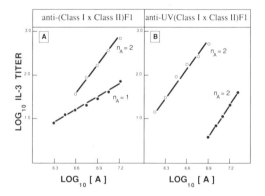

FIGURE 2. Dose response of C57BL/6 T'. Panel **A**: B6 lymph node cells were activated against gamma-irradiated (bm1 × bm12)F1 spleen cells and propagated as described in FIGURE 1. These T' then were triggered for lymphokine release with UV-irradiated bm1 (○-○) or bm12 (●-●) spleen cells. Panel **B**: B6 lymph node cells were activated against UV-irradiated (bm1 × bm12)F1 spleen cells in primary cultures supplemented with CS. (No activation occurred without the addition of exogenous factors.) These activated cells were propagated and triggered for lymphokine release with UV-irradiated bm1 (○-○) or bm12 (●-●) targets. Titers of IL-3 activity were calculated as previously described.[1]

the APC and provides evidence that T cells of one MHC specificity (class I) can influence the effector function of T cells of another MHC specificity (class II). These results are analogous to those reported by McCarthy and Singer[2] who found that the expression of cytotoxic function by class II T cells could be abrogated by a simultaneous response to class I alloantigens during activation. These studies do not represent T cell–helper function in the conventional sense, but rather describe conditions whereby MHC-reactive T cells can influence the qualitative nature of effector function by other MHC-reactive T cells. The mechanism by which class I T cells can alter the effector function of class II T cells remains unclear.

REFERENCES

1. GILL, R. G., S. K. BABCOCK & K. J. LAFFERTY. 1987. A quantitative analysis of antigen-triggered lymphokine production by activated T cells. J. Immunol. **138:** 1130.
2. McCARTHY, S. A. & A. SINGER. 1986. Recognition of MHC class I allodeterminants regulates the generation of MHC class II-specific CTL. J. Immunol. **137:** 3087.

Cleavage of the Influenza H3 Virus Hemagglutinin Does Not Alter Polyclonal Cytotoxic T Lymphocyte Recognition[a]

VIRGINIA S. HINSHAW, HANA VAN CAMPEN,
AND G. G. BROWNLEE[b]

School of Veterinary Medicine
University of Wisconsin
Madison, Wisconsin 53706
and
University of Oxford
Oxford, England

Cytotoxic T cell response to influenza A viruses is highly cross-reactive and primarily involves recognition of the nucleoprotein.[1] Specific recognition of the influenza virus hemagglutinin (HA) of the H1[2] and H2[3] subtypes, however, have been demonstrated with vaccinia-recombinant viruses. Our studies were concerned with examining the CTL response to the influenza virus HA of the H3 subtype and evaluating cleavage of the viral HA as a factor in recognition.

To determine whether the HA could be effectively cleaved on target cells, infected target cells were cultured for 4 or 16 hours in media containing 1 μg of trypsin/ml prior to their use in a 4 hour cytotoxicity assay. In addition, target cells were labeled with [^{35}S]methionine for 16 hours after infection; the HA was immunoprecipitated from the cell extract with monoclonal antibodies to the H3 HA (from R. G. Webster), followed by electrophoresis on a 10% SDS polyacrylamide gel and autoradiography.[4] As shown in FIGURE 1, the HA of X-31 and H3-Vac were uncleaved in the P815 target cells, whereas the treatment with trypsin effectively cleaved the viral HA into HA1 and HA2. The anti-nucleoprotein and anti-H5, an unrelated viral HA, were included as controls. Thus, the *in vitro* cleavage of the HA was effectively accomplished in these targets, so the next step was to determine whether cleavage of the HA altered CTL recognition.

To accomplish this, mice were inoculated intraperitoneally with X-31, an H3N2 influenza virus, H3-Vac (expressing the full-length HA of the H3 subtype from A/NT/60/68 virus), or H2-Vac (expressing the H2 HA of A/Jap/305/57 from B. Moss). After three weeks, splenocytes were cultured *in vitro* with gamma-irradiated, virus-infected syngeneic splenocytes. After five days, cytotoxicity was measured in a ^{51}Cr-release assay with virus-infected P815 mastocytoma cells. Percent specific release was calculated as [(experimental release − spontaneous release)/(total release − spontaneous release)] × 100. As shown in TABLE 1, the CTL from mice primed with X-31 were highly cross-reactive with equivalent cytotoxicity for Jap 305 (H2N2), and these cells did not lyse the H3-Vac recombinant virus. In addition, mice primed with H3-Vac demonstrated no recognition of X-31 and displayed equivalent recognition of targets infected with the H3-Vac and Vac. These results suggested that H3 HA-specific CTL recognition was not in-

[a] This work was supported by Grant MV295 from the American Cancer Society.

TABLE 1. Polyclonal CTL Recognition of Cleaved versus Uncleaved H2 and H3 Hemagglutinins on Infected Target Cells

Effectors (in vivo primary, in vitro secondary)	Percent Specific ⁵¹Cr-Release from Virus-Infected Target Cells							
	X-31		Jap 305		B/DB		H3-Vac	
	20:1	10:1	20:1	10:1	20:1	10:1	20:1	10:1
X-31 (H3), X-31 (H3)	35 (47)[a]	29 (30)	43 (36)	37 (23)	13 (0)	12 (0)	6 (0)	0 (0)
Vac-H3 (H3), X-31 (H3)	3 (0)	0 (0)	NT[b]	NT	10 (2)	4 (0)	27 (20)	31 (15)
Vac-H3 (H3), Vac H3 (H3)	12 (13)	9 (9)	19 (23)	13 (13)	14 (13)	9 (9)	30 (26)	15 (10)
Vac-H2 (H2), Jap 305 (H2)	6 (4)	0 (0)	46 (46)	26 (26)	10 (7)	6 (0)	NT	

[a] Number in parentheses = percent release from targets incubated with trypsin.
[b] NT = not tested.

duced. It was considered possible that lack of CTL recognition might be related to cleavage of the viral HA because viral replication in the host presumably exposes the immune system to cleaved, as well as uncleaved, HA. As a result, cytotoxicity assays were done with trypsin-treated targets.

As shown in TABLE 1, there was no difference in recognition of H3 when the HA was cleaved on the target cells. This suggests that cleavage of the H3 HA is not responsible for the lack of HA-specific cytotoxicity of the CTL from mice primed with H3. In the case of H2 HA, however, there is a more specific response, indicating that the HA is recognized. In this case as well, the presence of

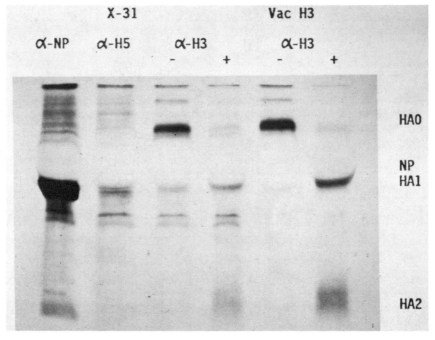

FIGURE 1. Radioimmunoprecipitation of the H3 hemagglutinin in X-31– and H3-Vac– infected P815 cells in the presence (+) or absence (−) of trypsin.

trypsin did not alter the cytotoxicity, suggesting that cleavage of the HA is not a factor in CTL recognition.

The above studies indicate that cleavage of viral HA is not a factor in CTL recognition. In addition, CTL response to the H3 HA was poor, in contrast to the H2 HA. The reason for this difference is not yet known.

REFERENCES

1. TOWNSEND, A. R. M. *et al.* 1985. Cell **42:** 457–467.
2. BRACIALE, T. J. *et al.* 1986. J. Immunol. **137:** 995–1002.
3. BENNINK, J. *et al.* 1986. J. Virol. **57:** 786–791.
4. BROWN, L. *et al.* 1983. Virology **130:** 134–143.

Intercellular Adhesion Molecule-1 (ICAM-1) Monoclonal Antibody Inhibits Cytotoxic T Lymphocyte Recognition

M. W. MAKGOBA, M. E. SANDERS,

G. E. GINTHER LUCE, E. A. GUGEL, M. L. DUSTIN,[a]

T. A. SPRINGER,[a] AND S. SHAW

National Cancer Institute
National Institutes of Health
Bethesda, Maryland 20892
and
[a]Dana Farber Cancer Institute
Boston, Massachusetts 02115

Recent studies have shown that cytotoxic T lymphocytes form conjugates with antigen-negative targets.[1] These studies have further demonstrated that this process of antigen-independent conjugate formation (AIC) is mediated by way of two adhesion pathways: one involving the T cell–CD2 receptor binding to the ligand LFA-3[2] on the target, and the other involving the T cell–LFA-1 receptor interacting with ICAM-1 and probably other ligands[3] on the target. While the roles of CD2, LFA-1, and LFA-3 in CTL-mediated lysis (CML) have been demonstrated abundantly,[4] very little is known about the role of ICAM-1 in such lysis. ICAM-1 was initially proposed as a ligand for LFA-1, based upon monoclonal antibody (mAb) inhibition of LFA-1–dependent T-cell adhesion to fibroblasts and the finding that inhibition occurred with pretreatment of the fibroblasts and not the T cell.[5,6] These findings have been extended to and confirmed in AIC using CTL clones.[3]

We initially investigated the role of ICAM-1 by mAb-inhibition studies of AIC formation, and showed that its utilization in LFA-1–dependent conjugates varied significantly between targets,[3] irrespective of the ICAM-1 level expressed on the target. To analyze its role in CML, targets that predominantly used ICAM-1 in AIC were selected. One such target is U937 (a promonocytic line).[3] The ability of the ICAM-1 mAb to inhibit antigen-independent, phorbol myristic acetate (PMA)/ionophore–triggered lysis of U937 by a CTL clone was studied. The results in FIGURE 1A showed that ICAM-1 mAb inhibits lysis by 70%; lysis is also inhibited well by the LFA-1 mAb (80%), and to a limited extent by CD2 (27%) and LFA-3 (38%) mAb. Following this result, a bulk population of allospecific T cells were prepared by two cycles of *in vitro* stimulation of peripheral blood mononuclear leukocytes with irradiated U937 as stimulator cells. The bulk population was tested in a standard CML assay. The result in FIGURE 1B showed 75% inhibition by the ICAM-1 mAb, compared with 95%, 20%, and 15% inhibition by LFA-1, CD2, and LFA-3 mAb, respectively. These results showed that ICAM-1 is critical for antigen-specific CTL recognition in this effector/target combination. Studies with various effector/target combinations revealed differing utilization and requirements for ICAM-1 in CTL recognition.[3] The results are consistent with the interpretation that ICAM-1 can serve as one ligand for LFA-1 in CTL recognition. The role of ICAM-1 in CTL recognition correlates closely with its ability to inhibit

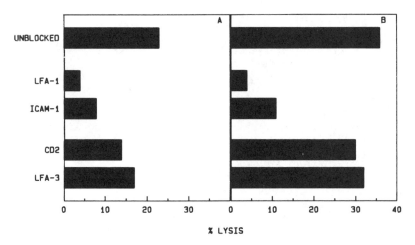

FIGURE 1. Monoclonal antibody inhibition of CML. Effector/target combinations tested include a DPw2-specific CTL clone 8.2, rendered antigen-nonspecific by PMA/ionophore, tested on U937 (**A**), and an allospecific bulk T-cell population sensitized against and tested on U937 (**B**). Both were tested at 10 : 1 E : T ratio in a 4 hr ^{51}Cr-release assay in the continuous presence of the indicated mAb.

AIC formation. The variable utilization of ICAM-1 in LFA-1–dependent interactions in both AIC and cell-mediated lysis strongly indicates the existence of alternative ligands for LFA-1. This variable requirement may explain why the ICAM-1 mAb would not be identified by screening for inhibition of CML in many effector/target combinations.

REFERENCES

1. SHAW, S., G. E. G. LUCE, R. QUINONES, R. E. GRESS, T. A. SPRINGER & M. E. SANDERS. 1986. Two antigen-independent adhsion pathways used by human cytotoxic T cell clones. Nature **323:** 262.
2. SELVARAJ, P., M. L. PLUNKETT, M. DUSTIN, M. E. SANDERS, S. SHAW & T. A. SPRINGER. 1987. The lymphocyte glycoprotein CD2 (LFA-2/T11/E-rosette receptor) binds to the cell surface ligand LFA-3. Nature **326:** 400.
3. MAKGOBA, M. W., M. E. SANDERS, G. E. G. LUCE, E. A. GUGEL, M. L. DUSTIN, T. A. SPRINGER & S. SHAW. 1988. Functional evidence that intercellular adhesion molecule-1 (ICAM-1) is a ligand for LFA-1 in cytotoxic T cell recognition. Eur J. Immunol. **18:** 637–640.
4. SANCHEZ-MADRID, F., A. M. KRENSKY, C. F. WARE, E. ROBBINS, J. L. STROMINGER, S. J. BURAKOFF & T. A. SPRINGER. 1982. Three distinct antigens associated with human T-lymphocyte-mediated cytolysis: LFA-1, LFA-2, LFA-3. Proc. Natl. Acad. Sci. USA **79:** 7489.
5. ROTHLEIN, R., M. L. DUSTIN, S. D. MARLIN & T. A. SPRINGER. 1986. A human intercellular adhesion molecule (ICAM-1) distinct from LFA-1. J. Immunol. **137:** 1270.
6. DUSTIN, M. L., R. ROTHLEIN, A. K. BHAN, C. A. DINARELLO & T. A. SPRINGER. 1986. Induction by IL 1 and interferon-gamma: Tissue distribution, biochemistry, and function of a natural adherence molecule (ICAM-I). J. Immunol. **137:** 245.

Recognition of Viral Antigens by Cytotoxic T Lymphocytes

G. M. VAN BLEEK, M. DE HULLU, J. SANDERS,
D. HOEKSTRA,[a] J. CALAFAT,[b] AND C. J. LUCAS

Central Laboratory of the Netherlands Red Cross Blood
Transfusion Service and
Laboratory for Experimental and Clinical Immunology
University of Amsterdam
Amsterdam, the Netherlands

[a] *Laboratory of Physiological Chemistry*
University of Groningen
Groningen, the Netherlands

[b] *Laboratory of Electron Microscopy*
Antoni van Leeuwenhoek Hospital
Amsterdam, the Netherlands

Cytotoxic T cells (CTL) are capable of eliminating virus-infected cells from the body. A prerequisite for recognition and subsequent elimination of virus-infected cells is the presentation of virus-derived antigens in the context of components of the major histocompatibility complex (MHC).[1] About the nature of this nominal antigen, very little is known yet. In the case of myxoviruses, membrane glycoproteins become expressed on the surface membrane of the infected cell. It was assumed, therefore, that the viral membrane glycoproteins that are serologically detectable on infected cell membranes could be candidates for recognition by CTL. It had to be supposed that they have sufficient lateral mobility to reach and interact with MHC molecules. Sendai virus is a member of the Paramyxoviridae, which injects its nucleocapsid into the cell cytoplasm after fusion of the viral envelope with the cellular plasma membrane. After fusion of the virus with cell membranes, virus-envelope components are diluted within 20 min in the cell membrane and are thus present for early recognition events. CTL recognition and lysis of target cells coated with Sendai virus occur within 30 min after virus treatment.[2] Combining these observations, it seemed reasonable to investigate the contribution of glycoprotein antigens in CTL recognition. We used reconstituted Sendai-virus envelopes (RSVE), containing the membrane glycoproteins hemagglutinin/neuraminidase (HN), and fusion protein F to make target cells for CTL. The capacity of these RSVE to bind and fuse with murine cells was determined. Binding and fusion studies were done with Sendai virus and RSVE, which were labeled with a fluorescent probe: octadecyl rhodamine B chloride, R18, in concentrations causing self-quenching. Relief of self-quenching occurs after fusion, when the viral envelope dilutes into the target-cell membrane. RSVE show a fusion and binding pattern similar to that of intact Sendai virus. From studies with trypsin (T) (T splices the F1 part from F protein) and dithiothreitol (DTT) (DTT reduces a disulfide bridge between F1 and F2 and, in higher concentrations, affects HN also), it can be concluded that RSVE-cell fusion is mediated exclusively by an intact F protein. By means of RSVE fusion, identical numbers of viral glycopro-

teins can be inserted into plasma-cell membranes. From immunoelectron microscopy experiments employing an anti-HN monoclonal antibody as well as a polyclonal anti-Sendai serum, it could be concluded that viral glycoproteins are
present in the plasma membrane in an outward projecting orientation. These
experiments also suggest that equal amounts of virus material are present in the
cell membranes after treatment with either Sendai virus or RSVE. Flow microfluorometry experiments were performed with cells treated with R18-labeled virus
and R18-labeled RSVE. Experiments performed with DTT-treated viral particles
that were fusion-inactive show that binding occurs with every cell in the population. With fusion-active viral particles, it was shown that like binding, fusion
occurs also with every cell in the population (Van Bleek *et al.*, submitted).

Subsequently, recognition of these well-characterized cell populations by CTL
was tested. Target cells treated with RSVE are recognized by anti-Sendai virus
CTL in an H2-restricted manner (TABLE 1). Lysis of the target cells treated with
RSVE is substantially lower as compared to the cells treated with the intact
Sendai virus, which suggests that the HN and/or F-specific reactivity is a minor
component of the total anti-Sendai CTL response. A number of different mouse

TABLE 1. Percent Lysis of Target Cells after Insertion of Sendai-Virus
Glycoproteins[a]

	Target Cells					
	C57BL/6 Sendai	C57BL/6[b] —	C57BL/6[c] RSVE	DBA/2J Sendai	DBA/2J —	DBA/2J RSVE
Effector cells						
C57BL/6	54.1	3.5	18.6	10.6	11.4	8.8
DBA/2J	3.4	5.6	5.6	58.3	6.2	20.5

[a] Effector cells: C57BL/6 and DBA/2J sensitive to Sendai; E : T ratio 5 : 1.
[b] Noninfected control target cells.
[c] RSVE: 7 μg of viral protein.

strains were tested, none of which showed elevated recognition. Apparently, viral
antigens to be recognized by CTL are not present in sufficient amounts or in
proper association with MHC. Possibly the glycoproteins inserted into the cell
membrane after fusion with RSVE behave differently than do the proteins derived
from intact Sendai virus, either in association with MHC or as a consequence of
minor alterations induced in the reconstitution process. A retarded or decreased
MHC association could be the result of changes in lateral mobility of the glycoproteins after RSVE fusion compared to Sendai-virus fusion. The alternative explanation could be that for Sendai virus, internal proteins would provide antigenic
structures for CTL recognition, as was reported for influenza virus,[3] vesicular
stomatitis virus,[4] and respiratory syncytial virus.[5] These authors used transfection or vaccinia virus to introduce viral material into target cells. These methods
need protein synthesis in order to occur before antigenic protein material has
formed. In the case of Sendai virus, CTL recognition possibly takes place early
after fusion of the virus with the target cells. This argues against the necessity for
the *de novo* protein synthesis. Furthermore, in experiments with emetine, which
precludes protein synthesis, we were not able to block CTL recognition of Sendai
virus–treated target cells. Neither did chloroquine (which inhibits lysosomal ac-

tivity) influence CTL recognition. This indicates that the epitopes to be recognized are formed independently of chloroquine-sensitive processing pathways.

The viral antigens somehow return, perhaps after processing by cytoplasmic enzyme systems, from the cytosol back on the cell surface. Further studies on the recognition of Sendai-virus proteins by cytotoxic T lymphocytes are in progress.

REFERENCES

1. ZINKERNAGEL, R. M. & P. C. DOHERTY. 1974. Restriction of *in vitro* T-cell mediated cytotoxicity in lymphocytic choriomeningitis within a syngeneic or semiallogenic system. Nature (London) **248**: 701–702.
2. SCHRADER, J. W. & G. M. EDELMAN. 1977. Joint recognition by cytotoxic T cells of inactivated Sendai virus and products of the major histocompatibility complex. J. Exp. Med. **145**: 523–539.
3. TOWNSEND, A. R. M., A. J. McMICHAEL, N. P. CARTER, J. A. HUDDLESTON & G. G. BROWNLEE. 1984. Cytotoxic T cell recognition of the influenza nucleoprotein and hemagglutinin expressed in transfected mouse L cells. Cell **39**: 13–25.
4. YEWDELL, J. W., J. R. BENNINK, M. MACKETT, L. LEFRANCOIS, D. S. LYLES & B. MOSS. 1986. Recognition of cloned vesicular stomatitis virus internal and external gene products by cytotoxic T lymphocytes. J. Exp. Med. **163**: 1529–1538.
5. BANGHAM, C. R. M., P. J. M. OPENSHAW, L. A. BALL, A. M. Q. KING, G. W. WERTZ & B. A. ASKONAS. 1986. Human and murine cytotoxic T cells specific to respiratory syncytial virus recognize the viral nucleoprotein (N), but not the major glycoprotein (G), expressed by vaccinia virus recombinants. J. Immunol. **137** (12): 3973–3977.

Induction of c-*ets* and c-*fos* Gene Expression upon Antigenic Stimulation of a Memory-like Cytolytic Hybridoma

Y. KAUFMANN,[a] T. SILVERMAN, B.-Z. LEVI,
AND K. OZATO

[a] Institute of Hematology
Chaim Sheba Medical Center
Tel Hashomer, Israel, 52621
and
Laboratory of Developmental and Molecular Immunity
National Institutes of Health
National Institute of Child Health and Human Development
Bethesda, Maryland, 20892

Upon mitogenic stimulation of normal lymphocytes, a number of proto-oncogenes are induced, suggesting the involvement of their expression in transition of lymphocytes from quiescence to competence. With normal lymphocytes, it is difficult to evaluate the contribution of proto-oncogene expression to differentiation of specific T cells because heterogeneous clones respond to the antigen (Ag), and stimulation leads also to cell proliferation. To overcome these difficulties, we studied proto-oncogene expression in a monoclonal memory-like cytotoxic T lymphocyte (CTL) hybridoma PMM1, whose proliferation is not induced by the stimulant. The PMM1 hybridoma has been derived from BALB/c anti-EL4 (H-2^d anti-H-2^b) CTL,[1] and it can be stimulated by H-2D^b–presenting cells to lyse specific target cells (TC) as well as to secrete interleukin-2 (IL-2).[2] In addition, the hybridoma can be activated with G7 anti-Thy-1 mAb,[3] which similar to Ag, induces IL-2 secretion and specific killing activity in the PMM1 hybridoma while causing a modest reduction in cell proliferation.

We have examined the expression of c-*fos*, c-*ets*-1, c-*ets*-2, and c-*myc* genes in PMM1 cells during induction of cytolytic activity. As shown in FIGURE 1, c-*fos* mRNA was not detected in nonstimulated PMM1 hybridoma. Thirty minutes following activation with irradiated EL-4 (H-2^b) cells, however, high levels of c-*fos* mRNA appeared, peaking at 45 min and subsiding to an undetectable level by 8 hours. Activation of the PMM1 hybridoma by G7 anti-Thy-1 mAb resulted in a similar rapid and transient induction of c-*fos* mRNA. The human c-*ets*-1 probe[4] revealed a weak but distinct band above 28S RNA in the nonstimulated cells, indicating a low constitutive expression of the c-*ets*-1 in the murine hybridoma. After Ag stimulation, an increase in c-*ets*-1 mRNA was observed by 90 minutes. It peaked 5-fold the constitutive level by 4 hr and then declined to the base line level by 8 hours. The c-*ets*-2 mRNA was constitutively expressed at high levels, and activation of the hybridoma with either specific Ag or G7 mAb did not cause major changes in its mRNA levels. The c-*myc* expression was high in the nonstimulated hybridoma. This level remained unchanged during the first 4 hr of stimulation and was reduced by 8–10 hr of activation with the Ag and anti-Thy-1 mAb (FIG. 1).

Were the induced proto-oncogenes, c-*fos* and c-*ets*-1, related to the activation of cytolytic function in the memory-like CTL hybridoma? This question was

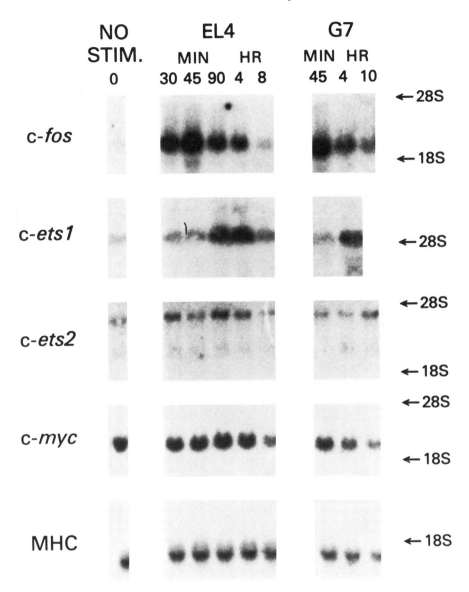

FIGURE 1. Induction of c-*fos* and c-*ets*-1 gene expression during activation of the PPM1 hybridoma with specific Ag or anti-Thy-1 mAb. The hybridomas were stimulated for the indicated times with irradiated EL-4 cells at a 10 : 1 ratio or with G7 mAb.[3] Total RNA (20 μg/ml) was electrophoresed and then transferred on to Nytran paper. Northern blot hybridization was carried out for 18 hr with probes containing 2–20 × 10[6] cpm. cDNA probes of murine c-*fos* and c-*myc* and human c-*ets*-1 and c-*ets*-2[4] were used. (0) Control of nonstimulated hybridomas.

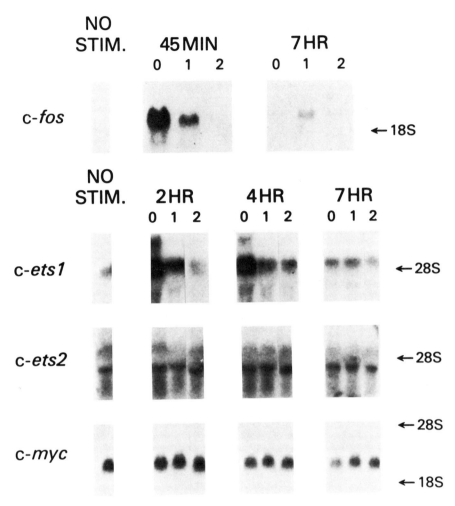

FIGURE 2. The induction of c-*fos* and c-*ets*-1 expression is blocked by inhibitors of CTL activation. PMM1 hybrid cells were preincubated with CsA (100 ng/ml) or anti-LFA1 mAb (1 : 10 dilution of M17.4 hybridoma, culture supernatant) for 30 min at 37°C. Cells were then stimulated with irradiated EL-4 for indicated periods of time. Northern blot hybridization was carried out as in FIGURE 1. No stim., nonstimulated hybridomas; (0), hybridomas stimulated with EL-4 in the absence of inhibitor; (1), stimulation in the presence of CsA; (2), stimulation in the presence of anti-LFA1.

addressed by examining whether the expression of these oncogenes is affected by cyclosporin A (CsA) or anti-LFA1 mAb that block the activation of the hybridoma.[2] CsA blocked induction of c-*fos* and c-*ets*-1 mRNA by more than 70%, and anti-LFA1 mAb completely abrogated their stimulation (FIG. 2). By contrast, the constitutive high expression of c-*myc* and c-*ets*-2 transcripts was not affected at all during the first 4 hr of stimulation. CsA and anti-LFA1, however, blocked down-regulation of c-*myc* that occurred in the hybridomas by 7–8 hr of Ag stimulation (FIGURES 1 and 2), suggesting that the inhibited c-*myc* expression in the stimulated cells was relevant to their activated state.

The finding that c-*fos* and c-*ets*-1 induction can be abolished by the inhibitors of CTL activation suggests that these oncogenes are involved in triggering of CTL differentiation. The c-*fos* gene expression seems to be associated with a very early step in the activation process, probably reflecting a general role for c-*fos* in coupling early events (like Ca^{++} influx) to long-term changes in gene expression. c-*ets*-1 stimulation that peaked by 4 hr postinduction may be associated with maturation of the lytic function that occurs in the hybrid cells subsequent to the triggering event.

REFERENCES

1. KAUFMANN, Y., G. BERKE & Z. ESHHAR. 1981. Proc. Natl. Acad. Sci. USA **73:** 2502.
2. KAUFMANN, Y. *et al.* 1985. *In* Advances in Experimental Biology and Medicine. p. 535. Plenum. New York.
3. GUNTER, K. C., T. K. MALEK & E. M. SHEVACH. 1984. J. Exp. Med. **159:** 716.
4. WATSON, D. K. *et al.* 1985. Proc. Natl. Acad. Sci. USA **82:** 7294.

Spontaneous Rosetting of T Lymphocytes to Reed-Sternberg Cells Is Mediated by the CD2/LFA-3 and LFA-1/ICAM-1 Pathways of Antigen-Independent Adhesion

M. E. SANDERS,[a] M. W. MAKGOBA, E. H. SUSSMAN,
G. E. G. LUCE, T. A. SPRINGER, J. COSSMAN, AND
S. SHAW

National Cancer Institute
National Institutes of Health
Immunology Branch
Bethesda, Maryland 20892
and
The Dana Farber Cancer Institute
Boston, Massachusetts 02115

Reed-Sternberg cells (RS) are a malignant cell type of uncertain origin that are found in diseased lymphoid tissues of patients with Hodgkin's disease. A well-described characteristic of RS is that they spontaneously form rosettes with autologous or allogeneic T lymphocytes without subsequent RS lysis.[1] The mechanism and pathophysiologic significance of this rosetting phenomenon have remained unclear. Recent studies from our laboratories have identified two pathways of antigen-independent adhesion used by T lymphocytes. T-cell CD2 is a receptor for target-cell LFA-3, and T-cell LFA-1 is a receptor for ICAM-1 and probably other ligands.[2,3]

We investigated the possible involvement of these previously described adhesion pathways in the phenomenon of RS/T-cell rosetting using the RS line L428.[4] This line was derived from a pleural effusion from a patient with Hodgkin's disease, and has morphologic and cell-surface marker patterns identical to freshly isolated RS.[5] L428 expresses high amounts of cell-surface LFA-3 and ICAM-1, and does not express CD2 or LFA-1, whereas peripheral blood T lymphocytes express high amounts of LFA-1 and CD2, but express very modest amounts of LFA-3 or ICAM-1. Monoclonal antibody (mAb) blocking studies showed that mAb to either CD2 or LFA-3 profoundly inhibited L428/T-cell rosettes (TABLE 1 and FIG. 1). Monoclonal antibody to LFA-1 inhibited moderately, and the combination of mAb to LFA-1 and LFA-3 completely inhibited rosettes. Monoclonal antibody to HLA class I or CD3 inhibited only marginally.

Conjugate formation of L428 with a T-cell clone that was noncytolytic for L428 showed a similar pattern of mAb blocking. CD2 or LFA-3 mAb blocked conjugates by greater than 50%, whereas mAb to LFA-1 or ICAM-1 blocked to a lesser degree. The combination of mAb to LFA-3 plus LFA-1 completely inhib-

---

[a] Present address: The Upjohn Company, 7214-24-2, Kalamazoo, MI 49001.

TABLE 1. Monoclonal Antibody Inhibition of L428/T-Cell Adhesion[a]

	Percent Inhibition	
Monoclonal Antibody	Rosettes	Conjugates
HLA class I	15	0
CD3	4	3
CD2	85	57
LFA-3	96	77
LFA-1	51	30
LFA-1 + LFA-3	100	100
ICAM-1	ND	10
ICAM-1 + LFA-3	ND	93

[a] Monoclonal-antibody inhibition of T-cell rosettes or conjugates with the RS line L428. Percent inhibition is calculated relative to rosettes or conjugates formed with media alone. ND indicates conditions not done.

ited conjugates, whereas the combination of mAb to LFA-3 plus ICAM-1 inhibited by 93% (TABLE 1). Monoclonal antibody to HLA class I or CD3 did not significantly inhibit conjugates.

These results indicate that RS/T-cell rosetting is a manifestation of exaggerated antigen-independent adhesion mediated predominantly by CD2/LFA-3, and to a lesser extent by LFA-1/ICAM-1 interactions. Such adhesion, in a lesser degree, is characteristic of normal T lymphocytes binding with a variety of targets. The exaggeration of normal antigen-independent adhesion seen in RS/T-cell rosetting may reflect alterations in RS surface–adhesion proteins associated with malignant transformation of RS. Our data indicate that RS/T-cell rosetting is not a manifestation of antigen-specific cell-mediated antitumor immunity, because it is not blocked by CD3 mAb and because it occurs with unprimed allogeneic T cells.

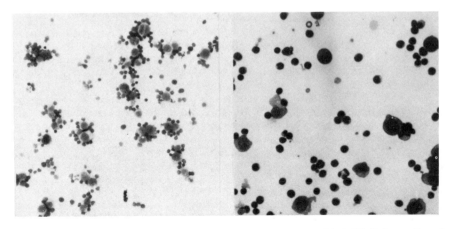

FIGURE 1. Spontaneous rosettes of peripheral blood T cells with L428 (left panel) and partial inhibition of rosettes with anti-LFA-3 (right panel).

REFERENCES

1. STUART, A. E., A. R. W. WILLIAMS & J. A. HABESHAW. 1977. Rosetting and other reactions of the Reed-Sternberg cell. J. Pathol. **122:** 81.
2. SHAW, S., G. E. G. LUCE, R. QUINONES, R. E. GRESS, T. A. SPRINGER & M. E. SANDERS. 1986. Two antigen-independent adhesion pathways used by human cytotoxic T cell clones. Nature **323:** 262.
3. ROTHLEIN, R., M. L. DUSTIN, S. D. MARLIN & T. A. SPRINGER. 1986. A human intercellular adhesion molecule (ICAM-1) distinct from LFA-1. J. Immunol. **137:** 1270.
4. SANDERS, M. E., M. W. MAKGOBA, E. H. SUSSMAN, G. E. G. LUCE, J. COSSMAN & S. SHAW. 1988. Molecular pathways of adhesion in spontaneous rosetting of T lymphocytes to Reed-Sternberg cells. Cancer Res. **48:** 37.
5. SCHAADT, M., V. DIEHL, H. STEIN, C. FONATSCH & H. H. KIRCHNER. 1980. Two neoplastic cell lines with unique features derived from Hodgkin's disease. Int. J. Cancer **26:** 723.

A Comparison of Trypsin-like Protease Activities in Extracts of Human and Murine Cytolytic T Cells

B. M. ASHE, W. E. BIDDISON,[a] J. T. BLAKE, G. NORTON,
M. POE, N. H. SIGAL, AND H. J. ZWEERINK

Merck Sharp and Dohme Research Laboratories
Rahway, New Jersey 07065-0900
and
[a]National Institute of Neurological and
Communicative Disorders and Stroke
Bethesda, Maryland 20205

To investigate whether human cytotoxic T cells contain novel proteases as were recently identified in murine cytotoxic T cells,[1-7] extracts from cloned antigen-specific human and mouse cytotoxic T cell lines were compared for amidase and esterase activities.

TABLE 1 shows that extracts from two human cytotoxic cell lines (8.3[8] and Q31) and a mouse line (AR1[1]) cleave trypsin-specific amidase substrates with arginine preferred in the P1 position. In noncytolytic murine CTLL-1 cells,[9] the chymotrypsin-specific substrate BOC-ala-ala-pro-phe-pNA is cleaved most effectively. Relatively low activity is observed in all extracts against the elastase substrate MeOSucc-ala-ala-pro-val-pNA. The trypsin-specific esterolytic substrates BLT and BAT are cleaved by all cell extracts in preference over the chymotrypsin substrate SPT. Control human leukemia T-cell extract (Jurkat) has negligible trypsin-like esterase activity, whereas it does contain significant trypsin-like amidase activity.

TABLE 2 shows that trypsin-specific inhibitors differ in their ability to block BLT and BAT esterase activities in extracts of mouse and human cells. Activities in both extracts are inhibited to nearly 100% by phenylmethylsulfonyl fluoride (PMSF), and to approximately 50% by antipain and not by $N\alpha$-p-tosyl-L-lysine chloromethyl ketone (TLCK). Inhibition in mouse-cell extracts is very effective with leupeptin and trasylol and effective to 50% with the high-molecular-weight inhibitors soy bean and lima bean trypsin inhibitors (SBTI and LBTI); inhibition in human cell extracts with leupeptin, trasylol, SBTI, and LBTI is insignificant.

These results show that the enzymes responsible for esterase activity in extracts of human cells differ from those in mouse cells. Partial inhibition by compounds, such as antipain, suggests that more than one enzyme is responsible for this activity.

TABLE 1. Amidase and Esterase Activities in T-Cell Lysates[a]

	Activities in				
	Human T Cells			Mouse T Cells	
Substrate	8.3	Q31	Jurkat	CTLL1	AR1
TOS-gly-pro-arg-pNA	210	61	38	101	168
TOS-gly-pro-lys-pNA	49	2	17	44	39
BOC-ala-ala-pro-phe-pNA	58	2	51	137	0
MeOSucc-ala-ala-pro-val-pNA	34	9	15	ND	9
Cbz-Lys-SBzl (BLT)	82	71	1	260	1224
Cbz-Arg-SBzl (BAT)	139	ND[b]	ND	450	720
Succ-phe-leu-phe-SBzl (SPT)	30	32	ND	85	90

[a] Antigen specific human [8.3[8] (anti-DPW2) and Q31 (anti-JY)] and mouse [AR1[1] (anti-H-2[d])] (from Dr. I. Weissman, Stanford University) were grown in the presence of appropriate irradiated stimulator cells and T cell–growth factor (TCGF). After 5 days in culture when *in vitro* cytotoxicity was maximal (70% target-cell lysis at E : T ratio ≤5), cells were harvested and cytoplasmic extracts prepared. CTLL-1 cells[9] were originally tumor-specific cytotoxic-murine cells, but they had lost their cytotoxicity while maintaining the ability to form granules. They were obtained from Dr. J. Young (Rockefeller University) and grown in the presence of TCGF.

Lysates were prepared by adding 0.01 ml of a 10% Triton X-100 solution to 10^7 cells in 1 ml 0.01 M Tris HCl (pH 8.0), followed by the removal of particulate material by centrifugation at 13,000 × g for 10 min.[6] Amidolytic activities were determined using peptido-*p*-nitroaniline substrates,[6] and esterase activities were determined using benzyloxy-L-lysine (or arginine) thiobenzylesters (BLT or BAT).[4] BAT was obtained from Dr. J. Powers (Georgia Institute of Technology).

One amidase unit corresponds to an increase in absorbance at 405 nm of 0.01 units in 20 hr at 37°C using extracts from 10^6 cells. One esterase unit corresponds to an increase in absorbance at 412 nm of 0.01 units per hour at 37°C with extracts from 5×10^4 cells.

[b] Not done.

TABLE 2. Inhibition of Trypsin-Like Esterase Activities in Extracts of Human and Mouse Cytotoxic T Cells[a]

Inhibitor	Inhibitor Specificity	Concentration (μg/ML)	Percent Inhibition	
			Human	Mouse
Leupeptin	Trypsin	50	8	84
Antipain	Trypsin	50	60	50
Trasylol	Trypsin	500	23	91
Soy bean trypsin inhibitor	Trypsin	500	0	52
Lima bean trypsin inhibitor	Trypsin	500	0	38
TLCK	Trypsin	50	6	0
PMSF	Serine and	10	89	74
	thiol proteases	50	94	65
Chymostatin	Chymotrypsin	50	6	0
Pepstatin	Pepsin	50	19	6
Phosphoramidon	Thermolysin	50	6	0
Elastatinal	Elastase	50	20	0

[a] Esterase assays using BLT and BAT were carried out for 1 hr as described previously (TABLE 1) in the presence of inhibitors at the indicated concentrations. Enzyme activities were compared to controls (samples without inhibitor), and percent inhibition was calculated.

Human cells used: 8.3; mouse cells used: CTLL-1 and AR1. Inhibition values obtained with BAT and BLT substrates were very close and therefore were averaged. Inhibition values for both mouse-cell extracts were close, and these values were also averaged.

REFERENCES

1. GERSHENFELD, H. K. & I. L. WEISSMAN. 1986. Science **232:** 854–858.
2. LOBE, C. G., B. B. FINLAY, W. PARENCHYCH, V. H. PAETKAU & R. C. BLEACKLEY. 1986. Science **232:** 858–861.
3. BRUNET, J.-F., M. DOSETTO, F. DENIZOT, M.-G. MATTEI, W. R. CLARK, T. M. HAQQI, P. FERRIER, M. NABHOLZ, A.-M. SCHMITT-VERHULST, M.-F. LUCIANI & P. GOLSTEIN. 1986. Nature **322:** 268–271.
4. PASTERNACK, M. S. & H. N. EISEN. 1985. Nature **314:** 743–745.
5. MASSON, D., M. ZAMAI & J. TSCHOPP. 1986. FEBS Lett. **208:** 84–88.
6. KRAMER, M. D., L. BINNINGER, V. SCHIRRMACHER, H. MOLL, M. PRESTER, G. NERZ & M. M. SIMON. 1986. J. Immunol. **136:** 4644–4651.
7. YOUNG, J.D.-E., L.G. LEONG, C.-C. LIU, A. DAMIANO, D. A. WALL & Z. A. COHN. 1986. Cell **47:** 183–194.
8. BIDDISON, W. E., P. E. RAO, M. A. TALLE, G. GOLDSTEIN & S. SHAW. 1984. J. Exp. Med. **159:** 783–797.
9. GILLIS, S. & K. A. SMITH. 1977. Nature **268:** 154–156.

Lymphokine-Activated Killer Cells (LAK) versus Natural Killer Cells (NK) in Graft-versus-Host Disease (GVHD) versus Control Rats[a]

JOHN CLANCY JR., JOANNA GORAL, JOHN TRINER,
AND TOM ELLIS[b]

Department of Anatomy
[b]Division of Hematology/Oncology
Loyola University Stritch School of Medicine
Maywood, Illinois 60153

GVHD in humans and rodents results in profound alterations in NK activity.[1-5] Early elevation followed by severe depression of NK during the later stages of GVHD have been reported.[3-5] The relationship of early augmented NK with LAK activity as well as the ability of human recombinant interleukin-2 (rIL-2) to reverse the late defect in NK activity have not been examined. A lethal GVHD was induced in unirradiated (DA × LEW) F1 rats with 1.5×10^6 DA lymphoid cells per gram body weight. Controls were injected with the same dose of F1 cells. GVHD animals died 18–22 days (d) after inoculation. At 4, 7, 10, 14, and 18–21 d postinjection, GVHD and control rats were exsanguinated and killed. Plastic nonadherent spleen or lymph node cells were either cultured directly with ^{51}Cr-labeled YAC-1 and DAUDI cells for 4 hr at 50:1 effector:target cell ratio or incubated for 2–9 d with 500 U/10^6 cells of human rIL-2 (Cetus) and then YAC-1 and DAUDI targets for 4 hours. Recombinant IL-2 increased the lytic efficiency of control spleen after 2 d in culture. Increased killing by lymph node cells was not evident until 7 days. Control spleen killed YAC-1 more readily than DAUDI after 2 d (FIG. 1). Whereas control spleen, at a 50:1 effector:target cell ratio, killed YAC-1 at 35 ± 3%, day 4 GVHD spleen caused 51 ± 5% of ^{51}Cr to be released from YAC-1. By day 10, however, only 19 ± 2% ^{51}Cr could be released from YAC-1. Not only control but also GVHD spleen cells did not kill DAUDI very readily (1–9%). This was somewhat unexpected, as it was assumed that during GVHD there would be an elaboration of endogenous IL-2, which could lead to activation of DAUDI killers.

When day 4–10 GVHD spleen cells were cultured with 500 U rIL-2 per 10^6 cells, there was a 3–7 × elevation in 4 hr DAUDI killing and a 1.5–1.8 × elevation in 4 hr YAC-1 killing (TABLE 1). The level of YAC-1 killing, however, was always approximately twice that of DAUDI killing at a 50:1 effector:target cell ratio. Day 14–21 GVHD spleen cells could not be significantly enhanced to become NK or LAK killers.

Morphologic observations indicate that rIL-2 increased the size and Ox-39 (CD25) expression but not the total number of spleen cells from day 4–14 GVHD

---

[a] This work was supported by NIH AI 23718.

TABLE 1. Ability of 500 U rIL Cells to Increase Spleen-Cell YAC-1 or DAUDI Killing after 2 Days *in Vitro* with rIL-2

	Targets	
Animal	DAUDI	YAC-1
Control	22 ± 1^a	61 ± 5^a
GVHD (days)		
4	31 ± 2^a	83 ± 7^a
7	28 ± 3^a	48 ± 4^a
10	15 ± 2^a	28 ± 3^a
14	6 ± 1	22 ± 4
18–21	2 ± 1	10 ± 1

[a] Mean of 4 experiments. Significantly different than control level at $p < 0.05$.

as well as controls. Five hundred units of rIL-2 per 10^6 cells are effective at repairing the NK and LAK deficit during GVHD, but to a different degree. Thus, either NK and LAK are different or they are the same cells with different threshold and kinetic requirements for rIL-2.

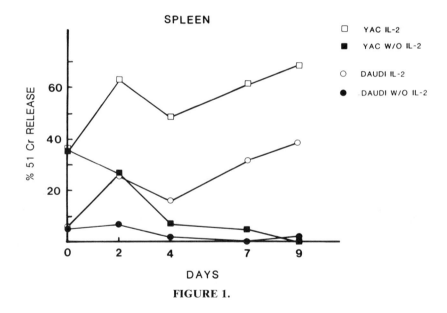

FIGURE 1.

REFERENCES

1. DOKHELAR, M. C., J. WIELS, M. LIPINSKI, C. TETAND, A. DEVERGIE, E. GLUCKMAN & T. TURSZ. 1981. Transplantation **26:** 61–65.
2. GRATAMA, J. W., M. A. LIPOVICH-OOSTERVEER, C. RONTELTAP, L. G. F. SINNIGE, R. J. VAN DER GRIEND & R. L. H. BOLHUIS. 1985. Transplantation **40:** 256–260.
3. ROY, C., T. GHAYUR, P. A. L. KONGSHAVN & W. S. LAPP. 1982. Transplantation **34:** 144–146.
4. GHAYUR, T., T. A. SEEMAYER & W. S. LAPP. 1987. Transplantation **44:** 254–260.
5. CLANCY, J., L. MAUSER & A. L. CHAPMAN. 1983. Cell. Immunol. **79:** 1–10.

T-Cell Activation along an
Alternative Pathway[a]

GIANNI GROMO,[c] LUCA INVERARDI,[c] ROBIN L.
GELLER, WALTER KNAPP,[b] AND FRITZ H. BACH

Immunobiology Research Center
University of Minnesota
Minneapolis, Minnesota 55455
and
[b]Institute of Immunology
A-1090 Vienna, Austria

The activation of cytotoxic T lymphocytes (T_c) involves a series of events, including proliferation and functional maturation.[1-4] In order to understand the relationship of the various signals that effect progress from a resting precursor (pT_c) to an effector cytotoxic T lymphocyte (eT_c), we have developed a series of "minimal signals," each of which stimulates cells to proceed to a further stage. The model system used involves activation along the "alternative pathway"[5] mediated by a pairwise combination of anti-CD2 monoclonal antibodies (mAb) or, as we have recently suggested, calcium ionophore.[6] Here we use the combination of mAb VIT 13 + 9.6[7-9] or the calcium ionophore A23187.

Peripheral blood lymphocytes (PBL), CD4- or CD8-enriched subpopulations (obtained by panning) were incubated for 3–4 days in tissue-culture medium (TCM) ± A23187 or VIT 13 + 9.6. Cells were then sorted for size (blasts versus small lymphocytes) and CD phenotype and returned to culture in TCM, TCM + rIl-2, or rIFN-γ for 2 days. Both [^{3}H]thymidine incorporation and lectin-dependent cytotoxicity (LDCC) were assayed before sorting and after the additional 48 hours of incubation. IL-2 receptor (Tac) was studied by indirect immunofluorescence; IL-2 production was measured by bioassay using CTLL 2.

The results are outlined in TABLE 1. Cells activated with VIT 13 + 9.6 or A23187 incorporate [^{3}H]thymidine, upregulate the IL-2 receptor (IL-2R), but do not produce measurable amounts of IL-2 or become cytolytic. We refer to these cells as pre-effector Tc (peT_c). Upon addition of rIL-2, CD8+ cells continue to proliferate and rapidly become cytolytic. If rIFN-γ is used instead of rIL-2, only the CD8+ cells activated with anti-CD2 mAb develop cytotoxicity. Positively selected CD4+ cells do not develop cytolytic activity when either lymphokine is added to cells previously stimulated for 4 days.

In this stepwise signaling system, we have been able to induce lytic activity in the CD8+ population, whereas the CD4+ cells do not become cytotoxic. Macrophages do not appear to be needed to allow VIT 13 + 9.6 or A23187-treated cells to increase expression of the IL-2R receptor. A model for these findings is pictured in FIGURE 1.

We here show that A23187 or VIT 13 + 9.6 stimulate pT_c to mature to poised T cells (poT_c) in the absence of macrophages, and to peT_c when adherent cells are

[a] This work was supported in part by NIH Grants AI 18326 and AI 19007.
[c] G. Gromo and L. Inverardi and recipients of fellowships from the Istituto San Raffaele, Milano, Italy. This is IRC paper #467.

TABLE 1. Summary of Activation along an Alternative Pathway

	CD8+		CD4+	
	VIT 13 + 9.6	A23187	VIT 13 + 9.6	A23187
[³H]thymidine incorporation	+++	+++	+++	+++
IL-2 production	—	—	—	—
IL-2 receptor expression	++	++	++	++
Macrophage requirement	+++	+++	+++	+++
LDCC	—	—	—	—
LDCC after signal 2: IL-2	+++	+++	—	—
IFN-γ	++	—	—	—
IL-1	—	—	—	—
TCM	—	—	—	—

present. Specific recombinant signals can affect the further progression to the effector stage. The minimal signals required to drive a poT_c to peT_c status are under investigation. The different sensitivity to IFN-γ observed in the two systems of activation tested (A23187 versus VIT 13 + 9.6) can be explained assuming that the cells are driven to a different point along the pathway of functional maturation. In this regard, a further subdivision of the peTc status may be needed. This step-wise model system may prove useful for better understanding the physiological relevance of the alternative pathway.

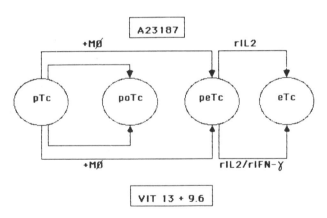

FIGURE 1. Cells stimulated with A23187 or VIT 13 + 9.6. The pT_c (precursor T cell) is a resting nondividing, noncytolytic T lymphocyte with no IL-2R on the surface; the poT_c (poised T cell) is a nondividing, noncytolytic T cell that expresses IL-2R; the peT_c (pre-effector T cell) is an IL-2R positive, dividing, noncytolytic cell; the eT_c (effector T cell) is a fully activated cytolytic cell. MØ represents the presence of macrophages in the culture.

REFERENCES

1. BACH, F. H., M. L. BACH & P. J. SONDEL. 1976. Nature **259**: 273–281.
2. MACDONALD, H. R. & R. K. LEES. 1980. J. Immunol. **124**: 1308–1313.
3. RAULET, O. H. & M. J. BEVAN. 1982. Nature **285**: 754–757.

4. NABHOLZ, M. & H. R. MACDONALD. 1983. Annu. Rev. Immunol. **1:** 273–306.
5. MEUER, C. S. *et al.* 1984. Cell **36:** 897–906.
6. GELLER, R. L., G. GROMO, L. INVERARDI, E. FERRERO & F. H. BACH. 1987. Stepwise activation of T cells: Role of the calcium ionophore A23187. J. Immunol. **139:** 3930–3934.
7. HOLTER, W. *et al.* 1986. J. Exp. Med. **163:** 654–664.
8. MARTIN, P. J. *et al.* 1983. J. Immunol. **131:** 180–185.
9. GROMO, G. *et al.* 1987. Nature. **327:** 424–426.

Cytotoxic Lymphocytes in the Lungs of Patients with Hypersensitivity Pneumonitis

Functional and Molecular Analyses[a]

G. SEMENZATO,[b,c] L. TRENTIN,[c] R. ZAMBELLO,[c]
C. AGOSTINI,[c] G. MARCER,[d] A. CIPRIANI,[e] R. FOA,[f]
AND N. MIGONE[g]

Departments of [c]Clinical Medicine, 1st Medical Clinic;
Clinical Immunology;
[d]Occupational Medicine; and [e]Pneumology
Padua University School of Medicine
Padua, Italy
[f]Department of Biomedical Sciences and Human Oncology
Medical Clinic Section
and
[g]Institute of Medical Genetics and Immunogenetics
Histocompatibility CNR Center
Turin University School of Medicine
Turin, Italy

INTRODUCTION

Although circulating antibodies to the offending antigens and the deposition of soluble immunocomplexes after interaction with inhaled etiological agents have long been demonstrated in patients with hypersensitivity pneumonitis (HP), strong evidence has recently provided for the delayed cell-mediated hypersensitivity mechanisms in disease pathogenesis.[1] Such a cellular response accounts for the infiltration of immunoinflammatory cells (mainly lymphocytes) into the bronchial and alveolar walls, resulting in an alveolitis, which is characterized by the expansion of lymphocytes with surface phenotype (CD2+, CD3+, CD8+, and HNK-1+) and functional *in vitro* properties of cytotoxic cells.[2,3] To better define the cytotoxic events taking place in the lungs of these patients, we studied cells recovered from the bronchoalveolar lavage (BAL) of seven HP patients. The lytic function of BAL lymphocytes was evaluated against natural killer (NK)-sensitive (K-562), NK-insensitive (Daudi) target-cell lines, and against specific antigen (*Micropolyspora faeni*)-sensitized autologous peripheral blood monocytes. To define the clonality of expanded populations, lung T cells from our patients were investigated at the molecular level by evaluating the T cell–receptor γ chain–gene rearrangement.

[a] This work was supported in part by Grant no. 12.01.063 from the University of Padua and by CNR P.F. Oncology (Rome).

[b] Address for correspondence: Istituto di Medicina Clinica, Via Giustiniani 2, 35128 Padova, Italy.

MATERIAL AND METHODS

Patients

Seven symptomatic HP patients were studied. The diagnosis was based on criteria usually reported.[4] All patients were nonsmokers and were studied 1 to 18 months after the last acute episode. They had never received therapy.

Functional in Vitro Assays

Pulmonary cells were recovered from the BAL and handled as previously described in detail.[3,5] Cells under study were tested, in resting conditions and after in vitro boosting (72 hr), with interleukin-2 (IL-2, 100 U/ml), to generate lymphokine activated killer (LAK) cells against the above-quoted targets. In addition, the cytotoxic ability versus the K-562 NK-sensitive cell line was determined a) following inhibition with CD3 and CD2 monoclonal antibodies (mAbs); b) after removal of NK-related cells, using CD16 and HNK-1 mAbs, according to the method already reported;[3] and c) following in vitro stimulation with lectins (3 days with 1 μg phytohemagglutinin (PHA)-M/ml/0.5 $\times$ 10[6] cells) and specific antigen (7 days with 125 μg Micropolyspora faeni/ ml/0.5 $\times$ 10[6] cells). Cytotoxic tests were assessed and the percent specific lysis calculated as previously reported.[3]

Gene Rearrangement Study

DNA extraction, digestion with Eco RI restriction enzymes, and hybridization to the $J_\gamma 1$ DNA probe to assess the configuration of the T cell–rearranging γ gene were performed as reported in detail elsewhere.[6]

RESULTS AND DISCUSSION

In resting conditions, cells obtained from the BAL of our patients were able to kill K-562 targets and, to some extent, the Daudi NK-resistant cell line (TABLE 1). In addition, IL-2–activated BAL cells showed an increased cytotoxic function not only against K-562 but also versus Daudi targets, as a proof of the LAK activity generation. On the other hand, neither resting nor activated HP-lung lymphocytes were capable of providing specific lysis of autologous monocytes previously sensitized with specific antigen (TABLE 1).

TABLE 1. Cytotoxic Function of HP-Bronchoalveolar Lymphocytes Tested in Different Experimental Conditions[a]

In vitro Conditions	Targets Used		
	K-562	Daudi	Autologous Monocytes Previously Sensitized with Micropolyspora faeni
BAL lymphocytes in resting conditions	22.5 ± 3.2	20.3 ± 4.0	0.1 ± 0.1
IL-2–activated BAL lymphocytes	48.1 ± 3.9	56.4 ± 5.3	0.1 ± 0.1

[a] ^{51}Cr-release at the 80:1 E:T ratio.

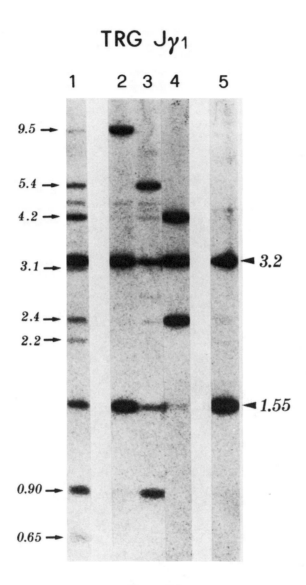

FIGURE 1. Southern blot analysis of one representative DNA sample of BAL lymphocytes, from a patient with hypersensitivity pneumonitis (lane 1), digested with Eco RI and hybridized to the T-rearranging gene (TRG) $J_\gamma 1$ probe. Lanes 2 to 4 are examples of monoclonal leukemic T cells (*i.e.*, showing J_γ rearrangement in one or both TRG-containing chromosomes). Note that multiple rearranged J_γ gene–containing segments are concomitantly shown in the BAL cells (line 1) indicating polyclonality. Lane 5 represents an unrearranged control DNA (fibroblasts).

Blocking experiments with anti-T3 and anti-T11 mAbs almost completely abolished the cytotoxic activity ($0.2\% \pm 0.1$ and $5.2\% \pm 1.2$, respectively). A decrease of cytotoxic function has been observed following removal of HNK-1–and/or CD16-positive cells; however in these experiments, the lytic activity was not completely eliminated (8.3% and 4.4%, respectively). Lymphocytic activation with PHA and *Micropolyspora faeni* determined an increase of the cytotoxic function ($43.8\% \pm 5.1$ versus $18.7\% \pm 2.0$ controls; $p < 0.01$).

The configuration of the T cell–receptor γ chain–gene region is reported in FIGURE 1. Note that multiple rearranged J_γ gene–containing segments are concomitantly shown in the BAL cells, which is indicative of polyclonality.

All these findings support the hypothesis that different types of cytotoxic cells (*i.e.*, NK cells, non-MHC–restricted cytotoxic T lymphocytes, and LAK cells) are present in the HP lung and might represent the response to the stimulus provided by inhaled antigens. Inasmuch as all these cytotoxic mechanisms are demonstrable on cells recovered from the lungs of these patients, it is reasonable to suppose that the etiological agent in this disease induces a polyclonal expansion of T cells. This is in line with the pattern observed with DNA analysis. These mechanisms may be relevant for specifying further the pathogenesis of this disease.

REFERENCES

1. SALVAGGIO, J. E. & R. D. DESHAZO. 1986. Chest **89:** 190S–193S.
2. LEATHERMAN, M. D., A. F. MICHAEL, B. A. SCHWARTZ & J. R. HOIDAL. 1984. Ann. Intern. Med. **100:** 390–392.
3. SEMENZATO, G., C. AGOSTINI, R. ZAMBELLO, L. TRENTIN, M. CHILOSI, G. PIZZOLO, G. MARCER & A. CIPRIANI. 1986. J. Immunol. **137:** 1164–1172.
4. FINK, J. N. 1984. J. Allergy Clin. Immunol. **74:** 1–9.
5. SEMENZATO, G., M. CHILOSI, E. OSSI, L. TRENTIN, G. PIZZOLO, A. CIPRIANI, C. AGOSTINI, R. ZAMBELLO, G. MARCER & G. GASPAROTTO. 1985. Am. Rev. Respir. Dis. **132:** 400–404.
6. FOA, E., G. CASORATI, M. C. GIUBELLINO, G. BASSO, R. SCHIRO, G. PIZZOLO, F. LAURIA, M. P. LEFRANC, T. H. RABBITTS & N. MIGONE. 1987. J. Exp. Med. **165:** 879–890.

Human Cytotoxic T Lymphocyte Responses to Cytomegalovirus and Herpes Simplex Virus[a]

CHARLES R. RINALDO JR., DAVID J. TORPEY III,
MARK D. LINDSLEY, AND QUAN CAI

*School of Medicine and
Department of Infectious Diseases
Graduate School of Public Health
University of Pittsburgh
Pittsburgh, Pennsylvania 15261*

Cytotoxic T lymphocyte (CTL) responses to cytomegalovirus (CMV) and herpes simplex virus type 1 (HSV1) may be significant in host immunity to these opportunistic pathogens. We have examined CTL responses in peripheral blood mononuclear cells from CMV and HSV1 immune, healthy donors after stimulation *in vitro* for 5 d at 37°C with UV-inactivated CMV or HSV1. CTL responses were assayed against CMV- or HSV1-infected autologous and allogeneic donor blood monocytes, which support only the early stages of CMV or HSV1 infection.[1,2] Both viruses predominantly induced CD4[+], HLA class II–restricted CTL that preferentially lysed autologous and HLA DR–matched allogeneic targets infected with the respective virus.[3,4] CD8[+], HLA class I–restricted CTL were also evident in cultures of certain donors. CTL responses were specific for the inducing virus, were not detectable in unstimulated cell cultures, and were not inducible in cells from nonimmune donors. Addition of recombinant interleukin-1 (rIL-1) or rIL-2 during culture enhanced CMV-specific CTL lysis an average of twofold. A significant, threefold increase in CTL response to HSV1 was detectable against HSV1-infected macrophages (derived by *in vitro* culture of monocytes) that support full-cycle HSV1 replication. Our studies indicate that CD4[+] antiviral CTL can be generated in short-term immune recall systems using appropriate HLA class II–expressing cells as targets. We are currently using these models to assay CD4[+] CTL responses in homosexual men infected with human immunodeficiency virus.

[a] This work was supported in part by NIH Grant R01-AI16212.

451

REFERENCES

1. RICE, G. P. A., R. D. SCHRIER & M. B. A. OLDSTONE. 1984. Cytomegalovirus infects human lymphocytes and monocytes: Virus expression is restricted to immediate-early gene products. Proc. Natl. Acad. Sci. USA **81:** 6134.
2. DANIELS, C., E. S. KLEINERMAN & R. SNYDERMAN. 1978. Abortive and productive infections of human mononuclear phagocytes by type 1 herpes simplex virus. Am J. Pathol. **91:** 119.
3. LINDSLEY, M. D., D. J. TORPEY III & C. R. RINALDO JR. 1986. HLA-DR-restricted cytotoxicity of cytomegalovirus-infected monocytes mediated by Leu-3-positive T cells. J. Immunol. **136:** 3045.
4. TORPEY, D. J., III, M. LINDSLEY & C. RINALDO JR. 1988. HLA-restricted cytotoxic T lymphocyte mediated lysis of herpes simplex virus-infected monocytes and macrophages. Submitted.

Cytolytic Lymphocyte Activity in Idiopathic Pulmonary Fibrosis and Sarcoidosis[a]

ALLEN J. NORIN[b] AND JILL KARPEL

*Departments of Medicine, Microbiology and Immunology, and
Surgery
Montefiore Medical Center
The Albert Einstein College of Medicine
Bronx, New York 10467*

Sarcoidosis and idiopathic pulmonary fibrosis (IPF) are interstitial inflammatory lung diseases of unknown etiology. Previous studies have shown alterations in the composition and function of immune cells in the lungs of patients with these disorders.[1,2] To assess the possible role of cytolytic lymphocytes in these diseases, cells were harvested from lung by a bronchoalveolar lavage (BAL) technique. A B-cell depleted and macrophage/monocyte–depleted fraction was obtained from the BAL fluid by the nylon column method and cytolytic-lymphocyte activity determined in a 3 hour concanavalin A–dependent cell mediated–cytotoxicity assay (CDCMC) by ^{51}Cr release from a xenogenic target-cell line (the murine line P815).[3] The lectin-dependent cytotoxicity assay measures the activity of cytolytic T lymphocytes (CTL) and interleukin-2 (IL-2) activated killer cells, but not natural killer cells (NK).[3,4] It is thus useful for detecting cytolytic lymphocytes in patients who have disease induced by unknown antigens. In some cases, NK activity was also determined on the K562 cell line. Activity was also determined on lymphocytes from peripheral blood.

Sarcoidosis patients were characterized by slight decreases in pulmonary function, whereas most IPF patients were characterized by moderate to severe impairment in pulmonary function (TABLE 1). Cell content studies of BAL fluid in the two patient populations revealed abnormal differential and total cell counts as compared to control subjects. Sarcoidosis patients were characterized by an increased percentage of lymphocytes, whereas IPF patients were usually characterized by an increased percentage of polymorphonuclear (PMN) leukocytes, with some patients having increased lymphocytes. Five of fifteen sarcoidosis patients and four of eleven IPF patients had >6% CDCMC in BAL fluid, whereas none of the normal controls had activity (TABLE 1). Although suggestive, these data are not statistically significant with present sample sizes. Most sarcoidosis and IPF patients had significantly greater levels of CDCMC activity in peripheral blood than normal subjects. Interestingly, 13 of 15 sarcoidosis patients had >10% CDCMC compared to 2 of 26 control subjects (Chi square, ≤.005). This latter finding is in contrast to previous reports, suggesting decreased systemic cell-mediated immune reactivity in sarcoidosis.[1,2,5]

[a] This work was supported in part by Grants from the United States Public Health Service (HL17417) and the Easter Seals Foundation.

[b] Present address: Department of Medicine, Pulmonary Division, SUNY Health Science Center, Brooklyn, NY 11203-2098.

453

TABLE 1. Summary of Pulmonary Function and Cell Mediated–Immune Activity in Patients with Sarcoidosis and Idiopathic Pulmonary Fibrosis[a]

Disorder	N	DLCO[b] Predicted Normal	Differential Cell Count in BAL			Cells/ml BAL × 10	Cytotoxicity			
			MØ[c]	Ly[d]	PMN		PBL NK	PBL CDCMC	BAL NK	BAL CDCMC
Sarcoidosis	15	77 (30–80)	36 (12–87)	64 (21–78)	0 (0–14)	2.2 (0.8–7)	61 (0–92)	19 (3–40)	0 (0–20)	4 (0–20)
Idiopathic Pulmonary fibrosis	11	48 (31–80)	57 (14–98)	23 (14–49)	24 (0–72)	11 (0.2–9)	32 (0–90)	9 (0–33)	0[e] (0–33)	0 (0–35)
Normal	4 BAL 28 PBL[f]	ND	80	20	0.04	58 (33–72)	0 (0–13)		0	0

[a] The median (plus the range) are reported for all experimental values.
[b] DLCO = diffusing capacity.
[c] MØ = macrophage.
[d] Ly = lymphocytes.
[e] 5 patients studied.
[f] PBL = peripheral blood leukocytes.

Serial BAL and pulmonary function studies were performed on six patients with IPF following corticosteroid therapy (TABLE 2). Three of the patients had no improvement in pulmonary function following treatment, whereas three other patients had significant improvement. The nonimproved patients had no evidence of cytolytic lymphocytes either before or after treatment. By contrast, the patients with improved pulmonary function had significant levels of CDCMC before treatment and decreased CDCMC after steroid therapy.

In conclusion, evidence of cytolytic T lymphocyte activity (in sarcoidosis and IPF) and evidence of decreased effector-cell activity associated with a positive response to therapy (in IPF) are consistent with a causal relationship between T-cell function and disease pathogenesis.

TABLE 2. Response of Patients with Idiopathic Pulmonary Fibrosis to Corticosteroid Therapy[a]

Patient	DLCO		CDCMC in BAL (%)	
	Before Tx[b]	After Tx	Before Tx	After Tx
• NIR	48	47	0	0
NIE	49	48	0	0
GAR	33	30	4	0
SCH	42	80	35	0
PER	31	60	8	0
ROS	42	70	18	6

[a] Patients were treated with 40 mg prednisone per day for approximately 30 days before the second study. CDCMC of ≤ 4% is below the limit of the detection of this assay and is therefore considered to be 0.
[b] Tx = transplantation.

REFERENCES

1. CRYSTAL, R. G., P. B. BITTERMAN, S. I. RENNARD, A. J. HANCE & B. A. KEOGH. 1984. Interstitial lung disease of unknown cause. I. Disorders characterized by chronic inflammation of the lower respiratory tract. N. Engl. J. Med. 310: 154–166.
2. CRYSTAL, R. G., P. B. BITTERMAN, S. I. RENNARD, A. J. HANCE & B. A. KEOGH. 1984. Interstitial lung disease of unknow cause. II. Disorders characterized by chronic inflammation of the lower respiratory tract. N. Engl. J. Med. 310: 235–244.
3. NORIN, A., J. KARPEL, J. FLEITMAN, S. KAMHOLZ & K. PINSKER. 1986. Concanavalin A dependent cell mediated cytotoxicity in bronchoalveolar lavage fluid of patients with interstitial lung disease: Evidence of cytolytic T lymphocyte activity. Chest 45: 144S–145S.
4. NORIN, A. J., S. L. KAMHOLZ, K. L. PINSKER, E. E. EMESON & F. J. VEITH. 1987. Cyclosporine induced tolerance in experimental organ transplantation: Evidence of diminished donor specific cytotoxicity relative to donor specific proliferative response. J. Immunol. 139: 332–337.
5. JAMES, D. F. G., E. NEVILLE & A. WALKER. 1975. Immunology of sarcoidosis. Am. J. Med. 59: 388–394.

Cytolytic T Lymphocyte Activity and Delayed-Type Hypersensitivity in Rejecting- and Tolerant-Lung Allografts[a]

ALLEN J. NORIN,[b] STEPHAN L. KAMHOLZ,[b]
KENNETH L. PINSKER, AND FRANK J. VEITH

Departments of Microbiology and Immunology,
Surgery, and Medicine
Montefiore Medical Center
Albert Einstein College of Medicine
Bronx, New York 10467

Considerable controversy exists as to the relative importance of various T cell–mediated effector mechanisms in the rejection of organ allografts. Depending on the experimental model, cytolytic T lymphocytes (CTL) or delayed-type hypersensitivity (DTH) reactions have been shown to play the major role in graft destruction. These studies have recently been reviewed.[1] One difficulty in assessing the relative roles of these two mechanisms in the rejection of allografts is that DTH reactions have not been amenable to quantitative *in vitro* analysis as compared to CTL activity. We examined effector mechanisms of allograft destruction in a canine single-lung transplantation model.[2] Intragraft effector cells were obtained from the transplanted lung by bronchoalveolar lavage (BAL). Cells were also studied from BAL fluid of the normal lung and peripheral blood. Intragraft CTL activity was quantified in standard ^{51}Cr-release assays against donor lymphocytes. To measure DTH reactions we used a lectin (concanavalin A, (Con A)–dependent cell mediated–cytotoxicity assay (CDCMC), which is known to detect CTL and interleukin-2 (I1-2)–activated killer cells, IAK (also known as lymphokine-activated killer cells, LAK), but not natural killer cells (NK).[3–5] We hypothesized that IAK cells may be generated in the allograft by stimulation with I1-2 that is released in a DTH reaction.

Serial studies were performed on lung transplant recipients during cyclosporine (Cys)-dose tapering. Most recipients had increased levels of CTL activity in BAL fluid from the transplanted left lung (representative data are shown in TABLE 1), but not the right normal lung (data not shown) when the Cys dose was ≦13 mg/kg/day. Concomitant evidence of rejection is shown by a decrease in blood flow to the allograft relative to the normal lung (TABLE 1). Maximum CDCMC activity preceded maximum donor specific CTL activity. Furthermore, persistence of specific CTL (but not CDCMC) during increased Cys dosage was associated with decreased lung function (recipient #84321). Prolonged high-dose Cys retreatment of recipients, such as #84321, usually resulted in diminished specific CTL activity and improved function. This delayed response to Cys is probably due to the relative ineffectiveness of the drug on mature CTL and its

[a] This work was supported in part by USPHS Grant HL17417 and the James Hilton Manning and Emma Austin Manning Foundation.

[b] Present address: Department of Medicine, Pulmonary Division, SUNY Health Science Center, Brooklyn, NY 11203-2098.

TABLE 1. Cytolytic Lymphocyte Activity and Pulmonary Function in Lung Allografts during Alterations in Cyclosporine Dosage[a]

Recipient	Days after Tx[b]	Cys Dose mg/kg/day	Percent Cytotoxicity CDCMC	DSCMC[c]	%Q_L[d]
#84321	64	17	0	0	40
	139	9	21	4	14
	183	20	5	19	22
	224	17	7	0	42
#4099	61	17	0	0	38
	96	9	11	0	43
	133	5	20	0	19

[a] Cytotoxicity assays of nylon column–purified lymphocytes obtained from bronchoalveolar lavage fluid of the transplanted lung were performed by the 3 hour ^{51}Cr-release method at an effector-to-target-cell ratio of 100:1.
[b] Tx = transplantation.
[c] DSCMC = donor-specific cell-mediated cytotoxicity.
[d] %Q_L = Blood flow to transplanted lung as a function of total blood flow to the transplanted lung plus the normal lung.[2]

inhibition of continued differentiation and proliferation of CTL precursors. In other recipients, decreased lung function with Cys-dose tapering has been associated with increased intragraft CDCMC activity, with no detectable specific CTL activity (as shown in the response of recipient #4099, TABLE 1). These findings suggest a DTH mechanism of rejection without specific CTL-mediated rejection.

In a small percentage of recipients (10–15%), Cys therapy could be terminated without signs of decreased lung function. These recipients had no specific CTL activity and low levels of CDCMC in BAL fluid. Recipient × donor mixed-lymphocyte cultures (MLC) performed before transplantation or in the early period after transplantation (before tolerance induction) showed high levels of donor-specific CTL activity and proliferation. Similar MLC performed after tolerance induction demonstrated greatly reduced or absent specific CTL activity (TABLE 2). By contrast, high levels of proliferative activity were still generated in

TABLE 2. Analysis of MLC and BAL Fluid Cytolytic Lymphocyte Activity of a Tolerant-Lung Allograft Recipient[a]

Source	Day after Tx	[^{3}H]Thymidine cpm/4 × 10^4 Cells	Percent Cytotoxicity Donor Specific	CDCMC
R × D[b]	69	11,191	44	65
MLC		±442		
BAL	69	NA[c]	8	35
R × D	239	13,937	3	41
MLC		±678		
BAL	258	NA	0	0

[a] MLC and cell mediated–immune assays were performed as previously published.[5] Rejection was detected at 69 days after transplantation when the Cys dosage was reduced to 13 mg/kg/day. Following an additional course of Cys therapy (35 days) at 17 mg/kg/day, treatment was terminated.
[b] R × D = recipient × irradiated donor.
[c] NA = not applicable.

the donor-specific MLC during the tolerant period. The proliferation of T cells in bulk MLC is predominantly a response against major histocompatibility complex (MHC)–class II molecules.[6] Such T cells belong to the subset involved in DTH reactions.[1,5] By contrast, specific CTL generated in bulk MLC are primarily directed against MHC–class I molecules.[7] The data are therefore consistent with the hypothesis that Cys induces long-lasting or permanent unresponsiveness to MHC–class I alloantigens while not similarly affecting the response to class II alloantigens.

REFERENCES

1. STEINMULLER, D. 1985. Transplantation **40:** 229–233.
2. NORIN, A. J., S. L. KAMHOLZ, K. L. PINSKER, E. E. EMESON & F. J. VEITH. 1986. Transplantation **42:** 466–472.
3. EMESON, E. E., A. J. NORIN & F. J. VEITH. 1982. Transplantation **33:** 365–369.
4. NORIN, A. J., J. KARPEL, J. FLEITMAN, S. L. KAMHOLZ & K. L. PINSKER. 1986. Chest **45:** 144S–145S.
5. NORIN, A. J., S. L. KAMHOLZ, K. L. PINSKER & F. J. VEITH. 1987. J. Immunol. **139:** 332–337.
6. THORSBY, E., E. BERLE & S. NOUSSAIZEN. 1982. Immunol. Rev. **66:** 39–56.
7. VIDOVIC, D., J. KLEIN & Z. A. NAGY. 1984. J. Immunol. **132:** 1113–1117.

Theileria-Specific Cytotoxic T-Cell Clones

Parasite-Stock Specificity in Relation to Cross-protection

BRUNO M. GODDEERIS AND W. IVAN MORRISON

International Laboratory for Research on Animal Diseases
P.O. Box 30709
Nairobi, Kenya

The protozoan parasite *Theileria parva* infects bovine lymphocytes, which subsequently undergo blast transformation and multiplication. Parasite and host cell divide synchronously, resulting in rapid clonal expansion of the parasitized cells and high levels of parasitosis in the lymphoid tissues. This acute, usually fatal disease of cattle in East and Central Africa is known as East Coast fever (reviewed in reference 1). Cattle immunized, by infection and treatment regimes, with the Marikebuni stock of the parasite are protected against challenge with the homologous stock and the antigenetically different Muguga stock. On the other hand, cattle immunized with, and subsequently immune to, the Muguga stock often remain susceptible to challenge with the Marikebuni stock. During immunization or homologous challenge, genetically restricted cytotoxic cells specific for parasitized target cells are detected transiently in the peripheral blood (reviewed in reference 1). These cytotoxic T cells have been propagated[2] and cloned[3] *in vitro*.

To analyze whether cytotoxic T cells of Muguga- and Marikebuni-immunized animals have different parasite-stock specificities, we derived a series of *T. parva*–specific cytotoxic T cell clones from cattle immunized with either the Muguga or Marikebuni stock of the parasite. The clones had the BoT4$^-$/BoT8$^+$ phenotype, as defined by monoclonal antibodies that recognize bovine analogues of CD4[4] and CD8.[5] The clones killed only parasitized target cells. Two clones, namely T20.40 and T21.7, which originated from a Muguga-immunized animal (class I MHC phenotype KN104/KN18) and a Marikebuni-immunized animal (class I MHC phenotype KN104/w6.2), respectively, were compared. Both clones were restricted by the class I-MHC specificity, KN104: this was based on analysis of cytotoxic activity on panels of parasitized target cells of diverse MHC phenotypes (FIG. 1) and blocking of cytotoxicity with alloantisera and monoclonal antibodies specific for polymorphic determinants on class I-MHC molecules. When analyzed for parasite-stock specificity, killing by T20.40, the clone derived from the Muguga-immunized animal, was restricted to targets infected with the Muguga stock (FIG. 2). By contrast, cytotoxic T cell clone T21.7, derived from the Marikebuni-immunized animal, killed targets infected with the Muguga stock as well as the Marikebuni stock (FIG. 2).

These results are consistent with findings of *in vivo* cross-immunity trials and thus suggest that cytotoxic T cells are important in protective immunity against *Theileria parva*.

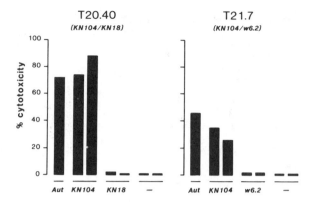

FIGURE 1. Analysis of cytotoxic activity of T-cell clones T20.40 and T21.7. The clones were tested in a 4-hour ^{51}Cr-release assay at an effector to target ratio of 2/1 against one autologous parasitized target, two parasitized targets matched with the effector for one MHC class I specificity, two parasitized targets matched for the other class I–MHC specificity, and two MHC-mismatched parasitized targets.

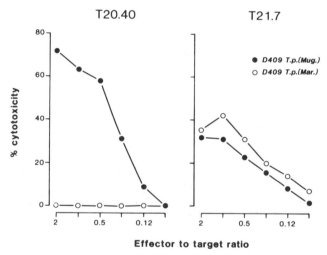

FIGURE 2. Analysis of cytotoxic activity of T-cell clones T20.40 and T21.7 on two cell lines infected with the Muguga and Marikebuni stock, respectively. Both parasitized cell lines were established *in vitro* by infecting lymphocytes of animal D409 (class I-MHC phenotype KN104/w7) with sporozoites of the Muguga stock and Marikebuni stock, respectively.

REFERENCES

1. MORRISON, W. I., P. A. LALOR, B. M. GODDEERIS & A. J. TEALE. 1986. *In* Parasite Antigens: Toward New Strategies for Vaccines. T. W. Pearson Ed.: 167. Dekker. New York.
2. GODDEERIS, B. M., W. I. MORRISON & A. J. TEALE. 1986. Eur. J. Immunol. **16:** 1243.
3. GODDEERIS, B. M., W. I. MORRISON, A. J. TEALE, A. BENSAID & C. L. BALDWIN. 1986. Proc. Natl. Acad. Sci. USA **83:** 5238.
4. BALDWIN, C. L., A. J. TEALE, J. NAESSENS, B. M. GODDEERIS, N. D. MACHUGH & W. I. MORRISON. 1986. J. Immunol. **136:** 4385.
5. ELLIS, J. A., C. L. BALDWIN, N. D. MACHUGH, A. BENSAID, A. J. TEALE, B. M. GODDEERIS & W. I. MORRISON. 1986. Immunology **58:** 351.

Virus-Specific CTL in SLA-Inbred Swine Recovered from Experimental African Swine Fever Virus (ASFV) Infection

C. MARTINS,[a,b] C. MEBUS,[a] T. SCHOLL,[a] M. LAWMAN,[c]
AND J. LUNNEY[d]

[a] Plum Island Animal Disease Center
Agricultural Research Service
United States Department of Agriculture
Greenport, New York 11944

[b] Escola Superior de Medicina Veterinaria
1100 Lisbon, Portugal

[c] Veterinary Infectious Disease Organization
Saskatoon, Saskatchewan, Canada S7N 0W0

[d] Animal Parasitology Institute
Agricultural Research Service
United States Department of Agriculture
Beltsville, Maryland 20705

African swine fever virus (ASFV) is an icosahedral cytoplasmic DNA virus that replicates primarily in the mononuclear phagocyte system of swine.[1,2] Virulent isolates, such as Tengani and Lisbon 60 (L60), are usually fatal, whereas less virulent isolates, such as the Portuguese nonhemabsorbing isolate (NH/P68) or Dominican Republic 2 (DR2), cause a less severe form of the disease. Infected swine, which recover, produce a significant humoral response to the virus, but these antibodies do not possess typical viral-neutralizing effects.[3,4] There is currently no effective vaccine, and slaughter is the control measure normally employed.

This study was aimed at analyzing T-cell responses to ASFV infection, to determine whether viral specific–cytotoxic T lymphocytes (CTL) could be produced and whether the porcine major histocompatibility complex (MHC) antigens, designated the SLA antigens, were restricting elements for ASFV-specific CTL. The latter analyses were facilitated by the availability of SLA inbred–miniature swine, which are homozygous for each of three separate SLA haplotypes: *aa* (SLA[a/a]), *cc*, and *dd*, and of the recombinant haplotype, *gg*, which expresses the SLA[c] alleles for the class I genes and SLA[d] alleles for the class II genes.[5]

RESULTS AND DISCUSSION

Pigs that recover from an ASFV infection clearly have significant levels of viral-specific CTL after *in vitro* restimulation (TABLE 1). In all experiments, viral-infected targets were killed more efficiently than uninfected macrophages. This killing was observed by effectors harvested and assayed directly, or assayed at 2 to 7 days after *in vitro* stimulation, with viral-specific lysis being most prominent at 2 to 4 days (Martins *et al.*, manuscript in preparation). The loss of ASFV-specific lysis after 4 days of *in vitro* secondary stimulation may have occurred due to the development of lymphokine activated–killer cells, inasmuch as high levels of interleukin-2 are produced in these cultures (Scholl *et al.*, manuscript submitted).

Viral specificity of these CTL was investigated using different isolates of ASFV as well as the unrelated hog cholera virus, which also infects pig macrophages. Effectors from swine infected and restimulated with ASFV/NH/P68 isolate preferentially killed macrophages infected with the homologous NH virus or

TABLE 1. Preferential CTL Killing of ASFV-Infected Targets[a]

Effector Cells			Percent Specific Lysis of Target Cells							
			Pig: 1284 *cc*		1769 *gg*		4134 *dd*		1101 *aa*	
			SLA: I^{c}II^c		I^{c}II^d		I^{d}II^d		I^{a}II^a	
Pig #	SLA[b]	E:T Ratio	ASFV[c] +	−	+	−	+	−	+	−
Exp. 1										
870	*cc* (I^{c}II^c)	100	36	0	34	5	7	0	19	5
		50	21	0	29	0	0	0	7	0
1481	*dd* (I^{d}II^d)	100	0	0	18	0	15	0	27	0
101	*aa* (I^{a}II^a)	100	10	0	17	0	6	0	13	0
		50	7	0	8	0	3	0	10	0
Exp. 2										
525.6	*cc* (I^{c}II^c)	50	44	22	49	12	16	0	13	17
		25	39	11	43	7	17	0	9	5
532.4	*dd* (I^{d}II^d)	50	12	0	24	0	24	0	20	0
		25	10	0	13	0	25	0	8	0
101	*aa* (I^{a}II^a)	50	10	1	18	3	17	0	19	0
		25	5	0	11	1	11	0	14	0

[a] CTL effectors are prepared from peripheral blood mononuclear cells (PBMC) isolated from swine that had been infected with the NH isolate of ASFV intranasally/orally 2–12 weeks previously and that were stimulated at 5×10^6 cells/ml with virus (multiplicity of infection, MOI = 0.2) for 3 days. Target macrophages are derived from PBMC of normal swine that had been cultured for 5 days with mouse fibroblast-derived growth factor at $2–5 \times 10^6$ cells/ml (Genovesi *et al.*, manuscript in preparation). Adherent macrophages were collected with EDTA, incubated for 1 hour with or without ASFV (MOI = 10), washed, and incubated for 4–6 hours, to allow the infection to progress before labeling with ^{51}Cr for 1 hour. CTL effectors were harvested, Ficoll-Hypaque purified, and added to round-bottom microtiter wells with 10^4 labeled targets for a 4 hour assay.
[b] SLA = porcine MHC type; *cc* = SLA$^{c/c}$; I^{c}II^c = SLA class I^c class II^c.
[c] Targets were cultured macrophages infected with ASFV (+) or control (uninfected (−)).

the related isolate L60, and exhibited lower reactivity against the less-related isolate Tengani. Macrophages infected with an unrelated virus, hog cholera, showed no specific lysis. Thus, viral-specific cytotoxic T cells are stimulated by ASFV infection.

The role of SLA antigens in restricting these viral-specific CTL is less clear. CTL from swine of different SLA haplotypes were analyzed for their ability to lyse various targets. The data in TABLE 1 show that *cc* effectors preferentially lysed *cc* and the SLA class I–matched *gg*, ASFV-infected targets, although in experiment 2, *cc* effectors also lysed some uninfected, and SLA mismatched, targets. In 13 of 16 assays, *cc* effectors exhibited preferential lysis of SLA class I–

matched targets, whereas *dd* and *aa* effectors exhibited such SLA preference in only 2 out of 7 or 1 out of 8 assays, respectively. All effectors preferentially lyzed infected targets. SLA class I–antigen involvement as a restricting element for the lytic response of *cc* swine was supported by the following: 1) anti-CD 8 (76-2-11), and not anti-CD 4 (74-12-4), pretreatment of the effectors depletes these cytolytic cells; and 2) class I-SLA–specific mAb block the ASFV-specific lysis. Recent data (Gonzalez-Juarrero *et al.*, unpublished data) suggest that virus infection leads to down-regulation of class I expression.

In summary, ASFV specific–swine CTL have been demonstrated, and this is the first observation of viral-specific CTL in this species. Because little or no effective neutralizing antibodies are produced during ASFV infection, the demonstration of these viral-specific CTL opens up new avenues for analyzing ASFV antigens for their T-cell reactivity and their potential as vaccine agents.

REFERENCES

1. BECKER, Y. 1987. African Swine Fever. Martinus Nijhoff Publishing. Boston. MA. p. 157.
2. VINUELA, E. 1985. African swine fever virus. Curr. Top. Microbiol. Immunol. **116:** 151.
3. WARDLEY, R. S., C. ANDRADE, D. BLACK *et al.* 1983. African Swine Fever Virus. Arch. Virology **76:** 73.
4. NORDLEY, S. G. & R. C. WARDLEY. 1983. Effector mechanisms in the pig. Res. Vet. Sci. **35:** 75.
5. LUNNEY, J. K., M. D. PESCOVITZ & D. H. SACHS. 1986. The swine MHC. *In* Swine in Biomedical Research. M. E. Tumbleson, Ed.: **3:** 1127. Plenum Press. New York.

Human T Cells Targeted with Hetero-cross-linked Antibodies Prevent Tumor Growth in Nude Mice

DAVID M. SEGAL, JULIE A. TITUS, TOBY T. HECHT,
MARIA A. GARRIDO, DAVID F. WINKLER, AND
JOHN R. WUNDERLICH

Immunology Branch
National Cancer Institute
National Institutes of Health
Bethesda, Maryland 20892

When human cytotoxic T lymphocytes (CTL) are coated with anti-T3, cross-linked to antitarget cell antibody (anti-T3 × antitarget), they lose their natural specificity and become cytotoxic for cells recognized by the antitarget cell antibody.[1] Fresh human peripheral blood T cells (PBT) will mediate such targeted lysis, and all *in vitro* cytotoxic activity resides in the T8+ subset.[2] These cells, when treated with anti-T3 × antitumor, will specifically lyse, *in vitro*, cultured or fresh tumor cells, but not fresh cells from normal tissue.[3] We have tested targeted PBT for the ability to prevent subcutaneous tumor growth of the LS174T human colon adenocarcinoma line in a Winn-type[4] tumor neutralization assay in nude mice.[5] PBT, coated with anti-T3(Fab) × 315F6(Fab) (315F6 is an antitumor antibody that cross-reacts on LS174T), prevent the growth of LS174T tumors at less than 1 : 1 T cell : tumor cell ratios (Table 1, rows, 4–6). Specificity controls established that an antitumor antibody must be physically linked to anti-T3 in order for tumor neutralization to occur.[5] Although Leu-11+ PBL mediate substantial antibody-independent, NK-like activity against LS174T cells *in vitro*, these cells are ineffective at preventing tumor growth *in vivo* (TABLE 1, rows 1 and 3). Removal of the T8+ subset of cells totally abolishes *in vitro* cytotoxicity, but has little effect on the tumor neutralizing activity of targeted PBT (TABLE 1, rows 4–6 and 8–10). Further studies (TABLE 2) showed that all of the tumor-neutralizing activity resides in cells expressing either T4 or T8 (TABLE 2, rows 9 and 10), with each subset exhibiting some tumor-neutralizing activity (rows 5–8). These studies show that targeted T cells are highly effective in preventing the establishment of at least one type of tumor. The studies also lay the groundwork for experiments involving the elimination of established tumors.

465

TABLE 1. Comparison of *in Vitro* Cytotoxicity with Tumor Neutralization by T-Cell Subsets

Effector Cells	Cross-Linked Antibody[a]	*In Vitro* Antitumor Activity (Lytic Units)[b]	E : T	*In Vivo* Antitumor Activity Tumor-Free/ Live Mice[c]	Tumor Size (mm)
PBL	−	17	7 : 1	0/5	16
PBL	+	33	7 : 1	5/5	—
Leu-11-PBL	−	2	7 : 1	0/5	16
Leu-11-PBL	+	14	7 : 1	5/5	—
			2.3 : 1	5/5	—
			0.8 : 1	2/5	15
Leu-11-T8-PBL	−	<2	7 : 1	0/5	19
Leu-11-T8-PBL	+	<2	7 : 1	5/5	—
			2.3 : 1	4/4	—
			0.8 : 1	0/5	19

[a] Effector cells were incubated with anti-T3(Fab) × 315F6(Fab) and washed.

[b] Lysis was measured in a 4 hr ^{51}Cr-release assay. Lytic units are calculated from the E : T ratio giving 20% lysis. Effector cells are peripheral blood lymphocytes (PBL) depleted of various subsets with either anti-Leu-11b or OKT8 and complement.

[c] LS174T tumor cells (5 × 10^6/mouse) were mixed with effector cells at room temperature and immediately injected subcutaneously into nude mice. Tumor positivity and average tumor diameter in tumor+ mice were assayed 31 days after tumor injection.

TABLE 2. Tumor Neutralization by T-Cell Subsets[a]

Effector Cells	Antibody	Relative Effector Dose	Tumor-Free Mice/ Surviving Mice (day 30)	Average Tumor Diameter (mm)
None	—	—	0/4	17
PBL	—	1	0/5	19
PBL	+	1	5/5	—
PBL	+	1/3	1/5	14
T4-PBL	+	1	3/5	14
T4-PBL	+	1/3	0/4	14
T8-PBL	+	1	5/5	—
T8-PBL	+	1/3	2/5	15
T4-,T8-PBL	+	1	0/5	21
T4-,T8-PBL	+	1/3	0/4	21

[a] Experimental procedure similar to TABLE 1, except that some cells were treated with OKT4 or OKT4 + OKT8 and complement prior to use.

REFERENCES

1. PEREZ, P., R. W. HOFFMAN, S. SHAW, J. A. BLUESTONE & D. M. SEGAL. 1985. Specific targeting of cytotoxic T cells by anti-T3 linked to anti-target cell antibody. Nature **316:** 354.
2. PEREZ, P., R. W. HOFFMAN, J. A. TITUS & D. M. SEGAL. 1986. Specific targeting of human peripheral blood T cells by heteroaggregates containing anti-T3 crosslinked to anti-target cell antibodies. J. Exp. Med. **163:** 166.
3. PEREZ, P., J. A. TITUS, M. T. LOTZE, F. CUTTITTA, D. L. LONGO, E. S. GROVES, H.

RABIN, P. J. DURDA & D. M. SEGAL. 1986. Specific lysis of human tumor cells by T cells coated with anti-T3 cross-linked to anti-tumor antibody. J. Immunol. **137:** 2069.

4. WINN, H. J. 1961. Immune mechanisms in homotransplantation. II. Quantitative assay of the immunologic activity of lymphoid cells stimulated by tumor homografts. J. Immunol. **86:** 228.

5. TITUS, J. A., M. A. GARRIDO, T. T. HECHT, D. F. WINKLER, J. R. WUNDERLICH & D. M. SEGAL. 1987. Human T cells targeted with anti-T3 crosslinked to anti-tumor antibody prevent tumor growth in nude mice. J. Immunol. **138:** 4018.

Activation of Tumor-Specific CTLP to a Cytolytic Stage Requires Additional Signals

PAUL VON HOEGEN AND VOLKER SCHIRRMACHER

Institute for Immunology and Genetics
German Cancer Research Center
D-6900 Heidelberg, Federal Republic of Germany

The aim of our study was the analysis of the activation status of tumor-specific T cells in a postoperative stage. In contrast to unspecific immune stimulation, the activation of specific T-cell reactivity can lead to long-lasting antitumor immunity. The mouse tumor line ESb is a spontaneous, highly metastatic variant of the methylcholanthrene-induced lymphoma Eb.[1] Tumor immunization/protection experiments revealed that the ESb line expresses a tumor-associated transplantation antigen (TATA), which can induce weak protective immunity[2] and which can activate specific cytotoxic T lymphocytes (CTL) following *in vivo* sensitization and *in vitro* restimulation protocols.[3] The strength of the host immune response depends on the site of tumor-cell inoculation. The strongest response was obtained by inoculation in the pinna, where even 5×10^4 living ESb tumor cells can be rejected; whereas in virtually all other sites of the body, progressive tumor growth was observed. Under these optimal priming conditions, the frequency of tumor specific–splenic CTL precursor (CTL-P) was estimated to be 1/15,000 by limiting-dilution analysis. The modification of the tumor cells with the paramyxovirus Newcastle disease virus (NDV) *in vivo* and *in vitro* leads to an increased frequency of tumor-specific CTL-P of 1/6,000. Bulk culture experiments revealed an effect of the ESb-NDV cells during *in vivo* sensitization and *in vitro* restimulation (FIG. 1). Interestingly, under these conditions, virus-specific CTL are not induced, and the effector cells are keeping the high specificity for the tumor antigen. We assume that the viral modification is acting as a second signal in the differentiation of CTL-P to mature active T cells, because additional tumor specific–CTL clones can be driven to a functional state. These CTL can only be activated in immunized animals, indicating that the respective antigen (*i.e.* the tumor antigen) is not able to trigger all antigen-specific CTL-P into a cytolytic-active stage. Nevertheless the *in vivo* preactivated CTL-P need a restimulation *in vitro* with the respective antigen for differentiation into a functional cytotoxic cell. When investigating the immune status in tumor-bearing animals, we found that the CTL-P could not be restimulated by the tumor antigen alone. When we tried to activate sensitized splenic T cells from tumor-bearing animals, we found that only restimulation with ESb-tumor cells, together with additional lymphokines, led to the activation of CTL (FIG. 2). Neither the tumor antigen alone nor lymphokines alone were sufficient for CTL activation. Not even in a situation of coexistence with micrometastases, leading to a permanent antigen presentation *in vivo,* can active CTL be found in the spleen. These spleen cells cannot, even with an excess of antigen in mixed lymphocyte tumor cell (MLTC) cultures, generate efficient cytolytic T cells. Additional signals apart from the tumor antigen are required for these CTL-P to become cytolytic active CTL.

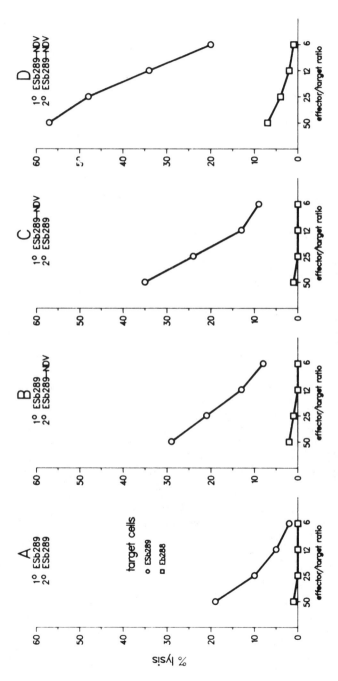

FIGURE 1. Effect of viral modification on the generation of ESb-specific CTL. ESb or NDV modified–ESb cells (ESb-NDV) were used for *in vivo* immunization (1°) (5×10^4 living tumor cells intrapinna, 9 days) or *in vitro* restimulation in MLTC (2°). 1.5×10^7 immune spleen cells were cocultivated together with 1.5×10^6 inactivated-tumor cells in 7 ml culture medium containing 10% fetal calf serum for 5 days and tested in a standard ^{51}Cr-release assay on the indicated target cells. 1×10^7 ESb cells were incubated for 1 hour with 160 HU NDV in 1 ml phosphate-buffered saline (PBS) and used after 3 washes. The cultures do not contain additional IL-2. The spontaneous release of the target cells was below 12 percent.

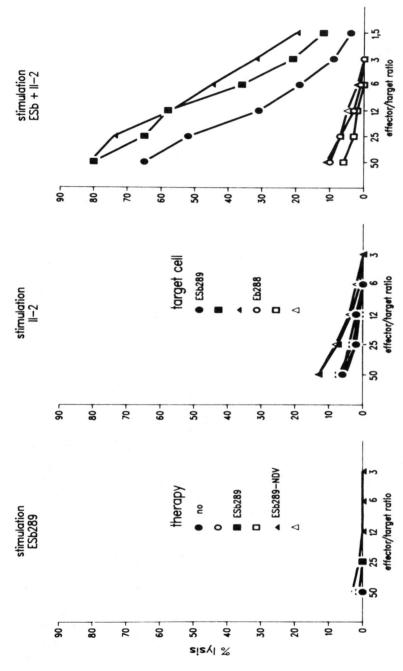

FIGURE 2. DBA/2 animals were injected intradermally with 2×10^5 ESb tumor cells. When the primary tumor had a diameter of 5–7 mm, it was removed by surgery. The animals were treated postoperatively with 2×10^7 inactivated ESb or ESb-NDV cells.[4] Nine days after surgery and treatment, pooled spleen cells of 2–3 animals were analyzed in MLTC for CTL activities. The CTL activity was measured in a standard ^{51}Cr-release assay on ESb and Eb-target cells. Part of the cultures were supplemented with 10 IU/ml IL-2 from EL-4 PMA supernatant. The spontaneous release of the target cells was below 10 percent.

We assume that a similar two-signal activation is achieved by IL-2 and/or T cell–differentiation factors, or when the ESb-tumor cells are coated with NDV and, as such, are used for activation of tumor-specific CTL-P. Further studies *in vivo* revealed that NDV modified–ESb cells had a greatly increased immunogenicity compared to ESb cells alone[4] and led in therapy studies to 50% long-term survivors.[4] In treatment with unmodified ESb cells, however, all animals died of disseminated metastases.

REFERENCES

1. SCHIRRMACHER, V., M. FOGEL, E. RUSSMANN, K. BOSSLET, P. ALTEVOGT & L. BECK. 1982. Cancer Met. Rev. **1:** 241–274.
2. BOSSLET, K., V. SCHIRRMACHER & G. SHANTZ. 1979. Int. J. Cancer **24:** 303–313.
3. SCHIRRMACHER, V., K. BOSSLET, G. SHANTZ, K. CLAUER & D. HÜBSCH. 1979. Int. J. Cancer **23:** 245–252.
4. HEICAPPELL, R., V. SCHIRRMACHER, P. VON HOEGEN, T. AHLERT & B. APPELHANS. Int. J. Cancer **37:** 569–577.

Biochemical Dissection of Human Tumor–Target Cell Surface Determinants

Relationship between Tumor N-Linked Glycoproteins and LAK Susceptibility

WILLIAM G. LOUDON AND ELIZABETH A. GRIMM

Department of Tumor Biology
Anderson Tumor Institute
University of Texas
Houston, Texas 77030

Nonantigen-primed peripheral blood lymphocytes activated with interleukin-2 (IL-2) rapidly acquire potent, non-MHC–restricted oncolytic activity against both fresh and cultured NK-sensitive and -resistant tumors while specifically sparing uncultured normal tissues.[1] The capacity of lymphokine-activated killer cells (LAK) to discriminate between normal tissue and all forms of tumor is an inherent characteristic of the individual effector cell, as cloned effector populations retain the target spectrum of the original population.[2] The target recognition mechanism used by LAK, therefore, represents a powerful biological probe for the identification of novel tumor-associated antigens.

We have previously reported preliminary data describing a trypsin-sensitive recognition site on tumor cells. Proteolytic treatment of tumor cells prior to testing in ^{51}Cr-release cytotoxicity assays renders these targets resistant to LAK-mediated lysis.[3] Pronase (0.05–1.5 mg/ml) and trypsin (0.05–1.0 mg/ml) (FIG. 1) treatments render targets highly resistant to LAK lysis, whereas chymotrypsin (0.05–1.0 mg/ml) effects only a minor reduction in susceptibility. Increasing the concentration of chymotrypsin (1.0–2.0 mg/ml) mediates no further reduction in susceptibility to LAK killing. At high effector-to-target ratios, residual target susceptibility can be detected in all enzyme treatment groups. Proteolytic cleavage sites may remain on the cell surface but are inaccessible to the enzymes due to steric hindrance. Alternatively, chemically distinct target structures may exist that are resistant to proteolysis.

The biological significance of the trypsinized tumor cells was addressed by assessing the ability of the treated targets to recover their original susceptibility to LAK. Initial recovery of susceptibility can be measured within four hours of trypsin degradation and is virtually complete within 18–22 hours. This recovery can be specifically blocked by inhibiting protein synthesis with cycloheximide or N-linked glycoconjugate synthesis with tunicamycin (FIG. 2), but not with mito-mycin-mediated ablation of DNA synthesis. The data suggest that LAK recognize a trypsin-sensitive N-linked glycoprotein epitope(s) in common to all tumors tested.

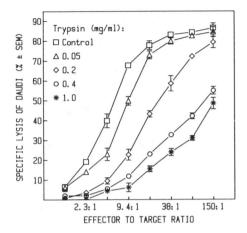

FIGURE 1. Trypsin treatment of Daudi induces resistance to LAK oncolysis. ^{51}Cr-labeled Daudi cells were incubated with the indicated concentration of trypsin for 30 minutes at 37°C. The targets were then washed three times and tested for susceptibility to LAK killing relative to untreated control Daudi in a standard ^{51}Cr-release assay.

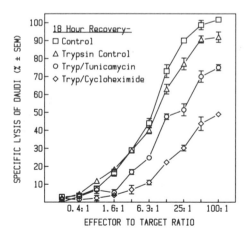

FIGURE 2. Inhibition of protein or N-linked glycoconjugate biosynthesis, by cyclohexi-mide or tunicamycin, respectively, of trypsinized Daudi, blocks the recovery of susceptibil-ity to LAK-mediated cytotoxicity. Daudi targets were trypsinized (0.5 mg/ml) and allowed to recover for 18 hours prior to testing for susceptibility to LAK killing relative to untreated controls. Cycloheximide (50 mcg/ml) or tunicamycin (1 mcg/ml) were added at initiation of culture of the trypsinized targets and washed prior to assay.

REFERENCES

1. GRIMM, E. A. & S. A. ROSENBERG. 1984. The human lymphokine-activated killer cell phenomenon. *In* Lymphokines. E. Pick, Ed.: 279–311. Academic Press. New York.
2. RAYNER, A. A., E. A. GRIMM, M. T. LOTZE & S. A. ROSENBERG. 1984. Demonstration of shared recognition and lysis of autologous and allogeneic fresh human tumors by cloned lymphokine activated killer cells (LAK). Surg. Forum **15:** 415–417.
3. GRIMM, E. A. 1986. Human lymphokine-activated killer cells (LAK cells) as a potential immunotherapeutic modality. Biochim. Biophys. Acta **865:** 267–279.

DNA Fragmentation in Tumor Cells Mediated by Human Natural Killer Cells and Lymphokine-Activated Killer Cells

P. J. LEIBSON, K. P. WINDEBANK, B. J. VILEN,
D. E. REGNERUS, AND L. R. PEASE

Departments of Immunology and Pediatrics
Mayo Clinic
Rochester, Minnesota 55905

Human natural killer cells (NK) ($CD16^+$/$CD3^-$) are a subpopulation of lymphocytes that can kill certain tumor cells without prior sensitization. These cytotoxic lymphocytes mediate their effects on target cells through a broad array of cytolytic and cytostatic proteins. The effector molecules include pore-forming proteins that can directly lyse target cell–plasma membranes. Recent studies have also suggested that one of the ways in which immune cells can inhibit tumor-cell growth is by irreversibly damaging the target-cell DNA.[1-4] In this study, we have investigated the induction of DNA damage in target cells by human NK and interleukin-2–activated lymphocytes.

In order to evaluate the mechanisms of NK-mediated cytotoxicity, we quantitatively determined target-cell lysis (using a ^{51}Cr-release assay) and target cell–DNA fragmentation (using radiolabeled DNA assays and agarose gel electrophoresis). We found that although NK lyse their sensitive targets at high effector-target (E/T) ratios, they also effectively fragment the target-cell DNA at low E/T ratios. This DNA damage of NK-sensitive human-tumor lines, such as K562 leukemia cells, can be mediated by fresh human NK, cloned NK lines (FIG. 1), and IL-2–activated mononuclear cells. The DNA fragments induced in the human K562 leukemic cells are heterogeneous in size, ranging from 500–23,000 base pairs in length (FIG. 2). The same effector cells induce multiples of 200 base pair fragments in mouse YAC-1 tumor-target cells, suggesting that the extent of DNA damage is target cell–dependent. These results suggest that human NK and IL-2–activated lymphocytes can inhibit tumor-cell growth not only by rapid direct lysis, but also by a distinct pattern of damage to DNA in the target cells.

DNA fragmentation has also been observed in several other experimental models of cell death, including steroid-induced killing of thymocytes, irradiation injury, withdrawal of IL-2 from dependent cell lines, and during normal embryological development. This DNA damage is accompanied by a morphologically characteristic pattern of cell death called apoptosis, in which the earliest changes include condensation of nuclear chromatin and blebbing of the nuclear membrane.[5] The data reported here suggests that human NK and IL-2–activated lymphocytes also contain the cytotoxic machinery necessary to mediate DNA damage in susceptible targets.

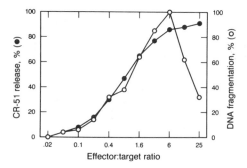

FIGURE 1. Cloned human NK induce DNA fragmentation and ^{51}Cr-release in K562 tumor cells. NKL.5, a cloned human CD16$^+$/CD3$^-$ cell line, was selected after fluorescence-activated cell sorting of CD16$^+$ cells and limiting dilution. These NK were then tested in 4 hour ^{51}Cr-release (●) and DNA fragmentation (○) assays.

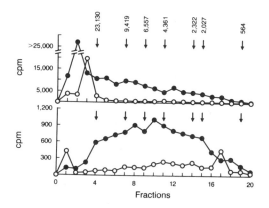

FIGURE 2. Analysis of DNA damage induced in K562 cells by NK. [^{3}H]thymidine–labeled K562 cells were incubated with (●) or without (○) NKL.5 cells for 4 hours at an E/T ratio = 3/1. DNA from either whole K562 cells (upper panel) or from the 12,000 g supernatant (lower panel) was run on a 0.4% agarose gel. The gel was then sliced and the cpm determined in each fraction. The base pair size markers (arrows) were determined by running Hind III–digested lambda DNA in parallel.

REFERENCES

1. RUSSELL, J. H., V. R. MASAKOWSKI & C. B. DOBOS. 1980. Mechanisms of immune lysis. I. Physiological distinction between target cell death mediated by cytotoxic T lymphocytes and antibody plus complement. J. Immunol. **124:** 1100.
2. DUKE, R. C., R. CHERVENAK & J. J. COHEN. 1983. Endogenous endonuclease-induced DNA fragmentation: An early event in cell-mediated cytolysis. Proc. Natl. Acad. Sci. USA **80:** 6361.

3. GROMKOWSKI, S. H., T. C. BROWN, P. A. CERUTTI & J. CEROTTINI. 1986. DNA of
    human Raji target cells is damaged upon lymphocyte-mediated lysis. J. Immunol.
    136: 752.
4. DUKE, R. C., J. J. COHEN & R. CHERVENAK. 1986. Differences in target cell DNA
    fragmentation induced by mouse cytotoxic T lymphocytes and natural killer cells. J.
    Immunol. **137:** 1442.
5. COHEN, J. J., R. C. DUKE, R. CHERVENAK, K. S. SELLINS & L. K. OLSON. 1985. DNA
    fragmentation in targets of CTL: An example of programmed cell death in the immune
    system. Adv. Exp. Med. Biol. **184:** 493.

Progressive Tumor Growth and Immune Responses[a]

LIONEL A. MANSON

Wistar Institute
36th Street and Spruce Street
Philadelphia, Pennsylvania 19104

A major question that dominates tumor immunobiology is why and how tumors grow progressively and overwhelm a host despite the immune responses triggered in the host. There has been a great deal of controversy as to whether autochthonous tumors are immunogenic. A consensus has emerged that most, if not all, tumors are immunogenic and clonal, but there is no agreement as to the nature of immunogenicity, tumor-specific antigens, immune responses in the tumor-bearing host, or how and if these relate to progressive tumor growth.

In studies carried out more than 10 years ago, we found that cytotoxic cells (CC) accumulated in the ascitic tumor mass of the syngeneic host, DBA/2 mouse, inoculated intraperitoneally (i.p.) with 1000 P815Y cells. By day 10, tumor load was approximately 5×10^7 cells per animal, and CC could be isolated from the ascitic tumor mass. These CC lysed tissue culture–grown P815Y and L5178Y (both H-2^d), as well as EL4 (H-2^b), but did not lyse two other cell lines, P815-X2 and L1210 (H-2^d). Cold target–inhibition studies, using a standard 4 h ^{51}Cr-release assay, demonstrated that the same CC lysed both P815Y and EL4 cells. P815Y tumor cells grown in the ascites for 10 days were sensitive to CC, whereas day 16 tumor cells, when tumor size had increased 10- to 20-fold, were resistant to CC. It was concluded that CC resembled T cells because they were nonadherent, sensitive to anti-Thy-1.2 serum treatment, and heat stable, yet not H-2–restricted. Progressive growth continued in the ascites because tumor cells underwent antigenic modulation, escaping the CC and overwhelming the host.[1,2]

A humoral response was also detected in DBA/2 mice inoculated with 1000 P815Y and L5178Y cells.[3,4] A specific antitumor IgM accumulated on the growing tumor cells. By day 16, the tumor cells had maximal amounts of IgM on their surface. Therefore, antigenic modulation leading to CC resistance was antibody-induced, and it was concluded that antibody-coated tumor cells are capable of unimpeded growth inside the animal.

We are now reporting that EL4 growing in C57BL/6 mice induce CC that can be isolated from a day 10 C57BL/6 ascites. In all four experiments (TABLE 1), CC were equally effective in lysing EL4 and P815Y. TABLE 2 shows that by day 16, antigenic modulation had taken place, and tumor cells were resistant to CC. Other experiments show that this antigenic modulation is also antibody-mediated. It appears that the tumor-specific antigen (EATI) of EL4 is cross-reactive with those of P815Y and L-5178Y.

We have also demonstrated that the anti-tumor Ig will sensitize mice to reject a tumor challenge,[3] most probably by inducing an anti-idiotype response, priming the animal to generate CC and causing tumor challenges to be rejected.

In conclusion, *in situ* immune responses were observed during progressive growth of a thymoma (EL4) in its syngeneic host C57BL/6 mice. Cytotoxic cells

[a] This work was supported by USPHS Research Grant from NCI, CA 34654.

TABLE 1. C57BL/6 Anti-EL4 Effector Cells (H-2^b) Have Equal Ability to Kill the DBA/2 Tumor P815Y (H-2^d)[a]

			Percent Specific Lysis		
Experiment	S (mm/h)	E/T	Hr Assay	El4	P815Y
1	4.3–6.6	150	5	9.4	7.1
2	3.8–4.9	50	5.2	20.6	34.9
3	1.6–6.7	150	4.0	7.6	14.1
4	0.8–6.3	150	17	39.1	38.4

[a] Labeling of target cells for ^{51}Cr-release assays. Tumor cells (4–5 × 10^6) were harvested from culture and resuspended in 1 ml of RPMI-1640 medium, supplemented with 10% heat-inactivated FBS, antibiotics, and MOPS, pH 7.2, to a final concentration of 5 mM (assay medium). Three hundred to 350 μCi Na$_2$^{51}CrO$_4$ (New England Nuclear, Boston, MA; specific activity ≥ 250 mCi/mg) were added and incubated with the tumor cells at 37°C for 90 min. Labeled cells were washed three times through FBS underlays and resuspended in cold assay medium. Viability of target cells was always ≥ 95%. Cytotoxicity assays. A standard 4 h ^{51}Cr-release assay for the measurement of cytotoxicity against tumor-target cells was performed as described elsewhere.[1,2] Briefly, effector cells and 5 × 10^3 ^{51}Cr-labeled target cells were added to triplicate wells of conical-bottom microtest plates (Linbro, New Haven, CT). The plates were centrifuged at 20 × g for 3 min and incubated at 37°C in a humidified atmosphere of 5% CO$_2$ in air. After 4 h, the supernatant fluids were removed for the determination of isotope release. Spontaneous release of ^{51}Cr from target cells was measured by incubation of the target cells with medium only, and the maximal release was determined by dilution of the target cells (1/20 v/v) in deionized water. Cytotoxicity was calculated by the formula:

$$\% \text{ specific lysis} = \frac{\text{experimental release} - \text{spontaneous release}}{\text{hypotonic release} - \text{spontaneous release}} \times 100.$$

were isolated from the i.p. tumor mass. Antitumor antibody (IgM) was found *in vivo* only on the tumor cells. Antibody-induced antigenic modulation is the most probable reason for progressive growth in the tumor-bearing host. We believe that these cytotoxic cells may be the precursors of TILS that have been used recently in adoptive immunotherapeutic experiments.[5]

TABLE 2. Modulation of EL4 Tumor Cells to Resistance to Intratumor Effector Cells[a]

Experiment	E/T	Time (h)	S (mm/h)	Percent Specific Lysis *in Vitro* EL4	Day 16 EL4 Tumor	Tumor Load 10^6/Mouse
1	67	4	2.8–3.8	38.4 ± 2.2	0.4 ± 0	1270
2	150	6	4.3–6.6	9.4 ± 1.8	1.0 ± 0.1	705

[a] For methods, see TABLE 1.

REFERENCES

1. BIDDISON, W. E. & J. C. PALMER. 1977. Proc. Natl. Acad. Sci. USA **74:** 329.
2. BIDDISON, W. E., J. C. PALMER, M. A. ALEXANDER, E. P. COWAN & L. A. MANSON. 1977. J. Immunol. **118:** 2243.
3. MANSON, L. A. 1984. Transplant. Proc. **16:** 524.
4. MANSON, L. A. 1987. Cancer Detect. Prevent. In press.
5. ROSENBERG, S. A., P. SPIESS & R. LAFRENIERE. 1986. Science **233:** 1318.

Evidence for Distinct IL-2 Receptors in Induction versus Maintenance of LAK Function

L. OWEN-SCHAUB, M. YAGITA, M. TSUDO,[a]
T. A. WALDMANN,[a] AND E. A. GRIMM

M.D. Anderson Hospital
University of Texas
Houston, Texas 77030
and
[a] Metabolism Branch
National Institutes of Health
Bethesda, Maryland 20892

Human lymphocytes respond to IL-2 with the generation of MHC-unrestricted oncolytic activity.[1] We have named this function lymphokine-activated killing (LAK). To investigate the mechanism by which IL-2 alone activates LAK, we have examined the role(s) of IL-2 cell-surface receptors.

Although we have shown that Tac expression accompanies and is necessary for LAK proliferation,[2,3] removal of cells expressing this epitope does not preclude the acquisition of LAK function. Therefore, we hypothesized the involvement of an alternate, non-Tac IL-2 receptor. Experiments using direct [^{125}I]IL-2 binding to Tac negative–LAK precursors suggested the existence of such a receptor (TABLE 1). Chemical cross-linking with disuccinimidyl suberate (DSS) followed by SDS-PAGE determined that the size of the non-Tac IL-2 binding protein was approximately 75 kDa.

Because preliminary experiments had demonstrated a positive correlation between expression of this non-Tac receptor and IL-2 responsiveness leading to LAK activity, we investigated the role of the p75 receptor in initial signal transduction. For these studies, Tac-negative precursors were activated by a brief IL-2 pulse. By limiting IL-2 exposure to an interval insufficient for detectable Tac up-regulation, non-Tac-mediated functional differentiation could be addressed. As shown in TABLE 2, the IL-2 ligand, interacting through an initial non-Tac pathway, rapidly transduced the signal for acquisition of LAK competence at 24 hours. The development of this lytic competence is proliferation-dependent, as mitomycin treatment has no effect at 24 hours. By contrast, progression (96 hr LAK) was shown to require continuous IL-2 exposure, Tac up-regulation,[3] and cellular proliferation.[2] These data strongly suggest that dissimilar IL-2 receptors (one independent of Tac expression and one Tac-dependent) are involved in the ontogeny of LAK.

TABLE 1. Specific [^{125}I]IL-2 Binding to Tac-Negative Peripheral Blood Lymphocytes (PBL)[a]

Cell Source	Specific Binding (CPM + SEM)
MLA-144	7241 ± 324
PBL	5126 ± 537
Tac (−) PBL	2641 ± 189
K562	< 0

[a] Tac-depleted PBL (2.5×10^6) were incubated with 5 nM [^{125}I]IL-2 (New England Nuclear) on ice for 1 hour. After incubation, cells were underlayered with 10% sucrose in phosphate-buffered saline and spun at 10,000 g for 1 min. The tips of the tubes containing the cell pellets were cut off and counted in a gamma counter. Nonspecific binding was determined in the presence of 200-fold molar excess unlabeled IL-2. Nonspecific counts have been subtracted from the total to obtain specific binding. Data presented are the mean ± SEM of triplicates.

TABLE 2. Tac-Negative PBL Pulsed with IL-2 Generate LAK Lytic Competence[a]

Activation Stimulus	Lytic Units/10⁶ Cells Generated against Raji 24 hr	96 hr
1×10^4 units pulse	10.7	<1.0
100 *units continuous*	24.4	142.0
None	<1.0	<1.0

[a] Tac-depleted PBL (1×10^6) were either pulsed with IL-2 for 30 min at 37°C, or exposed continuously at the indicated concentration (Cetus units IL-2/ml). For pulsing, exposure was terminated by stripping, washing, and reculturing in the presence of anti-IL-2 antibody.

REFERENCES

1. GRIMM, E. A., A. MAZUMDER, H. Z. ZHANG & S. A. ROSENBERG. 1982. J. Exp. Med. **155:** 1823.
2. GRIMM, E. A. & S. A. ROSENBERG. 1984. *In* Lymphokines. E. Pick, Ed.: **9:** 279. Academic Press. New York.
3. GRIMM, E. A., R. J. ROBB, J. A. ROTH, L. M. NECKERS, L. LACHMAN, D. J. WILSON & S. A. ROSENBERG. 1983. J. Exp. Med. **158:** 1356.

Chemoimmunotherapy of Spontaneous Mammary Tumors in C3H/OuJ Mice by Cyclophosphamide and Interleukin-2

YUTAKA KAWAKAMI,[a] MAURICE GATELY,[b]
AND JULIE Y. DJEU

Department of Medical Microbiology and Immunology
College of Medicine
University of South Florida
Tampa, Florida 33612
and
[b]Department of Immunopharmacology
Hoffmann LaRoche Inc.
Nutley, New Jersey 07107

INTRODUCTION

Successful chemoimmunotherapy has been reported in several animal models.[1-3] Syngeneic transplantable tumors, however, in young mice are most frequently used for these preclinical studies, which may not completely duplicate tumors that arise spontaneously in humans. In the present study, we attempted chemoimmunotherapy using cyclophosphamide (CYP) and interleukin-2 (IL-2) in old C3H/OuJ mice bearing spontaneous mammary tumors. These tumors developed due to a mouse mammary-tumor virus that the mice harbor. CYP, at an appropriate dose, reportedly has the ability to inhibit suppressor T cells and suppressor macrophages that are present in tumor-bearing mice,[4] as well as to reduce tumor burden by its direct cytotoxic effect. These actions of CYP may lead to increased tumor immunity and tumor rejection in mice. In addition, it is reported that CYP may enhance the delivery of effector cells to the tumor site,[1] increase tumor susceptibility to effector cells, and prevent adverse effects of IL-2 *in vivo*. IL-2 is a growth and differentiation factor for T cells and natural killer cells (NK), which may reconstitute some immune functions in mice after CYP treatment. Therefore, the combination of CYP and IL-2 was adopted as a rational therapeutic protocol for reduction of tumor load in C3H/OuJ mice bearing spontaneous mammary tumors.

MATERIAL AND METHODS

Human recombinant IL-2 was kindly provided by Hoffmann LaRoche Inc., Nutley, NJ. Eight- to twelve-month-old female C3H/OuJ mice that had developed palpable tumors of sizes between 0.2–3.0 cm^2 were randomized and inoculated

---

[a] Present address: Yutaka Kawakami, Surgery Branch, Division of Cancer Treatment, National Cancer Institute, National Institutes of Health, Bldg. 10, Room 2B51, Bethesda, MD 20892.

intraperitoneally with either 100 mg/kg of CYP or saline. Seven days later, either 1×10^5 units/mouse of IL-2 or saline was administered intraperitoneally daily for 5 consecutive days. The mice were then observed twice a week for tumor growth and survival. The results were analyzed in each group with initial tumor sizes of 0.2–0.5, 0.5–1.0, 1.0–1.5, 1.5–2.0, and 2.0–3.0 cm². The data were analyzed by Student's *t* test.

RESULTS AND DISCUSSION

Based on a previous report of the successful therapy by CYP and IL-2 of a transplantable MM46 mammary tumor in C3H/He mice,[3] we attempted a similar protocol for the treatment of spontaneous mammary tumors in C3H/OuJ mice.

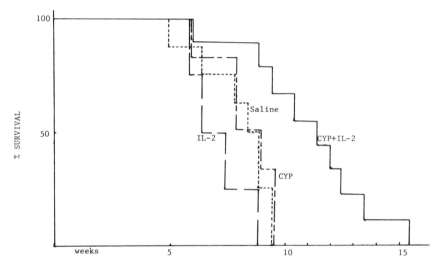

FIGURE 1. Effect of cyclophosphamide and interleukin-2 on the survival of C_3H/OuJ mice, whose tumors were initially 0.5–1.0 cm² in size. Only combination therapy of 100 mg/kg of CYP and 1×10^5 units/mouse of IL-2 prolonged the survival of spontaneous mammary tumor–bearing mice.

We found that CYP retarded tumor growth slightly for one week; however, either CYP alone or IL-2 alone had little influence on the late-tumor growth. The combination of CYP and IL-2 was effective in significantly retarding tumor growth (TABLE 1); CYP and IL-2 prolonged survival in mice that initially had tumors of less than 1.5 cm² (FIG. 1). Mice with larger tumors did not respond to this treatment regimen. These data suggest that CYP pretreatment prepared an *in vivo* environment in which IL-2 could effectively enhance effector cells against spontaneous mammary tumors. It is difficult to speculate what effector mechanisms might be responsible for retardation of tumor growth in the CYP/IL-2–treated mice. One of them could be the generation of lymphokine-activated killer cells (LAK), inasmuch as it has been reported that freshly isolated spontaneous mammary tumors in C3H/OuJ and C3H/HeN mice are susceptible to lysis by synge-

TABLE 1. Effect of Cyclophosphamide and Interleukin-2 on the Growth of C_3H/OuJ Spontaneous Mammary Tumors at Initial Sizes 0.5–1.0 cm^{2a}

Treatment	0 Week	1	3	5	7	9
Saline	0.8 ± 0.1(8)[b]	1.5 ± 0.3(8)	1.8 ± 0.4(8)	4.5 ± 1.1(8)	7.1 ± 2.0(6)	12.3 ± 4.6(2)
IL-2	0.8 ± 0.1(4)	1.2 ± 0.5(4)	2.1 ± 0.4(4)	5.0 ± 1.7(4)	6.1 ± 0.6(2)	(0)
CYP	0.8 ± 0.1(6)	0.9 ± 0.2(6)	2.1 ± 0.5(6)	4.6 ± 1.1(6)	7.7 ± 3.7(5)	10.5 ± 0.6(2)
CYP + IL-2	0.8 ± 0.1(9)	0.9 ± 0.2(9)	1.6 ± 0.5(9)	2.6 ± 1.4(9)	3.7 ± 1.1(8)	5.8 ± 1.7(7)

[a] The results are presented as the mean of tumor sizes (short × long diameter cm^2) ± SD. The data were analyzed by using Student's t test. Only combination therapy of 100 mg/kg of CYP and 1×10^5 units/mouse of IL-2 significantly retarded the tumor growth.
[b] Number in parenthesis indicates number of mice.
[c] $p < 0.01$.
[d] $p < 0.02$.

neic NK.[5,6] The generation and maintenance of LAK could also have been enhanced by prior CYP treatment, which could have eliminated suppressor cells that interfered with LAK generation. Further studies will be required to determine the exact effector mechanisms activated in these mice.

REFERENCES

1. HOSOKAWA, M., Y. SAWAMURA, F. OKADA, T. YABIKU, Z. XU, K. ITOH & H. KOBAYASHI. 1986. Proc. Jap. Soc. Immunol. **16:** 311.
2. YANG, J. C., I. PRATS, M. Z. PAPA & S. A. ROSENBERG. 1987. Fed. Proc. **46:** 1509.
3. IZAWA, M., K. OKADA, K. AMIKURA, N. KASHIMA & J. HAMURO. 1984. Proc. Jap. Soc. Immunol. **14:** 326.
4. SHATTEN, S., R. D. GRANSTEIN, J. A. DREBIN & M. I. GREENE. 1984. CRC Crit. Rev. Immunol. **4:** 335.
5. AMES, I. H., C. E. GATES, A. M. GARCIA, P. A. JOHN & R. H. TOMAR. 1987. Fed. Proc. **46:** 479.
6. SERRATE, S. A. & R. B. HERBERMAN. 1982. *In* NK cells and Other Natural Effector Cells. R. B. Herberman, Ed.: 1069. Academic Press. New York.

Index of Contributors